COWLES
ENCYCLOPEDIA
OF ANIMALS
AND PLANTS

COWLES ENCYCLOPEDIA OF ANIMALS AND PLANTS

from Cowles Volume Library

COWLES EDUCATION CORPORATION

CURRICULUM DIVISION
JAN 2 2 1970
LIBRARY

574
.03
C875
Ref

**COWLES ENCYCLOPEDIA
OF ANIMALS AND PLANTS**

Copyright © 1968
by COWLES EDUCATION CORPORATION
LOOK Building
488 Madison Avenue, New York, N. Y. 10022

All rights reserved. This volume may not be
reproduced in whole or in part in any form without
written permission from the publisher.

Published simultaneously in the United States and Canada.
Copyright under the International Copyright Convention.
Copyright 1967, 1966, 1965 by Cowles Education Corporation.

Printed in the United States of America

Library of Congress Catalog Number 68-29850

PREFACE

Cowles Encyclopedia of Animals and Plants is a wide-ranging survey of the world of nature. It is a handy, one-volume reference for everyone who has ever wondered about an animal or a plant. Here is a storehouse of information to meet the needs of the student, the animal lover, the armchair biologist, and the "just plain curious." Easy-to-read articles written by outstanding authorities cover key areas of knowledge and describe hundreds of animals and plants.

In addition to specific information on many individual animals and plants, authoritative articles provide the scientific background necessary to understand the rich and varied natural world about us.

A thorough discussion of animal life tells where animals live, what they eat, and how they are classified. A similar introduction to plant life discusses the classification of plants, plant structure, and plant physiology.

Essay-length articles give scientific background of the animal and plant worlds. Origins of Life discusses the theories on how life began. Microbiology tells about the world of the "invisible" creatures all around us. How living things transmit their unique characteristics is detailed in Genetics. And relationships among living things are explained clearly in Biological Relationships.

The Editors

COWLES ENCYCLOPEDIA
OF ANIMALS AND PLANTS

Managing Editor
ROBERT J. FELDMAN

Art Editor
JAMES T. ANDREWS

Assistant Editors
STEVEN P. DALBER, STEPHANIE L. DRANOFF,
M. T. v. GERLOFF, SARA DULANEY GILBERT, PHYLLIS G. ROSEN,
HILARY ROSS

Editorial Assistants
SUZANNE L. RINGER, D. D. WHEELOCK

Published by
COWLES EDUCATION CORPORATION

A subsidiary of
COWLES COMMUNICATIONS, INC.

GARDNER COWLES
Editorial Chairman

WILLIAM ATTWOOD
Editor in Chief

CONTRIBUTORS

HELEN BUTTFIELD, A.M.
Nature writer and photographer

RAYMOND F. DASMANN, Ph.D.
Director, Environmental Studies, The Conservation Foundation

RICHARD H. McBEE, Ph.D.
Dean, College of Letters and Science, Montana State University

STANLEY L. MILLER, Ph.D.
Associate Professor of Chemistry, University of California

LORUS J. MILNE, Ph.D.
Professor of Zoology, University of New Hampshire

MARGERY J. MILNE, Ph.D.
Lecturer in nature recreation and zoology

SELMA SILAGI, Ph.D.
Assistant Professor of Genetics, Cornell University Medical School

CONTENTS

PART 1

Animals 1
Animal life 1
Animals 11

PART 2

Plants 67
Plant life 67
Plants 78

PART 3

Biological Background 131
Origins of life 131
Microbiology 134
Genetics 142
Biological relationships 151

PART 4

Index 161

Animals

ANIMAL LIFE

The branch of science that deals with animals is called Zoology. Although it deals with the structures and functions of animals, perhaps its best-known aspect is the orderly classification of animal life, from the simplest to the most complex.

Although it is easy to see that a bear is an animal and that a pine tree is a plant, some of the smaller animals and plants are not obviously members of their respective kingdoms. Most animals can be distinguished by movement; yet there are microscopic water plants that swim as freely as animals do.

All animals large enough to be seen with the naked eye obtain energy by eating plants or other animals. Surprisingly, a few microscopic animals are like green plants in that through the process of photosynthesis they can capture energy from sunlight and can use simple chemical compounds dissolved in water as food.

Thus, it is obvious that methods must be found to distinguish animals from plants and to separate one kind of animal from another. One way to do this is an analysis of food habits. Another way is by studying habitat, or where an animal lives. The most important factors, however, are structure and function—how an animal moves, digests its food, breathes, and reproduces.

FOOD HABITS. The food habits of an animal will give information concerning its structure and function, some of the animals related to it, and a general idea of the environment in which it lives. Sometimes a broad category of food habits will cover a wide variety of creatures.

Herbivores. Any animal that eats only vegetable matter is a *herbivore,* or plant-eater. Herbivores eat grasses, leaves, twigs, succulent plants, and other types of vegetation. The classification encompasses such different creatures as caterpillars and cows.

Carnivores. Animals that eat the flesh of other animals are called *carnivores,* or meat-eaters. Animals as different as lions and ladybird beetles are in this category. When a cat pounces on a mouse, kills it, and eats it, the cat becomes a predatory carnivore, or *predator.*

Animals such as the vulture and hyena are also carnivores, although they usually prefer to feed on dead animals; this makes them *scavengers.* Domestic animals also become scavengers at times, such as when they rummage through refuse.

Omnivores. The most familiar *omnivores,* creatures that eat both animal and vegetable matter, are man himself and the domestic pig. There are, however, less familiar omnivores that are far more numerous.

The *aquatic omnivores* subsist on food so small that they must strain it from the water. Clams and oysters do so by producing a current within the shell, filtering out the food, and expelling the water. Worms that burrow in the ocean floor build U-shaped tubes, then wiggle in order to draw water in at one end; after they have strained the food from the water, they force the water from the other end of the tube.

Even the giant whales, which may be as long as 110 feet, filter their food. They swim, mouth opened, until small crustaceans, plankton, and other types of food are caught between thin plates known as whalebone that hang down in the mouth cavity. Then they close their mouths and swallow the contents.

Symbionts. Animals that form a beneficial partnership with animals of some other kind or a similar partnership with a living plant are *symbionts.* If both partners in a symbiotic arrangement benefit equally, the relationship is *mutualistic.* If one benefits without harming the other, it is a *commensal* relationship; if one gains at the expense of the other, it is *parasitic.*

Many termites illustrate mutualism. They chew and swallow wood but cannot digest the wood fibers until they are predigested by minute animals that inhabit the termites' digestive tract. These minute animals could not obtain wood fibers without the termites; the termites could not utilize wood fibers if the minute animals did not first digest them.

The shark sucker, also called pilot fish or remora, has a commensal relation with sharks. It attaches itself to the shark by means of a suction disk and is carried from place to place to share the shark's food. The shark sucker detaches itself while the shark is feeding, eats, and reattaches itself, to be carried elsewhere. Occasionally a shark sucker will be found attached to a sea turtle or a small boat.

Most parasites are harmless unless they have become numerous. One chicken louse will cause a bird mild discomfort; hundreds will cause a bird to scratch itself constantly, weaken, and grow ill. Such parasites as lice, fleas, ticks, and mosquitoes are called *ectoparasites.*

There are also *endoparasites,* which are internal parasites. They include tapeworms, which inhabit the digestive tract; flukes, which inhabit the lungs; and malaria parasites, which attack the red cells in the blood.

Certain minute insects parasitize plants by producing chemicals that irritate the plants into forming unnatural swellings on the leaf or stem, producing deformed terminal buds. These *galls* provide a place for the insects to live while they suck sap from the plant. Each type has a distinctive shape and inner structure.

HABITAT. The oceans are the home of the greatest variety of animals. Near the sea's surface, sunlight penetrates and enables the small, drifting plants called *phytoplankton* to carry on photosynthesis. Swimming weakly through the phytoplankton and feeding on them are *zooplankton.* Larger animals, called *nekton,* swim strongly and feed on the smaller forms of life. The largest of the nekton are the whales, which may migrate from the Arctic to the Antarctic and back again in a period of a single year.

Deep-sea Dwellers. Many inhabitants of the dark ocean depths are scavengers, dependent on material that sinks from the surface; a few are predators. Even in the muddy ooze that covers the sea floor at the greatest depths, there are animals utilizing the organic materials in the ooze. Many of them eat the bacteria that decompose material that sinks from the surface. Some animals at the deepest levels produce their own light; its function is not certain.

Coastal Dwellers. Much animal life is found near the shores, where the seaweeds are larger and more plentiful because the water is rich in minerals washed from the land. Wave action incorporates air bubbles in the water, thus providing more oxygen for the animal life.

The main danger to coastal dwellers is that of being thrown ashore by the waves. Some, like the sea urchins and sea stars, attach themselves to rocks by means of suction disks. Others burrow, or they live only in areas protected from wave action.

Marsh Dwellers. Animals that live in salt marshes and river estuaries must be able to tolerate great fluctuations of the water's salt content—from very low after a heavy rain to very high after a long drought. This is also true of the plants and animals on which they feed.

Freshwater Dwellers. Fresh water, whether flowing or still, supports fewer forms of life than salt water because it contains fewer dissolved minerals. It is often muddy, however, from undissolved particles. These reduce the amount of light penetrating the water and thus reduce the amount of plant food available to animals.

Fresh waters change level rapidly during floods and droughts, thereby altering the habitat of many creatures. They also freeze over in the winter, thereby greatly reducing the available oxygen and forcing some creatures, such as frogs and turtles, to hibernate.

Land Dwellers. There are many types of habitats to be found on the land, and various types of animals live in each. In the soil there are, among others, earthworms, moles, and many insects. Such animals as bears and deer choose forests or their edges.

The "edge" may grade off into willow or alder swamp, or into grassy field or pasture. In either case, there will be plants for herbivores, small herbivores for medium-sized carnivores, and large herbivores, such as deer, for large carnivores, for example, pumas.

Open plains, covered chiefly by grasses, have inhabitants like antelope, prairie dogs, rabbits, prairie chickens, and vast numbers of grasshoppers and ants. Wolves, coyotes, badgers, and snakes formerly were the main carnivores, but the spread of civilization has greatly reduced their numbers. Summer droughts have also served to curb predators, as well as to keep the herbivores from overgrazing the range.

Water is so scarce in deserts that few animals live there; those that do are generally small and have bodies specially adapted to their habitat. Only a few insects can live in ice or in hot springs. One or two kinds of flies have even been found living at the bottoms of shallow petroleum pools in oil fields, feeding on insects that happen to fall in.

Caves also have special animals that exist as external parasites on bats or eat the mold that grows on the bat droppings. Some of these animals prey on other cave creatures.

STRUCTURE AND FUNCTION. Any animal that is to continue to exist must at some time in its life perform the activities common to all animals: movement; food handling, that is, digestion, absorption, and excretion; respiration; coordination, both chemical and nervous; and reproduction, followed by the growth to maturity of new individuals able to carry on the same activities as the parents.

Structure. *Unicellular* (single-celled) marine animals are believed to have been the first form of life. Today there are about 30,000 species of animals that carry on all of their life processes within the one cell.

Most modern animals are *multicellular* (composed of many cells). Among these, the sponges are unique in that any cell can take over the function of any other cell. A sponge may evolve into a different kind of sponge, but it can never become any other kind of organism.

Function. All multicellular animals except sponges have their cells arranged in layers called *tissues;* each tissue is composed of cells with a definite structure and function. In the higher animals, the tissues are connected in *organ systems.*

A man is composed of organ systems, such as the digestive system; this system in turn is composed of such organs as the esophagus, stomach, intestines, and colon. The stomach is composed of a lining layer, muscle layers, and a covering layer; each tissue layer is composed of a definite type of cell. All multicellular animals have the same general types of tissues.

Contractile tissue, composed of tissues that shorten and lengthen, does the work of the body. This type of tissue forms either muscles moving the body or continuous sleeves around cavities, such as the digestive organs or the blood vessels.

Connective and *supporting tissue* is composed of cells that produce nonliving secretions between themselves. The tissue may be a solid mass in cartilage or bone; or tough strands in tendons, which connect bones; or it may be in ligaments, which connect muscle and bone. Connective tissues form the walls of capsules that hold the lubricant in each joint, as well as fine fibers resembling cobwebs that hold organs in place.

Epithelial tissue is composed of thin tilelike, cuboidal, or close-packed columnar cells that are on the surface of the body or are the lining layer of body cavities, ducts, and tubes. Epithelial cells produce such important nonliving substances as shells, hair, antlers, feathers, milk, sweat, and digestive juices. Some epithelial cells have microscopic extensions called *cilia,* which pulsate and propel fluids over the tissues.

Circulating tissue, or *blood,* is a fluid made of blood cells suspended in plasma. It is circulated by the pulsation of the heart muscles and of the blood vessel walls; it may also move incidentally when the body moves.

Endocrine tissue consists of cells that secrete hormones into the blood, to be carried throughout the body in order to coordinate its activities. The pituitary and thyroid glands are endocrine glands, or glands of internal secretion. *Exocrine* glands, or glands of external secretion, such as sweat glands, are epithelial tissue.

Conducting tissue is characteristic of the nervous system. Its individual cells, known as *neurons,* conduct impulses of electrochemical charge and help to coordinate the body by linking *receptors,* such as the light-sensitive cells of the eye, to *effectors,* the muscle cells or glands that respond. Large units of conducting tissue are *ganglia,* which are clusters of neurons, and such centers as the brain and spinal cord, from which many neurons extend in bundles known as *nerves.*

Reproductive tissue consists of egg cells produced in the female's *ovaries* and sperm cells produced in the male's *testes.* An egg is normally fertilized only by union with a sperm cell, becoming a new individual.

CLASSIFICATION

Animals are identified and grouped into a scheme of classes on the basis of their physical structure and the development of the body parts.

BINOMIAL NOMENCLATURE. The system of naming animals by specifying two names was developed in 1758 by Karl von Linné, a Swedish physician and naturalist. He is better known by his Latin signature, Carolus Linnaeus.

Under von Linné's system, a *species* is a group of creatures that can interbreed with complete fertility; several species may be included in a *genus* if they are very similar in structure, but crosses between two species either result in no offspring or in offspring with incomplete fertility. A familiar example is the mule, which is comparatively sterile. It is produced by a mating between a horse (*Equus caballus*) and a donkey (*Equus asinus*).

Von Linné also filled the need for levels of classification between the animal kingdom and the binomial nomenclature of the individual creature. He therefore set within the animal kingdom, in descending order, the *phylum,* the *class,* the *order,* and the *family,* which is composed of the *genus* and the *species.*

For example, the full classification of man is: phylum *Chordata* (vertebrates and near kin), class *Mammalia* (mammals), order *Primates* (mammals with nails and opposable thumbs or big toes or both), family *Hominidae* (man and manlike primates), genus *Homo,* species *sapiens.*

In some cases, additional levels of classification are added to show differences that are considered important. These include *subphyla,* each with one or more classes; *subclasses,* each with one or more orders; *suborders,* each with one or more families; and *subfamilies.*

TRINOMIAL CLASSIFICATION. Geographical divisions of a species are *subspecies,* also called *races.* The distinction among the members of a species is made by using *trinomial nomenclature.* Thus, for example, the white-footed mouse of Vermont is *Peromyscus maniculatus gracilis;* the white-footed mouse found in Canada north of Lake Superior is *Peromyscus maniculatus maniculatus,* the "typical" or "standard" member of the species. These and all other races of the species will interbreed freely if brought together.

EVOLUTION. The idea of evolution received little attention for more than a century after von Linné established the binomial classification. In 1859 Charles Darwin's *On the Origin of Species by Means of Natural Selection* gave evidence and explanation of change in body form over time.

Darwin pointed out that all animals reproduce faster than is necessary merely to maintain a stable population. Competition develops for food and habitat, and the weaker members of the species, unable to compete effectively, are likely to die before being able to reproduce. Only the fittest survive, and they pass on to their offspring any inheritable advantages.

Gradually a species adapts, splits into races, or dies out. Many extinct species, known only through their fossil records, have been classified through their similarities to living animals. All the animals of today are descended from those of the past and are ancestors of all future animals.

PHYLA

Of the more than one million species that have been named, all but 2 percent are classified in 14 phyla. Small additional phyla have been established for the remaining 2 percent, most of them inconspicuous deep-sea dwellers or parasites.

PHYLUM PROTOZOA. There are about 30,000 species of unicellular "first animals," most of them too small to be seen with the naked eye. They are commonly called *protozoans*.

Class Mastigophora. Because they propel themselves through the water by means of one or more whiplike projections from the body, these "whipcarriers" are called *flagellates*. Some, such as *Euglena*, have a single extension, or *flagellum*. Others have two or as many as ten.

Euglena is a large genus, including many species that contain chlorophyll and carry on photosynthesis. Some of these are so numerous in still water that after a period of heat and drought, the water appears bright green. Many colorless flagellates feed on bacteria. Still others are symbionts of termites, living in their digestive tracts and predigesting the wood fibers the insect swallows.

African sleeping sickness is caused by a parasitic flagellate, *Trypanosoma gambiense*, which is transmitted to man through the bite of the tsetse fly. Ordinarily the parasite lives in various wild animals, which seem to be unaffected.

Class Sarcodina. The most famous sarcodinians are the *amoebas*, the *radiolarians*, and the *foraminiferans*. All move about by extending lobes or networks of protoplasm, called *pseudopodia*, or false feet. Amoebas are extraordinary in that they have no definite shape; they flow into one pseudopodium after another as they travel in fresh water or in the digestive tract of an animal.

Radiolarians and foraminiferans, which live on bacteria and microscopic green plants, produce minute skeletons or chambered shells of either silica or lime, from the surface waters of the oceans. When these sarcodinians die, their skeletons sink to the bottom and build up great thicknesses of ooze. Radiolarian ooze becomes an inert powder suitable for making filters and bonding material in dynamite. Foraminiferous ooze gradually becomes a type of limestone.

Class Sporozoa. All sporozoans are parasites of multicellular animals and absorb their food in dissolved form directly from the *host*, the animal to which they attach themselves. They have no means of moving by themselves but must be transferred from one host to another by the activities of *carriers*, such as mosquitoes.

Perhaps the best-known sporozoan is *Plasmodium falciparum*, the cause of the most dangerous type of malaria in man. It penetrates the red blood cells, reproduces, and causes the cells to break open, releasing more parasites to attack other red cells. *Plasmodia* are spread by mosquitoes of the genus *Anopheles*, which feed on blood. If an *Anopheles* consumes infected blood, the parasites undergo changes and then migrate to its salivary glands. If the mosquito bites a healthy person, the *Plasmodia*, which go with the saliva into the victim's blood stream, start a new infection.

Class Ciliata. Ciliates are named for the many hairlike *cilia* that project from their microscopic bodies, beating in rhythmic waves and driving the cell through the water. The animals are unique in possessing two different kinds of cell nuclei—*macronuclei* and *micronuclei*.

Ciliates live in water and feed on bacteria and small protozoans. Among the best-known are the slipper-shaped *Paramecium*, the bell-shaped *Vorticella*, and the trumpet-shaped *Stentor*. In a strong light, all of these animalcules are large enough to be seen without a microscope.

PHYLUM PORIFERA. Phylum Porifera contains some 4,500 species of colonial animals that remain attached to the bottom of the sea or to other solid objects, while cells, known as *flagellated collar cells*, draw water and minute particles of food through small holes that lead to a central chamber or system of chambers. After the collar cells have caught the food particles, the water is released through one or more large openings.

Most of these animalcules, commonly known as *sponges*, are marine; a few live in fresh water.

Class Calcarea. *Calcarea* are marine sponges whose cells secrete needle-shaped or branching *spicules* of lime. The spicules usually project from the surface of the colony and mesh, giving it structural support; however, they are regarded as an internal skeleton. Common genera of this class include *Grantia* and *Leucosolenia*, some of whose species grow to an inch in length.

Class Hyalospongiae. *Hyalospongiae* are deep-sea sponges, often of great beauty, that produce a skeleton of silica. *Euplectella* is the Venus' flower basket sponge.

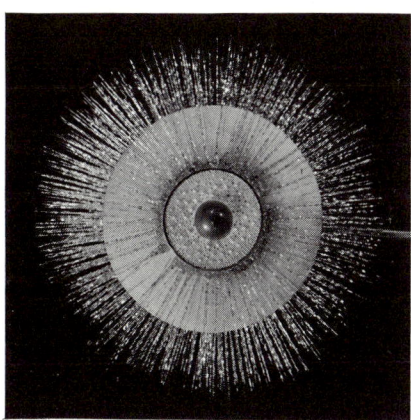

AMERICAN MUSEUM OF NATURAL HISTORY

THE RADIOLARIA has an inner skeleton of silica that houses the spherical nucleus.

Class Demospongiae. *Demospongiae*, the commonest sponges, either lack a skeleton or have one composed of a plastic-like secretion called *spongin*. Most of them live in relatively shallow seas, but one family lives in fresh water. The old-fashioned bath sponge is *Spongia*.

The freshwater sponges belong to the genus *Spongilla*; they are usually bright green or golden-green because they have microscopic plants as mutualistic symbionts.

PHYLUM COELENTERATA. The phylum *Coelenterata* is composed of some 9,600 species of aquatic animals, most of them marine, that have a saclike digestive cavity with a mouth opening at one end. The bodies of the coelenterates are radially or biradially symmetrical, with a ring of tentacles surrounding the mouth. On the tentacles, and often elsewhere, there are unique cells with which smaller animals are stung and paralyzed before they are thrust into the digestive cavity of the coelenterate.

Class Hydrozoa. Hydrozoans are characterized by their method of reproduction. Usually a *polyp* (hydroid) stage reproduces by asexual budding and releases free-swimming *medusae* (jellyfishes), which reproduce sexually; the embryos resulting from this mating settle to the bottom, become attached as polyps, and repeat the cycle.

Colonial hydroids include *Obelia* and *Plumularia*, also known as sea firs, and *Millipora*, or stinging coral. Freshwater hydras have no medusa stage, and some of the larger marine hydrozoan medusae have no known hydroid stage. Freshwater medusae are usually *Craspedacusta*.

Hydrozoans also include such free-floating colonies as the Portuguese man-of-war (*Physalia*), the by-the-wind sailor (*Velella*), and the porpita (*Porpita*).

Class Scyphozoa. *Scyphozoa*, the larger marine medusae, have armlike tentacles extending from the four corners of the pendant, tubular mouth. *Aurelia*, the moon jelly, is commonly found near shore; it is usually about eight inches in diameter. *Cyanea*, a giant medusa of the open ocean, may be seven feet across.

Class Anthozoa. All *anthozoans*, which are marine, lack a medusa stage; many are colonial. The most familiar are the sea anemones, the true corals, the sea fans, and the sea whips. They differ from other coelenterates in that they have additional cells in the usually noncellular *mesoglea*, or jelly, that separates the outer epithelium (epidermis) and the inner epithelium (gastrodermis). This additional cellular material makes the anthozoans' bodies firmer than those of other coelenterates.

The reef-forming corals obtain lime from seawater through their symbiotic relationship with microscopic green plants. Since reef-making corals depend on green plants, they occur only where sunlight penetrates warm seas.

PHYLUM CTENOPHORA. About 80 species of free-swimming marine animals with transparent, biradially symmetrical bodies make up the phylum *Ctenophora.* Comb jellies, as they are also known, swim by rhythmically beating eight lengthwise rows of paddle-like comb plates.

Ctenaphores feed on small planktonic animals that they usually capture by means of tentacles studded with adhesive cells. Many, such as *Mnemiopsis,* are thimble-shaped and glow in the dark when disturbed. *Cestus,* known as Venus' girdle, is ribbon-shaped and can be three feet long and two inches wide.

PHYLUM PLATYHELMINTHES. *Platyhelminthes* phylum, which is commonly known as flatworms, is composed of 15,000 species of flat-bodied animals that are bilaterally symmetrical and have well-organized muscle bands and muscle sheets. Flatworms also have a distinct nervous system consisting of at least one anterior ring of nerve fibers and lengthwise nerve cords.

Class Turbellaria. Turbellarians are free-living flatworms that glide on a ciliated lower epidermis or swim by bodily undulations. Most of these scavengers have a straight, Y-shaped, or multibranched blind digestive cavity. Although they are chiefly marine, *turbellarians* are also found in fresh water and in very moist soil. Freshwater turbellarians are known as *planarians.*

Class Trematoda. Trematodes are cilialess, parasitic flatworms that have one or more circular suckers with which to attach themselves to a host animal. The blind digestive tract is Y-shaped; the mouth, anterior.

Class *Trematoda* includes the flukes, such as the destructive liver fluke (*Fasciola*) found in sheep; intestinal and pulmonary parasites; and the dangerous African blood fluke *Schistosoma.* Some of the flukes, including *Schistosoma,* undergo a series of complex bodily changes that requires a sequence of hosts, one of which is usually a freshwater snail.

Class Cestoda. Cestodes, also known as *tapeworms,* are parasitic flatworms without digestive systems. They attach themselves to the intestine or body cavity of a vertebrate and absorb food directly.

Most tapeworms consist of an anterior individual (*scolex*) with suckers and hooks, and a series of posterior individuals. The latter are produced asexually by the anterior individual but can develop sex organs and produce fertilized eggs and embryos before breaking away from the oldest part of the chain and emerging from the host's body with the wastes.

Taenia solium, the tapeworm that attacks man when he eats improperly cooked, infected pork, can reach a length of 25 feet.

PHYLUM NEMATODA. The phylum *Nematoda* consists of about 10,500 species of cylindrical, unsegmented animals with a straight digestive tube from anterior mouth to posterior anus. Between the outer body wall, which has only lengthwise muscles, and the digestive tract is a bloodlike fluid that churns back and forth as the animal moves.

Some of these *roundworms* are free-living in moist soil and all aquatic situations, including hot springs and glaciers. However, parasitic nematodes are the best known. *Necator* and *Ancylostoma* are hookworms that attack man; *Euterobius* is the pinworm; *Trichinella* is a dangerous parasite acquired by eating infected, improperly cooked pork. *Filaria* causes elephantiasis.

PHYLUM ROTIFERA. Some 1,500 species of unsegmented aquatic animals, none over 1/16 inch long, compose the phylum *Rotifera.* The head region has a mouth with a muscular grinding mill nearby; two whorls of cilia move food particles toward the mouth and aid in swimming. Posterior to the anus, the wheel animalcule usually has a two-toed foot with cement glands that temporarily anchor the rotifer to a solid object.

Most rotifers are free-living freshwater dwellers. Although they are multicellular, rotifers are about the same size as the larger protozoans.

PHYLUM MOLLUSCA. There are about 100,000 living and 40,000 extinct species in the phylum *Mollusca.* All mollusks have a soft, muscular, usually unsegmented body with a dorsal mantle that generally secretes a limy shell. Usually the anterior head has a unique rasping instrument, called the *radula,* inside the mouth.

Class Amphineura. The class *Amphineura* consists of the *chitons,* all of which are marine. Most have a dorsal shell consisting of eight transverse overlapping plates. In dangerous situations, *chitons* curl up to protect the muscular ventral foot, exposing only the hard shell. The class name refers to the two pairs of ventral nerve cords that extend lengthwise from a nerve ring around the chiton's mouth.

Class Scaphopoda. Belonging mainly to the genus *Dentalium* and known as tooth shells, scaphopods are marine mollusks that have a slender, slightly tapered, tubular shell open at both ends. They use their muscular foot, somewhat resembling a horse's foot, to dig themselves into the ocean floor, leaving only the smaller opening of the shell exposed. Through this opening they draw in and expel water and minute particles of food.

Indians on the western coast of North America once used tooth shells as money; natives of New Guinea often wear them as ornaments in pierced ears, noses, and lips.

Class Gastropoda. Some two-thirds of the known species of mollusks are gastropods, known as snails if they have coiled shells, or slugs if they lack shells. All of them creep or cling on a flat, bilaterally symmetrical ventral foot; above the foot is a spiral body covered by the mantle.

Most gastropods are marine herbivores; but some, such as the whelk *Busycon* and the oyster drill *Urosalpinx,* are carnivorous predators.

Physa is a freshwater snail; *Helix pomatea* is the edible garden snail that has been cultivated in Europe for centuries.

Class Pelecypoda. Pelecypods are the *bivalves,* which have limy shells hinged and controlled by strong muscles between them. These aquatic mollusks are chiefly marine; they are unique in that they lack a head region and a radula. The best-known genera in-

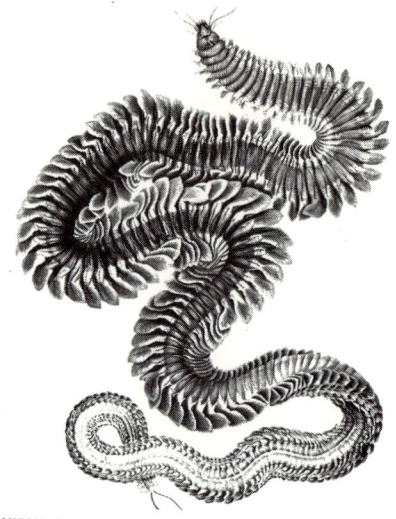

CLAMWORM, *Neries virens,* shows an evolutionary link between mollusks and annelids.

clude the scallop *Pecten;* the mussel *Mytilus;* the oyster *Ostraea;* the freshwater clam *Unio;* and *Tridacna,* the huge bear's-paw clam of the South Pacific reefs.

Class Cephalopoda. Cephalopods are marine mollusks that are "head-footed" in the sense that from eight or ten to as many as ninety tentacles extend from the part of the foot that contains the mouth; the rest of the animal is almost hidden by a high, conical mantle. Among fossil cephalopods a chambered shell was common; today, however, only the pearly *Nautilus* of the East Indies produces such a shell, in whose outermost chamber it lives.

Other living cephalopods have a greatly reduced shell, such as the "cuttlebone" of the cuttlefish *Sepia,* or none at all, as in the eight-tentacled *Octopus.* Most modern cephalopods have a pair of very large, camera-style eyes, much like those of vertebrates, and a highly developed brain.

All cephalopods are predators, most of them grasping their victims with suction disks on the tentacles, then rasping out flesh with the radula. Others are equipped with a special pair of concealed horny jaws, like the beak of a parrot, used for biting their prey.

Class Monoplacophora. Monoplacophorans, discovered alive for the first time in 1957, differ from all other mollusks in that they show signs of segmentation. A low, conical, one-piece shell characterizes and names this class, and is attached to the animal by from eight to twelve pairs of muscles. The sides of the flat foot bear a corresponding number of paired gills and excretory organs; the latter resemble those of the segmented worms.

Living species of *Monoplacophora* are members of the genus *Neopilina.* Regarded as "living fossils" because they show an evolutionary link between mollusks and annelids, they are found in the deep waters of the eastern Pacific. Fossils of this class have been found in stratified rocks of the early Paleozoic Era, covering a period from the Ordovician Age to the Devonian Age.

PHYLUM ANNELIDA. Some 7,000 species of cylindrical or flattened segmented worms are included in the phylum *Annelida*. The body cavity of annelids is transversely divided into definite segments, each of which usually contains a portion of the straight digestive tract that extends from anterior mouth to posterior anus.

The body cavity also contains a ganglion of the ventral nerve cord; branches of the closed blood-vessel system; a pair of excretory organs, called *nephridia*; and a set of bristles used in locomotion.

Class Polychaeta. Most members of the class *Polychaeta* are marine worms with a distinct head and a fleshy paddle on each side of most body segments. The paddles are supported and moved by the body bristles embedded in them, and both paddles and bristles are controlled by muscles within the body wall.

Many of these annelids, such as the clam worm *Nereis*, are free-swimming predators and scavengers. Others build U-shaped burrows in the bottom mud and use their paddles to create a current that brings a constant supply of food and oxygen through the burrow. Polychaetes include the lugworm *Arenicola* and the parchment worm *Chaetopterus*.

Class Oligochaeta. The best-known oligochaetes are the terrestrial earthworms, which burrow and scavenge in the soil for decaying plant material. Earthworms have no distinct head and no lateral paddles; they creep or cling by means of bristles that can be extended from each body segment.

The body usually has a swelling, the *clitellum*, about one-third of the way along the body from the head. The clitellum provides a sheathlike case for the eggs.

The most common earthworms are *Lumbricus*, *Allolobophora*, and *Eisenia*, which can be distinguished by the location of the paired pores that connect to the sex organs. Other smaller oligochaetes live in fresh water, where they burrow into bottom sediments.

Class Hirudinea. The class *Hirudinea* is made up of predatory bloodsuckers whose bodies are composed of exactly 34 segments that are concealed among transverse wrinkles. All these annelids have a large posterior sucker; many also have an anterior one surrounding the mouth, which has three horny jaws to capture prey or to cut through the skin of a victim in order to reach the blood vessels.

Most leeches live in fresh water, but a few are marine; there is also one that lives in the rainy Malayan jungles. The medicinal leech, *Hirudo medicinalis*, has long been used in the bloodletting thought to be a remedy for many diseases in various parts of the world.

PHYLUM ARTHROPODA. There are more than 770,000 species of arthropods, of which about 700,000 are insects. Typically, each arthropod has a segmented body enclosed by an external skeleton containing the polysaccharide *chitin*; this *exoskeleton* is shed periodically. Many of the body segments have a pair of jointed appendages, from which the phylum takes its name.

Almost 80 percent of the known animals are included in this phylum, which includes marine, freshwater, and terrestrial creatures of many types: free-living, *sessile* (attached by the base), commensal, and parasitic.

Class Onychophora. The onychophores are the "velvet worms" or "walking worms" of humid climates, chiefly the tropics. Their cylindrical bodies, which may be as much as eight inches long, have from 15 to 43 pairs of soft legs, each ending in two claws. The anterior head region is indistinct and bears a pair of simple eyes, a pair of short, flexible tentacles, and a pair of blunt *papillae* through which large salivary glands open near the mouth.

Distinct impressions of onychophorans have been found among the oldest fossils, and those species alive today are referred to as "living fossils" because they show features of both arthropods and annelids.

Like other arthropods, they have the periodically shed exoskeleton of chitin; the reduced body cavity, which is mainly replaced by large *sinuses*, or cavities, through which blood flows in an open circulatory system; the system of fine *tubules* through which air reaches inner organs; and claw-tipped legs.

Like annelids, they have paired excretory organs (nephridia) and simple eyes; they also lack a distinct head (or head plus thorax). The best-known members of *Onychophora* belong to the genus Peripatus.

Class Trilobita. Extinct marine arthropods, of which over 2,000 species are known from Paleozoic times, compose the class *Trilobita*. Each had a flattened, elliptical body marked by lengthwise furrows that separated a central lobe and two lateral lobes (the three lobes gave the class its name).

Transversely, the body was divided into a head with a pair of joined antennae, four pairs of jointed *maxillae* (mouth parts), and a pair of compound eyes; a thorax of 2 to 29 segments, each with a pair of jointed appendages used in swimming and creeping; and an abdomen made up of several segments fused into one plate.

All trilobites, the longest of which were 26 inches long, seem to have been scavengers. Their numbers decreased when fishes with jaws, their natural enemies, proliferated.

Class Crustacea. Although generally marine, crustaceans can also be found in fresh water and on land. A few are parasites that attach themselves to fishes. All crustaceans have a head region with two pairs of *antennae*, a pair of *mandibles* (jaws), and at least two other pairs of maxillae. Both the thorax and the abdomen may have paired appendages for swimming and walking.

Familiar genera of these creatures include *Artemia*, the brine shrimp of alkaline lakes; *Balanus*, the acorn barnacle of seacoasts; *Lepas*, the goose barnacle; *Oniscus* and *Porcellio*, terrestrial pillbugs; *Homarus* the Atlantic lobster; and *Callinectes*, the blue crab.

Class Diplopoda. The diplopods are the *millipedes*, or "thousand-legged worms." Each has a pair of antennae, a pair of jaws, and a pair of maxillae on the head; four segments and three pairs of legs on the thorax; and from nine to more than a hundred segments on the trunk. Each of these segments is really two that have been fused in the course of evolution; thus, as the class name indicates, each segment has two pairs of legs.

Most diplopods are harmless terrestrial scavengers that inhabit moist places.

Class Chilopoda. Terrestrial predators commonly known as *centipedes*, chilopods have flattened bodies and only one pair of legs per segment—there may be from 15 to 181 pairs of legs. The head has a pair of jointed antennae; a pair of jaws; and two pairs of maxillae, the second pair partially joined to form a lower lip that gives the class its name.

The first pair of legs are hooklike and have poison glands that open at the sharp tip of each; these poisonous hooks inflict painful or dangerous wounds.

Class Insecta. More than 700,000 species of insects, the only flying animals without backbones, are known today; and more are discovered every year. Insects are primarily terrestrial arthropods whose body is distinctly divided into head, thorax, and abdomen.

The head has a pair of jointed antennae, a pair of mandibles, a pair of jointed maxillae, and a *labium* (lower lip) that evolved from another pair of maxillae; the maxillae may be modified for chewing, sucking, or lapping. Typically, each of the three thorax segments has a pair of legs, in adult insects the second and third segments may also have a pair of wings apiece.

Insects may be classified by structure and by development. Structurally, the details of the maxillae and the wings are considered. The ancient insects are wingless, and change little in body form from hatching to maturity. The modern insects undergo indirect metamorphosis, a spectacular transformation from a specialized *larva* that spends most of its time eating and growing, to a quiet, nonfeeding *pupa* that encases the larval body while it is becoming an adult, to an adult that reproduces.

Intermediate insects experience direct metamorphosis, an incomplete transformation that lacks a pupal stage; the animal progresses from immature stage to mature stage. The wings of intermediate insects develop as pads on the back; the wings of modern insects develop internally, in the pupal stage.

Of the 16 orders described here, the first two are ancient, the next nine are intermediate, and the last five are modern.

Order Collembola is made up of the *springtails*, minute insects that are rarely more than ⅛ inch long and have chewing mandibles. They leap by flipping a special ventral springing organ on the fourth abdominal segment from under a hook on the third segment. The order includes

GEORGE A. SMITH

THE MONARCH BUTTERFLY is one of roughly 122,000 species of *Lepidoptera*. The butterfly shown is just emerging from its chrysalis.

some 2,000 species that live on land, in soil, and over water.

Order *Thysanura* is composed of about 700 species of *bristletails*, including the silverfish *Lepisma*. They grow to 1¼ inches long, and their bodies are covered with overlapping scales. Thysanurans have chewing mandibles and long, threadlike antennae. There is also a pair of antenna-like structures on the posterior end, and the last body segment of thysanurans may extend as a third antenna-like "tail."

Order *Dermaptera* includes the *earwigs*, which may grow to two inches in length and have chewing mandibles and, at the end of the abdomen, a pair of strong forceps. Some are wingless; others have a short pair of leathery wings that, when the animal is at rest, cover a large pair of membranous, semicircular hind wings. Order *Dermaptera* includes about 1,100 species, some of them harmful to crops.

Order *Orthoptera* includes some 23,000 species of insects, including cockroaches, stick insects, short-horned grasshoppers (locusts), long-horned grasshoppers (including katydids), and crickets. Some of these insects reach a length of 12 inches.

Most of them have as adults a pair of narrow forewings that cover the hind wings when the animal is at rest. The hind wings are folded fanwise. Certain species of the order *Orthoptera* cause considerable damage to crops.

Order *Isoptera* is made up of the social insects called *termites* or "white ants." All of the some 1,800 species of this class have chewing mandibles and may reach a length of two inches. Only adult sexual individuals have wings, of which there are two narrow membranous pairs. The wings lie flat on the back when the termite is at rest and are detached after the nuptial flight. The thorax and abdomen are joined broadly; there is no "waist" like that of a true ant.

Termites that eat wood depend upon intestinal flagellates to predigest the fibers. Some tropical termites cultivate fungus plants on chewed vegetation, then eat the fungi.

Order *Odonata* contains about 6,000 species of damselflies and dragonflies, which in their immature stages are freshwater predators. Members of the order have chewing mandibles and may reach a length of six inches, with a wingspread up to one foot—fossil dragonflies had wingspreads of as much as 28 inches. Adults have two pairs of membranous wings crisscrossed with many veins; a head with huge compound eyes; and a long, slender abdomen.

Order *Ephemeroptera* consists of the mayflies, of which there are approximately 1,500 species. They have chewing mandibles in the immature aquatic stages, but these become only vestigial at maturity. Mayflies reach a length of as much as two inches but may look longer because the abdominal tip has two or three filamentous "tails."

Members of the order *Ephemeroptera* are unique in that the flying creature that emerges from the immature aquatic stage is not yet an adult; it must shed its skin once more —even over the wings. The wings consist of a large forepair and a small hind pair, both pairs membranous and crisscrossed with veins. Mayflies rarely survive more than a day as an adult, but may require a year or more to reach this stage.

Order *Mallophaga* is composed of the biting lice, which grow to ¼ inch long and have chewing mandibles. Their bodies are flat and wingless, and they have either no eyes or small eyes. There are about 2,700 species of biting lice, all of them external parasites on birds and mammals. The genus *Menopon* includes the hen lice.

Order *Anoplura* includes some 200 species of sucking lice, whose flat, wingless bodies may be up to ¼ inch long. These lice have sucking mouthparts and small eyes—or no eyes. *Pediculus capitis* is the head louse, or "cootie," which transmits typhus fever and other diseases; *Haematopinus suis* is the hog louse.

Order *Heteroptera* is the order of the true bugs, which may grow to a length of four inches and have piercing, sucking mouthparts that arise forward on the head. Some *Heteroptera* are wingless as adults; those with wings have a forepair that is thick and horny at the base but membranous at the tips, where they overlap when held flat and slightly crossed at rest. The hind wings are membranous and fold slightly below the forewings.

Among the order's approximately 45,000 species are such water striders as *Gerris*, the stinkbugs *Pentatoma*, the milkweed bug *Lygaeus*, and wingless bedbug *Cimex*.

Order *Homoptera* contains the cicadas and their kin, about 25,000 species in all. These insects, many of them injurious to plants, grow to five inches long and have piercing, sucking mouthparts that rise far back on the head. Winged adults have forewings larger than the hind wings; both sets are membranous and at rest are held in tent fashion over the back. Some of the better-known *Homoptera* are the cicadas, aphids (plant lice), scale insects, leafhopper, and the spittle bugs.

Order *Lepidoptera* consists of the moths and butterflies, insects that may have a length of four inches and a wingspread of almost one foot. A caterpillar usually has biting mandibles, three pairs of thoracic legs, up to four pairs of soft abdominal prolegs, and labral openings of silk glands, used in spinning the cocoon. Adults have maxillae joined to form a coiled sucking tube, or *proboscis*. They also usually have two pairs of broad, membranous wings covered by overlapping scales.

There are roughly 122,000 species of *Lepidoptera*, including many that, as caterpillars, eat man's crops or possessions.

Order *Diptera* is composed of the two-winged, or "true," flies. These insects may attain a length of two inches and have a wingspread of three inches. The larval stages are usually legless maggots, some of which have chewing mouthparts. The adults have piercing and sucking, or lapping, mouthparts and one pair of membranous wings; the hind wings are represented by a pair of short, knobbed balancers.

Some of the roughly 90,000 species in the order are the mosquitoes *Anopheles*, *Aedes*, and *Culex*; the

GEORGE A. SMITH

FULLY EMERGED from its pupa case, the butterfly is in the final stage of its metamorphosis from egg to larva and finally to butterfly.

black flies *Simulium;* the beneficial tachinid flies that parasitize caterpillars; the fruit fly *Drosophila;* the housefly *Musca domestica;* and the wingless sheep tick or sheep ked *Melophagus.*

Order *Coleoptera* is made up of the beetles and weevils, which have biting mandibles in both larval and adult stages and may grow to six inches in length. The larvae are usually wormlike creatures with well-developed legs. Adults have a pair of thick, veinless forewings that, at rest, meet along the midline above the membranous hind wings, whose tips are folded when the wings are not in use.

Coleoptera is the largest order of insects, containing some 260,000 species. Many, such as the ladybug beetle *Coccinella,* are beneficial to man; others, such as the boll weevil *Anthonomus grandis,* are destructive.

Order *Siphonaptera* includes the fleas, which in the adult stage are external parasites on birds and mammals. The minute, legless larvae are scavengers with biting mandibles. The adults, about ¼ inch long, have laterally compressed, wingless bodies; their mouthparts are adapted for piercing and sucking.

Of the approximtely 300 species, two of the best known are *Pulex irritans,* which attack rats and humans, and *Xenopsylla cheopis,* the Indian rat flea, which transmits bubonic plague.

Order *Hymenoptera* takes in the ants, bees, wasps, and their kin, some 103,000 species. Some hymenopterans grow to three inches in length and may have a five-inch wingspread. Their larvae may be either legless maggots or caterpillar-like creatures; the latter are distinguished from caterpillars of the order *Lepidoptera* by having more than four pairs of fleshy prolegs. Some larvae are parasitic, usually attaching themselves to other insects.

Adults usually are solitary, but some species build colonies and organize societies that show distinct castes. Those adults that can fly have membranous forewings longer than the hind wings; the latter are hooked together in flight. The female's ovipositor is commonly modified as a saw, drill, or stinger.

Among the better-known species of the order are sawflies, with herbivorous, caterpillar-like larvae; beneficial *ichneumon* flies and *chalcids,* which parasitize harmful insects; gall wasps, ants, such as *Formica;* wasps, such as *Vespa* and *Polistes;* bees, such as the bumblebee *Bombus* and domesticated honeybee *Apis mellifera.*

Class Merostomata. Only four "living fossil" species of horseshoe crabs remain of the ancient "divided mouth" class, Merostomata. All of them dwell in shallow, offshore seas, where they scavenge on seaweeds, sea worms, and young mollusks.

Merostomates are armored creatures with an unsegmented *cephalothorax* joined broadly to an abdomen that ends in a bayonet-like tail spine; they lack antennae and true jaws. Food is chewed between the spiny bases of the four pairs of walking legs that flank the elongated mouth slit. Also near the mouth are two pairs of appendages, the usually pincer-like *chelicerae* and the *pedipalpi.*

Perhaps the best-known species is *Limulus,* of the American eastern coast, which comes to shore each spring to lay its eggs in beaches from Maine to Yucatan.

During the Paleozoic Era, the merostomates included sea scorpions, up to six feet long, whose clearly segmented, flexible, tapering abdomens suggest that they may have been the ancestors of land scorpions. Horseshoe crabs, by contrast, have an abdomen fused into a single unit; however, like the sea scorpions, they have a ventral series of five or six pairs of plates that are used in swimming and as protection for the gills.

Class Arachnida. The class *Arachnida* includes some 30,000 species of spiders and their kin. Each species has a cephalothorax and an abdomen, a pair of chelicerae, a pair of pedipalpi, and four pairs of legs, but lacks antennae, jaws, and paired appendages on the abdomen.

The class arachnida includes the scorpion *Scorpio,* the house spider *Theridion,* the orb-web spider *Argiope,* the harvestman *Phalangium,* the tick *Dermacentor,* and the spider mite *Tetranychus.* Scorpions, spiders, and many of the mites are predators; ticks and the rest of the mites are external parasites of animals or plants and may transmit diseases from infected hosts to healthy ones.

PHYLUM BRACHIOPODA. Brachiopods, known as lamp shells because of a resemblance between one type of shell and ancient oil lamps, are marine bivalves that secrete the dorsal half and the ventral half of the shell from the mantle. There are 260 living species and over 5,000 fossil species.

Most adult brachiopods remain permanently attached to their surroundings by means of a short posterior stalk that emerges through an opening in the ventral valve of the shell, near the hinge. The unsegmented body has two *lophophores,* spiral or V-shaped arms, from which the phylum takes its name; the lophophores bear ciliated tentacles that create currents to bring oxygen and microscopic food particles into the shell.

One class of brachiopods has a largely chitinous shell and no hinge teeth; these animals include *Lingula* and *Crania,* genera known longer than any others in the animal kingdom. A second class has a limy shell and teeth that keep the halves of the shell in alignment. These include *Terebratulina* and *Rafinesquina.*

PHYLUM ECHINODERMATA. There are roughly 5,700 species of echinoderms (or "spiny skins"), which begin life as bilaterally symmetrical embryos, then take on a false radial symmetry, and still later may become conspicuously biradial or even bisymmetrical; the symmetry usually has five parts.

If the creature has a skeleton, it is internal, composed of limy spicules or plates. Part of the large body cavity is separated to form a unique water-vascular system with special tube-like feet used in feeding and locomotion.

Echinoderms include the sea lilies and feather stars (class *Crinoidea*); sea cucumbers (class *Holothuroidea*); sea urchins, heart urchins, and sand dollars (class *Echinoidea*); sea stars, or starfishes (class *Asteroidea*); and serpent stars, or brittle stars (class *Ophiuroidea*).

7

PHYLUM CHAETOGNATHA. Roughly 50 species of arrow worms, all of them very slender, cylindrical, and unsegmented, compose the phylum *Chaetognatha.*

The lateral cranial lobes of these three-inch marine predators have chitinous bristles with which prey is captured and pushed into the mouth (hence the phylum name of "bristle jaws"). The digestive tract is straight, and the anus is just anterior to the tail. A pair of lateral fins, supported by fine chitinous rods, give the creature better stability and allow it to dart after minute crustaceans.

The arrow worms' remarkable transparency often causes them to be overlooked. They are plentiful, however, and provide an important source of food for whalebone whales.

PHYLUM CHORDATA. Chordates, of which there are some 45,000 species, are distinguished from all other animals by the development of a flexible supporting rod, called the *notochord.* This lies immediately below the hollow dorsal nerve cord and gives the phylum its name.

At some stage in development, gill slits connect the pharyngeal area to the outside of the body. Usually the body is bilaterally symmetrical and has a complete digestive tract, a closed circulatory system, and a tail posterior to the anus. Four subphyla are recognized.

Subphylum *Tunicata* is composed of about 1,600 marine species that have a notochord and a nerve cord only during the larval stage; the adult is a degenerate form surrounded by a secreted tunic, usually of cellulose.

The most familiar members of this subphylum are the sea squirts (class *Ascidiacea*). They are small and tadpole-shaped as larvae. The adult is permanently attached to the sea floor, where it draws in water, filters out microscopic food and absorbs oxygen, and expels the water.

Subphylum *Cephalochordata* includes about thirty marine species that retain the notochord and the nerve cord; both extend the full length of the body. Cephalochordates are the lancelets, or *amphioxi*, of the class *Leptocardii* and mainly of the genus *Brachiostoma.* They are slender, pointed at each end, and laterally compressed; they swim freely or make shallow burrows in the sandy sea floor near shore.

Subphylum *Agnatha* originally contained the earliest vertebrates, which are known through the fossilized covering of armor-like, bony scales over the head and much of the body; these members of the class *Ostracodermi* apparently were freshwater bottom dwellers during Ordovician, Silurian, and Devonian times.

Class Cyclostomata. Modern agnathans have a cartilaginous troughlike skull and a series of cartilaginous bars protecting the nerve cord. These smooth-skinned, cylindrical, unarmored creatures have horny teeth in their cup-shaped mouths, but no paired fins. They propel themselves by sinuous swimming movements of the whole body.

The hagfishes or slime eels, such as *Myxine*, are direct-developing marine scavengers that eat dead and dying fishes; the lampreys, such as *Petromyzon*, spend at least their larval stage in fresh water and then may move out to sea, where they attack living fishes. *Petromyzon marinus* spread through the Great Lakes in recent years and almost destroyed commercial fishing until recent efforts.

Subphylum *Gnathostomata* consists of chordates with an upper and lower jaw and blocks of cartilage or bone that serve as *vertebrae* and largely or completely replace the notochord in stiffening and supporting the body.

Usually these creatures have paired appendages—a pectoral pair of fins, legs, wings, or arms, and a pelvic pair of fins or legs. If the appendages are fins, the chordate is a fish; if they are limbs, it is a *tetrapod.* Six of the seven classes in the subphylum are represented by living species, the familiar vertebrates.

Class Placodermi. Placoderms (skin of plates) are extinct, jawed fishes that usually had an armor of bony plates or bony scales and two or more pairs of fins. These ancient fish are known from both freshwater and marine fossils of Upper Silurian to Devonian times; the best-known are *Dinichthys* and *Acanthodes.*

Class Chondrichthyes. About 275 living species, all primarily marine, compose this class of cartilaginous fishes that includes the sharks, skates, rays, and chimeras. All of them have cartilaginous rather than bony skeletons (hence the class name); in some, the cartilage is calcified. The scales are minute and usually have an enamel covering over a dentine base, similar to that of teeth.

Class Osteichthyes. A skeleton at least partly of true bone rather than of cartilage characterizes the approximately 25,000 marine or freshwater bony fishes in this class. Their bony scales either fit together in a diamond pattern or overlap like shingles.

Included in the class are the sturgeon *Acipenser*, whose eggs are caviar; the herring *Clupea*; the eel *Anguilla*; the sea horse *Hippocampus*; the cod *Gadus*; the freshwater perch *Perca*; the lungfish *Protopterus*; and the coelacanth *Latimeria*, sole known survivor of the lobe-fin fishes that are close to the ancestral line from which the tetrapods sprang.

Class Amphibia. Most of the nearly 2,000 species of amphibians transform from a gill-breathing immature stage (such as a tadpole) in fresh water to a lung-breathing, terrestrial adult stage. Most adults have forelegs and hind legs, the latter linked by way of a pelvic girdle to a specialized sacral vertebra. Unlike fishes, which have a two-chambered heart, adult amphibians have a three-chambered heart.

Common genera include the mud puppy *Necturus*, the salamander *Ambystoma*, the frog *Rana*, and the toad *Bufo.*

Class Reptilia. Some 5,000 living species of tetrapod chordates that have a dry skin, usually covered with overlapping scales, belong to the class *Reptilia* (creepers). Their skeletons are completely bony, and the pelvic girdle, if present, is linked to two sacral vertebrae.

These turtles, snakes, lizards, and crocodilians all obliterate the gill slits while developing within the egg; at no stage do they possess gills. Special membranes extend from the embryo to the eggshell and enable the embryo to breathe while surrounded by a watery egg "white" provided by the mother. Presumably the dinosaurs and all other extinct reptiles, including some that flew, were similar in general structure and development to modern reptiles.

Class Aves. More than 8,600 living species of birds are known, all of them warm-blooded and covered with feathers. They have a four-chambered heart and a system of blood vessels that carries all blood from the heart to the lungs for aeration before pumping it through the body again.

Other characteristics of birds are a mouth with a specialized beak; one pair of wings; and one pair of legs, which are linked to several vertebrae by way of a light but strong pelvic girdle. All birds lay eggs. Most can fly, but some—such as the ostrich *Struthio*, the kiwi *Apteryx*, and the penguin *Spheniscus*—are flightless and apparently had completely flightless ancestors.

Some well-known genera of class *Aves* are the domestic duck *Anas*, the fowl *Gallus*, the pigeon *Columba*, the crow *Corvus*, and the sparrow *Passer.*

Class Mammalia. There are more than 4,500 species of living mammals, all of them warm-blooded and at least partly covered with hair. The four-chambered heart pumps the blood through the lungs before it is circulated through the body. The pelvic girdle is fused to five vertebrae. Mothers secrete milk from special *mammary glands*, from which the newborn young gain nourishment. Twelve of the eighteen orders are of special interest.

Order *Monotremata* is composed of the egg-laying mammals. Some five genera belong to this order, all being found in Tasmania, New Guinea, and Australia; they include the duckbill or platypus *Ornithorhynchus* and the spiny anteater *Tachyglossus.* Only the young have teeth; adults have a horny beak. The large, yolky eggs are unique among mammals, as is the practice of incubating them.

The order is named to draw attention to the single body opening (cloaca) that serves the digestive, urinary, and reproductive tracts.

Order *Marsupialia* is made up of the pouched mammals, of which all but the American opossums inhabit Australasia. Unlike class *Monotremata*, the adult marsupials have teeth. The females have a pouch on the undersurface of the abdomen; the extremely immature newborn young creep in, attach themselves to a nipple, and remain attached until fully formed.

In all other orders of mammals (except *Monotremata*), the young are linked to the mother by a special membrane *(placenta)* formed by the embryo and used to transfer food and oxygen from the mother to the embryo, and wastes, including carbon dioxide, from the embryo to the mother. Such mammals are placental mammals.

Order *Insectivora* contains the insect-eating moles and shrews and their kin. These small mammals have pointed snouts and sharp teeth that are less specialized than those of other orders. The upper jaw has six to eight incisors, one pair of canine teeth, and three to four pairs of grinding teeth (molars and premolars); the lower jaw has no canines and often has fewer incisors.

Widely known genera are the mole *Talpa*, the shrews *Sorex* and *Blarina*, and the European hedgehog *Erinaceus*.

Order *Chiroptera* is composed of the bats, the only mammals that are capable of flapping flight. They fly by using their modified forelimbs, whose second to fifth toes are greatly elongated and support a thin, leathery membrane that extends to the hind legs, and usually to the short tail as well. The upper jaw often has one pair of incisors; the lower jaw, three.

Order *Primates* includes the monkeys and apes and their kin. Usually there are fewer incisors on both upper and lower jaws. Nails, rather than claws, are found on at least some fingers and toes. Characteristically, either the thumbs or great toes—or both—are opposable, and the shoulder girdle is linked to the breastbone by a collarbone on each side.

Modern man, *Homo sapiens*, and species of fossil man belong to this order, along with the chimpanzee *Pan*, the gorilla *Gorilla*, the orangutan *Pongo*, the rhesus monkey *Macacus*, the capuchin monkey *Cebus*, and the lemur *Lemur*.

Order *Edentata* includes the anteaters, sloths, and armadillos, about 30 different kinds of which live in tropical and warm-temperate America. The name means "without teeth," but actually only the anteaters are toothless. No kind has incisor or canine teeth, and there is no enamel on the premolar and molar teeth with which sloths and armadillos chew their plant food.

Order *Pholidota* consists of seven different kinds of pangolins, or scaly anteaters, of tropical Africa and Southeast Asia. These mammals are also toothless. They capture insects, particularly ants and termites, with a long, slender, sticky tongue and swallow the prey whole.

Order *Lagomorpha* includes rabbits and their kin. These animals may be distinguished by their teeth: two pairs of incisors in the upper jaw, one pair behind the other; one pair of incisors in the lower jaw; no canine teeth. The lower jaw can move from side to side but not from front to back; the jaws are not opposable. The tail is short. Some common genera are the pika or coney *Ochotona*, the hare *Lepus*, and the cottontail rabbit *Sylvilagus*.

Order *Rodentia* is made up of gnawing mammals that have only two incisors in the upper jaw and two in the lower; they have no canine teeth. Rodents have opposable jaws, and their lower jaws move forward and backward as well as from side to side.

Common rodents include the squirrel *Sciurus*, the marcot *Marmoto*, the rat *Rattus*, the mouse *Mus*, the beaver *Castor*, the porcupines *Hystrix* and *Erethizon*, and the South American capybara *Hydrochaerus* (the largest rodent, which grows to four feet in length).

Order *Carnivora* comprises land mammals with well-developed canine teeth used in tearing the flesh of their animal food. They have six small incisors above and below. Included in the order are the dog, wolf, and coyote *Canis*, the bear *Ursus*, the cat *Felis*, and weasel *Mustela*.

Order *Pinnipedia* consists of swimming mammals similar in many ways to carnivores, such as the seal *Phoca*, walrus *Odobenus*, and sea lion *Zalophus*.

Order *Tubulidentata* contains only the aardvark *Orycteropus* of Africa south of the Sahara. It resembles a large-size pig with teeth of a strange, tabular form found only in the sides of the mouth.

Order *Proboscidae* is now represented by only one type of animal, the elephant. These massive, thick-skinned mammals have a nose and upper lip that extend into a trunk tipped with nostrils.

The two upper incisors are elongated as tusks, and only one or two molars at a time are on each side of the upper and lower jaws; there are no canines or premolars. The teeth are large and have many folded rows of enamel.

An elastic pad behind the toes bears the animal's weight; the toes have nail-like hoofs on three to five digits, depending on the species.

Order *Artiodactyla* contains the even-toed hoofed mammals. These animals have two or four toes; on each toe is a horny hoof that reaches the ground. *Sus*, the boar or pig, and *Hippopotamus* have four toes on each foot. They also have a simple stomach.

Other artiodactyls have two toes on each foot and a four-part stomach; they chew regurgitated food in the form of a cud. Included in this second group are the camel, the caribou, the deer, the cow, the giraffe, the antelope, the sheep, the goat, and the musk ox.

Order *Hyracoidea* contains nine kinds of African and Near Eastern animals known as conies, dassies, or hyraxes, whose toes bear flattened nails resembling hoofs—four on the front feet and three on the rear. The

BIRTH OF AN OSTRICH. The egg, which is the largest laid by any living bird, is deposited in the sand and incubated by the heat of the sun. The ostrich, a flightless bird, lives in many parts of Africa.

EARL THEISEN

soles of the feet have special suction cups that help the animals climb on rocks and trees.

Order *Sirenia* is composed of four kinds of sea cows, large animals of the seacoasts that are said to have confused homesick sailors into believing in mermaids.

Order *Perissodactyla* is composed of the odd-toed hoofed animals. They bear their weight on either the middle toe or the three middle toes; there is a hoof on each functional toe. There are no canine teeth, but there are incisors and molars in both jaws. The stomach is simple, so no cud is formed. The best-known genera include the horse and zebra *Equus*, the tapir *Tapirus*, and the rhinoceros *Rhinoceros*.

Order *Cetacea* contains the whales and their kin. Toothed whales, such as the sperm whale *Physeter*, the killer whale *Orcinus*, and the dolphin *Delphinus*, have identical enamel-less teeth and are carnivorous, preying on fishes, squids, and other marine animals.

Toothless (whalebone) whales, such as the great blue whale *Balaenoptera* (which, at 110 feet and 150 tons, is the largest animal of all time) and the right whale *Balaena*, strain food from the sea between parallel fringed plates of whalebone that hang from the inside of the upper jaw.

Both types of whale have a body highly adapted for swimming and diving: the forelimbs are reduced to flippers, the hind limbs have disappeared (although a pelvic girdle remains), and the tail is flattened into a pair of transverse fleshy flukes.

ZOOLOGY IN PERSPECTIVE

The scientific study of animals, with information carefully arranged, began with the works (336–323 BC) of Aristotle—the "Father of Zoology"—a Greek physician and naturalist who studied under Plato and served as tutor to the prince who later became Alexander the Great. Through his works, Aristotle showed himself eager for knowledge for its own sake and ready to relate his knowledge of nonhuman creatures to man.

For some 1,800 years after Aristotle, few people realized that the ideas and information in his works were incomplete and erroneous, and that new discoveries could be important. Among the first to correct Aristotle's mistakes was Andreas Vesalius (1514–1564), a Belgian physician, whose illustrated work on human anatomy appeared in 1543 and earned him the reputation of the "Father of Modern Anatomy." A Swiss contemporary of Vesalius, the naturalist Konrad von Gesner (1516–1565), compiled information on the known kinds of animals in a five-volume encyclopedia he published between 1551 and 1587.

In the 1600s, 1700s, and 1800s, discoveries came so quickly that it was hard for zoologists to fit them all together, and some facts remained unappreciated for many years. Even details visible through the microscope did not lead to immediate understanding.

Milestones in this period included William Harvey's (1578–1657) proof that the human heart circulates blood (1628), Robert Hooke's (1635–1703) discovery and naming of cork cells (1665), Jean Baptiste de Lamarck's (1744–1829) conclusion that living things are evolving (1801—his theory that evolution came about through use and disuse was disproved), and Mattias Schleiden (1804–1881) and Theodor Schwann's (1810–1882) theory that all living things are either cells or composed of cells. Many zoologists after 1760 were content to improve upon the classification system established by Karl von Linné (1758).

EVOLUTION. Just as Schleiden and Schwann's cell theory provided a unifying concept among living things, so the theory of evolution provided an explanation for Sir Richard Owen's (1804–1892) principles of homology and analogy, set forth in 1843. Overwhelming evidence that evolution had occurred and a theory of its method through natural selection was provided in 1859 when Charles Darwin (1809–1882) published his book *On the Origin of Species.*

Darwin's lack of information on genetics forced him to assume that the visible variations he saw in each species followed an inheritable pattern. This first book and his later works stimulated zoologists all over the world to fresh research, which uncovered a wealth of new evidence supporting the theory of organic evolution.

The first experimental work to support Darwin's work came during his lifetime, in the statistical studies of inheritance in garden peas by the Austrian monk Gregor Mendel (1822–1884). This work, published in 1865, was not "discovered" until 1900, when three different research scientists brought it to the world's attention. In the meantime, W. Kuhne had discovered the nature of enzyme action (1878), W. Flemming had gained a consecutive understanding of the events in the cell division (1882), E. Van Beneden had discovered *meiosis* (1887), and Henry F. Osborne (1857–1935) had recognized the evolutionary principle of adaptive radiation.

MOLECULAR STUDIES. Many recent discoveries and theories have drawn attention to chemical similarities among animals, among plants, and between plants and animals. They have focused attention at the molecular level, leading to a greater appreciation of the steps in organic evolution—particularly those that occurred before the animals that have left fossils.

In 1916, Thomas H. Morgan (1866–1945) presented his theory of the gene; in 1953, the nature of the genetic code, in terms of the molecular structure of the DNA in the chromosomes, was visualized from the work of M. H. F. Wilkins, F. H. C. Crick, and J. D. Watson; today the fine details of the code are being worked out.

In 1929, K. Lohmann discovered ATP, the carrier of energy in living systems; in 1937, Sir Hans Krebs accounted for the citric acid cycle in the mitochondria of each cell as it carries on respiration, using oxygen and producing ATP.

Wendell Stanley (1904–) discovered in 1935 that a virus can be purified until it becomes a nonliving crystal without losing its ability to cause a disease; this reopened the question of the line between the living and the nonliving and led to new considerations of the origin of life and the chemical evolution that preceded the appearance of recognizable plants and animals. In 1953, in Harold Urey's laboratory, Stanley L. Miller demonstrated that organic compounds can form spontaneously under conditions very similar to those that geologists envision for the Earth during the Archeozoic Era.

NEW PERSPECTIVES. With all of this information, the zoologist is able to interpret the range of animal life, both extinct and living, in a new way. He sees the first long period after life began as one during which chemical systems evolved. To survive, each system had to meet the fundamental requirements for life: the ability to absorb from its environment the chemical substances and energy it needed and the ability to reproduce. The zoologist assumes that an almost infinite number of combinations was tried and that each successful one progressed by adding slight variations that improved its chances of survival.

Until a modern form of photosynthesis released quantities of oxygen into the atmosphere, it is believed that there was no basis for *aerobic respiration* on Earth. It is possible that some ancestors of protozoans lived without oxygen, and the same may be true of unicellular ancestors of other phyla.

Predatory animals could not have existed until oxygen was present, for only aerobic respiration allows rapid expenditure of energy for more than a few seconds. Multicellular parasites can thrive without oxygen, but only so long as they have larger, multicellular hosts that carry on aerobic respiration.

Since the Cambrian Age, which began some 550 million years ago, when animals reached a size and firmness of body that made fossils possible, essentially all the phyla—and many of the classes—are represented. Each ancestral line is of about the same length, but some animals have changed more in structure than others. To a great extent, the ones that have changed most have spread from the sea to fresh water and onto the land, into deserts, hot springs, and petroleum pools; today, the seas hold most of the animals that have changed least.

Although all animals have become more specialized in structure and function, some have become too specialized to survive a change in environment. An example is the dinosaurs, which became extinct with the advent of the Ice Age. Thus, the phyla of modern animals are regarded as alternative ways of living, all equally successful in their respective environments and all incorporating general features of life that evolved before the Cambrian Age.

—Lorus J. Milne and Margery Milne

ANIMALS

AARDVARK, an insect-eating mammal of Africa south of the Sahara and the Sudan. The aardvark (Dutch for earth pig) is about 5 feet long, including the tail. It uses its strong claws to burrow into the ground and to tear down the nests of termites (white ants). It licks up the termites with its long, sticky tongue. Although often called ant boar or earth pig, its small eyes and long snout are its only piglike features. Order Tubulidentata, specifically *Orycteropus afer*.

ABALONE, a sea snail of rocky coasts, which produces a low oval shell as much as 12 inches across. Abalones eat seaweeds, foraging for them while clinging to rocks by means of a large flat muscular foot. Only the edges of the foot project beyond the shell, which shows a slight spiral and usually a series of breathing holes near one side.

When disturbed, an abalone holds on like a suction cup, by contracting a strong muscle from the center of its foot to the center of its shell. This muscle has a high commercial value because of its delicate flavor. For their flesh and for the shells, which are lined attractively with mother-of-pearl, they are harvested in large numbers. Order Prosobranchiata, various species of genus *Haliotis*.

ADDER. See *Viper*.

AGOUTI, any of about 24 different rabbit-sized mammals native to the West Indies, South and Central America, and southern Mexico. For the most part, agoutis live on the ground eating roots, fruits, and foliage. They do not climb or dig to any great depth. When at rest or eating, they commonly sit on their haunches and hold food between their paws. They are considered good to eat and are sometimes domesticated. Agoutis can damage crops by eating the plant roots. Order Rodentia, member of genus *Dasyprocta*.

ALBATROSS, any of 13 different kinds of giant petrel-like sea birds. The extended wingspread may measure up to 12 feet, and the weight may exceed 20 pounds, making it the largest of all aquatic birds. Its plumage is white with black bands on the wings and back.

It has a strong, hard, long bill of a pale-yellow color with its nostrils near the tip; the flesh-colored feet are short and webbed, and the wings are long, narrow, and strong. Many species are frequently encountered in the South Pacific. Others have great nesting grounds on Laysan, an islet in the Hawaiian Islands Bird Reservation. Still another kind of albatross is seen in immense flocks about Bering Strait, in early summer, attracted by vast schools of migrating fish. Order Procellariiformes, the tube-nosed birds; members of genus *Diomedea*.

ALEWIFE, or sawbelly, a valuable herringlike fish as much as 15 inches long, with sharp projecting scales along its undersurface. Alewives are common near land along the western side of the North Atlantic Ocean from the Gulf of St. Lawrence to the Gulf of Mexico. Some are landlocked in Lake Ontario and lakes in New York State.

In spring, alewives from the ocean enter coastal shallows and streams in large numbers to spawn. The young, hatched from the eggs, remain in fresh water until they are about 4 inches long (usually by autumn), at which time they go downstream to the sea and mature there. Order Isospondyli, specifically *Pomolobus pseudoharengus*.

ALLIGATOR. See *Crocodile*.

ALPACA, the domesticated South American camel, which stands about 2 feet high at the shoulder, native to the higher portions of the Andes.

The Peruvians keep vast flocks of alpacas and esteem the silky luster and fineness of their wool. Order Artiodactyla, specifically *Lama huanaco*.

AMOEBA, any of several different microscopic one-celled animals, or protozoans, which move by flowing slowly. An amoeba has no head end, covering, or skeleton. Freshwater amoebas (chiefly of genus *Amoeba*, from a Greek word meaning change) flow around and digest smaller animals and plants. A few kinds of parasitic amoebas, such as the dysentery amoeba (*Entamoeba histolytica*) of man, found in contaminated water, reach the intestine and cause severe inflammation. Class Sarcodina, order Amoebida.

ANACONDA. See *Boa*.

ANCHOVY, a bony fish about 4 inches long, belonging to the herring family. It abounds in the Mediterranean, particularly along the coasts of Italy, Greece, Spain, and France. It is bluish brown on the back and silvery white on the belly. Order Isospondyli, specifically *Engraulis encrasicholus*.

ANGELFISH, any of several different kinds of tropical bony fishes in which the body is so narrow and high that they can hide easily behind a plant stem. Their dorsal and anal fins are usually elongated, giving the body the appearance of having a long wing above and below. Marine angelfishes as much as 2 feet long are conspicuous in the shallow waters of coral reefs, where they display their bright colors and gay stripes when not busy reaching with their small mouths among the crevices for food.

The freshwater angelfish (*Pterophyllum scalare*) has long been a favorite for tropical aquariums, but it is active mostly at night, very nervous by day, and fights with others of its own kind; it is a native of the Amazon River. Order Acanthopteri; various genera in family Cichlidae.

ANT, a social insect of the order Hymenoptera, family Formicidae, found in most temperate and tropical regions. Small and powerful, these insects have long been noted for their remarkable activities and interesting habits. Theirs is a well-defined community consisting of males, breeding females (much larger than the males), and sterile females called neuters, workers, or nurses.

The workers are wingless, and the males and breeding females acquire wings only for the nuptial flight, after which the males and females divest themselves of their wings and either return to established nests or found new colonies. The workers perform all the labor of the anthill, the community abode; they excavate the galleries, procure food, and feed the larvae or young ants, which have no organs of locomotion.

Some ants live on animal food, picking clean the skeletons of dead animals. Others live on saccharine matter, being very fond of the sweet substance called *honeydew*, which exudes from the bodies of aphids, or plant lice. These the ants keep in their nests or tend on the plants where the aphids feed; sometimes they even superintend their breeding. By stroking the aphids with their antennae, they cause them to emit the sweet fluid. Other insects are found living with ants in different types of association.

In temperate climates most of the male and female ants survive until cold weather. The next brood of ants appears in the spring from eggs laid the preceding summer. In colder climates the workers pass the winter in a state of torpor and require no food. They need food only during the season of activity, when they have a vast number of young to feed. Some species have stings as weapons, others have only their powerful mandibles or an acrid and pungent fluid (formic acid) that they emit.

ANTEATER, any of three different tropical mammals related to armadillos and sloths, which capture insects as food by means of their long, slender, sticky tongues, extensible over a considerable distance. All three have powerful front legs with strong hooked claws, which they use in climbing and in ripping apart the nests of termites and ants. They walk on the sides of their feet, with the claws incurved. Anteaters live in South and Central America.

The great anteater (*Myrmecophaga tridactyla*), which lives in humid forests from northern Argentina to southern British Honduras, weighs up to 50

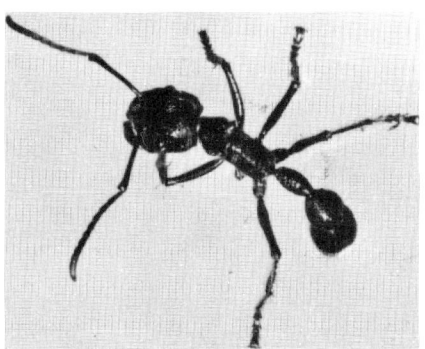

AMERICAN MUSEUM OF NATURAL HISTORY
ANT

pounds and is almost 7 feet long, counting the long bushy tail. The collared anteater (*Tamandua tetradactyla*) and the silky 2-toed anteater (*Cyclopes didactylus*) are smaller, with short hair, and a long naked tail which is used like a fifth hand in climbing; both are found mostly in trees, from southern Mexico to Brazil and Bolivia, and become most active at night. Order Edentata.

ANTELOPE, any of more than 100 kinds of graceful, plant-eating, cud-chewing mammals, which resemble deer but have permanent hollow horns instead of solid antlers that are shed annually. Africa south of the great deserts is the home of most antelopes—the various gazelles, gnus, hartebeests, and the springbok (*Antidorcas euchore*) and two kinds of elands (species of *Taurotragus*). Europe and Asia have two species: the chamois (*Rupicapra rupicapra*), which inhabits the Alps; and the saiga (*Saiga tartarica*) in the Soviet Union.

Antelopes have a timid and restless disposition and are among the swiftest runners in the animal kingdom. Most are gregarious, associating in herds. Order Artiodactyla, family Bovidae.

ANT LION, or doodle bug, any of several dozen kinds of larval insects with soft, egg-shaped bodies and large flat heads, equipped with sickle-shaped projecting jaws. An ant lion digs a funnel-shaped pit in the driest and finest sand it can find, using its big head to toss out the sand. When the pit is about an inch deep, with smoothly sloping sides, the ant lion buries itself at the bottom, projecting only its jaws. If an ant or other luckless insect stumbles into the pit, it skids down the sides into the jaws of the ant lion.

Generally the ant lion reacts to the sandslide produced by the skidding insect, confusing its victim by tossing still more sand. A full-grown ant lion pupates in the sand, and transforms to a flying insect resembling a dragonfly. Order Neuroptera; various members of genus *Myrmeleon*.

APE, the most highly developed wild members of the mammalian order Primates. All inhabit the Old World. They include baboons, mandrills, macaques, orangutans, chimpanzees, and gorillas. The nostrils of an ape are separated by a narrow septum; both fore- and hind-feet have opposing thumbs; the callosities on the rump are generally naked; some species have cheek pouches.

APHIDS, or plant lice, any of several hundred different kinds of small, soft-bodied insects with slender, sucking mouthparts. They are found all over the world, sucking the juices from the buds, leaves, flowers, young stems, or tender roots of plants. Growing rapidly, they attain adulthood by direct development and generally reproduce by parthenogenesis (virgin birth).

In the late summer, aphids develop wings and fly feebly to new locations. Toward winter, males are produced. Mated females lay eggs that can survive cold weather, whereas all young and adults die when frozen.

Generally an aphid reaches into the veins or conducting tubes where the plant is transporting sugary solutions and other organic substances. Excess water and sugar are excreted by the aphid in droplets, known as *honeydew*.

To get honeydew to eat, some ants carefully carry the aphids to suitable locations on plants, as though these "ants' cows" were domestic animals. Aphids that ants place in underground chambers on the roots of crop plants often cause serious loss to farmers, without being seen. Order Homoptera; various genera in family Aphididae.

ARMADILLO, any of about 20 different kinds of burrowing mammals encased by an armor of bony material divided into small, separate bands. The bands are connected by a membrane, except on the forehead, shoulders, and haunches, rendering the armor flexible and enabling the animal to roll itself into an armored ball.

Armadillos live mostly in Central and South America. They burrow in the earth, where they lie in the daytime, seldom going out except at night. They subsist chiefly on fruits and roots, sometimes on insects and flesh. They are inoffensive and can be eaten.

The largest (*Priodontes giganteus* of eastern South America) is 3 feet in length, with an 18-inch tail; the smallest (*Chlamyphorus truncatus* of Argentinean deserts) is 6 inches long with a 1-inch tail. The nine-banded armadillo (*Dasypus novemcinctus*), more than 2 feet long with a 12-inch tail, has spread recently through Mexico into Oklahoma and Florida. Order Edentata; various species in 9 genera.

ASS, either of two horselike mammals with conspicuous ears, an erect mane, a dark stripe along the back, and hair covering the hind legs where a horse has bare, horny areas. The African wild ass, or donkey or burro (*Equus asinus*), is native to Ethiopia, Somaliland, and adjacent areas of East Africa. It is easily domesticated.

The Asian wild ass (*E. hemionus*), which once ranged over the deserts and high plains from Asia Minor to Central Mongolia, has small differences in color and markings that can be used to distinguish the Syrian wild ass (Syrian deserts) from the onager (Iran to Turkestan), the Indian wild ass (western India and Baluchistan), the kiang (Tibet), and the kulan (Central Mongolia). Of these, the Syrian wild ass is almost extinct.

The long-legged and slender-headed tarpan, from which the domestic horse (*E. caballus*) was derived, is extinct. A related animal with shorter legs and thick head is the Mongolian wild horse (*E. przewalskii*).

Of the zebras, or striped horselike mammals, the one with the least markings is already extinct. It was the quagga (*E. quagga*) of southern Africa. Surviving zebras include the mountain zebra (*E. zebra*) of South Africa and Angola; Burchell's zebra (*E. burchelli*), which is common from the Transvaal to Uganda; and Grévy's zebra (*E. grevyi*) of Somaliland, northern Kenya, and parts of Ethiopia. Order Perissodactyla; family Equidae.

AUK, any of more than 20 different kinds of heavy-bodied sea birds of the Northern Hemisphere. They fly and swim many miles out to sea, feeding mainly on fishes, squids, crustaceans, and sea worms. Auks are most numerous in Atlantic waters from Newfoundland to Iceland and south to Scotland, and in the Pacific from northern California to Bering Strait and southeast along the Soviet coast. They come to land only in times of bad weather and during the breeding season.

The great auk (*Plautus impennis*) is now extinct; the last survivors were killed about 1845. It stood about 3 feet tall. The great auk could not fly, but used its wings to guide its underwater swimming. Like all auks, it propelled itself by paddling with its webbed feet.

Among the smaller auks still alive, the razor-billed auk (*Alca torda*) stands about 16 inches tall. Various auklets (genus *Aethia*) are barely 6 inches high. Other auks, all of which belong to family Alcidae, include the guillemots and the puffins. Order Charadriiformes.

AVOCET, any of 4 different kinds of long-legged shore birds, about 18 inches in length with a peculiar upcurved beak. The avocet of Eurasia and Africa is black and white; the two avocets of North America and Australia have a tan head and neck; the fourth species lives around salt lakes in the Andes of Chile and Bolivia. All of these birds wade sedately, swinging their slender beaks from side to side in shallow water to capture aquatic insects and small mollusks. Order Charadriiformes; species of genus *Recurvirostra*.

BABOON, any of eight different kinds of powerful apes distinguished by having an elongated, abrupt, doglike muzzle, fairly long tail, and naked pads on the buttocks. All but one kind—the most famous—are restricted to Africa. The exception, whose range extends from northeastern Africa to Arabia, is the Arabian baboon (*Comopithecus hamadryas*), which was sacred to the ancient Egyptians, who depicted it on their monuments, and mummified and entombed it. Old males have a heavy mane around the neck and shoulders.

More widespread in Africa are the Chacma, or pigtailed baboon, (*Chaeropithecus ursinus*) of eastern and southern areas; the yellow baboon (*C. cynocephalus*) of central and southern parts of the continent; the western baboon (*C. papio*) of central and western Africa; and the Doguera baboon (*C. doguera*) of Kenya and Ethiopia. West African forest areas are the preferred territories for the bearded mandrill (*Mandrillus sphinx*) and drill (*M. leucophaeus*), which have particularly colorful skin on the face and buttocks. Ethiopian mountains have the distinctive Gelada baboons (*Theropithecus gelada*), whose nostrils open on the sides of the nose.

All of these animals run and sit on the ground. They rarely climb trees or stand upright. They travel by day in troops of 25 to 300 individuals of all ages hunting for edible roots, fruits, eggs, reptiles, and insects. Sometimes they attack sheep or vege-

BEARS
U.S. DEPARTMENT OF THE INTERIOR

table crops, despite the efforts of herders and farmers. If pursued, they defend themselves, often by throwing stones and dirt. Order Primates, family Cercopithecidae, which includes also the monkeys of the Old World.

BADGER, any of 9 different short-legged mammals, related to weasels and skunks, which dig for their food with large forepaws armed with strong claws. The American badger (*Taxidea taxus*), found in dry open country from southwestern Canada to central Mexico, is somewhat smaller than the Eurasian badger (*Meles meles*) of wooded country from Scandinavia to southern China, which attains a weight of as much as 40 pounds and a length up to 3 feet.

The hog badger (*Arctonyx collaris*) of China, India, and Malaya, is equally large but more slender and has a long naked snout. Three kinds of ferret badgers (genus *Melogale*) and two of stink badgers (genera *Mydaus* and *Suillotaxus*) are found in the East Indies and adjacent parts of Southeast Asia. A honey badger, or ratel (*Mellivora capensis*), ranges over most of Africa and in Asia from Arabia to Turkestan and India.

Badgers feed on roots, fruits, insects, frogs, and ground squirrels. Most species have anal glands that secrete a malodorous fluid. Order Carnivora, family Mustelidae.

BARNACLE, any of about 800 different kinds of marine crustaceans that spend most of their lives permanently attached to rocks, submerged timbers, steel pilings, and ship bottoms. Their eggs hatch as free-swimming larvae, which feed, grow, and change their form. Soon each attaches itself to a firm support and begins to produce its limy shell of overlapping plates.

Shells of acorn barnacles (chiefly of the genus *Balanus*) are fixed directly to the support. Those of goose barnacles (genus *Lepas*) enclose the major parts of the body, which is held away from the support on a flexible, rubbery stalk.

Barnacles of all kinds cease feeding when exposed to air or when the water around them is muddy. In clear water, even during the crash of a wave, they extend from a gap in the shell several feathery extensions from their feet. In a combing motion, the barnacle captures minute sea animals as food and sweeps them into its shell, where it can get them into its mouth. Ships' hulls and wharf pilings often must be treated to prevent growth of barnacles on them. Order Cirripedia.

BASS, edible, perchlike bony fishes found throughout the world, most of them valued as food. Sports fishermen prize the American striped bass (*Roccus saxatilus*), which is native to the entire Atlantic coast from Florida north, and has been introduced successfully from California to Washington; it often reaches a weight of 60 to 70 pounds.

Almost as prominent among game fishes of freshwater are the small-mouthed and the large-mouthed black bass (species of *Micropterus*), which attain record weights of from 12 to 22½ pounds. The small-mouthed bass is sturdily built and dark in color; it frequents rivers and clear, cold water, and it is more active than the much heavier large-mouthed bass, which prefers quiet water and attains its greatest weight in semitropical regions. Order Percomorphi, the sea basses in family Serranidae, the freshwater basses in family Centrarchidae.

BAT, any of about 770 different kinds of mammals capable of flapping flight through use of wings formed from a thin webbing of skin stretched between the body and the elongated toes of the forelegs. Almost all land areas of the world, including remote islands, have their native bats or are visited by bats on migration. Most of these animals live in the tropical and subtropical regions, but a few kinds travel in season as far from the Equator as Scotland and Alaska.

Most bats are covered with short fur, have a pair of mammary glands in the chest region, and show their most distinctive features in the head—small eyes, small and numerous teeth, large ears, and nostrils often equipped with sensory lobes of peculiar shapes. Bats find their way about at night and in the dark places they choose for sleeping during the day by listening to the echoes of their own ultrasonic chirping. They can avoid obstacles as small as a stretched wire 1/16th of an inch in diameter, and pass through narrow openings without touching by the most dexterous use of their wings.

The majority of bats use the same type of echolocation to find flying insects and capture these as food. Tropical bats include a large number of kinds that seek out flowers that offer nectar at night, and unwittingly attend to pollination; others locate ripe fruits and crush them to get the juices. The largest of all bats is an Australian fruit-eating bat (the flying "fox" or kalong, *Pteropus giganteus*) weighing nearly 2 pounds and with a wing span of about 5 feet; it does much mischief in orchards.

Far more feared are the small vampire bats (*Desmodus* species) of tropical America, which use their razor-sharp front teeth to cut through the skin of sleeping people and large animals, add a saliva that prevents clotting of the blood, and lap up the blood as food. Still other bats in tropical America fly back and forth over the surface of quiet water, finding fishes of small size within reach of their long-clawed hind legs; these fish-eating bats (*Noctilio* species) either eat the fish in flight, or carry it home to the roost cave.

In caverns where many kinds of bats take shelter, each species clusters by itself, every bat suspended upside down. In cold regions, the bats either spend the winter hibernating where the temperature will always be above the freezing point, or they migrate toward the equator, where they can still be active and find food. All bats can bite in self-defense, and may be carriers of rabies. Order Chiroptera.

BEAR, any of 9 different mammals with large heads, large heavy bodies, short strong legs, and short tails. All except one (the polar bear, *Thalarctos maritimus*) live in temperate or tropical regions and tend to be active at night, sleeping by day.

All except one (the spectacled bear, *Tremarctos ornatus*, of northern South America) are animals of the Northern Hemisphere. The giants are the Alaskan brown bear (*Ursus arctos*) of the mainland and adjacent islands, which grows to almost 8 feet long with a weight of over 1,700 pounds, and the slightly smaller grizzly bear (*U. horribilis*) of the Rocky Mountains. Formerly, grizzlies ranged over much of western North America.

The Kodiak bear (*U. middendorffi* is a brown bear larger than the grizzly, found only on Kodiak Island, Alaska. American black bears (*Euarctos americanus*), which may be chocolate-brown, cinnamon-brown, blue-black, or even white, live in the forests all over North America except where they have been eliminated.

Asia has a black bear (*Selenarctos thibetanus*) in forests of the Himalayas, China, Japan, and Formosa; usually it has a white, crescent-shaped mark on the chest. The sloth bear (*Melursus ursinus*) lives in forests of Ceylon and of India as far as the foothills of the Himalayas, whereas the Malayan sun bear (*Helarctos malayanus*) is found in wooded areas of Southeast Asia from Burma to Indonesia.

All of these animals feed on fruits, roots, insects, and whatever small mammals they can catch. Grizzlies and the giant Alaskan brown bear are experts at flipping salmon out of streams during the annual spawning run. Polar bears eat seaweeds and carrion when other food is scarce; they swim readily, often from one ice floe to another in pursuit of seals. Unlike the other bears of the far northern regions they do not hibernate.

Hibernation, for a bear, consists of lying quietly, sleeping but capable of instantly being aroused, in a den of some kind during the winter months. The one or two young are ordinarily born at the end of this period of inactivity. Order Carnivora, family Ursidae.

BEAVER, either of two different gnawing mammals of the North Temperate Zone, with a broad flat naked tail and webbed hind feet. The European beaver (*Castor fiber*) and the American one (*C. canadensis*) are closely similar; both now occupy a small fraction of their previously wide range. In escaping from the attention of people who want to kill beavers for their fur, these animals have become nocturnal.

The European species makes its home inconspicuously in burrows along the banks of rivers, whereas the American beaver continues to construct a lodge of sticks and mud in the pond behind a special dam of the same construction. Beavers dive into the water for safety, propelling themselves with the hind feet while using the tail as a rudder, front paws folded against the chest.

Their food is exclusively vegetable matter, particularly the young twigs and thin bark of trees such as aspen and willow. A supply of this food is ordinarily collected during late summer and pushed into the muddy bottom of the beaver pond, where the beavers can go for it under the ice during the coldest weather. Order Rodentia, family Castoridae.

BEDBUG, a flat-bodied wingless insect that hides in cracks and bedding until night and then crawls out to suck human blood. Its saliva is poisonous to some people, its odor objectionable to almost everyone. It can live without a meal for as much as a year.

Related insects attack bats, swallows, and poultry, emerging from crevices in roosting sites to feed in darkness on their victim's blood. Order Heteroptera, specifically *Cimex lectularius.*

BEE, any of several thousand different wasplike insects with 4 membranous wings, the second pair much smaller than the first pair. The bee differs from the wasp in having a hairy body and mouthparts specialized for sucking as well as biting. Bees of many kinds inhabit virtually all land areas.

The bees eat and store honey made from the nectar of flowers and a material called "bee bread" made from pollen. On these nourishing materials the female bees feed the maggotlike larvae that hatch from their eggs.

Full-grown larvae transform to a pupa stage, during which their bodies are converted into the structure of the adult insect. While visiting flowers to gather nectar and pollen, bees unwittingly attend to pollination—usually cross-pollination—and hence are responsible for the efficient production of seeds and many kinds of fruits.

Bees differ greatly in their nesting habits. A majority of these insects make solitary nests, and are comparatively inconspicuous. Carpenter bees (of genus *Xylocopa*), which are as big as bumblebees, cut tunnels in timber, stock them with food and an egg in each of many chambers, and close up the opening afterwards. Leaf-cutter bees (of genus *Megachile*) snip out almost circular pieces of leaves and petals, particularly of roses, with which they line the burrows and construct the partitions separating one egg and its food store from the next.

Mason bees (such as the metallic green, bluish or purplish insects of genus *Osmia*) construct earthen cells under stones, in small holes in decaying wood, in deserted snail shells, and elsewhere. The cuckoo bees (species of *Nomada*) lack a means to collect pollen, and place their eggs in the nests of other kinds of bees. Social nesting is characteristic of bumblebees (of the genus *Bombus*) and honeybees (genus *Apis*). The bumblebees include about 50 different kinds in the North Temperate Zone and the Arctic, where they are the only bees present; they are rare in the Tropics.

Usually a bumblebee is about 1 inch long, heavier and larger than a honeybee, and covered with golden and black hair. Females build small separate cells on the ground, each one called a honeypot. Generally a few dozen bumblebees nest close together, building 200 to 300 honeypots.

Like most female bees, the female bumblebee has an effective sting. She can use it repeatedly until her supply of venom is temporarily exhausted, whereas a worker honeybee can sting only once because the act of stinging tears the stinger out of the honeybee's body. Bumblebees differ also from the honeybee in that the females of one colony never try to destroy one another; they do not swarm, and are regarded as showing only a simple social habit.

Few bees show so complex a social organization as the domesticated honeybee *(A. mellifera).* The most distinctive feature of this bee is its habit of continuing to store honey and bee bread not only for the breeding season but also to sustain the hive during the winter.

During the greater part of the year, the population of a honeybee hive is composed exclusively of two sorts of individuals—the mother, or queen bee, and the workers, or neuter bees, which are sterile females. The males, or drones, generally appear in May and are all dead by the end of July. The queen lives for several years, the workers only 1 to 2 months in seasons of activity, and the drones 1 to 2 months.

The queen has a longer body and shorter wings than the workers. She can use her sting repeatedly without rupturing herself, and normally will use it within minutes after escaping from her pupal cell. She will explore the hive thoroughly and sting to death all other queens present, even those that have not yet emerged as adults.

The old queen, with a large number of worker bees, has already left in a swarm, to find a new place for a colony. The young queen soon goes out on her nuptial flight, pursued by dozens of drones. Within 2 days, she is back in the hive, prepared to lay eggs at the rate of about 200 a day for the rest of her life. She lays each egg in a separate cell in the brood region of the hive, a short distance away from cells in which honey or bee bread is stored.

Development and hatching of the eggs, growth of the larva, pupation and transformation into an adult ready to emerge take an average of 24 days for the unfertilized eggs that mature into drones, 21 days for the fertilized eggs that mature into sterile workers on a low-protein diet, and 15½ days for the fertilized eggs that mature into new queens on a high-protein diet.

The life of a worker follows a regular schedule, with tasks changing to match development of various glands in her body. She produces saliva as a varnish for the cells in which the queen will lay eggs. She visits the honey stores and cells with bee bread to get food she can regurgitate for the larvae of different ages. The wax glands below her abdomen begin to secrete, and she takes wax scales in her jaws to work them into a material with which she builds new cells in the comb. Eventually, she crawls to the doorway of the hive and uses her wings there to create a current of air to ventilate the hive.

After a few days of this chore and of guarding the doorway from intruders, such as spiders or bees from other hives (which have the wrong "hive odor"), she becomes a field bee. Until their wings wear out, field bees daily gather nectar, pollen, resinous materials for sealing cracks in the hive, and water in hot weather when the inside temperature must be lowered by evaporation. A single hive may contain 60,000 workers at one time.

Only the workers possess special features on each of their 3 pairs of legs, which make these efficient tools in collecting and transporting pollen. The hind pair of legs—longer than the others—have on the outer surface a triangular depression (the palette) surrounded by stiff hairs; this forms a "pollen basket," into which the insect presses pollen combed from the surface of the body. The first segment of the feet on these legs is larger than the others, and bears on its inner surface a large number of short stiff bristles, forming a "pollen brush." The front pair of legs have notches through which the feelers are drawn carefully to clean them of pollen grains; an "eye brush" is on each front foot. Most of these and other special features are used by the bee while hovering in flight.

Worker honeybees appear to change their behavior according to the amount of a "queen substance" produced by their queen, and the amount of food stored in the hive. They communicate with one another in the darkness of the hive by special dances and sounds that tell other workers the direction and approximate distance to food they have found, as well as some measure of its abundance.

Order Hymenoptera, suborder Apoidea, and more than a dozen families.

BEETLE, any of more than 300,000 different kinds of insects in which the first pair of wings are hard, tough, and capable of meeting along the midline over the back to protect the membranous second pair of wings, which are used for flying. Beetles outnumber in variety all other insects, and are found on every continent, from forest to desert and fresh water.

Each beetle has a pair of strong jaws. Its eggs hatch to active larvae, which feed on living and dead parts of plants or on the remains of dead animals. Some bore in wood or live in tunnels eaten from the inner bark of trees. Upon reaching full size, a beetle larva pupates and transforms to the adult insect. Order Coleoptera.

BIGHORN, or mountain sheep, a wild sheep of the western mountain ranges of North America from New Mexico and California northward to British Columbia. It stands about 3 feet high at the shoulder; its horns are curved and spiraled back and outward, often to a full circle, and may measure from 32 to 40 inches in length. Its color varies from white to buffy brown to black with a large whitish rump patch. Order Artiodactyla, specifically *Ovis canadensis.*

BIRD OF PARADISE, any of 43 different kinds of perching birds related to crows, in which the adult male develops extraordinary feathers on the tail, wings, back, or head, used in courtship display. Females and young birds are inconspicuous and plain. Birds of paradise inhabit the remote forests of New Guinea and neighboring islands, and northeastern Australia. Field research has not yet provided full information on these magnificent birds. Order Passeriformes, family Paradisaeidae.

BISON, either of 2 kinds of large, cud-chewing mammals, remarkable for the great hump or projection over the fore shoulders, at which point the adult male is almost 6 feet high, and for the long shaggy rust-colored hair over the head, neck, and forepart of the body. In summer, from the shoulders backward, the surface is covered with very short, fine hair, soft and smooth as velvet. The tail is short and tufted at the end.

One, called the wisent (*Bison bonasus*), was once widespread in forested parts of Europe but survives now only in captivity. The other, the American bison (*B. bison*), was formerly numerous on the western plains of North America but is now present only in a few herds protected by law. The American bison is often incorrectly called a buffalo. Bison breed readily with domestic cattle, and their issue are fertile among themselves. Order Artiodactyla, family Bovidae.

BLACKBIRD, any of several American perching birds, related to orioles and meadowlarks. The red-winged blackbirds (*Agelaius phoeniceus*), which nest in marshes, often congregate in great flocks; the genus name *Agelaius* means gregarious. The related grackles are often called blackbirds. The unrelated European blackbird and the New Zealand blackbird are both songbirds of the thrush family. Order Passeriformes, family Icteridae.

BLACK DUCK, a common water bird of eastern North America, and a favorite with hunters. It is about 2 feet long and has dark-brown plumage with an iridescent bluish patch on the wings, and bright orange feet. It breeds from the Middle Atlantic States north to Labrador. The black duck and the closely related mallard are the two most abundant species of U.S. ducks. The nest of the black duck is a large structure made of weeds and grass; the 6 to 12 eggs are a pale greenish color. Order Anseriformes, family Anatidae, specifically *Anas rubripes*.

BLACK WIDOW, or hourglass spider, a small black spider with a black globular abdomen; a scarlet mark the shape of an hourglass on the abdomen's underside; and slender legs, the first and last pairs longer than the second and third. It is found in damp places from New England to Patagonia, more commonly in eastern North America and the far west.

The ¼-inch male is too small to be venomous, but the ½-inch female can puncture human skin where it is thin and soft, and inject a dangerous poison. She does so chiefly while guarding her 3 or 4 cocoons, each containing about 300 eggs, hung in a loose web in dark places such as cellars and outhouses. No deaths have been reported from such a bite in a healthy adult person. Related spiders with a similarly dangerous venom are found in Australia and New Zealand. Order Araneae, family Theridiidae, specifically *Latrodectes mactans*.

BLUEBIRD, any of 3 small perching birds of North America, with a soft twittering call and with blue feathers on much of the body. The eastern bluebird (*Sialia sialis*) was formerly much more common and was widely regarded as the harbinger of spring. Its breast and throat are earthy red, the rest of the body a solid blue. The western bluebird (*S. mexicana*) is similar except that the black is rusty red. The mountain bluebird (*S. currucoides*) is found from Mexico to Canada in high country; the male is azure blue, and the female is dull brownish with a blue rump, tail, and wings.

Bluebirds catch insects on the wing, but generally descend to the ground to eat them. They also eat fruits in season. Order Passeriformes, family Turdidae.

BLUEFISH, a mackerel-like marine fish, steely blue in color and beautifully shaped for speed and strength. It is widely distributed and abundant along the eastern coast of the United States.

Some individuals up to 20 pounds have been taken, but the average weight is from 3 to 8 pounds, and the length 20 to 30 inches. In addition to its food value, the fish is notable for the tremendous schools in which it congregates and for its feeding capacity. Young bluefish, called snappers, weigh about half a pound. Order Acanthopteri, family Pomatomidae, specifically *Pomatoma saltatrix*.

BLUE JAY. See *Jay*.

BOA, any of several dozen different nonvenomous snakes that resemble pythons in the way they capture and kill their prey, and in the possession of two functional lungs, not just the right lung as in snakes of other families. Unlike pythons, which lay eggs and are found only in the Old World, boas bear active young and most kinds inhabit the tropics of America.

In most boas and all pythons, a remnant of a hip girdle is attached to the backbone; in the male, further evidence of vestigial hind legs can be seen in a pair of protruding claws, one on each side of the vent. Like pythons, the boas lie in wait for prey, trying to capture mammals and birds far larger in diameter than the snake's head. Holding firmly with its mouth, the snake throws two or three coils of its body tightly around the victim and tightens still more every time the animal exhales. Prevented from breathing, the victim suffocates.

The snake swallows its prey whole, then seeks out some secluded spot in which to rest for a week or more while digesting its huge meal. Snakes with this habit are called constrictors. One referred to often as "the boa constrictor" is common from coastal Mexico to northern Argentina; it rarely exceeds 10 feet in length, but bears the name *Constrictor constrictor*.

The giant among boas is the anaconda (*Eunectes murinus*) of northern South America, which is reported to attain a length of 29 feet. It waits to prey along riverbanks, catching mammals and birds as they come to drink.

Beyond the New World, boas are represented in North Africa, Madagascar, the Mascarene Islands of the Indian Ocean, New Guinea, and on some islands of the South Pacific. Order Serpentes, family Boidae.

BOBOLINK, an American perching bird of southern Canada and the northern United States, except the west coast. It is related closely to the oriole, the blackbird, and meadowlark, and is known also as reedbird or ricebird in the southern states, through which it migrates to and from its winter home in central and southern South America.

The male bobolink is almost 7½ inches long. In spring and summer he is black and white on top and solid black underneath. By mid-summer, when bobolinks start south, and through the fall and winter, his plumage becomes buffy olive streaked with black, and the underparts olive or yellowish. Throughout the year the smaller female resembles the male in autumn plumage.

Order Passeriformes, family Icteridae, specifically *Dolichonyx oryzivorus*.

BOBWHITE, a quail native to the United States and Canada, named for its clear, loud two-part whistle. Both Rhode Island and Oklahoma have chosen the bobwhite as state bird. It has a conspicuous white patch on the throat and a pale mark from the beak over the eye and down the neck. At maturity the bird may be 11 inches long, including the short tail, and weigh 9 ounces.

Bobwhites benefit man by eating insects in summer and weed seeds in winter. They seldom fly far, but may

U.S. DEPARTMENT OF THE INTERIOR
AMERICAN BISON

attain more than 50 miles per hour. Order Galliformes, family Perdicidae, specifically *Colinus virginianus*.

BOLL WEEVIL. See *Weevil*.

BONY PIKE. See *Gar*.

BOTFLY, a parasitic fly often mistaken for a honeybee buzzing about the head and front legs of horses, mules, or donkeys. The female botfly keeps the tip of her long pointed abdomen curled under her until she alights, usually on a leg, and begins attaching her yellowish eggs to hairs of a horse. The horse gets the eggs into its mouth when it licks the hairs; the eggs hatch quickly, releasing legless maggots called bots. These find their way to the horse's stomach and attach themselves to the lining.

For about 8 to 10 months of the year the bots absorb what they need of the horse's food, grow to maturity, and pass through the digestive tract. From the manure they enter the ground, where they pupate and transform into adult flies. Related flies attack deer, moose, rabbits, squirrels, and other mammals. Order Diptera, family Gastrophilidae, specifically *Gastrophilus intestinalis*.

BRISTLETAIL, any of several similar wingless insects in which the head bears two long, slender feelers and three similar appendages extend from the opposite end of the body; these are the "bristles" for which the animals are named. Best known are the cosmopolitan silverfish, or fishmoth, (*Lepisma saccharina*) and the Europaen firebrat (*Thermobia domestica*), which inhabit human homes.

Like the firebrat, the bristletail uses its biting mouthparts in scavenging for food. Not content with crumbs, it dines on the glue that holds books together, or the sizing on coated paper, or the starch in clothes—often eating holes in garments and causing extensive damage. Lacking any transformation in body form as they mature, the bristletails are regarded as among the most primitive of insects. Order Thysanura.

BROWN THRASHER, a handsome songbird slightly larger than a robin and with a longer tail, a dark cinnamon-colored back, and rows of brown spots on its gray breast. Native to North America east of the Rockies, it hunts for insects, spiders, and worms among the fallen leaves below shrubs and woodland trees. Related to the mockingbird and catbird, the brown thrasher often sings loudly, mimicking other birds, usually repeating each phrase twice in quick succession.

For the winter, the brown thrasher migrates to the southeastern United States and eastern Mexico. Order Passeriformes, family Mimidae, specifically *Toxostoma rufum*.

BUFFALO, wild cattle of marshy places in the Old World tropics and subtropics. They are about 5 feet high at the shoulder. Some have been domesticated and used as beasts of burden.

The Indian or water buffalo (*Bos bubalus*) has been domesticated throughout Asia. The Cape or Kafir buffalo (*B. caffer*) of southern Africa is a larger, more powerful animal with a deserved reputation for being dangerous because it will charge and attempt to kill anyone who wounds it or threatens its young. The name buffalo was transferred by the early explorers to the bison of North America, a very different kind of animal. Order Artiodactyla, family Bovidae.

BUFFLEHEAD, or butterball, one of the diving ducks of North America, seen on lakes, rivers, and ocean bays, where it flies into and out of the water, pursuing fish and aquatic insects. In flight it displays conspicuous white patches on each wing. On the water, the dark back is often invisible and the body appears all white. The male's head is blackish green except for a large white area on the top. The female has a small slanting white patch on each cheek.

Buffleheads nest to the west and north of Hudson Bay, but spend the winter in most of the United States and Mexico. During migration, when they are hunted, each bird weighs 1 pound or less. Order Anseriformes, family Anatidae, specifically *Glaucionetta albeola*.

BULLHEAD. See *Catfish*.

BUNTING, any of several sparrow-sized birds with plump bodies and conical beaks. Europe has about a dozen different members of the genus *Embiriza*, including the corn bunting, the reed bunting, and the yellowhammer. In Eurasia and North America, the name "bunting" is used also for the snow bunting (*Plectrophenax nivalis*), which is the whitest of small land birds.

North America has 3 kinds of native buntings (*Passerina*), all spending the winter in Mexico but flying to separate nesting areas each spring. The indigo bunting (*P. cyanea*) goes to the central and eastern United States and Canada, where the males are the only all-blue birds; the mate is brown, faintly streaked below. The lazuli bunting (*P. amoena*) stays west of the Great Plains; the male is sky blue and on his throat, but has a chestnut breast band and white wingbars; his mate is brown, sparrowlike. The painted bunting (*P. ciris*) nests in the Gulf States and as far north as Missouri; the male is red, purple, and green, his mate all green.

Order Passeriformes, family Fringillidae.

BURRO. See *Ass*.

BUSHMASTER. See *Pit Viper*.

BUTTERFLY, any of a large group of scaly-winged insects with knobbed or hook-tipped feelers (antennae). They are closely related to moths, and develop in comparable stages: from an egg, to a plant-eating caterpillar, to a pupa, and to an adult with 2 pairs of wings and sucking mouthparts. The most conspicuous and useful of the mouthparts is a tube, which is coiled up like a watchspring when not in use.

Butterflies are active by day, and rest usually with the wings folded together vertically over the back, whereas moths are usually active at night, and rest with the wings more horizontal and to the rear. Most butterflies lay a single egg or a few in a place, and leave them unprotected. The caterpillars that hatch out are usually hairless, and pupate exposed, with no cocoon.

Of the 11 families of butterflies, 2 are composed of large insects found in the American Tropics: the brilliant iridescent blue *Morpho* butterflies (family Morphoidae), which conceal their display color when they close their wings; and the owl butterflies (*Caligo*, family Brassolidae), which have enormous eyespot markings on the underside of the rear wings, conspicuous when the insect is at rest.

Much more cosmopolitan are the skippers (most in family Hesperiidae), which are unique in having hooked, rather than knobbed, feelers, and of pupating in a cocoon; the swallowtails and their relatives (family Papilionidae), which include the giant birdwing butterflies of the Far East (*Troides*) and the familiar swallowtails (*Papilio*); the sulphurs, oranges, and whites (family Pieridae), including the cabbage butterfly (*Pieris rapae*); the blues, coppers, and hairstreaks (family Lycaenidae); the metalmarks (family Riodinidae); the huge family of brush-footed butterflies (Nymphalidae), such as the painted lady or thistle butterfly (*Vanessa cardui*), whose front legs, hairy and brushlike, are useless as legs; the wood-nymphs and satyrs (family Satyridae); the milkweed butterflies (family Danaidae), such as the migratory monarch (*Danaus plexippus*) of the Americas; and the heliconiids (family Heliconiidae), such as the zebra butterfly (*Heliconius charithonius*) of Florida, most of which are found in tropical America.

Order Lepidoptera, suborder Rhopalocera.

BUZZARD. See *Vulture*.

BY-THE-WIND SAILOR, a colonial marine coelenterate, resembling an oblong floating jellyfish but related to the Portuguese man-of-war. Native to warm waters of the Atlantic and Pacific oceans, by-the-wind sailors are often carried north and south to temperate latitudes and cast ashore, where they die. Unlike the Portuguese man-of-war, by-the-wind sailors are harmless to people.

Each colony is supported by a thin purple float containing gas chambers and bearing a low upright sail diagonally across the top. From below a healthy colony, a central tube hangs down, ending in a mouth. Around the rim of the float, small individuals of the colony bear many tentacles with which they capture food. This consists of miniature crustaceans and other small marine animals that drift in surface waters. The food is passed to the mouth, where it enters the diges-

CAMEL — UNITED NATIONS

tive cavity. Additional individuals below the float attend to reproduction. Class Hydrozoa, order Siphonophora, specifically *Velella mutica*.

CADDIS FLY, any mothlike adult insect with 4 hairy wings and soft nonfunctional mouthparts. Caddis flies are found in great numbers near lakes and streams because their caterpillar-like larval stages, called caddisworms, are all aquatic. Caddisworms usually are less than 1 inch long, are important food for fish, and are used as bait by anglers. The worms build cylindrical, portable cases of mineral or plant material or spin nets in swift waters to catch food particles carried by the current. Order Trichoptera.

CAMEL, a large cud-chewing mammal of North Africa and the Near East. There are two kinds — the Asiatic camel (*Camelus bactrianus*), which is about 9 feet tall and has two humps; and the African camel, or dromedary (*C. dromedarius*), which has only one hump. Camels can go for a long time without water but will lose weight and strength. When they are well fed, the hump is erect and plump, but when the camel is inadequately fed, the hump shrinks and falls over.

Fossil camels have been found in North America. The alpaca and llama of South America are closely related to the camels of the Old World. Order Artiodactyla, family Camelidae.

CANARY, a small songbird related to the sparrow, native to the Canary, Azores, and Madeira islands but domesticated in many countries for 300 years. Their acceptance of life in a cage and their sweet and powerful song have made canaries popular as household pets. The best singers, notably those raised in the Harz Mountains, bring high prices. Cage birds are usually yellow (canary color is a brilliant reddish yellow, named from the bird), but wild birds are a dull green with brown streaks. Order Passeriformes, family Fringillidae, specifically *Serinus canarius*.

CANKERWORM, either of 2 kinds of North American moth caterpillars that attack shade trees, orchard trees, and other woody plants. Both are described as measuring worms or inchworms because they move along by holding to the support alternately with the legs at the forward and the rear end of the body. When full grown, they let themselves down to the ground on long fine strands of silk, and burrow 1 to 4 inches into the earth before transforming into the adult stage—the moth.

Male moths have a wingspan of 1 to 1½ inches; the females are practically wingless, and merely crawl out of the ground, up a stem or tree trunk, and wait for a male to find them. Adults of the fall cankerworm (*Alsophila pometaria*) emerge in October or on warm days through the winter to as late as April. Adults of the spring cankerworm (*Palaeacrita vernata*) may appear as early as February or as late as May. The eggs of both species, laid in masses containing as many as 400, hatch about the time the leaves appear. Order Lepidoptera.

CANVASBACK. See *Duck*.

CARDINAL, or redbird, one of the most beautiful of American songbirds, the adult male being brilliant red, like a cardinal's hat, with a sharp crest of vermilion. The female and young are yellowish brown with some red, and with the same crest and heavy, red beak, which is black around the base. Its beautiful whistling song has given it the name, Virginia nightingale. The cardinal nests in bushes and thickets and constructs its nest of bark and twigs. Its food is almost equally divided among weed seeds, fruits, and insects. Order Passeriformes, family Fringillidae, specifically *Richmondena cardinalis*.

CARIBOU. See *Reindeer*.

CARP, a coarse bony fish of the minnow family. Carp are native to freshwaters in Europe and Asia, where they are raised in ponds as a source of protein for human use. In American streams and lakes, to which the carp was introduced many years ago, it causes serious damage by muddying the water, uprooting vegetation, and devouring the young of native fishes.

Usually a carp is brown in color, darker along the back. Close to its mouth are 4 soft projections, called barbels, which help the carp find vegetable food in muddy water. It also eats snails, worms, insects, and eggs and young of other fishes.

The carp attains maturity when about 12 inches long, and the female lays as many as 2 million eggs during the late spring. In ponds fertilized with farm manure, carp sometimes grow to 40 inches long and a weight of 60 pounds. Order Eventognathi, family Cyprinidae, specifically *Cyprinus carpio*.

CAT, any of several different mammals with retractile claws, teeth specially adapted for cutting, and vertically elongated pupils of the eyes. The name is used particularly for members of the genus *Felis*, which includes the domestic cat, the jaguar, leopard, lion, ocelot, and puma, and the genus *Lynx*, which includes the Canada lynx and the bobcat. Order Carnivora, family Felidae.

Domestic Cat. The common cat (*Felis domestica*) is probably a native of Egypt. Domesticated there, it was an object of worship and was frequently mummified. It was not known to the ancient Greeks and Romans who used domesticated martens to destroy rats and mice.

Domestic cats are fastidious animals, constantly washing their fur and paws. Different breeds vary widely in color, markings, size, shape, and length of tail. Notable are the tailless Japanese and Manx cats (coming from the Crimea as well as from the Isle of Man), the Angora or Persian cats with long silky fur, and the Siamese variety, a semialbino with blue eyes, a long pointed head, slender legs, and a long thin tail. The nose, ears, paws, and tail are darker than the body. The ancestor of the domestic cat was probably marked with black bars on a ground of tawny and white, these colors rendering it inconspicuous among the grasses and shrubbery where it ranged.

Wildcat. The name wildcat is applied in America to almost any cat (other than the domestic house cat). The lynx and puma are most commonly called wildcats. The true wildcat (*Felis catus*), however, is found only in Northern Europe and Asia. It is a striped animal, similar to other members of the cat family.

In the New World, the ocelot (*Felis pardalis*) is native to tropical America and has a limited range in the southern United States. Large specimens are about 3 feet long, excluding the 1-foot tail. The color is generally tawny-gray, barred or spotted with brown or black, with chin and underparts almost white. The ocelot preys mostly on birds in the deep forests. Individuals have been partly domesticated and trained for hunting, like the Asian cheetah.

The puma (*Felis concolor*), a little larger than the ocelot, is also native to America. It has a 2-foot tail. Slender, with long legs and small head, the puma is a fairly uniform tawny brown. This is the species referred to as mountain lion in the western United States, where it is notorious as a predator of young cattle and sheep. Elsewhere it is known as panther, painter, catamount, or cougar but the correct name is puma.

Leopard. The leopard (*Felis pardus*) is native to both Africa and Asia. The body of this fierce and rapacious animal is about 4 feet long. It is a superlative leaper, can swim and climb trees. The larger leopards are often called panthers, as are the American puma and jaguar. The leopard differs from the jaguar in having small spots thickly set; the jaguar's are large and open, making a beautiful pattern of dark rosettes on a tan or brown skin.

Jaguar. The jaguar (*Felis onca*), somewhat larger than the leopard, is one of the most formidable beasts of prey found on the American continent. It is typically South American but is found as far north as Texas. The banks of rivers are its favorite haunts, where it preys on such animals as the tapir and water hog or capybara. It kills by leaping on its victim's back, then twisting the neck with its heavy powerful paws until it breaks.

A noisy, heavy animal, it roams abroad at night, especially before the approach of bad weather. It is an expert climber and swimmer and sometimes catches fish for food.

Lion. The lion (*Felis leo*) is the most majestic member of the cat family. It is nearly a uniform tawny or yellowish, paler on the underparts; but the immature lions show stripes like a tiger's and some spots like a leopard's. The male usually has a great shaggy flowing mane and a long tufted tail. The whole frame is extremely muscular, and the foreparts, in particular, are remarkably powerful. The heavy shoulders, large head, bright eye, and copious mane give the animal a noble appearance that has led to its being called the king of beasts.

A lion of the largest size is not so big as a tiger. It measures about 8 feet from the nose to the tail, and the tail measures about 4 feet more. The lioness is smaller, has no mane, and is of a lighter color on the underparts.

The strength of the lion is such that it can carry off a heifer as a cat carries a rat. It is chiefly an inhabitant of Africa, although it is found also in Asia, particularly in certain parts of Arabia, Persia, and India. It was anciently much more common in Asia and was found in some parts of Europe (Macedonia and Thrace), according to Herodotus and other authors. The lion is an inhabitant of open plains in which the shelter of occasional bushes and thickets may be found. It hunts mostly at night and has a terrifying roar. It is easily tamed if it is taken young and abundantly supplied with food.

Tiger. The tiger (*Felis tigris*) is the largest and most danegerous of the cats, slightly exceeding the lion in size but far surpassing it in destructiveness. An Asian animal, the tiger reaches its highest development both in size and color on the hot plains of India. The full-grown male Indian tiger measures from 9 to 12 feet, and the tigress from 8 to 10 feet, from the nose to the tip of the tail, which has no tuft. The ground color is rufous or tawny yellow, white on the ventral surface, with vertical black stripes or elongated ovals and brindlings.

Although possessed of immense strength and ferocity, the tiger rarely attacks armed men, unless it is provoked, but often carries off women and children. When it is pressed by hunger or enfeebled by age and incapable of dealing with larger prey like buffalo, the tiger prowls around villages and, if it learns what easy prey humans are, it often becomes a habitual man-eater. Two varieties are the Bengal, or southern, type with short hair, and a northern variety, ranging as far north as Siberia, which has longer, softer hair. See also *Lynx*.

CATBIRD, a well-known American songbird, about 9 inches long, dark slate gray in color except for a rusty red area under the tail. During the summer it is found throughout the Middle Atlantic and New England States. During the winter it inhabits the extreme south of the United States, and is found also in Mexico and Central America. Order Passeriformes, family Mimidae, specifically *Dumetella carolinensis*.

CATERPILLAR, the wormlike immature stage in the development of a moth or butterfly. The name is said to be from the Latin *cata pilosa* (hairy cat), referring to the many caterpillars that are covered with hair. Most butterfly caterpillars are hairless.

Usually the head of the caterpillar, with its biting jaws, is followed by a portion of the trunk with 3 pairs of jointed legs. More posteriorly, the cylindrical body is generally supported on 6 pairs of stumpy, soft prolegs with many minute hooks; the last pair of prolegs are at the hind end of the caterpillar.

Some kinds of caterpillars do great damage to crops and other vegetation. An exception is the silkworm, which feeds on mulberry and grows to 1 inch long; it is economically valuable because commercial silk can be unwound from the cocoon it spins before pupating. Order Lepidoptera.

CATFISH, any of about 2,000 kinds of scaleless bony fishes with large, toothless mouths. Usually two or more long, soft, slender projections, called barbels, arise from the underjaw or from both jaws near the mouth. They help the catfish find food in muddy water.

Some kinds of catfishes have bony, platelike armor; other kinds are soft skinned. Generally the dorsal and pectoral fins have a stiff strong spine at the leading edge, which can serve as a dangerous weapon for self-defense. A species of catfish native to the Nile River and tropical Africa is capable of discharging an electric shock reaching 100 volts.

Most catfishes can live out of water for a few hours. Their flesh, which may be dark in color, is highly regarded in many parts of the world for human food. A common kind, attaining 20 inches long in American waters, is called the bullhead or horned pout (*Ameiurus nebulosus*), of order Ostariophysi, family Ameiuridae.

CATTLE, any of several kinds of large cud-chewing mammals useful to mankind as a source of power, meat, milk, hides, and horns. In India and other southern Asian countries, the zebu (*Bos indicus*) is used much as domestic cattle are in Europe or the United States. Zebus are humped animals with a great tolerance for hot weather. For meat, milk, and hides, they are less desirable than European and North African cattle (*B. taurus*), which have been bred into many particularly valuable lines of inheritance.

European cattle are especially productive of high-quality milk, and form the basis of the dairy industry. Among the dairy cattle, the Holstein breed (black and white) is perhaps the most important. Holstein cattle are great milk producers, but the percentage of its butter fat is somewhat less than in milk from other cattle. This variety originated in Holland, but has been imported to a considerable extent to the United States and now forms an important part of the milk industry.

Jersey cattle yield milk rich in butter fat. This breed originated in the Isle of Jersey, off the coast of France. Guernsey cattle are reddish, with white markings. They also originated on one of the Channel Islands. Their milk is probably the richest in fat, but the quantity is not so great as in other breeds.

Of the beef cattle, the English Shorthorns are a very sturdy breed. These vary from red to almost pure white. Shorthorns originated in England, but later were introduced into North America, South America, and to Australia. Another valuable beef animal is the Hereford. This has a red body and white head. Herefords are not so widely distributed as Shorthorns.

Sometimes male cattle are castrated to render them more amenable for draft or agricultural work. These are called oxen. When this is done to improve the quality of the beef for eating, the cattle are known as steers. Order Artiodactyla, family Bovidae, genus *Bos*.

CAVY. See *Guinea Pig*.

CAYMAN. See *Crocodile*.

CENTIPEDE, literally "hundred legged," any of about 2,000 different kinds of segmented terrestrial arthropod animals with biting jaws, one pair of feelers (antennae) on the head, and one pair of walking legs on each of 14 to 180 segments of the body. Centipedes are found on all continents and most major islands. North American kinds are mostly small and inconspicuous, living under stones or in and under decaying logs. In the tropics they often attain great size, some growing to 10 inches in length.

Most centipedes have the first pair of legs modified into poison claws. With them they can inject venom, which kills their prey. It causes considerable pain but rarely death to a person. Centipedes can run forward or backward with almost equal ease. Several orders of class Chilopoda.

CHAMELEON, any of about 80 different Old World lizards with independently roving eyes, a long tongue that can be shot out to capture insect prey, grasping feet, and a curled, prehensile tail. Half of the species are confined to the island of Madagascar, the rest living in Africa south of the Sahara, except one (*Chameleo chamaeleon*) found from Spain across North Africa to Asia Minor.

Chameleon is a Greek word meaning lion-on-the-ground, that is, a low or dwarf lion. These animals are famous for changing their color either in accordance with the environment or when disturbed. The change is due to the presence of clear or pigment-bearing contractile cells placed at various depths in the skin, their contractions and dilations being under the influence of the nervous system.

Chameleons can fast for weeks. When disturbed they inflate themselves with air. These habits gave rise to the fable that they live on air. In general they are slow-moving and completely harmless.

Unrelated lizards show less spectacular but still surprising changes of color, and the name chameleon has been applied also to them, especially the American chameleon (*Anolis carolinensis*) of the iguana family in the southeastern states. Order Sauria, family Chamaeleonidae.

CHAMOIS, a goatlike cud-chewing mammal closely allied to antelopes, native to high, inaccessible mountains in Europe and western Asia. A chamois stands 25 to 30 inches high at the shoulders, and wears horns 6 or 7 inches long, which are round, almost smooth, perpendicular and straight until near the tip, where they suddenly terminate in a hook directed backward and downward.

The hair is brown in winter, fawn in summer, and grayish in spring. The head is pale yellow, and a black band from the nose to the ears surrounds the eyes. The tail is black.

Its agility, the nature of its haunts, and its powers of smell render the pursuit of the chamois an exceedingly difficult and hazardous occupation. It can jump 20 feet and is proverbially sure-footed. A very soft yellow leather for linings and cleaning cloths is made from chamois skin and from inferior and less expensive hides. Order Artiodactyla, family Bovidae, specifically *Rupicapra rupicapra*.

CHEETAH, or hunting leopard, a large catlike mammal with nonretractable claws, and circular pupils in the eyes. It is native to the high plains and savannas of Africa and Iran. Longer legged than true cats, cheetahs race after antelopes and other prey; the world's fastest runners, they often attain a speed of 60 miles an hour.

Generally, however, a cheetah watches a herd of antelopes for an hour or more to select the weakest member as prey. During this time, the cheetah remains almost invisible because its sand-colored short fur and pattern of small black spots let it blend with its surroundings.

Unlike other cats, a cheetah cannot retract its claws. It growls, snarls, spits, mews, and makes a birdlike chirp, but can neither roar like a lion nor purr like a house cat. In Africa, cheetahs are often kept as pets. Order Carnivora, family Felidae, specifically *Acinonyx jubatus*.

CHICKADEE, any of several small plump active songbirds named from the sound of its cheerful call, *chick-a-dee-dee*. The common black-capped chickadee (*Parus atricapillus*) of Canada and the northern United States occurs also in Europe and Britain, where it is called the willow tit. Like the closely related titmice (singular, titmouse), chickadees eat many kinds of small insects, which make up about two-thirds of their diet, and various wild fruits. When offered suet, peanut butter, or sunflower seeds at a window feeder, chickadees become very tame.

All chickadees nest in small holes, such as in a decayed tree or branch, and lay 5 to 8 eggs finely spotted with reddish brown. Order Passeriformes, family Paridae, members of genus *Parus*.

CHICKEN. See *Fowl*.

CHIMNEY SWIFT, a fast-flying North American bird related to hummingbirds. It spends most of its life in the air and is often mistaken for a swallow. Its slender, cigar-shaped body is supported by narrow curved wings that seem very far forward because the beak is so short. The mouth is wide, and the bird uses it to catch insects and to drink while flying.

Originally, chimney swifts roosted for the night and built their nests in hollow trees and caves. With the arrival of Europeans in Canada and the United States, they changed to using chimneys and wells that are open.

The nests are of twigs, collected on the wing, held in place by a gluelike saliva. The birds cling with sharp claws, propping themselves up with their short stiff tail feathers. At the approach of cold weather, they migrate to a remote area of Peru.

Order Micropodiformes, family Micropodidae, specifically *Chaetura pelagica*.

CHIMPANZEE, a great ape with large conspicuous ears and short forearms, native to west and central Africa. A full-grown chimpanzee is almost 5 feet tall and weighs up to 150 pounds. It is not so large or powerful as a gorilla. The chimpanzee walks erect better than most apes, but not so well as the gorilla; when walking on all fours the feet are flat, whereas the fingers touch the ground with the knuckles.

The chimpanzee is more a tree-dweller than the gorilla. It feeds on fruits, often robs the gardens of the natives, and constructs a sort of nest among the branches of the trees. Order Primates, family Pongidae, specifically *Pan troglodytes*.

CHINCH BUG, a sucking insect less than ¼ inch long, with a black or dark gray body and white wings, if mature. Chinch bugs suck so much juice from corn and grain crop roots that they annually destroy thousands of dollars worth of crops. The adults seek protection near the roots and spend the winter under the soil. They emerge in the spring and lay eggs, which hatch in about 2 weeks.

When the young hatch, they start to feed at once. In about 3 months the adult stage is reached, and the insects lay eggs for a second brood. The young are yellow at first, then red, and later black. They are killed by heavy rains but survive from one year to the next in dry places. Order Heteroptera, family Lygaeidae, specifically *Blissus leucopterus*.

CHINCHILLA, a small South American rodent, strongly resembling a ground squirrel. The chinchillas inhabit the Andes of Chile and Bolivia, where they live gregariously in deep burrows, feeding on roots. They are more than 10 inches long and are highly prized and hunted for their lustrous gray pelts, which can be made into costly garments. An attempt has been made to domesticate them on fur farms in the United States. Order Rodentia, family Chinchillidae, specifically *Chinchilla laniger*.

CHIPMUNK, any of about 18 different kinds of small ground squirrels marked above with 5 lengthwise black or dark brown stripes separated by 4 paler stripes. One (*Tamias striatus*) inhabits most of the eastern United States and southeastern Canada. Another, the Siberian chipmunk (*Eutamias sibiricus*), is familiar from northern Japan westward through the northern Soviet Union.

The 16 others of this genus are denizens of forests and brushlands in western North America. Each chipmunk generally lives in a burrow, which it enlarges at intervals to make storage rooms for nuts, acorns, and seeds of many kinds. Four to 6 young are born in the burrow in early spring. Order Rodentia, family Sciuridae.

CICADA, any of about 1,500 different kinds of sucking insects with a short, heavy body and, when adult, 2 pairs of strong wings, the first pair much larger than the second. At rest, the wings are held tentlike over the body. Every continent and most large islands have cicadas; about 75 kinds are found in the United States, and 1 in Britain.

The call is among the most characteristic sounds of hot summer days in temperate zones, and a daily feature of the tropics. These loud sounds are produced by male cicadas, by means of a special pair of drumlike organs with resonators about midway back in the body. Females are attracted to the source of the sound and, after mating, lay eggs in slits cut into the bark of twigs on trees by means of a sawlike organ below the tip of the abdomen.

When the young cicadas hatch, they drop to the ground and spend the next 3 to 17 years (depending on the species) feeding on the sap from underground roots of trees and shrubs. Eventually the fully grown young

AMERICAN MUSEUM OF NATURAL HISTORY
CHIMPANZEE

20 Civet Cat

cicadas climb to the soil surface, walk up a tree trunk or other support, and shed their skins to emerge as winged adults. Order Homoptera, family Cicadidae.

CIVET CAT, any of about 21 different kinds of weasel-like mammals related to mongooses, with a slender body and long tail, and a head suggesting that of a cat, with short rounded ears and sharp muzzle. The various kinds are widespread in the Old World, but one (the African civet, *Civettictis civetta*) from Africa south of the Sudan and the great deserts is best known for the musky substance it secretes in a sac near the anus. This substance, called civet, is used in making perfumes. Probably the civet cat uses the substance for marking out its territorial boundaries. The animal feeds on reptiles, small mammals, birds' eggs, and large insects. Order Carnivora, family Viverridae, several different genera.

CLAM, any of about 11,000 different kinds of bivalve mollusks, known in British countries simply as bivalves. Mostly they live on sandy or muddy bottoms, in both salt and fresh water, all over the world. They create a current of water containing oxygen and microscopic food particles, which enters the gaping shell at one opening, is used for respiration and feeding, and then passes out carrying wastes through a second opening.

In the United States, an important industry has grown up around freshwater clams (species of genera *Lampsilis*, *Margaritana*, and *Unio*), from whose hard shells are manufactured such articles as buttons and knife handles. Many marine clams are of considerable economic importance, chiefly for food.

Along the U.S. Atlantic coast, a favorite is the Venus clam (or little neck, or quahog, *Mercenaria mercenaria*), which is rounded and thick shelled, a source of wampum, which formerly was used as money among Indians; another is the soft-shelled or sand clam (*Mya arenaria*), oval in shape, about 2½ inches long, with shells that are almost paper thin. The soft-shell has been introduced on the Pacific coast, and now rivals in popularity the native Pismo clam (*Tivela stultorum*).

Other clams include the giant bear's-paw clam (*Tridacna*) of coral reefs in the South Pacific, which is the largest shelled mollusk; and the edible cockle (*Cardium*) of British and European shore waters, which provides food for man and bait for fish; a cockle can jump several inches by using its long powerful foot. Class Pelecypoda, various orders.

COBRA, any of several different venomous snakes of the Old World, with fixed fangs at the front of the mouth and a more or less distensible neck region. Best known is the Oriental common cobra (*Naja naja*), which ranges throughout Africa and tropical Asia; it can spread its "hood" in the neck region more widely than any other cobra. It has been used extensively by snake charmers during the day largely because at that time it strikes (if at all) with its mouth shut, and hence does not bite.

The king cobra (*Naja Ophiophagus hannah*), native to Asia from India to the Philippines, attains a length of 12 feet and often stands its ground when disturbed; it eats other snakes as well as lizards, small mammals, and birds. South Africa has spitting cobras (of genus *Hemachatus*), which can discharge their venom with astonishing accuracy to a distance of 6 to 10 feet, apparently aiming for the eyes of prey or of people, and causing temporary blindness.

The asp of Egypt is a small deadly cobra (*Naje haje*), whose likeness is the dominant part of the headdresses for ancient Egyptian royalty. Order Serpentes, family Elapidae.

COCKATOO. See *Parrot*.

COCKLE. See *Clam*.

COCKROACH, any of a large number of different flat-bodied insects with long threadlike feelers (antennae), biting jaws, long spiny legs used in running rapidly, and usually a pair of short, sensitive projections from near the hind end of the body. Winged adults have two pairs of thin membranous wings, held flat over the back at rest.

Primarily tropical insects, they occur also in temperate woodlands. A few have adopted a life in human dwellings, stores, and factories where they can find food of many kinds. They require moderate or high humidity and are rare in very dry situations. Household pests include the 1-inch European cockroach (*Blatella germanica*), the 2-inch Oriental cockroach (*Blatta orientalis*), and the 3-inch American cockroach (*Periplaneta americana*). Order Orthoptera, family Blattidae.

COD, a marine bony fish with a projecting lower jaw, a barbel on the chin, a ductless air bladder, and soft-rayed fins. Formerly abundant in cold waters near shore on both sides of the North Atlantic Ocean, cod are still found in great numbers off the coast of Newfoundland.

The back of the cod is olive-green with darker spots, and the belly is white. At 4 years of age, the fish is about 2 feet long; at 5 years, it begins to mate and reproduce, a female laying as many as 9 million eggs.

The average length of cod caught for commerce is about 3 feet. Until about 1950, large quantities of oil were extracted from cod livers for medical use, because of the rich supply there of vitamins A and D. Now artificial vitamins can be made more cheaply and reliably.

Closely related to the cod (*Gadus callarias*) is the whiting (*G. merlangus*), a silvery fish with a black mark on the base of its pectoral fin but with no barbel on the chin. It is harvested from Norway to the Mediterranean and in Atlantic waters from Maine to Florida. Also lacking the barbel is the North Atlantic pollack (*G. pollachius*), which is greenish and has a jutting lower jaw. The coalfish (*G. virens*) is blackish and has a bar-

AMERICAN MUSEUM OF NATURAL HISTORY
COYOTE

bel but otherwise resembles the pollack.

A freshwater member of the cod family is the burbot (*Lota lota*), a slender fish of cold deep water found in the Great Lakes in North America, in Europe from the Arctic to mountain lakes in Italy, and in the far north of Asia. Order Anacanthini, family Gadidae.

CONCH, any of the large marine snails with heavy shells, which are powerful predators, seizing and eating the flesh of smaller snails, oysters and other bivalves, and sea urchins. Among the largest are the king conch (*Strombus gigas*) and the queen conch or cameo shell (*Cassis cameo*) of the Gulf of Mexico and warm waters of the Atlantic and Caribbean. A five-pound animal of this kind may have a shell 12 inches long.

The shells of the queen conch are shipped to Europe, particularly Italy, as the material from which cameo jewelry is carved. The trumpet shell (*Charonia tritonis*) is similar but more slender, with a higher spire and a long taper at the opposite end; it is sometimes made into a trumpet or shown as the musical instrument of the Greek sea demigods called Tritons. Class Gastropoda, order Prosobranchiata.

CONDOR. See *Vulture*.

CONE SHELL, any of a large number of different sea snails with smoothly conical chinalike shells. The spire of the shell is a short cone, and the opening is narrow. Cone shells live as vigorous predators in coastal waters of the tropics and the temperate zones, and are particularly numerous among the coral reefs of the South Pacific.

One of the most valued shells in the world is that of the fabulous glory-of-the-sea cone (*Conus gloria maris*) of the South Pacific, which combines beauty with extreme rarity. A collector of living cones must handle a snail with great care because it can jump part way out of its shell and drive into a person's hand a venomous organ, which normally is used to subdue fishes and other prey. A cone is very alert, watching with two eyes on long stalks for prey to come within reach. Order Prosobranchiata, family Conidae, various species of genus *Conus*.

CONY (known also as coney, cunny, and cunney), an ancient European name for a rabbit, a rabbitlike animal, or rabbit fur. The European rabbit (*Oryctolagus cuniculus*) has a diminutive, Latinized form of the word as its species name. The "coney" of the Bible (Leviticus 11:5) was probably the rabbit-sized hyrax or dassie (*Heterohyrax syriacus*) of Asia Minor and Africa, which are hoofed animals of order Hyracoidea, although they do not chew a cud and do not have a cloven hoof.

The rock cony or pika of northern Asia and the western mountains in North America (*Ochotona* species), which has no visible tail, and ears about as wide as they are high, is a member of the same order (Lagomorpha) as rabbits, but does not hop. The word is also used by fishermen for the burbot (*Lota* species), a codlike fish, and for a reef fish, the red hind (*Petrometopon cruentatus*) of the West Indies.

COOT, any of 10 different plump, short-tailed wading birds about 1½ feet long, whose individual toes have webbing on each side instead of between adjacent toes. Seven of the species are South American. Of the remaining 3, one breeds in southern Europe and winters in Africa south of the great deserts, another nests across Eurasia from Japan to the British Isles, and the third is found from southern Canada to northern South America.

All are expert swimmers and divers, inhabiting ponds and open water in marshes and swamps where they can find vegetable food. They pile up masses of vegetation in the water as the base for a nest. Coots are poor food, unsuspicious, and easily shot. This has led to the expressions "silly coot" or "queer as a coot" applied to persons who appear simple. Order Gruiformes, family Rallidae, members of genus *Fulica*.

COPPERHEAD. See *Pit Viper*.

COQUINA, or pompano shell, or butterfly shell, or variable wedge shell, a small marine bivalve 1 inch or less in length, living in sandy beaches from North Carolina to Florida and Texas. Rays of color mark the shell, diverging from the hinge region, often crossed by eccentric bands of the same or a different hue, in pink, yellow, green, blue, or lavender.

People collect them wholesale by scooping up the sand just below the edge of the tide, and passing it through a sieve. The coquinas are then cooked in their shells to make coquina soup. Other persons gather particularly colorful shells in pairs for use in jewelry. Order Teleodesmacea, family Donacidae, specifically *Donax variabilis*.

CORAL, any of a large number of lime-secreting, colonial marine coelenterates, or the limy external skeleton they secrete. Coral animals are mostly tropical. When the animals die, their skeletons remain so abundant and massive as to build up into the form of coral reefs and islands. The precious coral of the Mediterranean and of Japan is very solid and takes a high polish. Class Anthozoa.

CORMORANT, or shag, any of about 30 different large water birds which resemble geese when flying and loons while swimming. They are found all over the world, seldom out of sight of land, chiefly along coasts, inland lakes, and rivers. They dive and swim underwater in pursuit of fish, or to escape. Most kinds nest on cliffs and offshore islands in great colonies.

Most famous are the guanay birds (the white-breasted Peruvian cormorant, *Phalacrocorax bougainvillei*) off the Pacific coast of South America, whose nest areas provide guano as agricultural fertilizer. In China and Japan, trained cormorants are used for fishing, a brass ring being placed around their necks to prevent them from swallowing the fish.

Closely related are the 4 different kinds of snakebirds (*Anhinga* species) in which the beak is straight and sharp, not hooked at the tip. They are the original spear fishermen, impaling the fish or frog they catch on the closed beak, then tossing the victim into the air and catching it in the opened mouth. Both snakebirds and cormorants lack the usual waterproofing on their feathers, and must hold out their wings to dry after emerging from water. Order Pelecaniformes, families Phalacrocoracidae and Anhingidae.

CORNBORER, or corn-ear worm, the caterpillar of a moth native to Europe and now an introduced pest in America. It eats into the corn and makes it unsalable. Fermentation of the cornstalks in silos kills the overwintering insect; otherwise it lives through the winter in the plant, and emerges to reproduce the following summer. Order Lepidoptera, family Pyralidae, specifically *Pyrausta nubilalis*.

COTTONMOUTH. See *Pit Viper*.

COUGAR. See *Cat*.

COW. See *Cattle*.

COWBIRD, any of about 6 different kinds of dark-colored birds of medium size, which associate commonly with buffalo and cattle, eating insects disturbed by the grazing mammals. Most cowbirds lay their eggs in the nests of other birds (more than 90 species) and leave them there to be hatched and raised by the foster parents. Order Passeriformes, family Icteridae, chiefly members of genera *Molothrus* and *Tangavius*.

COWRIE, any of a large number of different sea snails with an egg-shaped shell, whose narrow aperture extends almost the full length. Through this opening, the animal puts out its foot and two short feelers, and two extensive folds of its soft mantle then expand, completely covering the shell.

Most cowries are tropical, living in shallow water. Each kind has a distinctive color pattern on its glossy shell, hence a collection of different cowries is particularly attractive. One of the smaller kinds in the South Pacific (*Cypraea moneta*) has been used for centuries as a kind of money by the inhabitants. Order Pectinibranchia, family Cypraeidae, members of genus *Cypraea*.

COYOTE, a medium-sized wolflike mammal of the western plains in North America. It eats chiefly rabbits, ground squirrels, and other small mammals, but occasionally attacks domestic sheep, particularly when lambs are being born or are very young and helpless. Order Carnivora, family Canidae, specifically *Canis latrans*.

CRAB, any of several hundred different crustaceans that spend their larval stages in the sea and then transform to possess 5 pairs of legs and a small abdomen folded under the anterior part of the body (the cephalothorax). The vast majority are marine, but a few come out on land after transforming and, as land crabs, return to the water only in breeding season to lay their eggs in the sea.

The edible blue crab (*Callinectes sapidus*) of the Atlantic coast of America south of Cape Cod is often kept captive until it sheds its hard outer covering, molting to grow larger. It is then a "soft-shell crab" for a few hours, and much easier to open for the table.

A similar crab of the Pacific coast is *Cancer magister*, with rounded sides to the cephalothorax instead of extended sharp spines there. Among land crabs, those with a huge pincer on one side in the male sex are called fiddlers (*Uca* species); at low tide they emerge from their burrows in the beach and search for small particles of food, often in armies of several thousand 1-inch individuals.

Hermit crabs differ in having a soft abdomen, which they conceal in the empty shell of a snail, carrying this shelter around with them wherever they go. A giant hermit crab (*Birgus latro*) of tropical islands in the South Pacific grows larger than any snail shell it can find; thereupon its abdomen becomes hardened, and the crab begins climbing coconut trees to feed on the fruit. Some of these coconut crabs weigh 20 pounds. Order Decapoda, several families and many different genera. See also *Horseshoe Crab*.

CRANE, any of 14 different long-legged birds that fly with the neck extended, not curved over the back in an *S* as among herons, and that stand on 3 toes on each foot because the fourth toe is raised well above the ground; herons have all 4 toes at the same level. The windpipe (trachea) of a crane is extensively convoluted, giving the voice resonance and letting the birds' calls be heard for great distances.

ANIMALS

MAINE DEPARTMENT OF ECONOMIC DEVELOPMENT
DEER

Cranes are native to all continents and major islands except South America, Malaya, New Zealand, and the Pacific Islands. They frequent large plains and marshes, where they can find insects, frogs, worms, mollusks, reptiles, fishes, and even small mammals. Cranes everywhere are becoming scarce. Those of North America are the rare whooping crane (*Grus americana*) of Great Slave Lake region, which winters in Texas, and the sandhill crane (*G. canadensis*) of northwestern and southeastern prairie country.

The European crane (*G. grus*) breeds in northern Europe and Siberia, but migrates south in winter, far into Africa. Order Gruiformes, family Gruidae.

CRAYFISH, or crawfish, a freshwater crustacean related to and resembling the North Atlantic lobster, but smaller (3 to 6 inches in length) and with claws proportionately smaller. The second syllable of the name was not originally fish, as the word is derived from French écrevisse and is like our word crevice—possibly from the burrows it digs. Originally applied to only one kind in Europe (*Astacus fluviatilis*), the name now refers to all fresh-water relatives in America.

Crayfishes in the southern United States are considered a table delicacy. Their extensive burrowing causes considerable damage to levees and dams. Blind crayfishes are found in the river of Mammoth Cave, in Kentucky. Order Decapoda, family Astacidae.

CRICKET, any of more than 900 different insects related to grasshoppers, with long threadlike feelers (antennae) and cylindrical bodies; those adults that have wings hold the fore pair flat over the back, with the sides turned down sharply. Females with long ovipositors seem to have thick needles projecting from the rear of their bodies; the ovipositors are never bladelike, as in the longhorned grasshoppers.

Only adult males produce the familiar chirping sounds, by rubbing together the bases of their forewings. Crickets are found all over the world, generally hiding during the day but emerging at night to feed on decaying plant material. The American black cricket (*Gryllus assimilis*) occasionally enters houses in cold weather. The European kind (*G. domesticus*) is the "cricket-on-the-hearth," which prefers living indoors on crumbs, and hiding in little chinks in the masonry of fireplaces.

Tree crickets (*Oecanthus* species) are slender, pale green, and stand on bushes while trilling continuously. Mole crickets (species of genus *Gryllotalpa*) have the front legs adapted for burrowing in soft soil. Cave crickets, known also as camel crickets because of their humped backs, are wingless members of a different family (Tettigoniidae), and remain permanently wingless; often they are found under bark or in cellars. Order Orthoptera, family Gryllidae.

CROCODILE, any of about 13 different formidable lizardlike reptiles whose long jaws gape widely and display strong teeth in bony sockets. They include the largest of living reptiles, and are found in tropical and subtropical shore waters and rivers in both hemispheres. They prepare nests of sticks and mud on shore, and guard their eggs until the young hatch.

Little crocodiles feed on insects and other small animals, but gradually change, as they grow, to larger food, often gorging on carcasses in a state of putrefaction. The nostrils at the end of the snout can be closed to prevent ingress of water.

Often a crocodile floats just below the surface, with only its prominent eyes and nostrils protruding into air. The long compressed tail forms a strong swimming organ. The legs are short, with 5 toes on the front pair and 4 on the hind, which are somewhat webbed. The skin is armored with square bony plates.

Best known is the Nile crocodile (*Crocodilus niloticus*), which was worshiped and embalmed by the ancient Egyptians. Today it has been exterminated from the Nile except in the Sudan and Uganda, but it is present in other rivers, such as the Congo and the Zambezi, and in Madagascar. The longest measured specimen was 16 feet; presumably it was old. The saltwater crocodile (*C. porosus*) of Indian, Malayan, East Indian, and north Australian coasts, is more dangerous and generally larger, the biggest known being 20 feet long. It swims from island to island, and often becomes a man-eater. Like other adult crocodiles, it seizes large prey in shallow water and then rolls over and over to subdue it, often drowning it in the process.

The American crocodile (*C. acutus*) of southern Florida, the West Indies, and northern South America often enters salt water. It and the long-snouted Orinoco crocodile (*C. intermedius*) have been measured at 23 feet long, which is the maximum that can be regarded as authentic for any of these animals.

The closest relatives of crocodiles (family Crocodilidae) are the alligators and caymans (family Alligatoridae) and gavials (family Gavialidae), all of which have cavities or pits in the upper jaw into which the long canine teeth of the lower jaw fit. Alligators and caymans have broadly rounded snouts, whereas the snout of a crocodile is pointed, and that of a gavial is very long, narrow, and ends in a soft tip that can be expanded at will. Alligators have a relatively soft skin, easily distinguished by touch from the skin of caymans, which have hard bony plates below the surface.

Of the two kinds of alligators, the larger is the now scarce American species (*Alligator mississippiensis*), which has been nearly exterminated for its hides, and a Chinese representative (*A. sinensis*). Of the 5 kinds of caymans, all inhabit swamps of northern South America and Central America. The sole species of gavial (*Gavialis gangeticus*) is a fish-eater of Indian rivers. Order Crocodilia.

CROW, any of about 10 different large perching birds about 20 inches long, with mostly black feathers and beaks. They are distributed throughout the world. The common North American crow (*Corvus brachyrhynchos*) is remarkable for its gregarious and predatory habits, as well as for its intelligence and cunning.

Crows pair in March; the old repair their nests, the young frame new ones; but they are such thieves that while the one is fetching materials the other must keep watch to prevent the rising fabric from being plundered by crow neighbors. As soon as the nest is finished and five bluish-green eggs with dark blotches are laid, the male starts to provide for his mate; he continues this during the period of incubation.

Crows frequent the same rookeries for years, but allow no intruders into their community. They feed chiefly on worms and the larvae of insects, consequently during outbreaks of insects the crows are beneficial; but they also eat grain and seeds and are thus injurious to the farmer. Chiefly because they destroy beneficial wild birds and their eggs, crows are often regarded as enemies of mankind.

The raven (*Corvus corax*) is the largest of perching birds and the most widespread of crows in the Northern Hemisphere. Because they destroy so many different crops, they have been driven out of the whole of the United States except the western region.

The fish crow (*C. ossifragus*) frequents the Atlantic and Gulf coasts of the United States. The carrion crow (*C. corone*) and the hooded crow (*C. cornix*) are closely related European birds. Most gregarious are the somewhat smaller rooks (*C. frugilegus*), which lose most of the feathers on the face as they mature. Well-populated nest sites in Britain and northern Europe have been used continuously for centuries. Order Passeriformes, family Corvidae, members of genus *Corvus*.

CUCKOO, any of about 200 different kinds of slender-bodied, long-tailed birds with downcurved beaks and pointed wings. They are widely distributed on land, and are of diverse habits. Literary references are generally to the common Eurasian and African cuckoo (*Cuculus canorus*) which has the familiar call of a striking cuckoo-clock. Like many other cuckoos, it is a parasite, laying its eggs in the nests of other birds.

Among the 40 kinds of cuckoos in the New World, the most familiar are the black-billed (*Coccyzygus erythrophthalmus*) and yellow-billed (*C. americanus*) cuckoos, which are shy, inconspicuous, about 1 foot long, and grayish-brown above, white below. They build their own nests, look after their own young, and make guttural, unmusical calls that have earned them the name of "rain crows," because some farmers claim that the sound generally precedes a rain. The cuckoos of both the Old and the New World are regarded as helpful to farmers, because they consume large numbers of caterpillars and other crop-damaging insects.

Ten of the 13 different ground cuckoos are American birds, the others living in Malaya and nearby Southeast Asia. One is the roadrunner bird, or chaparral cock (*Geococcyx californianus*), of the southwestern deserts in the United States and Mexico, where it runs about in search of lizards and snakes to eat.

Also related are the most sociable of the cuckoos, the three different coal-black anis (*Crotophaga* species) of the American Tropics, which make communal nests. Even immature anis appear to help in incubation and feeding of nestlings. Order Cuculiformes, family Cuculidae.

CUTTLEFISH, a squidlike cephalopod mollusk with 10 arms around the mouth and an enclosed, limy shell called a cuttlebone. Cuttlefishes are abundant in the Indian Ocean, and common in the Mediterranean Sea. They prey on fishes and grow to a length of 18 inches. Many persons in southern Europe eat cooked cuttlefish or use pieces for fish bait. When disturbed, a cuttlefish can discharge a black ink from an inkbag, clouding the water around its body. The pigment sepia originally was obtained from this source. Order Dibranchia, specifically *Sepia officinalis*.

DADDY LONGLEGS. See *Harvestman*.

DAMSELFLY, any of a large number of extremely slender adult insects with four slender membranous wings, ordinarily folded together at rest above the long abdomen, while the insect clings to some support, such as a plant stem. Damselflies are found near freshwater on most continents and large islands. Their flight is weak, yet rapid enough to capture some other small insects, such as plant lice and midges.

Damselflies lay their eggs under the surface film of ponds and streams. When full grown, each immature damselfly (called a naiad) creeps up a stem or a rock out of the water and then transforms into the adult. Order Odonata, suborder Zygoptera, several families and genera.

DEER, any of more than 50 different kinds of long-legged, cud-chewing mammals with long necks, small heads carried high, large ears, and large prominent eyes. Usually the male produces solid, branching antlers that fall off annually and are replaced.

Deer are native to the Northern Hemisphere and as far south in South America as Uruguay, in Africa to the great deserts, and in Asia to the East Indies. They have been introduced in New Guinea, Australia, New Zealand, Hawaii, and reintroduced into the British Isles, where they had been exterminated.

Largest of existing deer is the American moose (*Alces americanus*), which is very similar to the smaller European animal (*Alces alces*) called an elk. Both have broad blades with tines as antlers, and inhabit spruce bogs.

The large wapiti or American elk (*Cervus canadensis*) and the smaller European red deer (*C. elaphus*) are similar animals with heavy antlers and many upturned tines on mature bulls. Eastern North America is the home of the white-tailed or Virginia deer (*Odocoileus virginianus*), which has as western counterparts the large-eared mule deer (*O. hemionus*) in the Rocky Mountain states, and the blacktail (*O. columbianus*) near the Pacific coast.

The Old World has small roe deer (*Capreolus capreolus*), which can bark like dogs, and fallow deer (*Dama dama*), which retain their juvenile pattern of pale spots for life. The only deer in which both sexes wear antlers are the reindeer (*Rangifer tarandus*) of the Eurasian Arctic, where it is domesticated and herded by nomads, and the caribou (*R. caribou*) of the Far North in Canada and Alaska, which form herds that wander continually. Order Artiodactyla, family Cervidae.

DINGO. See *Dog*.

DOBSONFLY, a North American insect, of which the larval stage is an aquatic predator known as a hellgrammite. The eggs are laid at the edge of a stream or river, which the larvae enter as soon as they hatch. They need 3 years to attain full size, at which time the mature larvae creep out of the water and pupate among fallen leaves or in the upper levels of the soil, there transforming into the winged adult.

The dobsonfly's wings are gray, with many veins, and spread to as much as 6 inches, making this the largest member of the order Neuroptera in the United States and Canada. The male has enormously extended jaws, held crossed in front of the head. The female has much smaller and more powerful jaws, similar to those of the larva.

Fishermen collect hellgrammites as a favorite bait for trout and other fishes of running water. Order Neuroptera, family Corydalidae, specifically *Corydalis cornuta*.

DOG, any of about 12 different kinds of wolflike mammals popularly regarded as distinct from wolves, jackals, and foxes. The domesticated dog (*Canis familiaris*) is presumed to have been derived from tamed wolves, and now is remarkable for the almost infinite variety in size, shape, color, and hair.

A domestic dog will live on cooked vegetables, but prefers meat. To drink, it laps with its tongue. It never perspires, but loses heat through its moist nose and by panting with its dripping tongue hanging from the mouth. The female (bitch) goes with young 63 days, and usually has 6 to 8 puppies in a litter. Blind at birth, they do not acquire sight until the tenth day. A dog is full grown at the end of its second year, is old at 15, and seldom lives beyond 20 years.

The main types of domestic dogs are: Eskimo, sheep dogs, greyhounds, mastiffs, terriers, hounds, spaniels, and poodles. In Australia, the dingo (*C. dingo*), which has yellowish brown fur, is semiwild. It was probably introduced in prehistoric times by the aboriginal people. Asia has a single kind of raccoon dog (*Nyctereutes procyonoides*), which is valued for its meat and fur but has become rare in Japan and adjacent parts of the mainland, and a red dog (or Indian dhole, *Cuon alpinus*) which associates into hunting packs in Java, Sumatra, Malaya, India, and parts of east Asia far into Siberia. Similar habits are shown by the small African hunting dogs (*Lycaon pictus*), which hunt game animals systematically over most of the continent south of the great deserts.

South America has bush dogs (*Speothos venaticus*) on the savanna areas of Paraguay northward to the Guianas and Panama, and small-eared dogs (*Atelocynus microtis*) in tropical forest areas of the Amazon basin, but both are short-legged, nocturnal, secretive animals about which little is known. Order Carnivora, family Canidae.

DOGFISH, any of several different small sharks that swim in schools along seacoasts, often destroying fish that have been caught in nets and tearing the nets as well. Dogfish rarely grow longer than 5 feet, or heavier than 30 pounds. They seldom attack bathers along beaches. But the spiny dogfish (*Squalus acanthias*) of North Atlantic coasts often severely wounds fishermen who are freeing dogfishes from tangled nets.

This dogfish has a strong sharp spine with a venom gland at the leading edge of each of its two dorsal fins, and while struggling to escape, may drive these spines into a human limb. Order Selachii, several families.

DOLPHIN, any of about 41 different kinds of small sea mammals with pointed noses, many teeth, streamlined bodies, flippers as forelimbs, a distinct fleshy dorsal fin, and transverse tail fin, or flukes, whose total length does not exceed 13 feet. They are found in all oceans.

Frequently dolphins accompany ships, displaying by leaping singly or in groups, coming out of the water in a graceful arc and plunging in again with scarcely a splash. Sometimes they ride the bow wave of a ship for hours at a time. Best known is the bottle-nosed dolphin (*Tursiops truncatus*) of the eastern coast of North America, which feeds on a variety of fishes and squids.

Formerly caught commercially as a source of fine oil for clocks and chronometers, they are now being studied in detail to discover how they navigate, echolocate food and obstacles underwater, and communicate with one another. Order Cetacea, family Delphinidae.

DONKEY. See *Ass.*

DOVE. See *Pigeon.*

DRAGONFLY, any of nearly 4,000 different strong-flying predacious insects with biting mouthparts, prominent compound eyes, four similar membranous wings with many crossveins, and a slender abdomen. They are found near freshwater all over the world. They lay their eggs in water where the young hatch and live as predators. The fully grown young crawl up the stem of an aquatic plant and transform into the adult dragonfly.

The adults destroy mosquitoes and other small insects. Some of the larger kinds are reputed able to fly at a speed of about 60 miles an hour. Popularly called "devil's darning needles" and thought to be dangerous, they are in fact harmless. Order Odonata, suborder Anisoptera.

DROMEDARY. See *Camel.*

DUCK, any of about 115 kinds of web-footed, swimming birds related to geese and swans, but of smaller size and with necks shorter than the body. Most gooselike are the whistling or tree ducks, of Central America and the Southern Hemisphere, of which one from Mexico and Brazil called the Muscovy duck (*Cairina moschata*) has been domesticated as the largest of barnyard ducks.

Some of the shelducks, native to the Old World, are large enough to be called geese; they include the Egyptian goose (*Alopochen aegyptica*) of the Nile valley and Africa south of the great deserts. Most familiar are the smaller ducks of rivers and ponds, which tip their bodies tail up to reach food on the bottom; they include the mallard duck (*Anas platyrhynchus*) of northern North America and Eurasia, from which the all-white peking duck (*A. platyrhynchus*) became a favorite domestic breed. The tipping or dipping ducks are often called "true ducks," or freshwater ducks; they include also black ducks, pintails, shovelers, widgeons, and various kinds of teal.

The larger bay ducks, which include the canvasback and scaup ducks, dive for their food. The perching ducks, such as the handsome wood duck of North America and the decorative mandarin duck of Japan and eastern Asia, generally nest in a hollow tree or on a horizontal limb high above the water. The eider ducks nest in communities along arctic and subarctic rocky coasts, covering their eggs and young in the nest with a heavy layer of down feathers that have been pulled from the mother's winter coat.

The sea ducks, which include the mergansers, scoters, and goldeneyes, are fish eaters whose meat is generally considered inedible. Now extinct, the Labrador duck was formerly abundant along shores of the North Atlantic Ocean.

Most ducks and geese are expert fliers and highly migratory. But the stiff-tailed ducks, such as the ruddy duck (*Oxyura jamaicensis*), tend to be labored in flight, to be residents, and nonmigratory. Yet they swim and dive superbly and perform distinctive courtship displays with the tail stiffly upright, moving the head quickly up and down. Order Anseriformes, family Anatidae.

DUCKBILL, or platypus ("broad foot"), an Australian web-footed mammal whose toothless jaws have the form of a beak, like that of a duck. This animal lives in streams, feeding on worms and insects from the mud at the bottom. At maturity, a duckbill is about 1 foot long. The male has a horny spur on each heel, connected to a poison gland. The female lays eggs with a soft shell in a burrow dug from a stream bank, and takes the young that hatch out into a pouch. She has no nipples on her mammary glands, but the young lap the milk as it oozes out onto her fur. Order Monotremata, specifically *Ornithorhynchus anatinus.*

EAGLE, any of 27 different large birds of prey with broad rounded wings, feathers over most of the head and face, and well down on the feet almost to where the strong toes spread apart. Eagles fly and used to nest in most parts of the continents.

Largest and most widespread is the golden eagle (*Aquila chrysaetus*) of the Northern Hemisphere, which soars high above mountainous terrain, watching with sharp eyes for rabbits, marmots, woodchucks, ground squirrels, and other prey upon which to dive and snatch aloft. The spread of its wings is nearly 10 feet, although the length of the bird from beak to tail tip is only 33 inches. The eagle was the symbol of power of the Roman Empire, and it was trained like a falcon by Jirghiz Tatars to hunt antelope.

The emblem of the United States, the bald eagle (*Haliaeetus leucocephalus,* the "white head"), is actually a sea eagle, close relatives of which live in Africa, in Madagascar, in Malaya and the East Indies, the South Pacific islands, and in the northern regions from Siberia to Iceland and on to Greenland. Tropical jungles have their eagles in the powerful crested birds known as the harpy eagle (*Harpia harpyja*), which hunts for sloths and large parrots in southern Mexico, Central America, and south to the Argentine, and the monkey-eating eagle (*Pithecophagus jefferyi*) of the Philippines.

The harrier eagles, which specialize in catching reptiles, are native to Eurasia, Africa, and Madagascar; they include the splendid, short-tailed bataleur eagle (*Terathopius ecaudatus*) of African highlands. Almost all of these birds are in need of protection to keep them from becoming extinct. Order Falconiformes, family Accipitridae.

EARTHWORM, any burrowing segmented worm that swallows soil and digests out the organic matter before discharging the inert mineral particles as castings. These worms are found in practically all land areas of the world, with the exception of Madagascar and Antarctica.

Earthworms lack eyes and appendages, but are sensitive over their entire body surface and hold to the substratum by means of bristles under muscular control. They work through and loosen the soil, aiding the agriculturalist. In winter they burrow beneath the frost line.

Because they are used as bait by fishermen, earthworms are sometimes called angleworms. The common earthworms (usually *Allobophora foetida* or *Lumbricus terrestris*) are 3 to 5 inches long; in some tropical countries giant earthworms are 5 or more feet long. Class Oligochaeta, order Megadrili, family Lumbricidae.

EARWIG, any of about 1,100 different kinds of insects with biting mouthparts, a slender and somewhat flattened body, and a prominent pair of pincers at the posterior end. They live in temperate and tropical areas, subsisting chiefly on plant material, for which they scavenge at night. By day, earwigs hide among fallen leaves, under boards, in beach drift, or even in clothing that can provide shade. They use their pincers in self-defense, and to help adult earwigs in folding their transparent hind wings to fit under the opaque and horny forewings.

The European earwig (*Forficula auricularia*) has become established along both coasts of North America and in other parts of the world, where it often feeds on fruits, flowers, and garden plants. Females of the European and some other earwigs commonly guard their eggs and newly hatched young, which are called nymphs. Order Dermaptera.

EEL, any of about 350 different kinds of slender, bony fishes of snakelike form, the best known of which mature in brackish estuaries or fresh water but reproduce in the depths of the sea. The common eel of the North Atlantic coasts (*Anguilla anguilla*) is a valuable food fish 2 to 5 feet long. For breeding and egg laying they migrate from Europe and America to deep water near the Bahama Islands, where the spawning takes place.

The infant is a ¼-inch-long, ribbon-like creature so unlike the adult that it was long considered a different fish. When they are large enough, the young eels swim up and westward until they are carried along in the Gulf Stream. Young American eels leave to enter rivers along the coast. European eels remain longer in the Gulf Stream, until they can easily reach Europe's river mouths. Six to 12 years later these eels are mature,

PREHISTORIC ANIMALS

PHOTOGRAPHS FROM THE PRIMEVAL WORLD AT DISNEYLAND. ©WALT DISNEY PRODUCTIONS

FIN-BACKED EDAPHOSAURUS, a giant, plant-eating reptile, roamed through forests of exotic plants more than 300 million years ago.

TRIO OF ORNITHOMIMUSES, *left*, called "ostrich dinosaurs," around a drying water hole as the rain forests give way to desert lands.

GIANT PTERANODONS, *right*, flying lizards with leathery 25-foot wings and three-foot beaks, lived over 150 million years ago.

BIRDS

YOUNG TOUCANS

FRIGATE BIRDS

SANGUE-DE-BOIS

JANDAIA

PENGUINS

RED-FOOTED BOOBY CHICK

HARPY EAGLE

INSECTS

TARANTULA	WOLF SPIDER	SCORPION
HORNED BEETLE	RED-BANDED LEAFHOPPER	PRAYING MANTIS
BEE AT FLOWER	GRASSHOPPER ON THISTLE	CICADA

JAGUAR

PHOTOS © WALT DISNEY PRODUCTIONS

KOALA

RHINOCEROSES

BEARS

MAMMALS

BIGHORN MOUNTAIN SHEEP

GIRAFFES

PHOTOS © WALT DISNEY PRODUCTIONS

RACCOON

ANTEATER

RINGTAIL CAT

MUSTACHED TAMARING

REPTILES

CORAL SNAKE

PHOTOS © WALT DISNEY PRODUCTIONS

BRAZILIAN HORNED TOAD

LAND IGUANA

GILA MONSTER

MUSSERANA

RATTLESNAKE

TEJU LIZARD

and return to the spawning place and apparently die there.

Eels usually have minute scales, but the conger eel (*Conger conger*), a larger, strictly salt-water fish, is quite scaleless; it sometimes grows 8 feet long. Lampreys are sometimes called lamprey eels. Order Apodes, several families, especially Anguillidae.

EGRET. See *Heron.*

EIDER, any of 4 different kinds of large sea ducks, strikingly marked in the male with black and white. They are found in northernmost Europe, Asia, and America, going south beyond the limits of sea ice only in winter. Most species live wholly in the water and go to land only for breeding.

The female lines her nest with her own soft, downy breast feathers. In Iceland and many other arctic areas, people gather these feathers as soon as the nest is deserted, and use them to line pillows and quilts. Order Anseriformes, family Anatidae.

ELEPHANT, either of two gigantic land mammals in which the nose is greatly elongated to form a cylindrical prehensile trunk with the nostrils at the tip. Once widespread, the Asiatic (Indian) elephant (*Elephas indicus*) is now confined to forested regions of tropical India, Burma, the Malay Peninsula, and adjoining islands; and the African elephant (*Loxodonta africanus*) to Africa south of the Sahara.

The Indian elephant has a concave forehead and small ears; the African elephant has a convex forehead and large ears and is chiefly hunted for its ivory. A pygmy race of elephants (4 or 5 feet high, half the size of the regular African elephant) is found in the Congo.

In both species the two upper incisors or front teeth are often enormously developed, constituting long tusks. The lower incisors are lacking, and there are no other teeth in the jaws except the molars, or grinders, of which two are usually in use at one time on each side of each jaw. The molars are very large and expose a number of transverse plates or enamel united by dentine. As each molar is worn out another succeeds it. The feet have five toes, but these are barely indicated externally; the animal walks on the soles of its feet, each cushioned by a thick pad of skin.

Elephants are vegetable feeders, living almost entirely on the foliage of shrubs and trees, which they strip off by means of the prehensile trunk. As the tusks prevent the animal from drinking in the ordinary way, the water is sucked up by the trunk, which is then inserted in the mouth, where the contents are emptied.

Many species of extinct elephants are known, the most familiar of which are the mammoth and the mastodons. The mammoth (*Elephas primigenius*) formerly ranged over much of North America, Europe, and Siberia. In Siberia whole carcasses have been found preserved in the ice. Unlike the elephants of today, the mammoth was covered by long, thick hair. Its tusks reached a length of 15 feet, some weighing 250 pounds. The young of the Indian elephants have a hairy covering that sometimes lasts for several years—a vestigial remain of their remote ancestors which lived in colder climates.

The mastodons (*Mammut* species) at one time spread into South America. Some mastodons had a small pair of tusks on the lower jaw in addition to the large pair on the upper jaw. Order Proboscidea.

ELK. See *Deer.*

EMU, a flightless Australian running bird, similar in habits and appearance to the ostrich and second only to the ostrich in size, sometimes standing 7 feet high. The emu grazes in small groups on the level plains, relying upon keen vision and long legs to escape from danger. Order Casuariiformes, family Dromiceidae, specifically *Dromiceius novae-hollandiae.*

ERMINE. See *Weasel.*

FALCON, any of 58 different birds of prey with long-pointed wings, bare shanks and feet, loose-looking feathers on the thighs and, usually, a notch in the cutting edge of the upper beak. They are found on all major continents and large islands except New Zealand.

Largest of falcons is the powerful gyrfalcon (*Falco rusticolus*) of arctic tundras in both hemispheres; smallest is the Philippine falconet (*Microhierax erythrogonys*), which resembles a swallow. Most famous, and perhaps the most skilful flier, is the peregrine falcon (*F. peregrinus*), known in America as a duck hawk; the male is called a tercel. These falcons are the favorites of falconers, men who catch and train the birds to pursue and capture wild game. Order Falconiformes, family Falconidae.

FER-DE-LANCE. See *Pit Viper.*

FINCH, any of several hundred small seed-eating perching birds with heavy beaks, related closely to sparrows. Those of family Fringillidae are of New World origin and include the cardinal of the United States, Darwin's finches of the Galápagos Islands, and the Saffron finch of the West Indies and South America. Those of family Ploceidae come from the Old World, and include the bullfinch, goldfinch, house finch, and weaver finch.

The sexes may or may not be differently colored. Finches are to be found in all types of places, but especially in forests and open meadows. Seeds, insects, and fruits form the greater part of their food. Order Passeriformes.

FIREFLY, a nocturnal beetle with light-producing organs on the lower side of the abdomen used to bring potential mates together. The light is described as "cold" bioluminescence, since it includes little energy in the form of heat. It is caused by the oxidation of a secretion called *luciferin.* The larvae are luminous and called *glowworms.* In some species the eggs are luminous. Order Coleoptera, family Lampyridae.

FISHER. See *Marten.*

FLAMINGO, any of 4 different kinds of wading birds with longer legs and necks than any others. Their beaks have an angular downward turn, adapted to their use in filtering minute particles of food from shallow saline or alkaline water in which the birds stand.

Most widely distributed is the greater flamingo (*Phoenicopterus ruber*) of southernmost Florida, the Bahamas, Yucatan, northern South America, and the Galápagos Islands, and locally in Eurasia and Africa; those of tropical America have the brightest pink color. The Andean and James' flamingos inhabit alkaline marshes at high altitudes in South America. The lesser flamingo is found only in Africa south of the great deserts.

Flamingos nest in colonies of 4,000 to 5,000, on small isolated islands. They build volcano-shaped mud nests about 1-foot high, patting them into shape with feet and beak. One or 2 eggs are laid in the crater. For a time the young birds wear grayish white down and have difficulty standing up. Order Ciconiiformes, family Phoenicopteridae.

FLATFISH, any of a large number of bony fishes that swim or lie on the bottom with one side of the body regularly downward. During their development from symmetrical hatchlings, these fishes grow distorted. Both eyes come to be situated on the upper side of the head.

Flatfishes are found to moderate depths in all oceans, and ascend estuaries into almost freshwater. The one side that becomes the "belly" of the flatfish is usually white; the other side ("the back") often possesses remarkable powers of changing color and pattern. The fish matches the color of its surroundings so well that it is overlooked by small fishes of other kinds that it eats.

Largest of the flatfishes are the halibuts, the name meaning holy fish; they commonly weigh 50 to 120 pounds, and sometimes up to 720 pounds; much of this is white flesh of excellent flavor. Flounders are smaller and possess teeth in their twisted mouths; soles are still smaller and generally lack teeth. Order Heterosomata.

FLEA, a wingless jumping insect with a body strongly flattened from side to side, and mouthparts fitted for piercing flesh and sucking blood. Fleas are found all over the terrestrial world, as external parasites on particular kinds of warm-blooded animals. They lay eggs on the host or in its vicinity. Larval fleas hatch out, and scavenge for food, often in the bedding or nests of the host, or among organic matter in cracks. After transforming during a pupal stage, the adult flea emerges.

The human flea (*pulex irritans*) is about $\frac{1}{10}$-inch long. Fleas of cats and dogs (*Ctenocephalus* species) sometimes bite people when very hungry.

In the West Indies and other tropical areas, a small flea called the chigoe (*Tunga penetrans*) burrows into human skin, freeing her eggs and breathing through a small hole reaching the body surface. Order Siphonaptera.

FLOUNDER. See *Flatfish.*

FLUKE, any of about 5,800 different kinds of parasitic flatworms that are found all over the world and that cling to their host animals by means of two or more suckers. About 700 different kinds have a simple life history, attacking only a single host animal. They usually attach themselves externally to the skin or the gills of fishes. But some flukes have become adapted to living in the mouth, the nasal cavities, or the urinary bladder of amphibians and aquatic reptiles, such as turtles.

More than 5,000 different kinds of flukes have complex life histories, involving two or more hosts. Generally they live in the intestine of a vertebrate animal or in organs, such as the liver, that are connected to it.

The Chinese liver fluke (*Opisthorchis sinensis*), which reaches a size of ¾-inch in the bile passages of the human liver, lays eggs that reach the outside world in the feces. If an egg gets into freshwater and is eaten by an aquatic snail of the correct kind, the egg hatches into a parasite of a slightly different form, which goes through several larval stages. In the last larval stage it escapes from the snail and swims actively in the water, ready to penetrate the body of a fish in which it can go dormant.

Man becomes infected with the parasite by eating the dormant stage of the fluke in the flesh of fish that has been inadequately cooked. In many tropical countries a more serious parasitic fluke enters the human skin and reaches maturity in the blood vessels of the intestine. It is known as a blood fluke (*Schistosoma* species). Various orders of class Trematoda.

FLY, any of about 85,000 different kinds of insects in which the adult has 1 pair of membranous wings and 1 pair of knobbed balancers (halteres). Flies live on all land areas of the world. Most lay eggs that hatch into active maggots, which grow until they can pupate to transform to adult flies. Some, such as the flesh flies (species of *Sarcophaga*), whose maggots feed on carrion, and the biting tsetse flies (species of *Glossina*) of Africa, deposit active larvae that have hatched inside the body of the mother.

The larvae of mosquitoes, called wrigglers, are active aquatic insects, feeding on microscopic animals and plants. The floating pupae, called bullheads, can swim when disturbed.

Fly maggots of many kinds serve importantly as decomposers of dead plants and animals. Those of the tachina flies (members of family Tachinidae) are internal parasites of caterpillars, and help control infestations upon crop plants. The house fly (*Musca domestica*) and others that eat and drink food used by humans can transmit diseases; they can pick up infections because they seek out manure and other wastes as the places in which their maggots can find food for growth. Order Diptera.

FLYCATCHER, any of a large number of small to medium-sized perching birds with weak feet, which dart from perches on tree branches to capture insects on the wing. Flycatchers of the New World include 365 different kinds from northern Canada to Patagonia, including the eastern kingbird (*Tyrannus tyrannus*) of eastern and central North America, the tail-wagging phoebe (*Sayornis phoebe*) of the eastern United States and Canada, the spectacular scissor-tailed flycatcher (*Muscivora forficata*) of south central United States, the brilliant red vermilion flycatcher (*Pyrocephalus rubinus*) of Mexico, Central America, and the southwestern United States, and the great kiskadee (*Pitangus Sulphuratus*) which calls out its name from southern Texas to Brazil.

Flycatchers of the Old World include 378 different kinds, chiefly tree-dwellers, of Africa, Europe, Southeast Asia, and Australia, among them the 5 friendly gray birds with a reddish breast that Australians call robins (*Petroica* species). Order Passeriformes, families Tyrannidae (New World) and Muscicapidae.

FLYING FISH, any of many specially adapted bony fishes that can glide for considerable distances in air, either with the aid of enlarged pectoral fins (the "two-winged flying fishes") or with both pectoral and pelvic fins expanded (the "four-winged flying fishes"). All have the lower lobe of the tail fin enlarged as a sculling organ.

Flying fishes probably take to the air to escape from larger sea animals that are pursuing them in the water. Order Synentognathi, family Exocoetidae.

FLYING LEMUR, or colugo, either of 2 kinds of gliding mammals about 15 inches long with a 9- or 10-inch tail with a gliding membrane linking the neck to the tips of fingers, toes, and tail. They live in the forests of Malaya and the East Indies, where they climb slowly but skilfully head up, or cling suspended by their front claws.

They feed on seeds, fruit, buds, flowers, and leaves. Although quite helpless on the ground, they are active in the trees, leaping from branch to branch with remarkable agility, and gliding as much as 450 feet for each 40-foot loss in altitude. Order Dermoptera, family Cynocephalidae, specifically *Cynocephalus volans* in the Philippines and *C. variegatus* in Southeast Asia and the East Indies.

FOWL, a term originally referring to any bird, but now generally restricted to members of the Order Galliformes, which includes the domestic fowl (rooster and hen), the peafowl (peacock and peahen), the pheasant, turkey, partridge, grouse, quail, and the moundbuilder of Australia. Most of these are rather heavy in the body, with short wings and an ability to fly short distances only. Generally they run on the ground, using their strong feet to scratch for food. Most nest on the ground, laying numerous eggs, which the hen bird incubates alone.

Wildfowl, however, are now regarded as ducks, geese, and swans, all members of the Order Anseriformes. Waterfowl include pelicans and all other swimming birds, but not the herons and other wading birds.

FOX, any of about 15 different kinds of small to medium-sized doglike mammals with a sharp muzzle, long bushy tail, and a "foxy" odor arising from special glands near the base of the tail. They inhabit most of Africa, Eurasia, and the Americas. The pupil of a fox's eye is generally elliptical in strong light; ears are usually triangular and pointed.

The red fox (*Vulpes fulva*) inhabits most parts of Europe and America and extends also into northern Asia. Its senses are extremely acute, and it has learned to use them to avoid man. It usually remains concealed in a burrow during the day and ventures abroad chiefly at night in search of food.

It is one of the principal predators on voles and mice, but eats also insects, eggs, fruit, grass, and whatever small birds and mammals are easy to catch.

The arctic, or white, fox (*Alopex lagopus*) is remarkable for changing its color with the season, being brown or bluish in summer and white in winter. The soles of its feet are hairy. The gray fox (*Urocyon cinereoargenteus*) is common from southern Canada to northern South America, and often climbs trees when pursued, or to rest inconspicuously. The furs of all foxes are valuable, especially the silver foxes and blue mutant strains of arctic foxes now raised for the market on fox farms. Order Carnivora, family Canidae.

FRIGATE BIRD, or man-of-war bird, any of 5 different tropical, web-footed birds with a long hooked beak, very long wings that are bent at an angle while soaring or flying, and a deeply forked tail. The magnificent frigate bird (*Fregata magnificens*) ranges from the Bahamas and Baja California to Brazil and Ecuador; the male is solid black, except for the brilliant red chest pouch that he inflates at mating season; the female has a white neck and throat.

The great frigate (*F. minor*), also measuring 40 inches from beak tip to tail tip, and whose wingspan is about 7 feet, patrols coasts of the western South Atlantic, the central and western Pacific, and the Indian Ocean.

Smallest is the 32-inch long lesser frigate bird (*F. ariel*) of the South Pacific, Australian shorelines, Madagascar, and the coast of Brazil. These birds are all expert fliers, but can scarcely walk or swim. They pick food from the ocean surface, or snatch unguarded chicks from the nests of other sea birds, or like pirates attack any gull, booby, or cormorant that has caught a fish, forcing it to give up its prey. Order Pelecaniformes, family Fregatidae.

FROG, the common name for adult tailless amphibians that have smooth skin and webbed hind feet. Frogs inhabit moist places, near freshwater, all over

ANIMALS

the world. Females lay their eggs in long strings in the water. From these, fishlike larvae called tadpoles or polliwogs hatch out, each with a broad, swimming tail and gills on the sides of its head.

Tadpoles feed upon small aquatic plants that they scrape from sticks and stone with their horny jaws. As they increase in size, the legs grow out and the tail is absorbed. The anterior pair of legs forms first but remains concealed beneath the skin until the hind pair is well developed and conspicuous. With the growth of legs and the loss of tail, the gills disappear and the lungs come into use; nevertheless most species always remain in close proximity to water throughout life.

Adults live on animal food such as insects, mollusks, and small fishes. Some do not hesitate to eat members of their own species. Frogs are useful to man in keeping down certain species of insects. They are caught for the flesh in their hind legs, which is white meat of mild flavor.

The largest North American frog is the bullfrog (*Rana catesbiana*), 5 to 8 inches long, found almost everywhere east of the Rocky Mountains. The pickerel frog (*R. palustris*) is brown with green spots, and the leopard frog (*R. pipiens*) is brilliantly marked with black spots outlined in white on its bright-green skin. Order Salientia, family Ranidae.

FRUIT FLY, any of nearly 1,000 different kinds of 2-winged insects less than ¼-inch long, commonly found around bananas and other fruits in which its maggots can develop, feeding on yeasts in the fermenting juice. The Mediterranean fruit fly (*Ceratitis capitata* of family Trypetidae) is a destructive pest, especially on citrus fruits. Much that we know today about heredity has been learned from a study of fruit flies of the genus *Drosophila* (literally "honey-lovers"), of family Drosophilidae. Order Diptera.

GALLINULE, a marsh bird closely related to the coots and rails, with a plump body, suggesting that of a domestic fowl. Gallinules are found in many parts of the world, usually close to freshwater, in which they often swim about. Except on migration, they seldom fly far. They nest on platforms built of vegetation in the middle of marshes.

The common, or Florida, gallinule (*Gallinula chloropus*) of eastern North America and Central America is native also to Europe and Britain, where it is called a moorhen. The larger, purple gallinule (*Porphyrula martinica*) is a more conspicuous bird, with a purple breast and a blue shield on the forehead contrasting with a bright red, yellow-tipped beak, and with lemon-yellow legs.

Gallinules live along the Atlantic and Gulf coasts and in Central and northern South America. Similar, but flightless, birds in New Zealand are the pukeko (*Porphyrio melanotus*) of marsh edges and the rare takahe (*Notornis mantelli*) of valley tussock land, which until recently was believed to be extinct. Order Gruiformes, family Rallidae.

GAR (from an Anglo-Saxon word meaning pike or spear), any of about 8 different kinds of armored fishes with cylindrical bodies and needle-sharp teeth. They inhabit rivers and lakes of North America east of the Rockies and southward to the Isthmus of Panama.

Their covering is of rhomboidal scales, each with an enamel surface so hard that a fish spear will scarcely penetrate. The common gar, or bony pike (*Lepisosteus osseus*), sometimes attains a length of 5 feet and is easily distinguished by the long beaklike extension of the mouth region. The alligator gar of the lower Mississippi and of Mexico (*L. spatula*) is larger than the common gar, occasionally reaching 12 feet in length and a weight of 350 pounds. Order Ginglimodi, family Lepisosteidae.

GAZELLE, any of about 12 different exceedingly slender and long-legged antelopes, renowned for their long necks and graceful movements. They inhabit Africa, Asia Minor, and as far east as northern India and Mongolia. They include the dibatag or Clark's gazelle (*Ammodorcas clarkei*) of Somaliland, the gerenuk or Waller's gazelle (*Litocranius walleri*) of East Africa, the springbuk (*Antidorcas marsupialis*) of South Africa and Angola, the Mongolian gazelles (species of *Procapra*), and various gazelles (genus *Gazella*) in which lyre-shaped horns develop in both sexes.

The common gazelle (*G. dorcas*), 3 to 4 feet tall, is fawn or dun colored on the back; a brown or black line separates this coloration from the white hair on the belly. The horns, stronger in the male than in the female, were used for lyre frames in early days.

The gazelle inhabits the large plains and the Saharan region of northern Africa, as well as Arabia and Syria, and lives in herds. Order Artiodactyla, family Bovidae.

GECKO, any of about 300 kinds of slender lizards, with special suction discs on its toes, permitting it to creep on smooth vertical surfaces or even ceilings in pursuit of insects as food. Geckos sometimes bask in the sun, watching for danger through slit pupils suggesting those of a cat. Like cats, they prefer to hunt in twilight and darkness, capturing their food by sudden extension of a long, sticky tongue with an extended tip. Often geckos produce loud calls, which may sound like geck'-oh or like the chirp of an insect.

The banded gecko (*Coleonyx variegatus*) of the North American southwest, from Texas to California, is pale brownish gray, banded or speckled with dark reddish brown, and attains a length of 4 inches. Like all geckos it is harmless, despite superstitions to the contrary. Order Sauria, family Gekkonidae.

GIBBON, any of about 7 kinds of tailless anthropoid apes with extremely long arms and legs, enabling them to exceed all other mammals in the agility with which they swing through the tree tops from branch to branch. They

GIRAFFE

are native to southeastern Asia and the East Indies.

Rarely more than 3 feet high when standing erect, a gibbon usually balances itself by stretching its arms overhead. Let hang for a moment, the hands almost touch the ground. Gibbons have buttock pads and long canine teeth. They eat mostly fruit, leaves, buds, and whatever birds, eggs, and insects they can catch. By day they are active, but by night gibbons sleep upright in little groups, leaning on one another and some crouch in a big tree. Order Primates, family Pongidae.

GILA MONSTER. See *Lizard*.

GIRAFFE, the tallest mammal, a solid-horned cud-chewer with extraordinarily long neck and long legs. It inhabits African highlands, where it browses on the sides and tops of thorny trees. Formerly it was called the camelopard, because the neck was thought to resemble that of a camel, and the pattern of the skin the spots of a leopard. Actually it is related both to the antelopes, which have hollow horns, and the deer, which have solid antlers. In the giraffe the antlers are never shed, but continue to grow slowly under the hairy skin atop the head.

The giraffe uses its unusually long cylindrical tongue for stripping off the leaves from the trees on which it feeds. When the giraffe drinks it must spread its front legs wide apart to get its mouth to the water. Order Artiodactyla, family Giraffidae.

GNU, or wildebeest, either of 2 kinds of hollow-horned, cud-chewing African antelopes with a conspicuous beard, mane, tuft of hairs between the forelegs, and tuft of long hairs at the tip of the tail. Commonest and widespread on the African savannas is the brindled gnu or blue wildebeest (*Connochaetes taurinus*) which often forms mixed herds with zebras, each benefiting from the association. The white-tailed gnu (*C. gnou*), which has been exterminated except in South Africa, is about the size of a horse and has structural features suggesting a bison and a deer.

In both male and female the horns taper to points, curving forward from the skull and turning up at the ends. Order Artiodactyla, family Bovidae.

GOAT, any of 5 different hairy cud-chewing mammals, similar to sheep but differing in that the forehead is convex, rather than concave; in the possession of a beard and scent glands on the body of the male; and in the absence of scent glands on the feet of both sexes.

Goats inhabit Eurasia from Spain to Siberia, south to the Sudan, Ethiopia, and the Arabian peninsula. Mostly they are found in wild mountainous countries where they scramble among the high rocks. The domestic goat (*Capra hircus hircus*) may have been derived in ancient times from the bezvar goat (*C. hircus aegagrus*) of Asia Minor. It has been bred into many distinctive lines, such as the Angora, whose hair is woven into the fabric called mohair, and the Kashmir goat, whose hair becomes fine cashmere for India shawls.

The flesh, especially that of the kid or young goat, is used as food, despite its rather poor quality. The milk is very rich and nutritious, and, because it is free from tuberculosis germs, it is often fed to tubercular and other patients. Many cheeses are made from goats' milk. Some goats yield about 2 quarts. The skin is dressed as leather for many uses, particularly for gloves and other fine kinds of shoes. The horns, which are worn by both sexes, are used to make knife handles, and the fat to make candles.

The Rocky Mountain goat (*Oreamnos americanus*) is really a closer relative to the European chamois, intermediate between the antelope and the goat. It is about as big as an ordinary sheep, and it looks like a sheep of the Merino breed with long straight hair and spiky horns. Order Artiodactyla, family Bovidae.

GOLDENEYE, or whistler, a diving duck that nests in tree holes in the northern United States, Canada, Scandinavia, and northern areas of Europe and Asia. When feeding, it frequents lakes, broad rivers, and bays of the ocean, in which it can dive for crustaceans, plants, and aquatic insects. In flight, its wings make a characteristic high-pitched whistling sound.

Goldeneyes are dark colored toward the tip, with white patches above and below toward the body. In both sexes the body itself is white below and dark above. The male has a black head with a white spot between eye and beak, and a white neck. His mate has a brown head and a gray neck with a white collar. In the common goldeneye (*Bucephala clangula*), the white patches on the head of the male and the beak in both sexes are smaller than in Barrow's goldeneye (*B. islandica*), which nests farther north and at higher altitudes in North America, and only in Iceland in the Old World. Order Anseriformes, family Anatidae.

GOLDFINCH, a small songbird with a short, strong beak suited to opening seeds, and a quick, undulating flight. The American goldfinch (*Spinus tristis*) is common over most of settled Canada and all except the southernmost states of the Union in summer; it ranges down into eastern Mexico for the winter.

In summer the male goldfinch is often called a "wild canary," because he is then brilliant golden yellow with a black forehead, a black forked tail, and black wings marked with a white bar. His coloration in autumn and winter more closely resembles that of his mate and young goldfinches, which are brownish olive-yellow, darker above, with black tail and black wings similarly marked.

The European goldfinch (*Carduelis carduelis*), introduced into America in 1852 on Long Island, New York, is even more brightly colored, and equally in both sexes. Its face is brilliant red, snow-white at the sides; the crown of the head is jet-black, as are the nape of the neck, most of the forked tail, and the wings except for a broad band of bright yellow and white spots along the trailing edge. The body is brown except on the rump and belly, which are white. The call of the European goldfinch is usually a canarylike twitter.

In Europe and Asia, goldfinches are permanent residents of gardens, orchards, and cultivated land. They are rare or absent in Iceland, northernmost Scotland, and similar latitudes across the great continent of Eurasia. Order Passeriformes, family Fringillidae.

GOOSE, any of about 14 different kinds of web-footed birds related to swans, which are bigger and have longer necks, and to ducks, which are smaller and have shorter necks in proportion to the body. With the exception of the Australian magpie goose (*Anseranas semipalmata*), which is black and white, they are birds of the Northern Hemisphere. The legs of a goose are farther forward than a duck's, and thus better adapted for walking.

Geese spend much of their time on land, feeding on grass and other herbage, berries, seeds, and various kinds of vegetable food. Although large and bulky, they have great powers of flight. They strike with their wings in fighting; at the bend of the wings there is a hard callous knob or tubercle, which in some species becomes a spur.

Gray geese of 5 kinds include the domestic goose (*Anser domesticus*), which probably originated from the European gray-lag goose (*A. anser*), which is almost 3 feet long from the tip of the bill to the extremity of the short tail; the wingspread is about 5 feet. The weight of the largest bird is about 10 pounds. The other gray geese are the lesser white-fronted goose, the bean goose and the swan goose of Eurasia and the greater white-fronted of the North American arctic.

Three white geese are the snow goose (*Anser caerulescens*) of northern Asia and the American arctic, the blue goose of Baffin Land, and Ross' goose which comes from the Arctic Circle to winter in California.

The black geese include the Canada goose (*Branta canadensis*) and the smaller brant of North America, the barnacle goose of far northern Europe, the bar-headed goose of the Himalayas, and the rare nene of Hawaii.

Geese are kept for their eggs, for their flesh (a favorite Christmas dish), and for their feathers that are used for pillows and beds. Quill pens were made from goose feathers. Order Anseriformes, family Anatidae.

GOPHER, any of 21 different kinds of squirrel-like burrowing rodents of the open plains in the Northern Hemisphere. The name is from the French *gaufre* (honeycomb), alluding to the burrow.

Gophers search by day for seeds, nuts, roots, soft stems and leaves, insects, bird eggs, and whatever mice and birds they can catch. Near cultivated fields, they may raid by night, making themselves troublesome pests in some localities. They carry home dry foods to storage chambers, but also become very fat by midsummer and often go early into winter dormancy. Order Rodentia, family Sciuridae, species of genus *Citellus*.

GORILLA, the largest of the manlike apes, which may reach a height of 5½ feet and a weight of 400 pounds. Gorillas live in the bamboo forests of tropical West Africa. Their arms in relation to the body are shorter than those of any other ape. Gorillas are very strong, but they usually retreat before man. When grown to more than 100 pounds, they rarely climb. Usually they make beds of leaves and boughs.

Little was known of them until 1859 when Paul Du Chaillu, a French-American explorer, brought skins and skeletons to Europe. He brought back to the United States the first gorillas ever seen there. Order Primates, family Pongidae, specifically *Gorilla gorilla*.

GRACKLE, either of 2 large blackbirds, about 14 to 17 inches long, including the long tail, found in Canada and the United States east of the Rocky Mountains. The bronzed grackle (*Quiscalus quiscula*), sometimes called crow blackbird, nests as far north as Great Slave Lake and Newfoundland, and winters in the southeastern United States. The boat-tailed grackle (*Cassidix mexicanus*), which is slightly larger (up to 16 inches long), is a bird of Atlantic coastal states and Mexico. Order Passeriformes, family Icteridae.

ROTHSTEIN/LOOK

GORILLA

GREBE, any of 18 different kinds of diving water birds, each of whose toes has horny flaps at the sides, like individual webbing, used particularly in swimming underwater. Grebes are found on all continents as inhabitants of slow streams and ponds. When disturbed, grebes usually dive below the surface where they swim long distances. They are good flyers, however, but have some difficulty in leaving the surface of the water because of their small-sized wings.

They feed mainly on small fish, frogs, crustaceans, and insects. They build nests near or on the water and the matted plant material sometimes actually floats. Grebes carry their young pick-a-back, sometimes even diving to escape with the young birds still hanging on. Order Podicepediformes, family Podicepedidae.

GROSBEAK, any of several songbirds with a conical, heavy beak well adapted to opening thick-shelled seeds. They are distinctly larger than sparrows, and frequent trees and brush, seldom coming to the ground. They are birds of the Northern Hemisphere. Generally the two sexes are unlike in coloration; the males are much more brilliantly marked. Many individuals associate together in winter, often showing little fear of man.

Among the grosbeaks of North America are the cardinal (*Richmondena cardinalis*), which has a crest; the rose-breasted grosbeak (*Pheucticus ludovicianus*); the black-headed grosbeak (*P. melanocephalus*); the blue grosbeak (*Guiraca caerulea*); the evening grosbeak (*Hesperiphona vespertina*); and the pine grosbeak (*Pinicola enucleator*), which is found also in coniferous forests of northern Europe, where a much smaller bird (*Carpodacus erythrinus*) is called the scarlet grosbeak, although it is a close relative of the American purple finch (*C. purpureus*). Order Passeriformes, family Fringillidae.

GROUSE, any of 18 different kinds of the fowl-like birds with thick soft feathers, usually brown and reddish in inconspicuous patterns. Grouse are widely distributed in the Northern Hemisphere. Their short wings beat very rapidly in flight with a whirring sound, giving them great speed and agility over distances up to a few hundred yards. In general grouse prefer the deep woods and spend most of their lives on the ground where they find seeds, fruits, buds, and insects.

The ruffed grouse (*Bonasa unbellus*), sometimes called partridge in the northern states, is regarded as the finest of all upland game birds over its whole area of distribution, coast to coast in Canada, and southward to Georgia and northern California.

During the mating season, the male ruffed grouse drums with his wings at some open spot on or near the ground, the sound sometimes carrying more than a mile, and serving as a call to the female or as a challenge to combat for other males.

Spruce grouse (*Canachites canadensis*) occupy much the same area in coniferous woods rather than in cutover forests. Most beautiful is the black grouse (*Lyrurus tetrix*) of forests in northern Eurasia, and largest among grouse the capercaillie (*Tetrao urogallus*) of Scandinavia, which is almost as large as a turkey. The heath hen (*Tympanuchus gallo*), which became extinct on the American mainland about 1835 and on Martha's Vineyard Island in 1932, was an eastern race of the prairie chicken (same name) which is growing scarce over its range from the Canadian prairies to the Appalachians and Arkansas. Order Galliformes, family Tetraonidae.

GUINEA FOWL, any of 7 different kinds of short-tailed, pheasantlike birds that run, rather than fly. They are native to Africa and Madagascar. Because of their tasty meat they are now widely domesticated even though they are almost too noisy to be raised on a small farm. They are mainly vegetarian, digging and scratching for seeds and roots. The common domestic guinea fowl (*Numida meleagris*) prefers grassy areas in which to hunt for seeds, fruits, slugs, and insects, but it needs trees in which to roost at night. In Africa, flocks sometimes number 2,000. Order Galliformes, family Numididae.

GUINEA PIG, or cavy, any of about 20 different kinds of stout-bodied, tailless, vegetarian rodents about 10 inches long. They are native to brushlands in mountainous South America, where one kind (*Cavia cobaya*) was domesticated in pre-Columbian times by the Incas as a convenient source of meat. In the wild, this guinea pig produces small litters, but in captivity it is extremely prolific: it begins to breed when 10 months old, and produces several families in a year, each family consisting of about 8 young. The popular name is inappropriate; the animal is not a pig and it does not come from Guinea. Order Rodentia, family Caviidae.

GULL, any of 43 different kinds of web-footed, scavenging birds, larger than terns, with a hooked tip on the upper beak and the habit of directing the beak forward, not down, while in flight. Gulls are common along seacoasts and large bodies of inland water, and on garbage dumps all over the world. They are usually white below with the upper parts varying from a light gray to black.

They can run and walk readily and often help in controlling plagues of grasshoppers and crickets. The Pacific gull (*Larus pacificus*) patrols the shores of Australia and the Great Barrier Reef for young turtles as they hatch and scamper over the beach toward the water. The herring gull (*L. argentatus*) and others of North and Central America drop mussels and sea urchins on rocks, paved areas, and parked cars to break open the shells and get at the meat inside. Order Charadriiformes, family Laridae.

GUPPY, or mosquito fish, a small top minnow from freshwaters of northern South America and the islands of the West Indies. It is named for Robert J. L. Guppy, who in 1866 discovered fishes of this kind in Trinidad.

At 1 inch in length the male guppy attains full size, and develops a long anal fin that shows his sex. The female grows twice as large, with an anal fin of normal size. During courtship, the male uses his special fin to transfer sperm cells to the female. Fertilization is internal, and the embryos develop into active little fish before emerging from their mother. From a single mating, a female guppy may produce 200 young in a month, and 200 more each month thereafter for about 8 months.

Because young fish can take care of themselves if the parents do not eat them, and reach maturity quickly, guppies have become popular as the "million fish" for tropical aquariums in the home. Supposedly a pregnant female guppy could give rise to 1 million descendants in a year or less, if the offspring were supplied with enough food and space that includes vegetation wherein the young can hide from older fish.

The common name mosquito fish refers to the readiness of the guppies to eat small aquatic insects. In captivity they may be supplied with water fleas (*Daphnia*) or young brine shrimp raised for the purpose. Order Cyprinodontes, family Poeciliidae, specifically *Gambusia affinis*.

HADDOCK, a marine bony fish resembling a cod in having the dorsal fin divided into 3 parts and the anal fin into 2, but with only a white line along the side instead of a pattern of markings. Haddocks are common in cold waters of the North Atlantic, where they eat virtually anything edible, especially mollusks. Haddock is one of the most important of the food fishes, and exceeds all other fishes in tonnage caught and sold annually. It is often smoked for sale as "finnan haddie." Order Anacanthini, family Gadidae, specifically *Melanogrammus aeglefinus*.

HAKE, any of several different marine food fishes differing from cod in details of the skull bones and ribs; the dorsal fin consists of a long forward part and a shorter rear part (not three parts, as in the cod), and the lower jaw bears no projections (barbels) with which to detect smaller fishes and other animals as prey upon the sea bottom.

Despite this lack, hake, which are widely distributed, catch fishes, crustaceans, and squids in large numbers. Apparently they do so with little exertion, for their flesh remains soft. Like the cod, hakes have soft fins and an air bladder with no connection to the outside world.

The European hake (*Merluccius merluccius*) inhabits deep water in the Mediterranean Sea and along Atlantic coasts from Norway to northwestern Africa; it attains a weight of 20 pounds, and is fished for at depths as great as 2,400 feet. The silver hake (*M. bilinearis*) along the Atlantic coast of North America and the Pacific hake (*M. productus*) are of smaller size. The South African hake, or stockfish (*M. capensis*), grows to as much as 4 feet in length, and is caught at depths to 1,800 feet by trawling, as the most valuable single commercial fish of that region. Order Anacanthini, family Merluccidae.

HAMSTER, any of several different kinds of small burrowing rodents from Mediterranean countries and Asia. The common, or black-bellied, hamster (*Cricetus cricetus*) is a short-tailed species, which makes extensive burrows in which to spend the day and the winter. A hamster may store as much as 200 pounds of grass seeds, dry small fruits, and even potatoes in its burrow. In summer these animals eat large numbers of insects as well as frogs, worms, and other smaller animals.

In some areas of Europe and Asia Minor, hamsters are trapped for their furry skins, which are usually light brown above, marked with white on the sides, and black below. During recent years, large numbers of common hamsters have been raised in captivity on a diet of dog biscuits, corn, and lettuce. They make interesting pets, and have become a valuable experimental animal for medical science. Order Rodentia, family Cricetidae.

HARE, any of about 30 different kinds of short-tailed, long-eared, jumping mammals with a short palate and the habit of bearing young that are fully haired, open-eyed, and ready to run with the mother. Native to North America and Eurasia as far south as Malaya, they have now been introduced into South America, Australia, New Zealand, islands off the northwest coast of Africa, and the northeastern United States.

The popular names hare and rabbit are often incorrectly used interchangeably. For example "jack rabbits" and "snowshoe rabbits" are not rabbits, but hares, whereas the "Belgian hare" is a rabbit.

Most kinds of hares live in open grassy country, but the varying hare (*Lepus americanus*) inhabits evergreen forests, where its fur is white in winter and dark brown in summer; its large feet make huge prints in the snow, hence the name "snowshoe rabbit" for this animal. The arctic hare (*L. arcticus*) is not found south of Hudson Bay. The black-tailed jack rabbit (*L. californicus*) occupies the U.S. southwest and Mexico.

All of these animals supply important food for the larger predators, and might contribute important meat and fur for mankind if raised in captivity, as is the European hare (*L. europaeus*) in many parts of Europe, to keep the animals free of disease. In the wild, they carry tularemia, a severe bacterial disease to which people who handle infected hares are susceptible. Order Lagomorpha, family Leporidae.

HARVESTMAN, or daddy longlegs, a spiderlike land animal with extremely slender long legs and a small, compact, often hard body bearing a pair of eyes on an elevated turret on its back.

Harvestmen are abundant in field and forest in all parts of the world from May to October. Eggs are laid in the fall and hatch the following spring. A few species sleep through the winter, but the majority of the adults die each fall after the breeding season. Their food consists mainly of small insects and other minute animals. They are harmless, but may produce an unpleasant odor when molested. Order Phalangida of class Arachnida.

HAWK, any of about 80 different medium-sized birds of prey, larger than falcons, smaller than eagles, kites, and vultures. Hawks are found in all parts of the world except New Zealand and Oceania. They are almost wholly carnivorous and rarely take food that has not recently been killed. The plumage is usually brown or white, although gray is not uncommon. The nests are built in trees and on rocky cliffs; occasional ground nests are found.

The principal kinds are the sharp-winged members of genus *Accipiter*, and the broad-winged hawks of genus *Buteo*. The sharp-shinned hawk (*A. velox*) is small, measuring only 11 to 13 inches in length, grayish on the back with bars of brown, whitish underneath, and with yellow legs and feet. Cooper's hawk (*A. cooperi*) is similar in plumage to the sharp-shinned, but larger.

The goshawk, originally goose-hawk (*A. gentilis*), is circumpolar and a great favorite with falconers for hunting marsh birds and rabbits. The marsh hawk (*Circus hudsonius*), one of the harriers, is a highly beneficial and almost cosmopolitan bird which kills such pests as rats, mice, and grasshoppers; it rarely feeds on birds.

The broad-winged hawks prefer reptiles, amphibians, and small mammals no larger than a rabbit; they include the red-shouldered hawk (*Buteo lineatus*) of eastern North America, which winters in southern Florida and Cuba, and the birds called buzzards (*Buteo buteo* and *B. lagopus*) in Europe. Order Falconiformes, family Accipitridae.

HEATH HEN. See *Grouse*.

HEDGEHOG, any of about 12 different small mammals bearing barbless spines among the fur on the back and sides, and able to roll up into a ball surrounded by spines when disturbed. They are Eurasian and African animals, which feed on animal matter, live or dead, although they willingly eat bread and milk or other food put out for cats and dogs.

Hedgehogs measure from 10 to 12 inches in length; the legs are short; the snout is long; and the spines are usually about 1 inch long. They are nocturnal in habits; during the day they hide in logs and stumps. In winter hedgehogs hibernate in protected places. Their flesh is sometimes eaten in Europe. There are no true hedgehogs native to the northern hemisphere: the North Amercian porcupine (*Erethizon*) is sometimes erroneously called a hedgehog. Order Insectivora, family Erinaceidae, particularly the Eurasian *Erinaceus europaeus*.

HIPPOPOTAMUS

HERON, any of the long-legged wading birds that have straight or slightly downcurved beaks, toothlike points on the side of the claw on each middle toe, and carry the head and neck in an S curve, particularly during flight. They are widespread, and commonly seen standing on one leg in shallow water, although they fly when disturbed.

Herons are generally subdivided into the bitterns (12 kinds), the tiger herons (6 kinds), the night herons (9 kinds), the day herons (35 kinds), and the agami heron of central and northern South America. Egrets are day herons with snowy plumes, the aigrettes of the milliner. The snowy, the white, and the reddish egrets live in the southern United States.

There are 2 American blue herons —the great blue (*Ardea herodias*), sometimes called blue crane, about 50 inches high, with a black crest; and the little blue heron (*Hydranassa caerulea*), only about 24 inches high. The European heron (*A. cinerea*) is so swift and strong that it was the favorite prey of trained falcons. Herons nest in high trees, in structures built of grass and twigs, sometimes in communities called heronries. The bitterns live in marshy places and the British species are becoming rare as marshy grounds are reclaimed.

The Old World bittern (*Botaurus stellaris*) is about 30 inches in length and about 44 inches in wingspread. Its usual color is a dull yellowish brown, with spots and bars of black or dark brown. It has long, loose breast feathers, a short tail, and a bill about 4 inches long. It is remarkable for its booming or bellowing cry, from which come the provincial names, miredrum, butterbump, and stake-driver. The eggs are 4 or 5 in number. The North American bittern (*Botaurus lentiginosus*) resembles the common European bittern, and is 26 inches long. The little bittern (*Ixobrychus minutus*) of Eurasia to New Zealand and South Africa is not more than 15 inches in length. Order Ciconiiformes, family Ardeidae.

HERRING, any of about 175 different kinds of small, soft-finned, bony fishes with deciduous scales and a knifelike ridge along the undersurface of the compressed body. Some live in the freshwaters of Africa and the Amazon basin, but most are marine and commonly come to river mouths at spawning time.

These fishes occur in large schools; they swim through the sea with open mouths, scooping up the minute life for food. Immense numbers are caught. The young herring, also taken in quantity, are preserved as American sardines. Order Isospondyli, family Clupeidae.

HIPPOPOTAMUS (Greek for river horse), either of 2 kinds of large mammals with a broad snout, large mouth, bulky body, and short stout legs ending in 4 toes. The large hippopotamus (*Hippopotamus amphibius*) is a river dweller of many parts of Africa, whereas the pygmy hippo (*Choeropsis liberiensis*) lives only in swamp forests of West Africa.

The large hippo adult weighs about 4 tons, the pygmy about 550 pounds. Both feed on shrubs, grasses, and other vegetation, and spend most of each day almost submerged in a favorite water hole. The stomach is 3-parted, but the animal does not chew a cud. Order Artiodactyla, family Hippopotamidae.

HOG. See *Swine*.

HONEYBEE. See *Bee*.

HOOKWORM, any of several different small parasitic intestinal roundworms, which have special attachment spines around the mouth. They attain maturity while firmly anchored in the wall of the human small intestine where they often cause severe bleeding, with consequent anemia and weakness. Their eggs pass out with undigested wastes, and hatch if exposed to air on the soil.

The active larvae can bore through bare human skin, particularly along the sides of the foot, between the toes, and around the ankles, thus reaching the bloodstream. The blood carries them to the lungs where they bore through into the air cavities, opening an avenue for infection by tuberculosis bacteria and other diseases. The larval hookworms ride the mucous film up to the throat, are swallowed, and thus reach the intestine.

Millions of persons are infected by hookworms, primarily in warm countries where sanitary conditions are poor and bare feet are usual. Order Rhabditida, particularly genera *Ancylostoma duodenale* and *Necator americanus*.

HORNET, any of a number of wasplike insects about 1 inch long with conspicuous white or yellow markings on a brown or gray body. The name hornet is loosely applied to a number of stinging wasps, but referred originally to the European brown kind (*Vespa crabro*), which is justly noted for the virulence of the sting and the irritability of the female insects so equipped.

The widely distributed European hornet, now introduced accidentally near New York City, builds communal nests in hollow trees, constructing the nest itself of wood fibers chewed to form a gray papery material.

The large gray hornet (*V. maculata*) found in eastern North America builds a similar "carton" nest, but suspends it from the limbs of trees. Inside the nest are cells like those of a honeycomb. The smaller yellow jackets (*V. communis* and *V. diabolica*) usually nest underground.

Hornets eat sweets of all kinds and steal honey from bees; they also feed on other insects. Order Hymenoptera, family Vespidae.

HORSE, either of 2 kinds of large herbivorous mammals that stand or run on a horny hoof capping the single elongated toe on each foot. Compared with the related asses and zebras, horses have small ears; they grow long hairs from the outer half of the tail, not at all from the end of the tail in a tuft as in these related animals.

Living horses are native to Africa north of the great deserts, and to central and eastern Asia. The only wild horses today are Mongolian, named *Equus przewalskii* after their discoverer the Russian explorer Nikolai Przhewalski; they are short-legged, thick-headed, stocky horses with an erect mane. The domesticated horse (*E. caballus*) is longer legged, more slender in the head, and graceful in body and legs. It probably is the descendant of an extinct horse of the same scientific name, the tarpan, which was an important source of food for mankind in prehistoric times.

Like other domestic animals, the horse has been developed into many special breeds, such as the Arabians for riding, the perchrons for draft use, thoroughbreds for racing, and ponies for work in mine passageways. Order Perissodactyla, family Equidae.

HORSESHOE CRAB, or king crab, any of 4 different marine arthropod animals, in which the heavily armored body as seen from above shows conspicuous subdivisions into a front division that is the shape of a horse's hoof and as much as 22 inches wide, a rear division that is roughly triangular, and a terminal long tapering tail spine.

The front division of the body bears a large compound eye on each side, and 2 small simple eyes near the midline far forward. Below this portion of the body are 4 pairs of walking legs, arising from the sides of the mouth, and 2 pairs of special appendages used for tasting and handling food, anterior to the mouth.

The rear division of the body bears below it a series of hinged plates to which the leaflike gills are attached. Waving these hinged plates and beating with its legs, a horseshoe crab swims upside down. After swimming, it often sinks to the bottom back downward and must turn over to walk along in search of worms and other soft food. It uses its tail spine to turn itself over onto its feet. Order Xiphosura of class Merostomata, family Limulidae.

One kind of horseshoe crab (*Limulus polyphemus*) lives along Atlantic and Gulf coasts of North America. The other 3 are found along coasts of Southeast Asia and the East Indies. These animals are not true crabs, but distant kin of scorpions and spiders (Class Arachnida); all of their nearest relatives, the sea scorpions, have been extinct for more than 200 million years.

HOUSE SPIDER, a small dust-colored spider not over ¼ inch long with slender legs 3 times the length of the body and several dark chevron markings on both the upper and lower surfaces of the egg-shaped abdomen. House spiders seldom live outdoors, having adopted human dwellings. They spin loose silken webs that catch small insects as well as dust; the spider flings strands of silk at its prey, using a special comb on its last pair of legs to handle the silk. Order Araneae, family Theridiidae, mostly *Theridion tepidariorum*.

HUMMINGBIRD, any of 319 different kinds of small day-active birds, with long slender bills and very small feet, which hover while sipping nectar from flowers and produce a humming sound by rapidly vibrating their wings. They are natives to the New World from southern Alaska and northern Nova Scotia to Tierra del Fuego. They are represented by the largest variety in tropical South America.

About 18 species are found in the United States, many of them only on the borders of the country. Only one species, the ruby-throated *Archilochus colubris*, is found east of the Mississippi River. It is 3¼ inches long and beautifully colored. Their beaks are long and curved allowing the birds to reach into deep-throated flowers, many of which they pollinate. Order Apodiformes, family Trochilidae.

HYDRA, any of several freshwater coelenterate polyps with a cylindrical, contractile body some ¾ inch long and about the diameter of the lead in an automatic pencil. It is ordinarily attached at one end to underwater vegetation; from the free end, which bears the mouth, 8 or more long threadlike tentacles extend into the water like fishing lines waiting for minute animals. Each tentacle is studded with microscopic nettling cells, which discharge when suitable prey touches them. Some of these cells inject a poison that quiets the prey, such as a water flea (*Daphnia*), while lassolike extensions of other cells hold on to the victim.

Slowly the hydra pushes the prey animal into its mouth, which opens into a sac-shaped digestive cavity. After all digestible materials have been absorbed, indigestible remains are ejected through the mouth in a spitting movement.

Well-fed hydras may develop from the side of the body new small individuals called buds, or produce sex cells in simple sex organs. Fertilized eggs grow to become swimming embryos, which eventually attach themselves somewhere and transform into the polyp form of the adult hydra.

The name hydra refers to a monster in Greek mythology, which grew new heads when old heads were cut off. The name was given to these polyps because of their powers of regeneration when mutilated. Class Hydrozoa, order Hydroidea, species of *Hydra* and other genera.

HYENA, any of 3 kinds of doglike mammals with disproportionately large head and forequarters but weak hindquarters. They inhabit the semi-arid portions of Africa and Asia, the spotted or laughing hyena (*Crocuta crocuta*) being widespread in Africa south of the great deserts, the brown hyena (*Hyaena brunnea*) in southern Africa, and the striped hyena (*H. hyaena*) from Asia Minor to West Pakistan.

The hyena is covered with coarse, bristly hair, short over most of the body, but forming a mane along the ridge of the neck. The hind legs are shorter than the forelegs, giving the body a slope from the withers to the haunches. The hyena is somewhat larger than a shepherd dog. The cheek muscles are greatly developed, and the large grinding teeth have great conical crowns that enable them to smash the thighbones of animals as large as the horse.

All hyenas are nocturnal in their habits. They are useful scavengers. Order Carnivora, family Hyaenidae.

IBIS, any of 23 different kinds of medium-sized, long-legged wading birds, which have no feathers on the face. Some lack feathers on the entire head and neck. Ibises are found in all warm and temperate regions except Oceania.

The sacred ibis (*Threskiornis aethiopica*) of Africa and Madagascar was worshiped in ancient Egypt; many legendary powers were ascribed to it. Today the bird has been virtually exterminated north of the great African deserts, although it is still common to the south. Far more widely distributed is the glossy ibis (*Plegadis falcinellus*) of southern Eurasia, Africa, Madagascar, Australia, the West Indies, and southern Florida.

The white ibis (*Eudocimus albus*), whose face and long down-curved beak and legs are reddish orange, is over 2 feet long with pure white plumage and a few black wing feathers. It nests generally by the thousands in immense rookeries in Florida, the West Indies, central and northern South America.

The scarlet ibis (*E. rubes*) of South and Central America has bright scarlet wings tipped with black. The American bird called a wood ibis is actually a kind of stork. Order Ciconiiformes, family Threskiornithidae—literally birds of worship, referring to the sacred ibis.

IGUANA, any of a number of tropical herbivorous lizards with a laterally compressed body and tail, and a number of soft spines that extend from the head to the tip of the tail, giving a crested appearance.

Iguanas are native to tropical America, including islands of the West Indies. A Galápagos iguana (*Amblyrhynchus cristatus*) lives on the lava rocks along the seashore and is partly aquatic, feeding on seaweeds, and growing to be 4 feet long. Even larger is the common green tree iguana (*Iguana iguana*) of Central and South America, which is sometimes 6 feet long.

Iguanas resemble more the legendary Chinese dragons than real animals. Their flesh has a delicate flavor, and their eggs, almost all yolk, are eaten in Latin America. Order Sauria, family Iguanidae.

JACKAL. See *Dog.*

JAY, any of about 50 different kinds of perching birds, smaller and more brightly colored than the closely related crows and magpies. They are found throughout the temperate and tropical zones, except in New Zealand and some oceanic islands. The common blue jay (*Cyanocitta cristata*) of eastern and central North America has beautiful bright-blue plumage, a conspicuous crest on its head, and a very harsh cry.

The Canada jay (*Perisoreus canadensis*) has sooty plumage, a black cap, white forehead, throat, and collar, but no crest. It is an accomplished thief, frequenting hunters' and prospectors' camps; it is called moose bird and whisky jack. Steller's jay (*Cyanocitta stelleri*) of America west of the Rockies is dark blue and black, with a crest, and inhabits coniferous forests. If they have a chance, nearly all jays will eat nestlings of smaller birds and their eggs. Otherwise they live on a wide variety of food, preponderantly of vegetable origin. Order Passeriformes, family Corvidae.

JELLYFISH. See *Medusa.*

JUNCO, any of several different sparrow-sized birds, characteristically slate-gray above, white below, and with white along each side of the tail. The feathers show no streaks or spots, but in some species provide red or pink color to the sides and some areas of the back. All are North American. Most widespread is the slate-colored junco (*Junco hyemalis*), which has a pink beak; it nests in Canada and the northern United States and winters throughout the United States and northern Mexico.

The western yellow-pine forests of the American Southwest are the sole home for the white-winged junco (*J. aikeni*), which has 2 white wing bars. Dry mountain forests and adjacent plains of the southwestern United States and northwestern Mexico have a gray-headed junco (*J. caniceps*), which has a gray head and a red-brown back. More widespread along the provinces and states of the Pacific slope and over the Rocky Mountain area into northern Mexico is the Oregon, or pink-sided, junco (*J. oreganus*).

All juncoes are often called "snowbirds," because they hop around on the winter snow while searching for dry seeds. During the summer they

AUSTRALIAN NEWS AND INFORMATION BUREAU
KANGAROO

eat large numbers of insects and feed their young exclusively on insects until the young birds leave the nest. Order Passeriformes, family Fringillidae.

JUNE BUG, or May Beetle, any of several kinds of flying adult beetles, which often fly to lights in late spring. Some are scarabs, such as *Phyllophaga* and *Cotinus;* others are stag beetles (*Pseudolucanus*). These types emerge from the ground where their larvae, called white grubs, pass a year or more feeding upon roots of grasses, vines, and trees. The adults, usually about an inch long, often chew vegetation; they are, however, most noticed when they fly through open windows and tumble to the floor. Order Coleoptera, chiefly families Scarabaeidae and Lucanidae.

KANGAROO, any of about 52 different kinds of mammals with a particularly strong, long tail serving as a third leg or as a prop while seated, with large, strong hind legs and small forelegs, and with a small head bearing a deerlike snout and large ears. Kangaroos and tree kangaroos, rat-kangaroos, wallabies, and wallaroos are found in Australia, Tasmania, New Guinea, and some adjacent islands. Females carry their young in a pouch (marsupium).

The largest kangaroo is the great gray (*Macropus giganteus*), which may stand 8 feet tall and weigh 150 pounds. Formerly plentiful over Australian plains, it is being eliminated to make space for cattle. While grazing, kangaroos walk on all fours. When alarmed or in a hurry, they leap along on their hind legs, 10 to 15 feet at a hop, the body being carried in a nearly horizontal position, and the tail extended to balance it. The forepaws are chiefly used for handling, and with these the females lift their young and place them in the pouch. The kangaroo skin is very soft and pliable and is used in making shoes and gloves. Order Marsupialia, family Macropodidae.

KATYDID, the popular American name for several different, large long-horned grasshoppers, which are active at night and make distinctive calls at night. In many parts of the country their loud, persistent "katy-did" notes are the most familiar sounds of a summer evening, being audible for ¼ mile or more on quiet nights. The sound is produced by the male rubbing the base of one forewing against the other. The katydids resemble common field grasshoppers in structure but are larger—almost 3 inches long—with bright-green bodies. Order Orthoptera, family Tettigoniidae.

KINGBIRD, any of several tyrant flycatcher birds of North America, about 9 inches long. The common eastern kingbird (*Tyrannus tyrannus*) is crested, dark gray with white underparts, and has a white band across the end of its black tail. It is famous for fighting off any attacker at its nest, and in chasing crows from the vicinity.

Yellow underparts are distinctive of the western or Arkansas kingbird (*T. verticalas*) and of Cassin's kingbird (*T. vociferans*) of the American southwest. Kingbirds are commonly seen on bare limbs of trees from which they dart to catch flying insects. The call note is rather harsh and shrill. Order Passeriformes, family Tyrannidae.

KINGFISHER, any of 84 different kinds of stout carnivorous birds with long strong beaks, large heads, short necks, short tails, and short legs on which the front toes are joined for more than half their length. Kingfishers are found all over the world, except in the Arctic and on some oceanic islands. Europe has only one kind, the Eurasian kingfisher (*Alcedo atthis*) of northern Africa, and from Portugal eastward to the Solomon Islands. Only the belted kingfisher (*Megaceryle alcyon*), a crested blue and white bird, lives in America north of Mexico.

Kingfishers eat mainly small fish, which they get by diving. Sometimes they also eat insects. Their nests are usually built in tree trunks or in the banks of streams.

The laughing jackass, or kookaburra (*Dacelo gigas*), of eastern and southern Australia is a kingfisher as large as a crow, feeding chiefly on reptiles and insects and seldom going near water. The popular name comes from the bird's loud braying cry, which is like a noisy laugh. Order Coraciiformes, family Alcedinidae.

KINGLET, a very small plump bird of the forest, with a brilliant streak of feathers on its crown when mature. In the golden-crowned kinglet (*Regulus satrapa*) of North America and the goldcrest (*R. regulus*) of Britain and Europe the crest is bright orange-yellow bordered with black. In the ruby-crowned kinglet (*R. calendula*) of North America and the firecrest (*R. ignicapillus*) it is red.

All kinglets build nests in conebearing trees other than pine, suspending the nest below a branch or twig. In summer, these birds flit quickly through the dark evergreen forests, hunting for insects for themselves and their young. In winter, kinglets are more often seen on bare trees and evergreens around suburban homes. Order Passeriformes, family Sylvidae.

KINKAJOU, a tropical American mammal with a rounded head, short face, sharp claws, and a strong, prehensile tail. It lives in trees, hunts by night, eats insects, eggs, and honey, and is sometimes called a honey bear. A kinkajou is about as big as a house cat; it has soft wooly fur and is easily tamed. Order Carnivora, family Procyonidae, specifically *Potos flavus*.

KITE, any of about 25 different kinds of long-winged birds of prey with weak feet, which restricts their diet to small prey and carrion. All are strong fliers, graceful in the air.

Largest of the four kinds in the United States is the swallow-tailed kite (*Elanoides forficatus*), about 25 inches long, which spends most of its life on the wing, often in flocks of 20 or so. It hovers before pouncing on snakes, lizards, frogs, and other small reptiles, as well as grasshoppers, caterpillars, and grubs.

The other American kites, which differ in plumage but are similar in form and habits, are the white-tailed kite (*Elanus leucurus*), the Mississippi kite (*Ictinia mississippiensis*), and the Everglade kite (*Rostrhamus sociabilis*), which is dwindling toward extinction—perhaps because it feeds almost exclusively on one kind of snail. Order Falconiformes, family Accipitridae.

KITTIWAKE, a middle-sized gull of the open sea, which nests in colonies on steep rocky cliffs of Britain, Scandinavia, Iceland, and arctic Canada as far south as Gaspé peninsula of Quebec. Adults are distinctive because each wingtip appears to have been dipped in black ink, and the feet are black, not brown as in the immature bird.

Kittiwakes are rare inland, but common far out at sea, where they frequent the northern fishing areas. Often they pick food from the waves without stopping. At times they swim on the surface or dive deeply, apparently swimming underwater in pursuit of fishes. Order Charadriiformes, family Laridae, specifically *Rissa tridactyla*.

KIWI, any of 3 different plump-bodied flightless birds with virtually no wings and with a long slender beak at the tip of which the nostrils open. All kiwis are New Zealand birds, about the size of a domestic hen. They use the beak to reach into soft forest soil for earthworms and insects, locating them by scent. The wing stubs end in a claw; the feathers are hairy. The legs are strong, and used both for running and defense.

The female lays 2 eggs, each weighing about a third as much as she does after her laying is completed; her eggs are larger relative to her body than those of any other bird. Order Apterygiformes, family Apterygidae, species of genus *Apteryx* ("wingless").

KOALA, an Australian mammal as much as 33½ inches long, 33 pounds in weight, with a large head, big rounded hairy ears, a black bare nose, strong legs with opposable claw-bearing toes, and a vestigial tail. Native only to eucalyptus forests in eastern Australia, it feeds on about 12 different kinds of these trees, eating foliage, buds, and flowers. It clings tightly, using remarkable hands with thumb and forefinger both opposable to the other three fingers.

The young koala is carried in the mother's pouch for about 6 months and then on her back until it is a year old. Both appeal to people as living toylike "teddy bears." Order Marsupialia, family Phalangeridae, specifically *Phascolarctos cinereus* ("the ash-gray pouched bear").

KUDU, either of 2 African antelopes, second in size only to the eland. They frequent forests, where they browse on shrubbery. Unlike most other antelopes, they are heavy and rather ungainly.

The greater kudu (*Tragelaphus strepsiceros*, meaning twisted horn) inhabits southern Africa from Angola to Ethiopia, and stands almost 5 feet at the shoulder, 8 feet long not counting the long tufted tail; the male has massive horns up to more than 4 feet long, spirally twisted and beautifully curved.

Both sexes are grayish brown with a white stripe down the middle of the back and numerous vertical white stripes on the sides. The lesser kudu (*Strepsiceros imberbis*) of Somalia and East Africa is about 3½ feet tall at the shoulder, and its horns grow to more than 2 feet long. Order Artiodactyla, family Bovidae.

LAC BUG. See *Scale Insect*.

LACEWING, or goldeneye, or green fly, any adult insect that develops from an aphis lion. Lacewings are worldwide on land areas. Their 4 broad wings are pale green, with many cross veins, held at rest like a tent over the body; when spread, their span is about 1 inch. The head bears two large, bulging, golden-colored compound eyes and a pair of long threadlike antennae (feelers), as well as a pair of strong small jaws with which the insect attacks and devours aphids (plant lice).

Female lacewings lay their white eggs singly atop ½-inch slender stalks, seemingly to prevent the first larva that emerges from eating all unhatched eggs. The larva, called an aphis lion, devours large numbers of aphids. It attains full size in about 2 weeks, and spins a cocoon in which to transform to the winged adult lacewing. Often winter is spent in the cocoon. Because aphids cause so much damage to plant crops, lacewings are regarded as extremely beneficial insects. Order Neuroptera, families Chrysopidae and Hemerobiidae, members of *Chrysopa* (literally "golden eye").

LADYBEETLE, or ladybird beetle, or ladybug, a small hemispherical beetle, often orange or red with black spots, and ½ inch or less in diameter. It is a harmless beetle found in temperate and tropical climates. Lady beetles lay eggs on plants. The larvae that hatch out are usually black with a flattened pear-shaped body, the head with biting jaws, and six legs at or near the larger end.

In the Middle Ages, when it was seen that these insects and their larvae destroyed aphids (plant lice) and scale insects, they were dedicated to the Virgin and became "Beetles of Our Lady," hence ladybeetles. Most ladybeetles benefit agriculture, although a few kinds, when adult, such as the Mexican bean beetle (*Epilachua varivestis*) eat plants.

An Australian ladybeetle (*Vedalia cardinalis*) was introduced in California to control the cottony cushion scale, a mealy bug (also from Australia), which threatered the orange orchards. The countless descendants from 500 ladybeetles checked the pest in a few years. Order Coleoptera, family Coccinellidae.

LAMPREY, a cylindrical, jawless fish with a circular sucking mouth and no paired fins. Most lampreys live in the sea but ascend freshwater streams to lay eggs. They make nests by moving rocks on the pebbly bottom. The young hatch as small slender larvae, called *ammocoetes*. For 3 or 4 years, each larva burrows shallowly in mud or sand, drawing in water for respiration and filtering out microscopic particles of food. When ready to transform to the adult shape of body, it migrates to salt water to finish growing. Finally it returns to a stream to mate and die.

At maturity, a sea lamprey (*Petromyzon marinus*) is nearly 3 feet long. It uses the horny teeth in its mouth and suction to fasten itself as an external parasite on larger fishes, on whose blood and flesh it feeds. It has a single nostril and seven gill openings on the side of the neck.

Allied to the lampreys are the scavenging hagfishes or slime eels (genus *Myxine*), which sometimes burrow into the body of a dead or dying fish and eat it from the inside. Hagfishes, although uncommon along the Atlantic coast of North America, are abundant in European and Californian waters. Order Hyperoartia of class Cyclostomata.

LANCELET, or amphioxus, any of about 30 kinds of slender marine animals 2 to 3 inches long, about the shape of a willow leaf, sharp, pointed, and thin like a lance at both ends. Lancelets live near shore along temperate coasts all over the world, usually burrowing shallowly in sandy bottom materials during the day and emerging to swim about rapidly at night. The sexes are separate, but fertilization occurs in the open sea. Fertilized eggs develop into free-swimming larvae, which are distributed widely by water currents before they settle to the bottom and transform slightly to adult form.

At one end of the adult body is a narrow oval mouth opening into an extensive throat region (pharynx), which has multiple slits through which sea water passes. These slits allow the lancelet to filter from the water microscopic particles of food, and to absorb oxygen and get rid of carbon dioxide. The food, caught in sticky mucus, proceeds onward through a straight intestine.

Lancelets in some features resemble vertebrate animals in their embryonic development. They have a hollow dorsal nerve cord, a lengthwise supporting rod called a notochord, slits in the side walls of the pharynx that resemble gill slits in fishes, a closed circulatory system with arteries, capillaries, and veins, and a body cavity lined by a thin layer of cells called a peritoneum. But there are no indications of head or brain, nor of the blocks of cartilage or bone that form the internal skeleton of a vertebrate animal. Presumably lancelets represent an ancestral form of chordate animal, relatively unchanged for the last 600 million years or more. Subphylum Cephalochordata of phylum Chordata.

LARK, any of about 75 different kinds of songbirds the size of a large sparrow, noted for the song flights of the males. Most larks are African, but the group is represented in Eurasia, Australia, and North America.

The skylark of temperate Eurasia and North Africa (*Alauda arvensis*) begins its song early in the spring and continues to sing the whole summer. It is quietly colored in brown, buff, and creamy white, and in many countries is prized as food. The horned lark (*Eremophila alpestris*) of the same areas and the New World as far south as Colombia, has a black collar, yellowish throat, black tail, and black head "horns."

Meadowlarks of North America are about the size of a robin, with a black V on the yellow breast. They thrive, as the Old World larks do, on developed farmland and are highly regarded as destroyers of insect pests. The western meadowlark (*Sturnella neglecta*) is slightly smaller than the eastern (*S. magna*), and its whistled call is lower in pitch and less shrill. Meadowlarks are, however, totally different from true larks; they are related to blackbirds in family Icteridae, whereas the true larks comprise family Alaudidae, both families of order Passeriformes.

LAUGHING JACKASS. See *Kingfisher*.

LEAFHOPPER, any of more than 2,000 kinds of small insects resembling miniature cicadas, with a short head (often pointed) and compact body, and the 4 wings held tentlike lengthwise above them at rest.

They are found in all terrestrial parts of the world. With sucking mouthparts, they get nourishing juices from leaves, young stems, flower buds, and soft fruits, often doing much damage by introducing the carriers of disease.

The largest leafhopper is less than an inch long when mature, and most do not exceed ¼ inch in length. The eggs hatch into small wingless insects of the same body form and similar habits. Development is direct, with no pupal stage.

In some species, such as the rose leafhopper (*Empoa rosea*), two generations attain maturity in vast numbers each year, the first generation attacking one kind of plant (in this case almost any type of rose) and the second generation a quite different plant (in this case apples). Adults of the second generation generally fly back to plants suitable as food for members of the first generation, there to lay eggs that will survive the winter. Order Homoptera, family Cicadellidae.

LEECH, a flattened segmented worm with a sucker surrounding the mouth at the front end, where the animal has 3 knifelike jaws, and usually a second sucker at the hind end. Leeches mostly inhabit freshwater shallows, where they catch small crustaceans and snails, and have a chance to attach themselves to fish, turtles, or a mammal that is drinking or wading. With their jaws, leeches can cut through the skin and reach blood, making a quick meal of it before dropping off.

Half a century ago freshwater leeches (*Hirudo medicinalis*) 2 or 3 inches long were used extensively by physicians to relieve certain diseases by bloodletting, but since it was found that the human system is weakened by bloodletting, the use of leeches has diminished.

A few kinds of leeches live in the ocean, attacking fishes and turtles. In wet forests of Southeast Asia, one kind of leech waits for victims along game trails on land. Several orders of class Hirudinea, phylum Annelida.

LEMMING, any of about 12 kinds of small, short-eared, short-tailed rodents found in tundras, coniferous forests, and mossy bogs of northern Eurasia and North America. The lemming (*Lemmus lemmus*) of Scandinavia and northwestern Russia, about 5 inches long with a heavy, rounded body, short legs, and a large head, is famous for its periodic migrations suddenly every 8 to 10 years. At these times, huge numbers of lemmings travel downhill from overpopulated and food-scarce high country. If their migratory urge persists, they do not stop even when they reach the ocean but plunge in and drown.

Normally lemmings eat reindeer moss (a lichen) and other plants, and serve as the principal food of predatory animals in the Far North. Order Rodentia, family Cricetidae.

LEMUR, any of about 16 kinds of long-tailed monkeylike mammals, from 5 to 17 inches long not including the tail. They are native to Madagascar and the Comoro Islands. Most are arboreal, associating in troops of up to 20 individuals. Their very large eyes, staring appearance, and nocturnal habits earn them their name—*lemures* is Latin for ghosts. Lemurs eat fruit and insects. Lemurlike but unrelated animals (order Demoptera) that glide from tree to tree are known as flying lemurs. Order Primates, family Lemuridae.

LEOPARD. See *Cat*.

LIMPET, any of a large number of marine gastropod mollusks having a low, conical shell widely open below, where the body of the animal expands into a large flat foot with which it clings by suction to solid supports. They are common along rocky shores between high-tide mark and a few feet below low tide. Those most abun-

ANIMALS

dant in this location around Britain and Europe belong to genus *Patella*, named for a fancied resemblance to the bone in the tendon of the human knee; the most familiar limpets along American shores belong to genus *Acmaea*. Keyhole limpets, which have a hole at the tip of the shell and use it for discharge of water from which they have taken their oxygen, often belong to genus *Fissurella*.

All limpets browse on the film of minute seaweeds that grow on rocks along coasts, and resist both the pounding of waves and the combination of dry air and sun when exposed by the tide. They arch the central portion of the soft muscular foot to create a vacuum like that in a suction cup; they can be dislodged easily by pressing a thin knife blade between the rock and the foot, thus releasing the vacuum. Large numbers of limpets are collected along British and European coasts for use as food and fish bait. Order Aspidobranchia.

LING, or lingcod, a large marine bony fish resembling the closely related cod in having short soft projections (barbels) from the lower jaw, used to detect small fishes, crustaceans, worms, and other food on the sea bottom. Ling are caught in the North Atlantic Ocean off the coasts of Europe and Greenland. Like a hake, a ling has a dorsal fin divided into a small forward part and a much more extensive hind part, whereas a cod has a three-part dorsal fin.

Ling is a term derived from a Middle English word, meaning long, and refers to the proportions of the body. In some parts of the world remote from Europe, the same name is given to quite different fishes in which the body appears longer in proportion to height than is customary among familiar fishes. Order Anacanthini, family Gadidae, specifically *Molva molva*.

LION. See *Cat*.

LIZARD, any of about 3,140 different kinds of scale-covered reptiles in which the 2 sides of the lower jaw are joined together, not merely linked by a flexible ligament as among snakes. Usually the eyelids are movable and an external opening of the ear can be found; most commonly a lizard has 4 legs with distinct toes, but a few are legless and often mistaken for snakes.

Lizards live in temperate and tropical countries all over the world. Largest are the monitor lizards of Africa and tropical Asia to Australia; one, the Komodo dragon (*Varanus komodoensis*) discovered in 1912 on the small Komodo island in the East Indies, grows to a length of 9½ feet and is a formidable predator. Only the 2 kinds of beaded lizards in deserts of southwestern North America are venomous: the Gila monster (*Heloderma suspectum*) of Arizona and Mexico, and the Mexican beaded lizard (*H. horridum*) have a poisonous saliva that seeps into wounds made when the animal bites.

The tree iguanas (*Iguana iguana* and near relatives) of tropical America eat foliage high among the tall trees of the rain forest. Most other lizards are insectivorous or eat small invertebrate animals. This is the habit of the nocturnal geckos, the horned lizards (or horned "toads"), the fence lizards, the chameleons, and most of the legless lizards known as "worm" lizards or as "glass snakes" from their habit of breaking off the tip of the tail into separate twitching fragments when handled. Order Squamata, suborder Sauria (or Lacertilia).

LLAMA, a deer-sized, cud-chewing mammal of the Andes of South America. Although lacking a hump, it is related most closely to camels and, like them, has been domesticated as a beast of burden, capable of carrying 200 pounds for 17 miles in a day over mountain trails.

When annoyed, a llama spits and bites. From its long hairy coat, fine cloth can be made. The Andean Indians depend greatly on the llama for milk and meat. Order Artiodactyla, family Camelidae, specifically *Lama peruana*.

LOBSTER, a large marine "long-tailed" crustacean whose strong adominal muscles are sought for food. At the front of the head are two pairs of sensitive feelers (antennae) and a pair of eyes on the end of short stalks.

The North Atlantic lobster (*Homarus americanus*) along coasts of both the Old and New World is distinguished by the exaggerated size of the front pair of legs, each ending in pincers, and one being larger than the other. Lobsters scavenge for decaying fish, and may be caught in large traps called *lobster pots*, made of lath and baited with decaying fish.

The number of lobsters taken is enormous, but overfishing has so greatly reduced their numbers that laws have been enacted almost everywhere to protect them. The annual catch on the New England coast is estimated at about 30,000,000 pounds, the weight of an average lobster being between 2 and 3 pounds.

The spiny, or rock, lobster, or sea crayfish (*Palinurus*), has no pincers on its 5 pairs of legs, but defends itself with antennae that are particularly thick and strong. They generally project from the rock crevices where the animal takes shelter. In the Mediterranean is found *P. vulgaris*, the langouste of French menus; similar animals are caught in the West Indies, southern Florida, Bermuda and the Bahama Islands, and along the coast of South Africa. Order Decapoda.

LOCUST, a loosely used word applied to (1) short-horned grasshoppers, (2) cicadas, and (3) several kinds of trees with edible seeds, belonging to the pea family. No one is sure which of these is referred to in the Bible as a food approved for Israelites (Leviticus 11:22) and as the food eaten with wild honey by John the Baptist (Matthew 3:4; Mark 1:6). Those that came in swarms and ate the crops were certainly the migratory grasshoppers (*Schistocerca peregrina*) of North Africa and Asia Minor.

LLAMA
BRANIFF INTERNATIONAL

A similar habit is shown by the smaller short-horned grasshoppers (*Melanoplus spretus*) of prairies near the Rocky Mountains in North America. Order Orthoptera, families Locustidae and Acrididae.

LOON, or diver, any of 4 large, handsome, fish-eating water birds whose legs are enclosed within the body all the way to the ankle joint. They normally come ashore only to nest, for their long, heavy body and short neck, as well as the position of the legs, make them clumsy and awkward on land. They cannot take flight from land at all, and even from the water they must run along the surface, frantically flapping their short wings.

Loons frequent coastal salt water and inland lakes, particularly far north in the Northern Hemisphere. They are rather solitary birds, and their favorite haunts are mostly in wild places unfrequented by man.

Most widespread is the red-throated loon (*Gavia stellata*) which nests around small arctic pools and winters as far south as Formosa and California around the Pacific, and the Gulf of Mexico and Mediterranean Sea around the Atlantic Ocean. The arctic loon (*G. artica*) and the yellow-billed loon (*G. adamsi*) are circumpolar but rarely come near human communities even in winter. The common loon (*G. immer*) of northern North America, Greenland, and Iceland is best known for its eerie calls, sometimes likened to the laughter of the insane. Order Gaviiformes, family Gaviidae.

LOUSE, any of a large number of wingless parasitic animals that cling to the body of a host animal or plant and feed from the surface. The blood-sucking lice that attack man and other mammals are classified in the insect order Anoplura. They include the worldwide head louse (*Pediculus humanus*), or cootie, which has often been the principal carrier of typhus fever, trench fever, and relapsing fever; and the hog louse (*Haematopinus suis*), which infests uncared-for domestic pigs, and occasionally spreads to people who walk among the pigs, causing intense itching but no harm.

The biting lice that feed on the feathers of birds are insects of the order Mallophaga; they include the common chicken louse (*Menopon gallinae*). So numerous do the chicken lice often become that the tickling by their feet of a fowl so distracts the bird from eating, sleeping, and social activities that its health declines. The whale lice that crawl over the surface of whales, feeding on the skin, are crustaceans of order Amphipoda.

These diverse parasites show remarkable adaptations in their legs, which help them hold to hairs or among feathers. Most lice are highly specialized to feed on one or a few closely related kinds of animals; they soon die if they cannot find the correct host.

Plant lice, or aphids, are insects that feed by placing their beaks into leaves and stems and sucking the juices; they are members of the family Aphididae in order Homoptera.

LOVEBIRD, any of several kinds of small plump parrots (*Agapornis*) of Africa and Madagascar, so named because they apparently choose a mate for life at a very early age and thereafter stay close together in pairs, giving frequent evidence of affection for one another.

In their native countries, lovebirds fly in large flocks, and generally nest close together. Like other members of the parrot family, they feed principally upon seeds and soft fruits, and produce a great deal of noise by their frequent chirps and calls and by the whir of their short wings as they fly from one branch to the next.

Each kind of lovebird has its distinctive color pattern, which usually is almost identical in the two sexes, and its own method for making a nest from plant fibers collected or cut with the beak in the forest.

The name lovebird is sometimes applied also to the Australian budgerigar (*Melopsittacus undulatus*) and to various South American parakeets (*Psittacula* species), all of which are attractive as cage birds. Order Psittaciformes, family Psittacidae.

LUNGFISH, any of about 5 different kinds of bony fishes in which the nostrils connect with the mouth cavity, instead of ending as blind pits, and the long slender body contains a pair of lunglike air sacs opening into the throat region. They are river fishes of Australia, South America, and Central Africa, living where the water dries up for part of the year. When the dry period comes, the fish burrow into the damp earth and breathe by means of air bladders that are similar to lungs. When water again appears in the river, the fish leave the burrow, and the gills function as in other fish.

Only the Australian lungfish, called the barramunda (*Neoceratodus forsteri*), has leaflike fins; the South American one (*Lepidosiren*) and the African kinds (*Protopterus*) possess only filamentous paired fins. Order Dipnoi, families Ceratodontidae and Lepidosirenidae.

LYNX, any of 4 different kinds of short-bodied, strong-legged, short-tailed, catlike mammals with conspicuous tufts of fur on the ears. Formerly these powerful predators ranged more widely in Europe and North America, and in Africa and Southern Asia. The European lynx (*Lynx lynx*) and the North American lynx, or catamount (*L. canadensis*), are forest animals, which attain a length of 3 feet and weigh as much as 40 pounds. The northern variety, larger and darker in color than its southern relative, is trapped in large numbers for its fur.

The bobcat, or bay lynx (*L. rufus*), which is pale brown with black streaks and spots, differs from other lynxes in having a slightly longer tail (6 inches, instead of 4) with a black mark only above at the tip; it occurs in southern Canada, northern Mexico, and most of the United States. The caracal lynx (*L. caracal*) of Africa and southern Asia prefers hilly country and scrub-covered plains. All lynxes are efficient killers of rodents, but sometimes attack poultry and livestock. Order Carnivora, family Felidae.

LYREBIRD, either of 2 different shy, solitary songbirds about the size of a domestic hen. The mature male possesses a spectacular array of showy tail-covert feathers as much as 25 inches long; in a courtship display, he turns them forward over his back and head in the shape of a graceful lyre. The female has a long straight tail and no special covert feathers.

Lyrebirds are forest dwellers in eastern Australia, the superb lyrebird (*Menura novaehollandiae*) occurring farther south than the Albert's lyrebird (*M. alberti*). They live on the ground, scratching among the leaf litter for insects, centipedes, snails, and other small animals as food. Lyrebirds whistle sweetly, and mimic expertly the calls of many other birds. Order Passeriformes, family Menuridae.

MACKEREL, any of about 10 different tunalike marine bony fishes with smoothly contoured bodies, widely forked tails efficiently linked to the last part of the backbone, and a series of dorsal and ventral finlets just in front of the tail. They are found in all oceans, from cold to tropical; many migrate along routes well known to fishermen.

Most important economically is the North Atlantic mackerel (*Scomber scombrus*), weighing up to 4 pounds, which is caught on hooks and with seine nets. A mackerel fleet from Gloucester, Mass., follows these fish yearly from Chesapeake Bay in April to the St. Lawrence River, which they reach in May. Among Spanish mackerels (species of *Scomberomorus*) in the North Atlantic, the largest is the king mackerel, or kingfish (*S. cavalla*), which grows to 100 pounds and a length of more than 5 feet. Frigate mackerels, such as the common *Auxis thazard* found in tropical seas around the world, are less valuable because their meat is dark. Order Acanthopteri, family Scombridae.

MAGPIE, or pie, any of a number of medium- to large-sized birds with predominantly black-and-white plumage in a bold design, and long oval tails. The name is given to birds of this appearance on all continents, following an old English tradition. There the black-billed magpie, or pie (*Pica pica*), of Eurasia and western North America long ago became a favorite cage bird, enjoyed because of its crafty behavior and its ability to imitate words; they were called Margaret or Mag (just as a parrot is Polly), hence magpie.

Wild magpies take a wide variety of food, animal and vegetable, often robbing other birds' nests of eggs and young. The Old World has also red-billed blue magpies, Ceylon blue magpies, and in Australia black-and-white magpies that are actually crow shrikes (*Gymnorhina* species). Western North America has a yellow-billed magpie (*P. nuttalli*), chiefly in the central valleys of California. Order Passeriformes, chiefly family Corvidae.

MALLARD, a large handsome dabbling duck with a glossy green head (purplish in some lights), a broad yellowish-green beak, a white ring around the neck, a brown back, and a whitish tail; the underparts are mottled gray, and the feet an orange red. Mallards are among the commonest ducks of the Northern Hemisphere, often flocking with black ducks in North America.

Mallards feed on plant rootlets, mussels, snails, small fish, frogs, fruits, and grain and other seeds. They nest inconspicuously in marshland near water, laying 6 to 10 olive-colored eggs. Domesticated mallard ducks have given rise to a number of hardy and prolific breeds for the barnyard. Order Anseriformes, family Anatidae, specifically *Anas platyrhynchos* (meaning broad-beaked duck).

MAMMOTH. See *Elephant*.

MANATEE. See *Sea Cow*.

MANDRILL. See *Baboon*.

MAN–OF–WAR. See *Portuguese man-of-war*.

MANTA. See *Ray*.

MARLIN, any of about 5 different kinds of spearfishes, in which the head is prolonged into a slender, sharp beak with a fancied resemblance to a marlinspike—a pointed metal tool used to splice rope. They are giant fishes of temperate and tropical seas, the largest being the black marlin (*Istiompax marlina*) of the Indo-Pacific, which grows to as much as 14½ feet long and 1,560 pounds. The striped marlin (*Makaira mitsukuri*) of the Pacific and blue marlin (*M. ampla*) of both the Pacific and Atlantic are slightly smaller. Order Percomorphi, family Istiophoridae.

MARMOSET, any of about 33 different kinds of small, monkeylike mammals in which the great toe is opposable and bears a flat nail, but the thumb is not opposable and, like the other fingers and toes, bears a sickle-shaped claw. They live in the forests of tropical South America and Panama, where they climb and leap jerkily from branch to branch in small groups, hunting for insects, spiders, and fruits. They have long, silky fur, elongated hind legs but short arms, and generally tufts of hair on their ears.

The one most often kept as a pet, called the common marmoset (*Callithrix jacchus*), has gray fur and produces a variety of birdlike chirps. Order Primates, family Callithricidae.

MARMOT, or woodchuck, or groundhog, any of about 16 different kinds of large burrowing rodents with pointed heads, small ears, short legs, and a tail about one third as long as the rest of the body. They inhabit cooler parts of the Northern Hemisphere, at lower elevations in the north and higher in the south.

When numerous in any area, woodchucks are the bane of the farmer. They devour many garden crops and are very fond of alfalfa and red clover. The burrow is deep and has several compartments in which the woodchuck hibernates from September to March. February 2, Candlemas, is known as Ground-hog Day or Woodchuck Day from the popular belief that then the animal comes out of his burrow and if he sees his shadow runs back again— cold weather will continue. Order Rodentia, family Sciuridae, species of genus *Marmota*.

MARTEN, any of 8 different kinds of tree-climbing, weasel-like mammals with a long bushy tail. In the New World they are denizens of coniferous and mixed forests; in the Old World they are found from the northern limits of forests to the Mediterranean and Malaya and the East Indies. Martens eat mice and squirrels, which they pursue relentlessly, and carrion, insects, and fruit. They have been trapped extensively for their fine fur.

In the New World, the larger of two kinds is the fisher, or pekan (*Martes pennanti*), sometimes 3 feet in length; the smaller is the pine marten (*M. americana*). Old World martens are often called sables, although one (*M. zibellina*), resembling the pine marten, is the only true sable; it is found chiefly in Siberia and Kamchatka where it is hunted for its fur, the darker shades being the most desired. Order Carnivora, family Mustelidae.

MASTODON. See *Elephant*.

MAY BEETLE. See *June Bug*.

MAYFLY, or shadfly, any of about 1,500 different kinds of adult flying insects with 2 or 3 long filamentous "tails" from the tip of the abdomen, and ordinarily 2 pairs of membranous wings, the front pair much larger than the rear pair. Mayflies are found near freshwater on all continents and major islands. Very few of them have functional mouthparts or live beyond a few days, during which they fly about, find mates, and deposit eggs.

The immature mayflies that hatch out are naiads or, incorrectly, nymphs. They have biting mouthparts, but feed principally on minute plant matter adhering to underwater vegetation or to rocks, or buried in the bottom sediments among which they burrow.

After a period of growth that lasts from 1 to 5 years according to the species, the naiad comes to the surface of the water and molts, freeing into air a flying individual that still is not mature. No other kind of insect includes in its development this winged stage, called subimago, which has wings but must molt again. Mayfly subimagoes and adults are consumed in great numbers by bats, swallows, and other insect-eating birds; the naiads form an important food for fish. Order Ephemeroptera.

MEDUSA, or jellyfish, any of several hundred different kinds of solitary, free-swimming coelenterates, whose soft body has a jellylike consistency and the shape of a bell with a pendant tube where the tongue of the bell would be. These animals are widespread in the oceans; a few live in freshwater.

The mouth, at the end of the pendant tube, leads into a digestive cavity which branches out toward the edges of the domed body. Around the rim of the bell are pendant tentacles, studded with nettling organs used to subdue or kill small animals as prey. These writhing tentacles led to the use of the name medusa, from the mythical Greek Gorgon whose hair consisted of writhing snakes.

The venom of some medusae can cause severe irritation to human skin. Medusae produce eggs that hatch into minute swimming larvae. The larvae settle to the bottom and there transform into colonial polyps (in class Hydrozoa) or special reproductive individuals (in class Scyphozoa) from which new medusae arise by asexual budding. After becoming free, they transform into little medusae, and swim away by expelling water from under the bell through muscular contractions.

MENHADEN, a large marine fish with a large head and special strainers on the gills used to filter from sea water the minute plankton animals and plants that form its diet. Menhaden live in coastal waters of the Atlantic Ocean from Nova Scotia to Brazil.

Mature fish, which average about 12 inches in length, are generally caught in the fall of the year while they are migrating to spawning grounds that remain unidentified. Their eggs float up to the surface and are carried along by oceanic currents, as are also the young fish when they hatch out.

Adult menhaden form large schools and are easily caught, but they are little used for human food because the flesh is very oily. The oil and eggs are often made into poultry food; the flesh from which the oil has been extracted is used for fertilizer. Order Isospondyli, family Clupeidae, specifically *Brevoortia tyrannus*.

MERGANSER, any of several fish-eating ducks with a slender beak that is hooked at the tip, and saw-toothed along the sides. They are waterfowl of the Northern Hemisphere, along coasts and in freshwaters. The bird (*Mergus merganser*), known as the American merganser in the New World and as the goosander in the Old World, is slightly larger than a mallard duck, and has a conspicuously red bill and feet; unlike other mergansers, it lacks a crest; it prefers freshwater lakes, reservoirs, and large rivers, and builds its nest in proximity to water, usually in a hollow tree or a hole in the bank, chiefly in Canada and northern Eurasia to beyond the tree-growth limit.

The red-breasted merganser (*M. serrator*) is smaller, with a rakish crest, and red or pink low on the neck; it generally remains close to the ocean, nesting among grass or trees near water in Canada, Alaska, Eurasia, Iceland, and Ireland. A hooded merganser (*Lophodytes cucullatus*) in many of the same regions lives more often along slow streams, and nests in wooded areas, generally in a hollow tree or stump; its diet includes fish, but also frogs, tadpoles, crayfish, insects, and vegetable matter. Order Anseriformes, family Anatidae, subfamily Merginae.

MIDGE, in general any small, 2-winged fly of feeble flight. More specifically, a member of the family Chironomidae, especially those of *Chironomus*, which resemble mosquitoes but do not bite. Midges often form immense swarms over shrubs or over water, within which the individual flying insects seek out mates; the combined humming of their wings can sometimes be heard for a considerable distance.

Generally midges lay their eggs in large masses at the edge of the water, into which the cylindrical larvae go. Some of these larvae are bright red with hemoglobin, and are known as "bloodworms."

Most midges are scavengers; some live so successfully where there is an almost complete lack of dissolved oxygen that they are indicators of organic pollution. After 1 or 2 years of growth as larvae, these insects transform into a pupal stage that floats near the water surface until the adult insect is ready to emerge, using the floating pupal case as a raft while escaping into air.

Midge larvae are an important food for many kinds of fish, and the adults provide nourishment to bats, swallows, and other insect-eating birds. Order Diptera.

MINNOW, a popular name for small fishes that swim in schools, are easily netted, and serve as live bait for fishing. Scientists reserve the word minnow for about 1,200 different kinds of fishes from 1½ to 110 inches long, found in all watery habitats in the temperate and tropical regions except South America, Madagascar, and Australia.

Minnows lack teeth in the jaws, but have teeth in the throat; they have soft rays in their fins, and lack an adipose fin (between the dorsal fin and the tail fin on the back). Among the more familiar minnows are the silvery-scaled shiners (genus *Notropis*), and the goldfish (*Carassius auratus*) and carp (*Cyprinus carpio*) of Eurasia. Order Ostariophysi, family Cyprinidae.

MITE, or spider mite, any minute globular arthropod with 3 or 4 pairs of legs and an apparently unsegmented body. They are found all over the world as predators on microscopic animals in the soil or on the surface of plants, or as parasites on or in many kinds of animals and plants. Like the larger and closely related ticks, mites hatch from eggs as active creatures with 3 pairs of legs; at the first molt they gain another pair; the 4 pairs of legs are characteristically present for the rest of their lives.

In the itch mite (*Sarcoptes scabiei*) and similar species, the first two pairs of legs on the female are adapted into the form of suckers with which she pulls herself into a hair follicle on a person or other mammal. Protected within the skin, she extends her mouthparts to draw blood as food. In this position she can be reached for mating by male mites, which creep over the skin surface, and can extrude oval eggs, which she forces into furrows cut into the skin.

The skin develops an intense itching, and often scales off in large areas, partly from being scratched. The condition is commonly called sarcoptic mange or scab disease. It can be transferred easily to other individuals by contact or by infected cloth, since the mites themselves are less than 1/50 inch long and easily overlooked. Order Acarina of class Arachnida.

MOCCASIN. See *Pit Viper*.

MOCKINGBIRD, an inconspicuous ash-gray songbird slightly larger than a catbird, showing white on its wings when it flies. It is native to the southern United States, where it rivals the Eurasian nightingale in the variety of its song both day and night. It mimics other birds with special skill, but has a song of its own as well, full and varied. Order Passeriformes, family Mimidae, specifically *Mimus polyglottos*.

MOLE, any of about 40 different kinds of burrowing mammals with a pointed nose, small eyes, many tiny teeth, powerful forelegs, a cylindrical body, and usually a short tail or none. About half of them are golden moles (family Chrysochloridae) of Africa, with a metallic luster to their fine fur; they burrow by pushing their noses into the soil. The remaining moles (family Talpidae) live in Eurasia and North America, and dig with their front feet; they are grayish black.

For all moles, earthworms and insects provide the main diet. Moles build amazing subterranean fortresses or nests, consisting of an intricate system of chambers connected by tunnels at varying depths.

Largest of moles is the Eurasian desman (*Desmana moschata*), as much as 8½ inches long with a tail of equal length; except for the long flexible nose, it might be mistaken for a muskrat. The common Eurasian mole (*Talpa europaea*) is less than 6 inches long, as is the American star-nosed mole (*Condylura cristata*), which burrows in damp or muddy soil. The eastern mole of North America (*Scalopus aquaticus*) has partly webbed feet, but seldom swims. Order Insectivora.

MONGOOSE, any of about 30 different kinds of weasel-like mammals with pointed muzzles, mostly about the size of a house cat. They are persistent predators of the Old World, roaming alone or in small groups by day or night.

The Indian mongoose (*Herpestes griseus*), a 15- to 18-inch animal with a furry tail of almost equal length, has thick reddish-gray fur, and special agility used in killing poisonous snakes such as cobras. It was introduced as a rat- and snake-killer into Jamaica, Hawaii, and many other islands. In those places, it turned its attention to reptiles that were easier to catch and to native birds, often endangering the survival of rare kinds. In 1902 a law was enacted to forbid the bringing of a live mongoose into the United States.

The ichneumon (*H. ichneumon*) is a mongoose of North Africa and Asia Minor, that was kept like a house cat in ancient Egypt because of its efficiency in devouring rats, mice, crocodile eggs, and other pests. Order Carnivora, family Viverridae.

MONKEY, any of a large number of small tropical mammals with long tails, having opposable thumbs and great toes, and nails instead of claws. Most New World monkeys can support themselves by their tails; they have widely separated nostrils that open sidewise. Old World monkeys do not have prehensile tails; their nostrils open forward and downward, as in man.

Most monkeys anywhere choose fruits and soft greenery for their diet; however, they also eat insects, young birds, and eggs whenever they can. Order Primates, superfamilies Cercopithecoidae in Africa and Asia, and Ceboidae in America.

MOOSE. See *Deer*.

MOSQUITO, any of about 1,500 different kinds of delicate flies with long, slender sucking mouthparts. They are found in most parts of the world, feeding on sap from plants and blood from vertebrate animals.

Only the females "bite" animals. Usually they lay their eggs on the surface of water or in it, where larvae called wrigglers hatch out. These are unusual among fly larvae, in that they have eyes, well-developed biting mouthparts, and the ability to swim by wriggling until they can suspend themselves from the water's surface film while inhaling a fresh supply of air. With their mouthparts, mosquito wrigglers collect small particles of food from the water.

When fully grown, the wrigglers transform into pupae called bullheads, which are buoyant and float at the surface with breathing tubes reaching the air. If disturbed, a bullhead swims downward, but soon rises again. Inside the bullhead skin, the insect continues its transformation (metamorphosis) until it can break through into air as an adult mosquito, winged and ready to fly.

Males live on plant juices. Females of some species seek blood meals only and cause irritation and transmit disease. As a lubricant, anesthetic, and anticoagulant, a small amount of saliva is pumped into the wound made with the mosquito's mouthparts. The saliva contains proteins that later cause itching and often induce local swelling of the skin. Often the saliva contains live parasitic agents, such as the protozoan of malaria, the bacteria of myxomatosis (a disease fatal to European rabbits), the virus of yellow fever, and the filaria worm causing elephantiasis. Each of these diseases is carried only by a particular kind of mosquito; eradication of the disease can be achieved by elimination of the carrier mosquitoes, or by preventing the mosquitoes from becoming infected by "biting" people with the disease. Order Diptera, family Culicidae.

MOTH, any adult insect with 2 pairs of wings covered with overlapping scales and during flight linked together (as those of butterflies are not) by a special bristle or group of bristles on the leading edge of the hind wing. Moths are found on all habitable land areas of the world. They are usually recognized by having threadlike or feathery feelers (antennae), not knobbed or hooked ones as among butterflies; in folding their wings horizontally over the back at rest, not vertically as do butterflies; and in being active by night, rather than by day.

Like butterflies, however, moths lay eggs that hatch into caterpillars, most of which feed on foliage and other parts of plants. A large number of moths are regarded as major pests because of the damage their caterpillars do. After the caterpillar pupates, however, it no longer eats. Usually moth pupae lie in cocoons spun by the full-grown caterpillar. The moth that emerges from the pupa generally uses its long tongue to sip nectar from flowers that are open at night, and thus pollinates many of these plants, ensuring that seeds will form. Order Lepidoptera, suborder Heterocera.

MOUSE, the popular name for any small rodent. Mice are native to all continents except Australia and Antarctica, and of many islands, but not New Zealand. The house mouse (*Mus musculus*) of Eurasia has adopted man and gone with his belongings everywhere; in captivity the albino genetic strain has proved valuable in medical research. In Britain, most of Europe and parts of Asia, the wild harvest mouse (*Micromys minutus*) lives among tall undergrowth, while the various wood or field mice (species of *Apodemus*) frequent grasslands and open woods.

In North America the deer or white-footed mice (*Peromyscus* species) with very large eyes, occupy the woodland areas, while the short-tailed, short-nosed meadow mice or voles (species of *Microtus*) live in pasturelands and grain fields. Order Rodentia, family Muridae.

MULE, a hybrid bred from the horse and the ass, differing in size, strength, and beauty, according to the predominance of its parental species. Hybrids from a male ass and a mare are far superior to those from a she-ass and a horse, which are sometimes called hinnies to distinguish them from the other mules.

MULES

In mountainous countries mules are highly serviceable, for no beast of burden is more sure-footed or more capable of enduring fatigue. In beauty of form they fall short of the horse, and usually cannot reproduce. The mule has a large, clumsy head, long erect ears, a short mane, and a thin tail. Order Perissodactyla, family Equidae.

MULLET, the popular name given to several types of fishes that are unrelated. In Britain, fishmongers distinguish between gray mullets of family Mugilidae and red mullets of family Mullidae. In the western United States, plain mullets are actually suckers, of family Catostomidae.

Gray mullets are bottom feeders, living close to shore along seacoasts or in brackish estuaries. Most of them are small, weighing 3 pounds or less, with small mouths and a special muscular gizzardlike stomach used in grinding up the vegetable matter they swallow. The striped mullet (*Mugil cephalus*) reaches a weight of 15 pounds and length of 3 feet, growing faster than other mullets and supporting commercial fisheries at many places around the world — chiefly where the water is warm.

Red mullets are generally called goatfish because they have two tactile projections (barbels) under the chin. The common red mullet (*Mullus barbatus*) of the Mediterranean and Atlantic coasts northward was once a great favorite among Romans, who kept them in salt ponds and trained them to respond to the sound of a bell or a voice at feeding time. Orders: Percomorphi (Mullidae) and Mugiloidae (Mugilidae).

MUSK OX, a hairy arctic cud-chewing mammal about the size of a small ox but with shorter legs, a shaggy brown coat of long hair hanging almost to the ground, and thick hollow horns that curve and taper down and forward below the eyes. Its range in glacial times was over the whole of Europe and in the United States as far south as Kentucky; now it is confined to the arctic regions of Greenland and North America, where the steadily decreasing herds are hunted by Eskimos.

The animal is named for its musky odor, which—apparently not emitted by scent glands—is noticeable at a considerable distance from a herd and also in the flesh, which the Eskimo eats. The musk ox has gregarious habits, runs in herds of 30 to 40, and feeds on grass, shoots, moss, and lichens. Order Artiodactyla, family Bovidae, specifically *Ovibos moschatus*.

MUSKRAT, or musquash, a medium-sized rodent with a small round head, close-set ears, short neck, and bulky body covered with soft dense fur, brown on the back and gray below; the feet are partially webbed, the tail bare, round, and tapering. A marsh animal of North America, the muskrat has been introduced in Europe with mixed results. The fur, called Hudson seal, is useful. But the animal digs holes in dikes and shows a liking for vegetable gardens near water.

Normally muskrats eat aquatic roots, fish, worms, mollusks, vegetables, insects, and fruits. They are especially fond of apples and mussels, often traveling a considerable distance to procure them. Mostly nocturnal in habits, muskrats are not often seen, but their abundance is proved by the millions that are annually trapped for their skins. They do not seem to be on the decrease despite constant persecution by man and natural enemies.

The muskrat's home is built near water, usually burrowed into the bank of a stream with the entrance under the surface of the water. Order Rodentia, family Cricetidae, specifically *Ondatra zibethica*.

MUSSEL, a name loosely applied to members of 2 unlike types of bivalved mollusks. Marine mussels attach themselves to solid objects or to one another by means of strong threads of secretion. Often they form a wave-resistant "scalp" over sandbars and other soft bottom sediments, preventing erosion by storms.

In Europe the edible mussel (*Mytilus edulis*) is harvested from natural mussel beds, and also cultivated by driving leafless trees into the sea bottom to give mussels a place to cling.

Freshwater mussels, of which nearly 1,000 kinds are known, are widely distributed. Some are abundant in tributaries of the Mississippi River, attaining a length of 8 inches. They are used less for their meat and as a source of occasional pearls than as shells from which pearl buttons can be cut; shell waste is ground up to make lime fertilizer. Order Filobranchia, family Mytilidae, and order Eulamellibranchia, family Unionidae.

NAUTILUS, any of several shell-bearing cephalopod mollusks, distantly related to the octopus and squids. They live in the warm waters of the Indian and Pacific oceans close to the Equator, propelling themselves by squirting out sea water through a special nozzle. A nautilus has 4 gills instead of the 2 on all other cephalopods, and a large number of tentacles for capturing food. Unlike the tentacles or arms of an octopus or a squid, however, those of a nautilus lack suction cups which would give it a stronger grip.

The shell of a nautilus is a flat spiral, divided at intervals by curved partitions into a number of chambers. The animal lives in the outermost and largest chamber, but maintains control of the mixture of sea water and gas in the smaller chambers, using the mixture as a flotation device with which to rise or sink through the tropical sea in search of food.

The eyes of a nautilus lack a lens, and resemble a pinhole camera. Unlike most other cephalopod mollusks, the animal lacks an ink sac, and consequently cannot cloud the water about it while escaping from a predatory fish. About 300 different fossil species of nautilus are known, but only 4 remain alive today. Order Tetrabranchiata, genus *Nautilus*.

NEWT, or eft, any of several small aquatic, tailed amphibians or salamanders, with narrow compressed tails. The giant newt (*Triturus torosus*) of humid western parts of North America grows to be 6 inches long; it has red or orange underparts. The red eft (*T. viridescens*) is brick-colored with red and black spots. It is found in ponds and damp woodlands of eastern North America. A crested newt (*T. cristatus*) and a spotted one (*T. vulgaris*) are common in similar sites in Britain and Europe. Eft and newt are the same word; "an eft" was misdivided to "a neft" and rewritten "a newt." Order Caudata.

NIGHTHAWK, or bullbat, a medium-sized bird of the United States and Canada, allied to the whippoorwill and the nightjars. It has a short beak, an enormous mouth with which it catches flying insects while on the wing, pointed wings with a white spot near the tip, and a forked tail. The feet are so small and weak that the bird seldom walks. Instead it flutters to a stop on the ground, or a rooftop, or the tip of a fencepost, or a horizontal branch of a tree. On a branch it turns parallel, and appears to be only a swelling of the wood, its mottled brown feathers matching bark of many kinds of trees.

Nighthawks build no nest; they lay their 2 eggs in some open area where they can see any animal or person approaching. On dull days, in twilight and at night, nighthawks fly erratically in search of food, often beating their wings 3 times in quick succession and uttering a harsh *peenk*. At intervals, a bird closes its wings for a sudden dive, then, with a loud *zing-g-g*, spreads them again to check its descent. For the winter, nighthawks migrate to South America, some of them as far as Argentina. Order Caprimulgiformes, family Caprimulgidae, specifically *Chordeiles minor*.

NIGHTINGALE, either of 2 different small, inconspicuous brown thrushes of Europe, whose sweet melodious song from dense cover is enjoyed by night and by day. The nightingale (*Luscinia megarhyncha*) that visits Britain in summer is widespread in Europe south of Scandinavia. The thrush nightingale (*L. luscinia*), which has a few streaks on its underparts, visits eastern Denmark and southern Sweden in summer, but it is an eastern European and western Asian bird. The song resembles that of the American hermit thrush, which is a distantly related bird.

Nightingales build a nest of dry leaves, lined with grass, fine roots, and hair, and lay 4 or 5 eggs of olive-brown color. Order Passeriformes, family Turdidae.

NIGHTJAR, any of several kinds of Eurasian birds related to the whippoorwill of America with short beaks, enormous mouths, and long wings. The nightjar is active only at night, feeding in flight, eating large moths and smaller insects, which are caught in the widely open mouth as though the bird were trawling through the sky. By day the nightjars crouch motionless on the ground or on a tree branch, their mottled brown feathers camouflaging them well.

They build no nest, laying their eggs on the bare ground. The name refers to the loud jarring night song that rises and falls continuously for as much as 5 minutes at a time. Order Caprimulgiformes, family Caprimulgidae, members of genus *Caprimulgus*.

NUTHATCH, any of several small perching birds with strong beaks like those of woodpeckers, and large powerful feet, used in climbing down and up the bark of trees while searching for hidden insects to eat. Nuthatches do not use their short stubby tail as a prop the way a woodpecker does. They live principally in the coniferous forests of Eurasia (as far south as Malaya) and North America.

Nuthatches get their name from the habit of pecking at nuts that are wedged in the bark, probably to reach insects inside the nut. They do eat some fruits and many seeds, especially in winter, and will often visit a feeding shelf to get sunflower seeds.

Nuthatches nest in holes such as the abandoned cavities cut by woodpeckers, sometimes making their own holes by excavating the rotting wood in a dead tree. The female, whose size and coloration are closely similar to those of the male, attends to most or all of the incubation of the eggs; both sexes, however, bring insects as food for the nestlings.

Often the owner of the nest can be guessed before the bird is seen, because nuthatches commonly smear resin from coniferous trees or mud around the 1-inch opening to their nest. Order Passeriformes, family Sittidae, members of genus *Sitta*.

NUTRIA, or coypu, a South American rodent resembling a large rat, with a body weighing as much as 20 pounds; it is about 22 inches long and bears a 14-inch tail covered by scales and short hairs. The fur is long, grayish or brownish when seen at a distance, but thick because of a dense yellowish underfur visible when the outer guard hairs are parted. The large incisor teeth are bright orange-yellow. Only the hind feet are webbed. With them a nutria swims well. These animals dig burrows in the banks of rivers and marshes, and emerge principally at night to feed on many kinds of vegetation. Order Rodentia, family Myacastoridae, specifically *Myacastor coypus*.

OCELOT. See *Cat*.

OCTOPUS, or devilfish, any of a number of soft-bodied, shell-less marine cephalopod mollusks with 8 sucker-studded arms. These animals are found along most of the world's seacoasts, where they catch crabs and other animals as food. The common octopus (*Octopus vulgaris*) of the Mediterranean Sea, which is caught for food, often grows arms that can stretch 8 feet tip to tip. One (*O. apollyon*), found along the Pacific coast of North America from northern California to Alaska, is almost twice as large. Small ones are surprisingly abundant in tide pool and reef crannies in the tropics.

When it senses danger, the octopus squirts a dark inkish substance from a sac. It seems to have a high-domed head, although this actually is its body—above the head. The mouth is below, where the arms come together; in it is a pair of horny jaws and also a rasping organ (*radula*) with which an octopus can make a hole right through a heavy conch shell to reach the meat inside. Order Dibranchia, family Octopodidae.

OKAPI, a large cud-chewing mammal standing 4 feet high at the withers, with head and ears like those of a giraffe but a much shorter neck. It is found only in humid forests of Africa's Congo River basin. Its body is a curious mixture of deep red and black; the legs are cream-colored below and striped black and white where they join the body.

Sir Harry Johnston discovered the okapi in 1900. Order Artiodactyla, family Giraffidae, specifically *Okapia johnstoni*.

ONAGER. See *Ass*.

OPOSSUM, or possum, any of about 101 different kinds of short-legged, long-tailed marsupial mammals, most of which have a clawless, opposable big toe and a prehensile tail. All but one of the New World representatives live in the Tropics or in temperate South America; the exception is the Virginia opossum (*Didelphis marsupialis*), which is about the size of a housecat, occurring now from Florida north to eastern Canada and west to the Missouri River. When disturbed, it "plays possum," going into a sort of trance and giving no sport to animals that want live prey.

Possum is the official spelling for the Old World representatives, all members of family Phalangeridae, inhabiting Australia and New Guinea. The brush-tailed possum (*Trichosurus vulpecula*), which occurs in all humid forests of Australia, was introduced into New Zealand in 1900 as a fur bearer; too late was it recognized as a serious defoliater of native New Zealand trees.

All except 7 of the New World opossums belong to family Didelphidae. The 7 are small "rat" opossums from western South America, which have claws on their big toes and cannot grasp objects with their feet or their very long tails; they are grouped in family Caenolestidae. In these 7, as in some representatives among opossums and possums, a distinct pouch (marsupium) is lacking; the young must cling to the underside of the mother between two lengthwise folds of skin. Order Marsupialia.

ORANGUTAN, the Malay name (meaning man-of-the-woods) for a large manlike ape with dark brown skin and scanty reddish-brown hair. It is found in lowland swamps and forests of Borneo and Sumatra, where it grows to a height of slightly more than 4 feet. The arms of one big male, 4 feet 2 inches tall, spread 7 feet 9 inches; and when he stood erect, his hands nearly touched the ground. Such an orangutan weighs 250 to 300 pounds.

Orangutans live almost entirely in trees. They eat fruits, flowers, buds, and insects, and build for each night a new nest of leaves and boughs. The animal never jumps, but progresses through the forest by swinging itself from limb to limb. Order Primates, family Pongidae, specifically *Pbngo pygmaeus*.

ORIOLE, any of about 65 different kinds of starling-sized birds that frequent tree tops, build saucer-shaped or sac-like nests suspended from high branches, and are brightly colored, with yellow or orange generally conspicuous on the plumage. Oriole is a variant spelling of aureole, from the Latin *aureus* for golden. In Europe, Asia, and parts of Africa, more than 30 kinds of such birds are found, all members of the Old World family Oriolidae. Only the golden oriole (*Oriolus oriolus*), which winters in Africa, is common in Europe and comes as far as Britain. Australia has 2 members of this family, called figeaters (*Sphecotheres* species).

Curiously, unrelated birds in the New World show similar body form, coloring, and nesting habits. They are the 30 kinds of American orioles, including the Baltimore oriole (*Icterus galbula*), the male of which is bright orange with a black head and throat; this bird nests over much of the eastern United States and Canada, and winters in southern Mexico and Central America. However, American orioles are related closely to the blackbirds, grackles, and cowbirds, in family Icteridae. Order Passeriformes.

OSPREY, or fish hawk, a large hawk with a wingspread of as much as 72 inches, which eats fish exclusively, catching them by a spectacular plunge into the water and then grasping the prey in its strong feet. Ospreys were at one time numerous about large rivers and lakes and along coasts of North America, Central America, parts of South America (Peru, Chili, Paraguay), Asia, Australia, Europe, and Greenland. Now their numbers are reduced; and the bird is disappearing or has disappeared from many of these regions.

Ospreys generally return year after year to nest at the same site, adding sticks to a bulky mass built atop a dead tree, a utility pole, or even on the ground. Both parents defend the nest and tend the 2 to 4 eggs, the young that hatch out blind and helpless, and the young birds that grow rapidly on fishes brought to them all day long.

The female osprey is larger than her mate, weighing between 4 and 5 pounds; a male bird rarely is heavier than 3 pounds 3 ounces. In flight, both appear to hold their wings in a bent position. Often an osprey with a fish in its grasp is robbed of its prey by an eagle that attacks it in mid-air. Order Falconiformes, family Pandionidae, specifically *Pandion haliaëtus*.

OSTRICH, the largest of living birds, males growing 8 feet tall and reaching 250 pounds in weight. They graze on grasses and other low plants on African savannas south of the great deserts.

Ostriches are flightless because of their great size, but not wingless although their wing muscles are small and weak. Feathers from wings and tail formerly were used for decorating hats, but today the chief uses for ostrich plumes are in feather dusters and feather boas for stage costumes. To supply these, and ostrich meat and ostrich eggs, ostrich farms have been developed in South America, South Africa, and California.

A hen ostrich lays 10 to 12 eggs on the sand. Two or 3 hens of a single male may lay eggs in the same nest. The male stands guard over them by day, shielding them from the sun or warming them with his body, depending on the temperature. At night the females take turns incubating the eggs. Each egg has about the volume of 24 eggs of domestic fowl. Order Struthioniformes, family Struthionidae, specifically *Struthio camelus*.

OTTER, any of about 17 different kinds of short-legged, heavy-bodied, swimming mammals with durable, valuable fur. Most are river otters (species of *Lutra*), playful animals that live on fish in the Americas, much of Africa and Eurasia, including East Indian islands. They slide down mud banks and snow banks, headfirst into streams. One kind is the rare sea otter (*Enhydra lutris*) of kelp beds along North Pacific coasts from California to Alaska and Kamchatka, where it feeds on sea urchins, sea snails, and mussels. The mother sea otter plays with her pups for hours and sometimes is seen asleep on a tangle of seaweed in the water, lying on her back with the little otter in her front paws. Order Carnivora, family Mustelidae.

OWL, any of about 123 different kinds of predatory birds with extremely large heads; huge eyes directed forward; short, stout beaks hooked at the tip; and very large ear openings. Owls have feathered legs and 4 toes, the outer one capable of being directed backward to make a clutching fist. Their plumage is remarkably soft, and the feathers of the face form disks around the eyes.

Owls are found over the whole globe. Species vary in size from 5 inches to 2 feet in length. They feed on small mammals, birds, fishes, and insects, swallowing the prey whole. Afterward they disgorge the hair, bones, feathers, and scales in the form of pellets. They nest on the ground, among rocks, in hollow trees and in buildings; some resort to the old nests of other birds. They lay from 2 to 5 roundish, white eggs.

Several species have feathered tufts of either side of the top of the head and are called horned owls or cat-owls — notably the eagle owl (*Bubo bubo*) of Europe and Asia and the North American great horned owl (*B. virginianus*), both about 25 inches long. The snow owl or snowy owl (*Nyctea scandiaca*), despite its scientific name meaning nocturnal, hunts in the long daylight of the Arctic in both hemispheres; it occasionally winters in northern United States; it has no horns and is almost snow-white.

One of the smallest owls is the 5½-inch elf owl (*Micropallas whitneyi*) of the American Southwest and Mexico, which often nests in abandoned

OWL

woodpecker holes in large saguaro cactuses. The burrowing owl (*Speotyto cunicularia*) of the American plains lives in the deserted holes of prairie dogs and viscachas. It is 9 or 10 inches long, and its legs are longer and barer than those of other owls. Order Strigiformes, family Strigidae.

OX. See *Cattle*.

OYSTER, any of a number of different marine bivalved mollusks that, at an early age, cease swimming and attach themselves by the left shell valve to the ocean bottom or a mangrove root or a wharf piling. Oysters live near shore along most coasts. Most valuable as a source of luxury food is the Atlantic-coast oyster (*Ostraea virginica*) of the United States from Cape Cod to the Gulf of Mexico. Formerly it extended to the coast of Maine, and even now there are scattered beds in the Gulf of St. Lawrence.

The European oyster (*O. edulis*) is smaller than the American and has a coppery taste. Both sexes are united in the same individual, whereas in the American species the sexes are separate.

In tropical waters, divers seek pearl oysters, *Avicula* and *Pinctada*, which are especially abundant around Ceylon, and *Margaritophora* near Bermuda. These oysters habitually secrete mother-of-pearl, which is the ordinary lining material for their shells, around sand grains, small worms, or other foreign particles that get between the body and shell. Layer after layer is added until a hard lump is formed; if it is spherical or of some interesting shape and suitably lustrous, the lump is a precious pearl. Order Prionodesmacea, family Ostreidae.

PANTHER. See *Cat*.

PARROT, any of about 315 different kinds of brightly colored birds in which both upper and lower beak are hinged movably to the skull, and the foot grasps strongly with 2 toes forward and 2 in back. Parrots live in all countries and major islands in the Tropics and also in some adjacent temperate lands.

In the southeastern United States there formerly lived a Carolina paroquet (*Conuropsis carolinensis*), but it was exterminated before 1910; tropical American parrots include 25 kinds of large macaws (species of *Ara*) with long slender tails, and another 25 of green parrots with short tails (species of *Amazona*), as well as numerous conures, parakeets, and parrotlets.

Africa is the home of the gray parrot (*Psittacus erithaceus*) with a red tail, which is particularly desirable as a cage bird because it excels in imitating human speech; other African relatives are the small colorful lovebirds (*Agapornis* species) of many kinds. Australia and New Guinea have numerous kinds of cockatoos, lorikeets, and the popular budgerigars (*Melopsittacus undulatus*) that now rival canaries as house pets.

New Zealand parrots include three plump kinds that are almost as big as a chicken: the flightless owl parrot, or kakapo (*Strigops habroptilus*), a rare ground bird of forest glades; the equally rare kaka (*Nestor meridionalis*), which feeds on fruit, nectar, and insects; and the mountain kea (*N. notabilis*), which now stays near camps and sheep-butchering stations, feeding on scraps and waste fat from sheep carcasses. No other parrot seems to have changed thus far from a diet of seeds and fruits in the treetops. Order Psittaciformes, family Psittacidae.

PARTRIDGE, any of several fowl-like birds with short beak, short legs, and short tail, and which produce a loud whirring sound when frightened into flying away.

Originally the word partridge referred to particular birds of Eurasia and Africa, specifically the Hungarian, or European, gray partridge (*Perdix perdix*), and the red-legged, or Chukar, partridge (*Alectoris rufa*) of Europe, Corsica, and the Canary Islands; both have been introduced widely into North America, New Zealand, and elsewhere as upland game birds that offer good targets and good eating.

In North America, the word partridge is often applied to quail in the southern states, and to the ruffed grouse farther north. Order Galliformes, family Phasianidae.

PEAFOWL, any of 3 different large pheasantlike birds with a slightly curved beak, a small distinctive crest on the head, short wings, long stout legs and, in the male, a magnificent set of long gold and green tail coverts that the peacock during courtship raises vertically like a semicircular screen extending from the ground on one side to the ground on the other.

The domesticated peafowl (*Pavo cristatus*) is native to India and Ceylon; both peacock and peahen have a blue neck and crest feathers with the little vanes only at the tips; the tail-covert feathers of the male are elaborately patterned with large eyespots, which show even when the plumes are lowered to make a "train" behind the bird. White peafowl, with no markings, are not uncommon in domestic flocks.

A Javanese peafowl (*P. muticus*) with a green neck and crest feathers with vanes the whole length lives in humid forests of Java and adjacent Southeast Asia. A Congolese peafowl (*Afropavo congensis*) is a glossy black bird with a patch of white in its crown. Order Galliformes, family Phasianidae.

PECCARY, either of 2 different kinds of New World wild pigs, whose tusks point downward instead of outward or upward, whose 2-chambered stomach shows special complexity, and whose long slim legs are peculiar in that the hind feet have only 3 toes, instead of the usual 4 among pigs.

Native to the New World, peccaries are forest animals, usually seen in bands containing both sexes and all ages. The larger white-lipped peccary (*Tayassu pecari*), which associates in groups of 50 to 100 or more, may if threatened, counterattack, slashing effectively with its sharp tusk.

Peccaries live from Paraguay to southern Mexico. The collared peccary (*T. tajacu*), found from Arizona and Texas to Patagonia, travels in bands of 5 to 15, often roaming desert regions as well as tropical forests.

Members of both species use their snouts to dig for vegetable food, grubs, snakes, and other small animals; sometimes they raid cultivated fields and inflict damage. Generally the presence of peccaries in an area is indicated by the strong-smelling substance their musk glands secrete whenever they are excited. Order Artiodactyla, family Tayassuidae.

PELICAN, any of 6 different kinds of fish-eating, swimming birds with a large pouch of skin between the halves of the lower jaw.

In the New World, the brown pelican (*Pelecanus occidentalis*) ranges along coasts from the southern United States to Venezuela and Chile; the white pelican (*P. erythrorhynchus*) is an inland bird, nesting from British Columbia to Ontario, and migrating to Mexico and the Gulf States in winter. Old World pelicans are largely white and venture far inland in Africa, southern Europe, southern Asia, to southeastern Australia.

All pelicans can hover, fold their wings, and plunge into water after fish. Sometimes they fish in groups. They scoop the fish into the pouch and swallow it while flying again or after returning to the shore. Order Pelecaniformes, family Pelecanidae.

PENGUIN, any of 15 different short-tailed swimming birds of the Southern Hemisphere, in which the strong wings lack flight feathers and are stiff, moving only at the shoulder as paddles for underwater propulsion or as weapons in self-defense. Except for the Galápagos penguin (*Spheniscus mendiculus*), which lives on the Equator surrounded by icy water, they are birds of the Antarctic and the southernmost coasts of Africa, Australia, New Zealand, South America, and remote islands.

Tallest is the emperor penguin (*Aptenoides forsteri*), 4 feet high, which lays its eggs and raises its chicks on Antarctica during the winter night there. The only other penguins on Antarctica are the Adélies (*Pygoscelis adeliae*), 30 inches tall. Of medium size and with a call like a donkey's bray is the jackass penguin (*Spheniscus demersus*) of South America and South Africa. The smallest is the fairy penguin (*Eudyptula minor*) of Australia and New Zealand, 16 inches tall.

Newly hatched penguins are covered with down, but the grown birds have stiff scalelike feathers. Their food consists chiefly of fish and squids. Order Sphenisciformes, family Spheniscidae.

PERCH, either of 2 small, edible, fresh-water fishes in which the pelvic fins are far forward, close to the pectoral fins, the dorsal fin has its spiny and its soft portions separated from one another, and there are 3 anal spines instead of 2, as in sunfishes.

The European perch (*Perca fluviatilis*), found through most of Europe to Siberia and in brackish waters of the Black Sea, sometimes grows to weigh 6 pounds. The yellow perch (*P. flavescens*) of North America lived only east of the Rocky Mountains until it was introduced elsewhere; a 15-inch fish weighing 2 pounds is a large one. Its orange-yellow sides have 6 to 8 dark vertical stripes, and its pelvic fins are reddish. Order Percomorphi, family Percidae.

PERIWINKLE, or winkle, any of several different kinds of small snails of the seacoast, with a compact top-shaped shell and a horny plate on the side of its foot with which to block the shell opening after the animal has withdrawn inside. Originally native to European coasts, periwinkles have now been introduced widely around the world. Periwinkles feed almost exclusively on small seaweeds, and their meat is delicately flavored.

Unlike many snails, a periwinkle has its foot divided into a right side and a left, and creeps by swinging alternately from side to side with a peculiar rolling gait. To reach its food, a periwinkle extends its tonguelike rasping organ (radula), which sometimes is twice as long as the 1-inch foot of the animal. Order Aspidobranchia, family Littorinidae, members of genus *Littorina*.

PETREL, any of 26 different kinds of small, web-footed sea birds, which have their nostrils opening at the end of a tubelike part of the upper beak. Four are plump-bodied diving petrels (family Pelecanoididae), resembling auks, flying with rapidly whirring wings, which they use also in swimming underwater in pursuit of fish. The others are slender-bodied storm petrels (family Hydrobatidae), which flutter over the sea surface but seldom alight, while feeding on squid, floating mollusks, surface shrimp and other crustaceans, or the galley scraps from passing ships.

Petrels are found far out at sea on all oceans, except at nesting time, when they return to offshore islands or the slopes of coastal mountains, generally coming in at dusk or after dark to burrows 2 to 3 feet deep or crannies under loose rocks. Leach's petrel (*Oceanodroma leucorhoa*) of the North Atlantic and North Pacific has a forked tail, the storm petrel (*Hydrobates pelagicus*) of European coasts, a rounded or square tail; both have become well known from their habit of following ships day after day, and are called Mother Carey's chickens—from the Latin *mater cara*, the divine virgin, referring to the Virgin Mary who is guardian of all seafarers. Petrel is believed to be a diminutive of St. Peter, alluding to the apparent ability of petrels to walk on water.

The name petrel is often given also to a shearwater, the giant fulmar or giant petrel (*Macronectes giganteus*) of southern oceans, a bird 3 feet long with an 8-foot wingspan. No true petrel is longer than 10 inches; they are the smallest of all pelagic birds. Order Procellariiformes.

PEWEE, or wood pewee, a small inconspicuous woodland flycatcher whose olive-gray body blends with the shadows while it perches on a branch, awaiting a flying insect. The pewee flits out quickly, catches the insect, and returns to the same or another branch, often calling *pee'-a-wee'* or *pee'-wee* in a plaintive way.

The bird has a forked tail, 2 pale wing bars, and often raises the feathers on its head to form a low crest. It builds its nest on an outstretched branch of a deciduous tree, constructing it of rootlets and other plant fibers, frequently covering it with lichens as though for camouflage.

For the winter, pewees migrate to northwestern South America, where they mingle with closely related birds from western North America. The western wood pewee (*C. sordidulus*), which inhabits more open woodlands and calls *dear* or *dear-me*, often sings at night. Order Passeriformes, family Tyrannidae, specifically *Contopus virens*.

PHALAROPE, any of 3 different shore birds of the Arctic, resembling large sandpipers, in which the female is larger than the male, with a wingspread from 14 to 16 inches, and does the courting; she is more brightly colored but often leaves the building of the nest and incubation of the eggs she lays in it to her mate. All

ANIMALS

nest in the Arctic, their small pear-shaped eggs hatching in about two weeks, and the young birds hiding themselves among grasses near the simple nest.

The northern phalarope (*Lobipes lobatus*), known as the red-necked phalarope in Britain and Europe, flutters over salt water, using its long beak to catch minute crustaceans and other small plankton animals as food. The red phalarope (*Phalaropus fulicarius*), called the gray phalarope in the Old World, swims more frequently in freshwater and performs characteristic spinning movements that appear to disturb insects, snails, and other prey into moving and being seen.

The Wilson's phalarope (*Steganopus tricolor*) of Arctic America nests farther south, to California and Indiana, feeding itself and young on terrestrial insects, crustaceans, spiders, and snails found near the marshlands where it nests. As soon as their young are ready to fly, all phalaropes migrate far south to cold waters off the coasts of South Africa and South America, particularly where ocean currents from the Antarctic enrich the surface waters and support large numbers of plankton, crustaceans, and small fishes. Order Charadriiformes, family Phalaropodidae.

PHEASANT, any of about 50 different kinds of large, long-tailed, grouselike birds. They are native to central and southern Asia and the East Indies, but many of them have been introduced elsewhere. The ringneck, or English or Mongolian pheasant (*Phasianus colchicus*) probably reached Britain during Roman times; it is a well-known and popular game bird. The argus pheasant (*Argusianus argus*) of Southeast Asia is almost as big as a peacock. Female pheasants are dull and plain compared to the males. In some parts of the United States, the name pheasant is used loosely for grouse and quail. Order Galliformes, family Phasianidae.

PHOEBE, a medium-sized flycatcher, is olive-gray in color, slightly paler below; continually wagging its tail up and down, it frequently calls its name *phee'-be* or (more insistently) *phee'-beee'*. Like other flycatchers it perches on bare branches where it can see flying insects coming, and dart out to catch them. It builds its nest under a cover, such as alongside an overhanging bank above a stream or under a bridge or porch roof.

In winter it migrates to Florida, the Gulf States, and Mexico. It was a nestful of young phoebes that John James Audubon marked along a stream in Pennsylvania, using loose bracelets of silver wire, in the first experimental study to determine whether birds return after a winter's absence to the region where they were hatched. Of 5 phoebes marked in this way, 3 returned the following spring to nest along the same stream. Order Passeriformes, family Tyrannidae, specifically *Sayornis phoebe*.

PICKEREL. See *Pike*.

PIG. See *Swine*.

PIGEON, any of almost 300 different kinds of small-headed, stout-bodied birds with short, rounded beaks topped by a fleshy part (the cere) through which the nostrils open. They are represented on every continent and most islands. Generally the term pigeon refers to birds with square or rounded tails, and the term dove to more slender-bodied related birds with pointed tails.

Domesticated and city pigeons are derived from the common rock pigeon (*Columba livia*), about 13 inches long, native to southern Eurasia and north Africa. Careful breeding has produced from this bird distinctive strains excelling in racing speed, homing ability, aerial acrobatics, showy feathers, and quick production of meat for people who enjoy eating young birds (squabs) that have just reached full growth.

The extinct passenger pigeon (*Ectopistes migratorius*) that vanished in the wild about 1899 had occupied vast oak and beech forests in central and eastern North America. Colonists destroyed their habitat, and also netted, shot, and trapped the birds for shipment to market until there were no more.

The giants are the 3 kinds of crowned pigeons in New Guinea, as much as 33 inches long. They have a crest of lacy feathers, and 16 instead of the usual 12 tail feathers. Nearby Australia has big, metallic-colored pigeons called bronzewings (the common one is *Phaps chalcoptera*), which eat so many seeds from a poisonous plant that their bones and internal organs are deadly to predatory animals, although their flesh is unharmed and edible. Order Columbiformes, family Columbidae.

PIKE, any of about 8 different kinds of predatory fishes of northern freshwaters, with a long pointed head, large mouth with formidable teeth, no spines in any of the fins, the dorsal fin far back—behind the pelvic fins and above the anal fin—and with a body slender and spear-shaped, as the name pike suggests.

Most widespread is the northern pike (*Esox lucius*) of Eurasia and the northern United States and Canada, a fish that has been recorded as attaining 54 inches in length and a weight of 46 pounds. It is exceeded in both ways by the muskellunge (*E. masquinongy*) of the upper Great Lakes and adjacent waters, which may grow to 102 pounds.

Smaller relatives of these large fish are called pickerels ("little pikes"), and differ in details of the scale pattern on the head and body, as well as in distribution and habits. Aside from the northern pike, the only member of this group in Eurasia is the black-spotted pike (*E. reicherti*) of Siberia. Order Haplomi, family Esocidae.

The fish called a walleyed pike (*Stizostedion vitreum*), found in eastern North America, and the pikeperch (*Lucioperca lucioperca*), found in Eurasia, are members of the perch family.

U.S. ARMY SIGNAL CORPS
PIGEON

PINTAIL, a dabbling duck of freshwaters, in which the male has 2 long middle tail feathers 5 to 9 inches long stretching out behind his 28-inch body. Pintails breed in northern Eurasia, Canada, and the northwestern United States, migrating southward and to the Pacific coast in winter.

The male has a reddish-brown head, gray back, and white throat and underparts. The female is smaller and is streaked with brown. They nest on the ground, concealed in bunches of grass or weeds, usually near water. Seven to 10 greenish eggs are laid in March or April. Order Anseriformes, family Anatidae, specifically *Anas acuta*.

PIRANHA, any of several South American freshwater fishes 7 to 24 inches long, with elliptical bodies, strong lower jaw, and many razor-sharp teeth. Four kinds of piranha are greatly feared in their native rivers and lakes, because they attack in large numbers any person or mammal that enters the same water—particularly if it falls in and splashes about.

Most widely distributed is the 4-inch *Serrasalmus nattereri* of the Brazilian river systems, particularly the Amazon, whose normal diet consists of other fishes. This piranha might be mistaken for a small sunfish until it darts at a victim and uses its incredibly strong jaws and sharp teeth to cut out pieces of flesh and bone. Fishermen seek piranhas, an excellent food, but use strong wire leaders on fishing lines to prevent the piranha from cutting itself loose and swimming away with the baited hook. Order Ostariophysi, family Characidae, species of *Serrasalmus*.

PIT VIPER, any of several poisonous snakes, which possess between nostril and eye a distinctive pit that is sensitive to radiant heat. They live in eastern Asia and the New World. Using its paired pits, the snake even in complete darkness, can find animals as prey because these are warmer than their surroundings—as a sleeping bird or a mammal would be, or cooler—as a frog would be because of evaporation from its wet skin. The pit viper strikes its prey with two erectile fangs in its upper jaw, within which venom canals are connected to large glands that secrete the poison.

Most feared of these snakes is the bushmaster (*Lachesis muta*) of northern South America, Panama, and parts of Costa Rica, which lies in wait for small mammals along their trails through forest and scrubland where its mottled brown color makes it almost invisible. No less deadly is the smaller fer-de-lance (*Bothrops atrox*) which sometimes attains a length of 8 feet and frequents coconut plantations from southern Mexico to southern Peru, through all of northern South America. Like most pit vipers, but unlike the bushmaster which lays eggs, the fer-de-lance mother brings forth active young, as many as 71 at a birth, each with its sensory pits and venom apparatus fully developed.

Far less dangerous are the copperhead (*Ancistrodon contortrix*) of forest regions in eastern North America, the cottonmouth moccasin (*A. piscivorus*) of swamplands in the southern United States, and related members of the same genus in Mexico and the Old World from the southern edge of the Russian steppes to Ceylon, Malaya, and Japan.

Rattlesnakes (*Crotalus* and *Sistrurus*), which are exclusively North American, represent a more venomous group of pit vipers. In these snakes, only part of each old skin is shed at molting time, and the remainder contributes to the accumulated loose sections of the "rattle" at the end of the tail. Because the terminal "button" and additional parts of the rattle commonly break away and the snake may shed its skin more than once a year, it is impossible to learn the age of a rattlesnake by counting the pieces in its rattle.

The amount of venom that a rattlesnake can inject, and hence the danger offered by the snake, is roughly proportional to the length of the animal. This varies from one species to another, the giant being the eastern diamondback rattlesnake (*C. adamanteus*), one of which was found to be 98 inches long. Next in size, so far as known, are the western diamondback (84 inches), the western Mexican rattlesnake (80 inches), and the South American rattlesnake (78 inches).

The famous timber rattlesnake (*C. horridus*), which was the first kind encountered by the English colonists, sometimes reached a length of 75 inches. It is still found in many parts of the area from northern New England to northern Florida, west to eastern Texas and north to Wisconsin. From this territory westward to the Pacific coast and northward into Canada, the prairie rattler (*C. viridis*) takes its place, sometimes becoming as much as 60 inches long. Order Serpentes, family Crotalidae.

PLATYPUS. See *Duckbill*.

PLOVER, any of 38 different kinds of shore birds with legs of moderate length and beaks no longer than the head, slightly enlarged toward the tip. They are found almost all over the world, nesting on open beaches and fields, where their spotted eggs blend inconspicuously and are easily overlooked. In England and on the Continent plovers' eggs are a great delicacy.

As a group, plovers are noted for covering enormous distances on their migratory flights. The golden plover (*Pluvius dominica*), about 11 inches long, a beautiful but fast-diminishing species, breeds on the Arctic coasts but winters in southeastern Brazil and Argentina; its annual southern flight takes it many hundreds of miles out to sea, although it takes an overland route flying north.

One of the most familiar plovers is the killdeer of North America (*Charadrius vociferus*), so called because the Latin word *vociferus* (loud) describes its noisy, reiterated cry. Killdeers, often found in the uplands many miles from water, are recognizable by their brown back, tail and wings. They are 10 inches long, brownish above and with 2 black bands on the white breast and 2 on the head.

The pole-backed, 7-inch piping plover (*C. meloda*) is nearly always found on the beach where it is often difficult to distinguish from the sand whose color it matches; it has a plaintive, melodious whistle, as indicated by its name. Order Charadriiformes, family Charadriidae.

POLECAT, any of several weasel-like predatory mammals in which the anal musk glands are well developed, producing a fetid secretion when the animal is threatened. Native to northern Africa and Eurasia, they have contributed one member which can be domesticated—the ferret, which is usually an albino and is valuable in driving rabbits from burrows or in destroying rats.

The wild form of the ferret is the most widespread polecat (*Mustela putorius*); it grows to 20 inches long with a 7-inch tail, is dark brown to black in color with a yellow patch on each side of the head between ear and eye. Its pelt is sold in the fur trade as "fitch." A marbled polecat (*Vormela peregusna*) lives in steppes of southeastern Europe and across to Mongolia, differing markedly from other polecats in its mottled dark and pale coloration. Order Carnivora, family Mustelidae.

POLLOCK. See *Cod*.

PORCUPINE, any of about 43 different kinds of rodents in which the back, and often the head and tail as well, bear large hollow barbed quills that pull out easily from among the shorter fur. In the Old World, 20 kinds in family Hystricidae live mostly on the ground, eating carrion and plant materials, in Africa, southern Europe to southern China, Indonesia, and the Philippines. In the New World, 23 kinds in family Erethizontidae are more tree-dwellers, as vegetarians, ranging from coast to coast and from the Arctic to southern South America.

When disturbed, a porcupine tries to hide its unprotected and sensitive nose, while presenting its quills by raising them at right angles from the body. The North American porcupine

PORCUPINE

(*Erethizon dorsatum*) may back up, swatting vigorously with its quill-studded tail. Porcupines in Central and South America have prehensile tails that help them hold on while eating leaves high in the trees. The porcupines of Europe and Africa are as much as 32 inches long, weigh as much as 56 pounds, and have some quills 12 inches long. At birth, the quills are soft, but they harden in a few hours. Order Rodentia.

PORPOISE (from old French for hogfish), any of about 7 different kinds of small-toothed whales less than 6 feet long, with a blunt nose. Almost all of the world's coasts, estuaries, and harbors are visited by these animals as they hunt for unarmed fishes of modest size, squid, and crustaceans; sometimes they are seen following schools of fish, singly or in pairs or in groups of nearly 100. Unlike dolphins, they rarely follow ships.

Formerly they were caught in Europe for meat and an oil useful for lubrication and for burning. Porpoise fisheries still operate along the coasts of some Oriental countries. Order Cetacea, family Delphinidae, chiefly genus *Phocaena*.

PORTUGUESE MAN-OF-WAR, a dangerous colony of marine coelenterate animals, 1 member of which at a time grows to become a pinkish blue, gas-filled balloon as much as 8 inches long and 5 high. The float provides buoyant support for the colony; floating high in the sea surface, it catches the wind and hence pulls the colony along. Below it dozens of other members of the colony extend slender contractile tentacles, deep blue in color and as much as 60 feet long.

The tentacles hang down like fishing lines, waiting for fishes and other edible animals to bump into them. Special nettling cells on the tentacles can inject poison into a victim, stunning or killing it, while other cells cling to the prey and the whole tentacle (or group of tentacles) shortens to haul up the victim right under the float. There are other individuals with soft flexible mouths begin digesting the prey. The digested food is then shared throughout the colony. In season, special reproductive individuals are formed, providing eggs and sperms for sexual multiplication.

The Portuguese man-of-war is common in tropical American waters, and is often carried northward by the Gulf Stream, to be blown ashore. Even dead colonies on the beach can sting painfully if their tentacles are touched, and live ones in water can sting a human swimmer worse than a nestful of wasps. Order Siphonophora, family Physalidae, specifically *Physalia pelagica*.

PRAIRIE CHICKEN. See *Grouse*.

PRAIRIE DOG, any of 5 different kinds of short-tailed, short-legged burrowing squirrel-like mammals. They live sociably in prairie-dog "towns" where bison used to roam, on the plains east of the Rocky Mountains, from the Canadian prairie provinces to northern Mexico. Like their relatives, the marmots, prairie dogs have well-developed claws on all the toes of the forefeet and shallow cheek pouches. They feed on herbs and grasses but store little.

The best-known species is the plains prairie dog (*Cynomys ludovicianus*), about 1 foot long with a 4-inch tail, reddish-brown above, variegated with gray. The name refers to their alarm cry, which suggests the barking of a small dog. Order Rodentia, family Sciuridae, all members of genus *Cynomys*.

PRAYING MANTIS, any of about 1,500 kinds of predatory insects with special grasping forelegs, thought to be the only insect with a neck so flexible it can turn its head and look backward. For hours a praying mantis may remain motionless or may sway slightly on the 4 long slender legs that support it, waiting for some other insect to come within snatching distance. Victims are held firmly by the forelegs, which are folded once again in a prayerful attitude, while the head is moved and the jaws are brought into play.

A female mantis may even eat her mate and incorporate his nourishment into the mass of eggs she will lay. As many as 1,000 eggs go into each mass, which is affixed to a plant stem or other support and coated with a brown froth that hardens as it dries. In the spring, miniature praying mantises emerge and are distributed by the wind. Those that survive will grow slowly, molt by molt, until they acquire wings and become mature—usually by autumn.

The largest mantises in the United States are the kind introduced from China (*Paratenodera sinensis*), of which females may be nearly 6 inches long. The introduced European mantis (*Mantis religiosa*) is rarely more than 2 inches long. There is only 1 mantis (*Stagmomantis carolina*) native to the United States. Order Orthoptera, family Mantidae.

PRONGHORN, a handsome antelope-like mammal, which differs from all true antelopes in possessing on the head of both sexes an unusual kind of armament—a pair of horns with a bony core, covered by a horny sheath that is shed each year. This is the swiftest mammal of the New World, able to run at least 65 miles per hour and to "cruise along" at 48 mph, often traveling 20 miles a day in its native western North America.

A full grown male (buck) pronghorn weighs about 125 pounds and stands 3 feet high at the shoulder. A female (doe) may reach 90 pounds. Both are marked alike, the back, 3 collars, and a streak down to each leg being reddish brown, the hind-quarters shining white, and the rest of the animal sand-colored.

Pronghorns feed on a wide variety of vegetation in open country, in herds and as individuals at short distances from one another. When alarmed they flash their white rumps in many directions, alerting all pronghorns in sight. Order Artiodactyla, family Antilocapridae, specifically *Antilocapra americana*.

PTARMIGAN, any of 4 different kinds of grouselike birds with feathers all the way down the legs and out on the toes. They live in the Arctic and on high mountains, nesting in thickets on the ground, eating buds, insects, berries, and roots.

Ptarmigans, with one exception, are reddish-brown in the summer, but turn snow-white in winter—a remarkable example of protective coloration. The exception is called the red grouse (*Lagopus scoticus*), and is found now only in Ireland and England. Britain has also the rock ptarmigan (*L. mutus*) and the willow ptarmigan (*L. lagopus*), both of which are circumpolar. A distinctive white-tailed ptarmigan (*L. leucurus*) living above the snowline in Alaska and the Rocky Mountains retains the white color of its tail in summer. Order Galliformes, family Tetraonidae.

PUFFIN, or sea parrot, any of 3 kinds of sea birds with heavy bodies, short tails, short-pointed wings, short necks, and enormous triangular beaks marked with red, yellow, and blue. At the end of the breeding season, the bright covering of the beak is shed, and a new one grown, bearing an extra ridge and colored stripe by which the age of a puffin can be estimated. A puffin feeds mostly on fish, crustaceans, and small mollusks.

Nesting in colonies on offshore islands along northern coasts, these birds produce a single large egg, then tend the single young in a hole in the ground or a natural crevice among boulders. The young bird becomes enormously fat, heavier than the parents, and is then deserted. It completes its development, taking on adult form, finds its way to the coast, and dives into the sea to get its food.

The Atlantic puffin (*Fratercula arctica*) is abundant in Iceland and breeds in smaller numbers as far south as Maine and Britain. Pacific puffins of the Far North include the horned puffin (*F. corniculata*) which has a small, fleshy appendage like a horn on its upper eyelid, and the tufted puffin (*Lunda cirrhata*), named for the yellow plume of feathers extending backward like a great eyebrow on each side of the head. Order Charadriiformes, family Alcidae.

PUMA. See *Cat*.

QUAIL, any of about 40 different kinds of small, grouselike birds with short beaks, wings, and tails, but strong legs and plump bodies. The 33 in the New World are nonmigratory, lack spurs, and have a notch in the cutting edge of the upper bill. They include the 4 different bobwhite quails (*Colinus* species) that live in fields and woodland edges from Canada to South America, whistling loudly the 2-note call for which they are named; and the valley quail (*Lophortyx californicus*) of the American Southwest and Mexico, in which the male has a fancy little recurved plume over his forehead.

The 7 kinds of quails in the Old World are migratory, lack the notch in the beak, and mostly have spurs. One is the European quail (*Coturnix coturnix*), which ranges widely over Eurasia and Africa. Three others have spread from Southeast Asia all the way to Australia and New Zealand: the Australian brown quail (*Synoicus ypsilophorus*), the Chinese painted quail (*Excalfactoria chinensis*) no bigger than a sparrow, and the stubble quail (*Coturnix novae-zealandiae*) which vanished in New Zealand in 1870. Order Galliformes, family Phasianidae.

QUETZAL. See *Trogon*.

RABBIT, any of about 18 different kinds of long-eared, long-legged, short-tailed mammals similar to hares but differing in being born naked, blind, and helpless in a nest prepared by the mother. They are generally smaller than the hares and live only on grasses or other herbaceous matter.

In the New World they are represented by 13 kinds of cottontails, marsh rabbits, and tropical forest rabbits (all in genus *Sylvilagus*) from southern Canada to Argentina and by the volcano rabbit (*Romerolagus diazi*) of highland Mexico, trotting instead of hopping.

In the Old World, the most widespread kind of rabbit is the European rabbit (*Oryctolagus cuniculus*), which makes extensive burrows in the wild, and is raised for food, fur, experimental medicine, and for esthetic purposes; the "Belgian hare" is one true-breeding strain.

Additional kinds of rabbits are found locally in the Ryukyu Islands near Japan, in the foothills of the Himalayas, in forests of Sumatra, and in African equatorial forests. Order Lagomorpha, family Leporidae.

RACCOON, or coon, any of several different kinds of doglike forest mammals with a black masklike mark across the eyes, fore paws that are almost as flexible and versatile as a monkey's, hind feet that make footprints like a child's, and a well-furred tail marked with 5 to 10 black rings.

Raccoons are forest dwellers from southern Canada to northern South America. They climb and swim well, and prefer food found close to water, in which they habitually manipulate it, perhaps to free it of grit. From this comes the name of the most widespread species, *Procyon lotor*—the

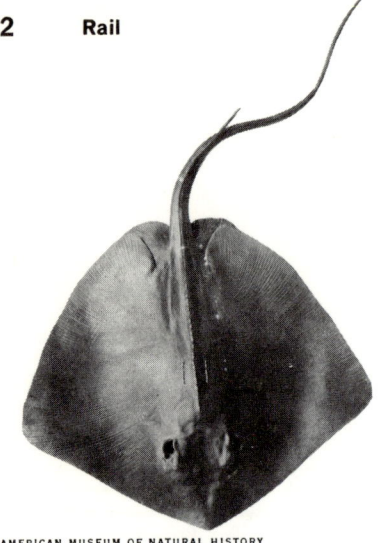

STING RAY (American Museum of Natural History)

washer. During the day the raccoon curls up in a tree to sleep. Order Carnivora, family Procyonidae, all members of genus *Procyon*.

RAIL, any of about 100 different kinds of running, swimming, and wading birds of marshes and tussock land, distinguished from the closely related coots and gallinules by the narrowness of their bodies, which helps when they run through thick marsh vegetation. They are "thin as rails."

Rails are found throughout the world except in polar regions. Living almost exclusively in marshlands, they are shy and use their wings only as a last resort, when they fly feebly for a short distance, immediately settling back into the swamp grass from which they were flushed.

Long-billed rails include the largest kind, the king rail (*Rallus elegans*) of the eastern United States. It grows to about 19 inches long, is dusky brown in color, and similar to the 11-inch Virginia rail (*R. virginianus*). Short-billed rails, called crakes in Europe, include the common American sora rail (*Porzana carolina*), 9 inches long, brown above and gray below. Rails are largely nocturnal in habits, and so elusive by day that gunners generally try to approach them silently by boat. Order Gruiformes, family Rallidae.

RAT, a vague term applied to almost any medium-sized rodent with a pointed nose, unspecialized legs, and long, usually naked tail. New World rats include rice rats, water rats, climbing rats, vesper rats, Andean rats, web-footed rats, cotton rats, pack rats, wood rats, fish-eating rats, mole rats, maned rats, and sand rats, all in family Cricetidae. Old World rats include climbing rats, spiny rats, tree rats, thick-tailed rats, shaggy-haired rats, bush rats, swamp rats, soft-furred rats, water rats, pouched rats, prehensile-tailed rats, cloud rats with bushy tails, shrewlike rats, and the two most destructive rats—the Norway rat (*Rattus norvegicus*) and the black rat (*Rattus rattus*).

The Norway rat probably is native to Japan and eastern Asia, and reached Europe about 1730 and America by 1775, to both by ship. The black rat comes from Asia Minor, and came to Europe with the returning Crusaders. It is a better climber than the Norway rat, and lives better under tropical conditions. Both kinds harbor and carry bubonic plague, typhus fever, trichinosis, rabies, tularemia, and other diseases deadly to man. The laboratory white rat is a domesticated variety of the black rat. Order Rodentia, family Muridae.

RAVEN. See *Crow*.

RAY, any of about 340 different kinds of cartilaginous marine fishes in which the body is flattened or extended to the sides, the pectoral fins greatly enlarged, the gill slits on the lower surface, the pelvic fins small, and the tail often long and whiplike.

Rays are most abundant and varied in the Tropics, but are found also along cold coasts and in the great abysses. The giant manta rays, or devilfishes, measure as much as 22 feet from side to side, and probably weigh more than 3,500 pounds; they cruise slowly near the surface, using a special pair of feeding fins to drive small crustaceans and other food toward the cavernous scooplike mouth.

Sawfishes have the head prolonged into a flat "saw," studded on each side with sharp teeth; they use this strange tool to dislodge edible animals from sandy bottoms, and to slash sideways through schools of fishes, maiming and impaling many victims, which they can then eat at a leisurely pace. Rays of 2 different families have venom spines on their tails, and are called stingrays. Perhaps 25 different kinds of rays can discharge jolts of electricity in self-defense or to stun prey; they are called torpedoes or electric rays. Most rays, however, are relatively harmless, feeding on mollusks, crustaceans and small fishes they catch along the sea bottom and crush with teeth that have flat surfaces fitting together like tiles in a mosaic.

All rays swim with special grace, undulating their large pectoral fins (which form the edges of the body) as though they were the wings of a bird in leisurely flight. In Europe, some of the smaller and flattest rays, called skates, are sought as food. Order Batoidea, several different families.

REDSTART, any of several small, active dark-colored birds in the Northern Hemisphere. Redstarts in Eurasia are members of the thrush family (Turdidae), related closely to the nightingale; they continually flicker their rust-colored tails and display a rusty rump patch; they are classified in genus *Phoenicurus*.

Colonists to America, who were used to seeing Eurasian redstarts transferred the name to American birds of similar size, color, and behavior, without realizing that those of the New World were essentially different, being wood warblers of family Compsothlypidae. The common American male redstart (*Setophaga ruticilla*) is mostly black, with bright orange areas on wings and tail, and a white belly; the female is olive-brown where the male is black, and yellow where he is orange.

Members of both sexes continually droop their wings and display their colorful tail feathers while they hunt among the foliage for small insects. In the Southwest, a painted redstart (*S. picta*) is found in high mountains; it is black with white patches on the wings and tail, and a bright red patch on the breast. Order Passeriformes.

REINDEER. See *Deer*.

RHINOCEROS (from Greek words meaning nose horn), any of four kinds of massive, thick-skinned, 3-toed, hoofed mammals. Equatorial and South Africa have the largest two kinds, both with 2 nose horns: the square-lipped or white rhino (*Ceratotherium simus*), which is slate-gray and a grazer, and the slightly darker black rhino (*Diceros bicornis*)—both names mean two-horned—with a more pointed, prehensile lip, used in browsing. Next to the elephants, these are the largest land animals.

The Asian rhinos are smaller: the one-horned Indian rhino (*Rhinoceros unicornis*), often seen in zoos, comes from marshes of Southeast Asia and Java, and is threatened with extinction; the two-horned Asiatic rhino (*Didermocerus sumatrensis*), which is the smallest, is rare now in Southeast Asia, Sumatra, and Borneo, where it inhabits dense forests near streams. Order Perissodactyla, family Rhinocerotidae.

ROBIN, any of several different kinds of plump-bodied birds that are dark on the back, red or orange on the chest, and seen commonly near homes. The European bird (*Erithacus rubecula*), for which all the others were named, is about 5½ inches long; it is distinguished from the native redstart mostly by appearing neckless and having dark brown instead of chestnut-colored feathers in the tail. The British introduced "their" robin in Africa, India, Australia, and North America; it became naturalized in all except North America.

The New World robin (*Turdus migratorius*) is a bigger bird, 10 inches long, gray on the back, reddish on the breast, with the outer corners of the tail white; it nests throughout Alaska, Canada, the continental United States, Mexico, and the West Indies, migrating south well into the continent for the winter, except in regions along the coasts.

The European and American robins are both members of the thrush family (Turdidae). The Pekin robin (*Leiothrix lutea*), 6 inches long, in southern China and the Himalayan foothills, and five Australian robins (of genus *Petroica*) are unrelated babblers (Timaliidae) and flycatchers (Muscicapidae), respectively. Order Passeriformes.

SABLE. See *Marten*.

SALAMANDER, any of about 240 different kinds of Eurasian and North American amphibians with a distinct head, a trunk, and permanent tail, usually with clawless-toed limbs of about equal size. The young have gills and resemble the adults, having teeth in both jaws. From the characteristically moist cool skin has come the superstition that a salamander can live in fire, and the use of the name "salamander furnaces" for heating buildings during construction.

The common European spotted salamander (*Salamandra maculosa*) is 6 to 8 inches long, black with yellow or orange patches, sluggish, very shy, and perfectly harmless. The olm (*Proteus anguinus*) of caves in southeastern Europe is pink, unpigmented, and blind, its eyes covered by skin. The related mud puppy, or water dog (*Necturus maculosus*), of eastern North America grows to 17 inches long in rivers, but never loses its gills, although at maturity it develops lungs.

North America also has many kinds of lungless salamanders, mostly under 6 inches long, that respire through their moist skins after they lose their larval gills. The axolotl (*Ambystoma mexicanum*) of Mexican lakes and marshes is sought as food, and interests scientists because in places where water is permanent it becomes sexually mature and reproduces while still a larva in body form—8 to 10 inches long, with gills on each side of the neck region. Given hormone treatment, it transforms and develops adult body pattern and other features not normally acquired.

The giants among salamanders are the Japanese *Cryptobranchus maximus*, sometimes over 5 feet long, and the related hellbender (*C. alleganiensis*) about 18 inches long in streams of the Ohio Valley. Various orders in subclass Caudata.

SALMON, any of a number of different kinds of edible carnivorous fishes with a small soft adipose fin between the dorsal fin and the tail, directly above the anal fin, with pink or red flesh, and with a habit of migrating at spawning time. They are native to the Northern Hemisphere, particularly along seacoasts and in landlocked lakes that once were connected to the oceans by rivers up and down which the salmon could swim.

Atlantic salmon (species of genus *Salmo*) are large trout, which make seasonal spawning runs into rivers of eastern North America and western Europe, returning to the sea afterward. Pacific salmon (6 species of genus *Oncorhynchus*) enter rivers on the west coast of North America and the east coast of Asia, and die there after mating and laying eggs. All of these salmon commonly attain a length of 3 to 4 feet, and a weight of about 30 pounds; record individuals weigh 100 pounds or more. The king, or chinook, salmon (*O. tschawytscha*) has been successfully introduced into New Zealand, where it has set up a new migration pattern.

Only the landlocked salmon feed in freshwater. The others enter rivers full fed in and in fine condition, but fast while they swim and leap past rapids and small waterfalls to reach the headwaters where they lay their large eggs.

The hatchling salmon, known as parr, feed in freshwater for various lengths of time from 1 to 7 years, depending upon the species and the latitude. They descend to the ocean, losing their crossbands and becoming silvery as they go, and are known as grilse when the change is completed; they are almost indistinguishable, except for size, from full-grown salmon.

The remainder of their feeding is done in the ocean, over a period of 6 to sometimes more than 7 years, and while traveling 1,000 to 2,500 miles away from the coast. Eventually, many of them find their way back to the same tributaries of the identical streams in which they spent their immature lives. Order Isospondyli, family Salmonidae.

SAND DOLLAR. See *Sea Urchin*.

SANDERLING, a small, active, 3-toed sandpiper, seen virtually wherever in the world waves break against sandy shores. Feeding in small flocks on mollusks, worms, crustaceans, and insects, it follows each receding wave onto the wet sand, probing for food until the last moment before being overwhelmed by the next wave.

A conspicuous white stripe shows on the wing when the bird flies, helping give it a common name of *whitey*. The sanderling lays its eggs in a slight hollow, lined with grass or leaves, on the upper beach. Usually there are 4 eggs, which hatch to downy chicks that hide among the nearby grasses. Order Charadriiformes, family Scolopacidae, specifically *Crocethia alba*.

SANDPIPER, any of 23 different kinds of small wading birds in which the slender, straight, or slightly downcurved beak is as long or longer than the head; all except the sanderling have 4 toes on each foot. Almost all breed in the Northern Hemisphere, mostly in the arctic and subarctic barren grounds. They seldom are found far from water, even on their long migrations, which take them to the limit of land in the Southern Hemisphere.

Largest is the 10-inch knot (*Calidris canutus*), sometimes called the robin sandpiper because its breast is red in spring and summer; it nests in the arctic and antarctic barrens, visiting western Europe and the North American Atlantic and Gulf coasts on migration.

Smallest is the least sandpiper, or stint (*Erolia minutilla*), a 6-inch bird seen frequently on marshes and along the open beach; it nests from Newfoundland to Alaska, and winters in the southernmost United States, Mexico, Central and northern South America.

The best-known in America is the spotted sandpiper (*Actitis macularia*), a 7-inch bird that teeters its tail up and down, bobbing its head at the same time. The Eurasian common sandpiper (*A. hypoleucos*) has the same habit. Order Charadriiformes, family Scolopacidae.

SAPSUCKER. See *Woodpecker*.

SARDINE. See *Herring*.

SAWFISH. See *Ray*.

SAWFLY, any adult insect with 4 membranous wings, the fore pair larger than the hind pair, and biting mouthparts, differing from the ant, bee, and wasp in that its abdomen is broad where it joins the thorax portion of the body, never constricted to a narrow waist. Female sawflies possess a sawlike egg-laying organ, with which they produce narrow slits in plant stems that hold the eggs securely.

From the eggs, larvae resembling caterpillars emerge. They are leafeaters, and usually can be distinguished by having soft paired appendages (prolegs) on almost every body segment, not just 4 pairs in the middle region of the abdomen and a pair at the rear, as in a caterpillar. Commonly the full-grown larva of a sawfly creeps down into the soil to pupate, and emerges for a relatively brief period of adult life. Order Hymenoptera, family Tenthredinidae.

SCALE INSECT, any of a large number of soft-bodied sucking insects that secrete over themselves a hard protective scale or a series of fluffy projections that fend off ants and hungry birds. Found on all continents and most islands, scale insects attach themsleves to plant stems while sucking the juices. For most of the year they produce young by the process of parthenogenesis, one female often giving birth to thousands of offspring during one summer season. Generally the young remain for a while close to the mother, benefiting from her shelter; they they go off on their own to grow quickly.

The pernicious San José scale insect (*Aspidiotus perniciosus*), which attacks citrus and shade trees, is individually only about 1/16-inch long; it produces infestations so dense that the bark of the tree appears covered with dark-gray scurfy patches of overlapping sucking insects. The cottony scale of maple, Virginia creeper, and other plants (*Pulvinaria innumerabilis*) places its eggs in a mass of cottony secretion.

The cochineal insect (*Coccus cacti*) of tropical America sucks the juice from stems of prickly pear cactus, and was the source of a famous red dye called cochineal, now replaced by synthetic colors from coal tar. The lac insect (*Tachardia lacca*) of Asia secretes a substance from which shellac and also several dyes can be prepared.

In the Near East, the manna scale insect (*Gossyparius manifera*) on tamarisk trees produces an edible secretion, which is said to have been the food called manna, used by the Israelites as described in Exodus 16. Order Homoptera, many genera of family Coccidae.

SCALLOP, any of more than 100 different kinds of marine bivalved mollusks, in which the shell valves are shallowly saucer-shaped, almost circular, and serve in swimming to expel jets of water from the ends of the hinge at the back. Scallops live along most of the world's seacoasts, below low-tide mark and to depths of about 100 feet.

Around the edge of a scallop's shell, minute eyes look out, attached to the edge of the soft mantle. Generally the shell has ridges radiating from hinge to edge, which is wavy in the pattern said to be scalloped, from the name of the mollusk. Scallops are caught with nets and dredges, chiefly during July and August, after their spawning is completed. The edible part is the strong muscle that pulls the two valves together. Order Filobranchia, family Pectinidae.

SCAUP, either of 2 very similar ducks of northern latitudes in America and Eurasia, feeding and swimming along seacoasts except when nesting in the far north.

The distinctive markings of the male scaup include a pale blue beak, dark head, neck, and tail, and pale gray back and wings. The female is brown where the male is black, and has a white face. The greater scaup (*Aythya marila*) is 19 inches long, the lesser scaup (*A. affinis*) 17 inches, with a more angular head and less white on the wing.

Scaups fly swiftly and erratically in large flocks; they are often seen sitting on the water in so-called *rafts* that number several thousand; many are shot each year by hunters. Order Anseriformes, family Anatidae.

SCORPION, any of a large number of terrestrial arthropod animals walking on 4 pairs of legs, with a pair of pincers on the most anterior appendages, and with a slender elongated jointed portion of the flexible abdomen ending in a venomous stinger.

They live in tropical and warm lands, on all continents, preying upon insects and spiders, holding them in their pincers and often stinging a struggling captive to subdue it before bringing it to the mouth. Like spiders, scorpions lack both jaws and feelers (antennae). They crush their animal prey, squeezing out drops of liquid they can take in through the small, sucking mouth.

After an elaborate courtship and mating ceremony, female scorpions give birth to as many as 60 young of identical appearance, and carry them about on their backs for a week or so until the growing youngsters become independent. Scorpions are active chiefly at night, and often hide by day in shoes and clothing. Particularly in the tropics, where scorpions are often large and venomous, it is wise to shake out every garment before putting it on. Order Scorpionida of class Arachnida, family Scorpionidae.

SEA ANEMONE, any of about 1,000 flowerlike, marine, coelenterate animals found attached to piles and floating timber. Sea anemones usually do not have a free-swimming jellyfish stage. From their attached positions they extend arms or tentacles in all directions to find food, which consists of microscopic organisms. When a sea anemone is irritated, it contracts violently, expelling water from its central digestive cavity. Several orders of subclass Zoantharia of class Anthozoa.

SEA COW, any of 4 different massive aquatic mammals with a rounded head, small mouth, short neck, paddlelike forelimbs, no hind limbs, and a tail that is horizontally flattened. They are found in tropical waters along coasts, estuaries, and marsh-bordered rivers on both sides of the Atlantic and Indian oceans, from the Red Sea to the Philippines and the northwest coast of Australia.

The Indian Ocean representative is the dugong (*Dugong dugon*), which usually feed in groups of 2 or more, eating marine plants in shallow waters; they grow to 9 feet in length and a weight of nearly 400 pounds.

The Atlantic Ocean sea cows, called manatees, include one (*Trichechus manatus*), which inhabits the coast from Florida and the West Indies to northern South America; another (*T. inunguis*) in the Amazon and Orinoco River drainage areas of South America; and one (*T. senegalensis*) in West Africa. Manatees have a rounded tail, rather than a notched one, and feed mostly at night.

Sea cows are hunted in many areas for their tasty flesh and for a clear oil that does not turn rancid. Order Sirenia, families Dugongidae and Trichechidae.

SEA CUCUMBER, or bêche-de-mer, or trepang, any of about 500 different kinds of sausage-shaped, soft-bodied echinoderms that maintain their shape through hydraulic pressure of liquid in their voluminous body cavities. They are exclusively marine and occur in all oceans, but most commonly in the tropics. Their only skeletal support consists of tiny limy plates in the outer part of the body wall.

Many sea cucumbers are regarded as food; others are used as the source of a fish poison with which to force edible fishes in tide pools to come out of hiding, anesthetized and helpless. Many orders of class Holothurioidea.

SEA FAN, a colonial coelenterate animal of shallow warm seas, attached to a rock or some dead coral or other solid support, and growing upward in the form of a branching tree with all the branches in one plane. In the large sea fans (*Gorgonia*) of semitropical waters, the branches grow together to form a lacy network, upon the surface of which the individual polyps live. Each is a tiny, soft-bodied sac with a microscopic mouth at the center of a ring of tentacles.

Nettling cells on the tentacles help the sea fan catch and subdue equally small swimming animals in the nearby water, and to pull each victim into the mouth for digestion inside the body. Each polyp contributes toward the growth of the tough, hornlike protein which forms the core of the fan, and toward secreting the surface coating of limy spicules, which may be pastel yellow, lavender, pink, or purple.

In season, sea fans produce reproductive cells and liberate free-swimming larvae that eventually settle to the bottom where they may begin new colonies. Each colony grows toward whatever currents come regularly in the water, letting the polyps on both sides of the fan benefit equally from food in the passing water. Order Gorgonacea of class Anthozoa.

SEA HORSE, any of about 50 kinds of small, marine, bony fishes with a head strongly resembling that of a horse or the knight chessman. The mouth is round, at the end of a tubular snout, and used for sucking in minute animals and plants for food. The whole body is covered with bony plates. Generally a sea horse swims in an almost vertical position. It prefers quiet brackish waters and coils its long, prehensile tail around seaweeds and sea grasses to keep from being swept away by the currents.

The female sea horse lays her eggs in a pouch on the belly of the male, where they develop to the hatching stage, at which time he expels them. The common sea horse of the east coast of North America (*Hippocampus hudsonius*) is about 5 inches long; the Pacific coast sea horse (*H. kuda*) grows almost twice as large. Order Solenichthyes, family Syngnathidae.

SEAL, any of 18 different kinds of fin-footed marine mammals with only a wrinkle to show where the ear opens, with a tail of moderate length that is inconspicuous between hind legs so specialized for sculling through water that they cannot be folded forward, but merely drag when the animal hauls out on land. The harbor seal (*Phoca vitulina*), found along Pacific and Atlantic coasts of the Northern Hemisphere, sometimes follows shad and other fishes far into rivers. Leopard seals (*Hydrurga leptonyx*), which grow to 11½ feet long, prey on penguins and other birds. Order Pinnipedia, family Phocidae.

SEA LILY, any of about 630 different kinds of marine echinoderms in which the body is cup shaped, protected by limy plates that fit together closely just under the skin, and bearing 5 arms that divide close to the base into 2 equal feathery extensions. Almost all sea lilies live at great depths in temperate and tropical oceans, but those of polar seas live in shallower water.

All of the deep-water sea lilies seem permanently attached by long cylindrical armored stalks with rootlike clasping parts that can hold to firm objects on the sea bottom. Some shallow-water sea lilies, called feather stars, live in the Tropics on coral reefs, where they soon free themselves from their short stalks and move about from time to time; some can even swim feebly. Fossil sea lilies of the Paleozoic era are found in great numbers. Several orders of class Crinoidea.

SEA LION, any of about 12 different kinds of fin-footed marine mammals with a small protruding ear, a short tail, and hind legs sufficiently flexible to be folded forward and used for awkward walking or running on land. They live along coastlines of western North America and South America, Australia, New Zealand, some oceanic islands, and southern Africa.

ANIMALS

The trained "seals" of circuses and vaudeville shows are California sea lions (*Zalophus californianus*), which are found also along the shores of the Galápagos Islands and Japan. Related are the fur seals (*Callorhinus ursinus*) of the Aleutian Islands and Alaska, of which about 90,000 of an estimated 2 million are harvested annually for their fur; and the Antarctic fur seals (6 species of genus *Arctocephalus*), of which about 30,000 are taken each year. Order Pinnipedia, family Otariidae.

SEA SQUIRT. See *Tunicate*.

SEA STAR, or starfish, any of about 2,000 different kinds of marine echinoderms in which the body is star-shaped, 5-angled, and generally extended into from 5 to 50 flexible arms below which are grooves containing tubefeet used for locomotion and for holding to the substratum. Sea stars are found in all oceans, and some kinds tolerate being exposed to air a few hours while the tide is out. Most are predatory, feeding on mollusks and sand dollars. Many orders of class Asteroidea.

SEA URCHIN, any of about 860 different kinds of marine echinoderms in which the body is made firm by interlocking limy plates just beneath the skin, and protection is given by movable spines operated by muscles and located on ball-and-socket joints on the limy plates. These animals are found in all oceans, at many depths, but rarely where they are exposed by the receding tide.

A sea urchin holds on and moves about by means of a large number of fine flexible tube feet. Its mouth, on the surface next to the substratum, has 5 hard, sharp limy jaws with which it can bite out pieces of seaweed to swallow. Most sea urchins are circular, and their shells show impressive detail in a radially symmetrical pattern. Some urchins, mostly burrowing kinds, are heart shaped. Others, known as sand dollars, are very flat-bodied and live in the surface ooze over sand bars below low-tide level. Many orders of class Echinoidea.

SECRETARY BIRD, a long-legged, fast-running hawk about 4 feet high, with a crested head that gives the bird its popular name—as if it were a secretary with several pencils stuck in her hair. It is common in Africa south of the great deserts, and protected because of its fearless attacks on snakes, even large and poisonous varieties, which it kills with its talons and wings. It is sometimes domesticated as a snake-killer. Order Falconiformes, family Sagittariidae, specifically *Sagittarius serpentarius*.

SHAD, any of several edible, herring-like fishes about 2 feet long, which in spring seek out freshwater shallows to mate and lay their eggs. Many, such as the American shad (*Alosa sapidissima*) of the Atlantic coast, return to the sea, where they feed on plankton. Others, such as the Ohio shad (*A. ohiensis*), are restricted to river life. Although the meat is full of small bones, shad are caught in large numbers for table use. Their eggs (roe) are also a delicacy. Order Isispondyli, family Clupeidae.

Related gizzard shad (6 kinds in genus *Dorosoma*, family Dorosomidae) live in salt water and freshwaters as forage fish. Their name refers to the specially modified muscular stomach with which they grind up their food.

SHARK, any of more than 250 different kinds of cartilaginous fishes with a torpedo-shaped body, a wide mouth underneath the head, separate gill slits on the sides, and a two-lobed tail of which the upper lobe is much the longer. They are found in all seas, and occasionally ascend rivers into freshwater, as in Lake Nicaragua.

The giants among sharks are the whale shark (*Rhincodon typus*), sometimes 45 feet long, and the giant basking shark (*Cetorhinus maximus*), which is nearly as big; both eat only tiny sea animals. The slender blue shark (*Prionarce glauca*), 12½ feet long, and the great white shark (*Carcharodon carcharias*, named from Greek words meaning sharp tooth because its teeth are shaped like arrowhead flints), up to 36½ feet long, is a fast-swimming predator of open oceans, and the most famous of the man-eaters. It can swallow a 100-pound sea lion, a 50-pound seal, or a Newfoundland dog at a single gulp.

Almost as dangerous to skin divers and men overboard (or in flimsy life rafts) are the tropical Atlantic, 18-foot, mackerel shark, or porbeagle (*Lamna ditropis*), which is sharp-snouted, and the hammerhead shark (species of genus *Sphyrna*), whose head is extended on both sides like the top of a T, with the eyes at the extreme corners. Many tales of man-eating sharks are exaggerated and overdrawn.

Small sharks include some called dogfishes, which destroy fish caught in fishnets; spiny dogfishes, with a spine in front of each of the 2 dorsal fins, include many species of the genus *Squalus*. Smooth dogfishes lack these spines, and may be species of genus *Mustelis*. Both are caught for sale in Europe and the Orient, often as "grayfish" with edible flesh. Order Selachii, many families.

SHEEP, any of 9 different kinds of hollow-horned, cud-chewing mammals with narrow noses and pointed ears, distinguished from goats by the lack of a scent gland at the base of the tail. They are native to northern mountains of Eurasia and North America, and to Sardinia and Corsica, North Africa and the Sudan across to the north bend of the Niger River. The largest are the African aoudads, or Barbary sheep (*Ammotragus lervia*), which have a mane of long hairs on the throat, chest, and upper parts of the forelegs.

Slightly smaller are the Rocky Mountain sheep, or bighorns (*Ovis canadensis*) and Dall sheep (*O. dalli*) of western North America, and the argali, or Marco Polo sheep (*O. ammon*), of the central U.S.S.R. to Nepal and western China. The massive horns

MONTANA HIGHWAY COMMISSION
SHEEP

on the males reach impressive size, and are used in ceremonial butting activity at mating season. The mouflon (*O. musimon*) of Mediterranean islands has been introduced widely.

The original of the domestic sheep (*O. aries*) is no longer known in the world. It probably originated in Asia, and has been bred into many distinctive races. The Shropshire is a popular breed in the Middle States and is a good mutton sheep. The most important wool sheep is the Merino breed, Spanish in origin but found today largely in America and Australia, where its fine wool is a product of great importance.

In addition to their furnishing of wool and meat products, sheep are of considerable importance to farming because of the manure that they produce. Order Artiodactyla, family Bovidae.

SHINER. See *Minnow*.

SHIPWORM, any of several highly specialized marine bivalve mollusks that settle on wood soaked with seawater and spend most of their lives burrowing into this material. They are found in most parts of the world, doing great damage to wooden ships and pilings by weakening their structure.

The shipworm, also called teredo, uses its small valves as boring tools, while its elongated siphon (part of the mantle) extends to the surface of the wood to get seawater containing microscopic food and oxygen, and to discharge wastes, carbon dioxide, and reproductive cells. A thin limy tube is secreted around the wormlike siphon. Order Eulamellibranchia, family Teredinidae, chiefly members of genus *Teredo*.

SHREW, any of more than 200 different kinds of small, short-legged mouselike mammals with long-pointed noses and many small teeth; only the upper middle incisors are enlarged, and they are not fitted for gnawing. Shrews are found in most land areas, but not on arctic islands, the West Indies, Australia, Tasmania, New Zealand, or South Pacific islands. They include the smallest known mammal, the dwarf shrew (*Suncus etruscus*) of Mediterranean coastal countries, 1½ to 2 inches long with a 1-inch tail, weighing about 1/15 ounce.

Except in breeding season, shrews are solitary, voracious predators, spacing out their meals on insects, snails, and worms with seeds and other plant materials. The commonest shrew in the United States and Canada is the short-tailed *Blarina brevicauda*, which might be mistaken for a mole except for its delicate legs and feet. Order Insectivora, family Soricidae.

SHRIKE, or butcherbird, any of 73 different kinds of small to medium-sized birds with large heads, stout beaks hooked and notched at the tip, strong legs, short rounded wings, and, usually, long tails. They are found in both hemispheres, with 39 bush shrikes and 9 helmet shrikes in Africa.

Only 2 of the other shrikes live in America; one (the loggerhead shrike, *Lanius ludovicianus*) migrating from southern Canada to Mexico and central America, the other (the northern shrike, *L. excubitor*) ranging farther north and also across Eurasia. Like many shrikes, they are gray above, white below, black and white on wings and tail, and have a mask mark across the eyes.

Shrikes have the peculiar habit of impaling insects, frogs, and small birds on thorns or barbed wire fences, perhaps because the shrike's feet are not strong enough to hold its prey while its powerful bill tears the food apart. Order Passeriformes, family Laniidae.

SHRIMP, or prawn, any of a number of different aquatic crustaceans, 6 inches or less in length, with laterally compressed bodies or abdomens. Most shrimps are marine, and some 1½ to 3 inches long are caught in enormous numbers for human food. Those from the Gulf of Mexico (especially *Penaeus setifer*) are a delicate gray-green color spotted with brown; when cooked they turn pink and white. Order Decapoda.

The name shrimp is given to unrelated crustaceans: brine shrimps (*Artemia salina*) of salt lakes and fairy shrimps (*Eubranchipus vernalis*) of freshwater ponds in early spring belong to order Anostraca; freshwater shrimps, or scuds (species of *Gammarus*), live in shallows of streams and ponds, and belong to order Amphipoda; opossum shrimps, most of which are marine (species of *Mysis*), belong to order Mysidacea.

SILKWORM, any of a number of different moth caterpillars that spin a viscous secretion from their salivary glands into a single, continuous, fine silk strand with which to construct the egg-shaped cocoon that is to protect them during their pupal transformation.

Only one, the oriental silkworm (*Bombyx mori* of family Bombycidae), has achieved commercial importance. It supports an industry where cheap labor is available to keep captive caterpillars fed with fresh mulberry leaves, and to unravel and wind up the silk strands from the finished cocoons.

The caterpillar itself is yellowish gray, about 3 inches long when fully grown, with a hornlike projection on the last segment of the body. After the cocoon is complete and has hardened, it is plunged into hot water to kill the enclosed pupa and to free the silk fibers. As reeled, the raw silk fiber may be bright orange, tan, or almost white. Order Lepidoptera.

SILVERFISH. See *Bristletail.*

SKATE. See *Ray.*

SKIMMER, any of 3 coastal birds in which the lower bill is longer than the upper and used in a peculiar method of fishing. The black skimmer (*Rhynchops nigra*), which ranges along the Atlantic coast of North America from Long Island southward, and down both sides of Central and South America, is the largest. Its wingspan may be as great as 50 inches, and its red beak 4½ inches long from the lower jaw and 3 inches from the upper.

The African skimmer, found along the coasts and larger rivers of Africa, has a bright yellow beak. The Indian skimmer, with a bill black at the base and yellow at the tip, patrols the rivers of India and Southeast Asia.

All skimmers cruise low over the water by steady beating of their long-pointed wings, while they lower the underbill into the water. If the tip of the bill encounters an obstacle, such as a fish or a crustacean at the surface, the bird quickly bends its head and closes its mouth, picking up the trophy as food. Skimmers feed mostly in the early evening and before dawn, when the water is calm and prey tend to come to the surface.

By day, skimmers roost in flocks on open beaches, and withstand the intense light by closing to a narrow slit their unusual pupils, which suggest those of a cat. Their nests are mere unlined depressions in a sandflat or beach near the water, with 4 eggs blotched with brown. The young birds have both bills equal until almost full grown. Order Charadriiformes, family Rhynchopidae.

SKUNK, any of 10 different kinds of short-legged, bushy-tailed mammals marked strikingly in black and white, and armed with a special gland under the tail, secreting an ill-smelling fluid that can be squirted to 10 to 15 feet with fair accuracy.

Skunks live only in the Americas, where they seek under logs and stones for insects, and catch mice and frogs; occasionally skunks attack birds, including poultry. Hog-nosed skunks (6 species of *Conepatus*) are the only ones in South America; their range extends to the southern United States. Spotted skunks (*Spilogale* species) are found from British Columbia to Central America, and striped skunks (*Mephitis* species) from eastern Canada to Central America. Order Carnivora, family Mustelidae.

SLIPPER SHELL, or boat shell, or quarterdeck, any of several kinds of marine snails that increase the surface area for attaching themselves to their oval shells by producing one half a horizontal shelflike platform.

Boat shells feed on minute animals and plants that become stuck in a film of mucus over the gills on each side of the foot. At intervals of about 4 minutes, the snail twists its head to right or left and sucks up the loaded mucus into its mouth. It swallows large particles at once but stores larger ones in a pouch for a later meal. The snail can feed on these at low tide when it must clamp its shell down tightly and hold on.

Often slipper shells are found holding on to horseshoe crabs or larger snails, or even to other slipper shells in a cluster of several dozen, all rolling together on the sea bottom. Female boat shells produce about 50 membranous egg cases, each containing about 250 eggs, and stand guard over these until the young hatch out. The young swim freely for about 2 weeks, then settle on some firm surface where they can become more or less permanently attached. Order Prosobranchiata, family Crepidulidae, species of genus *Crepidula*.

SLOTH (meaning slowness, laziness), any of 7 different kinds of tropical mammals with round heads, ears that are barely visible, eyes directed forward, and all feet with long, curved strong claws from toes not exceeding 3 in number, bound together for most of their length. Sloths live only in the Americas.

Sloths hang by their claws below horizontal branches, progressing slowly while feeding upon the leaves. The young, only 1 at a birth, holds tight to the mother's back and is almost hidden by her long hair.

There are 2 genera: *Bradypus* (which means slow foot), having 3 claws on the front feet; and *Choloepus* (lame foot), having 2 claws on the front feet. On the ground, sloths are practically helpless. They are usually 1½ to 2 feet long. Order Edentata, family Bradypodidae.

SLUG, any snail-like mollusk that is unprotected by a limy shell. Some of the land slugs that are classified in Order Pulmonata because they breathe air through a lunglike organ, have concealed a small shell that they secreted at a very early age and then outgrew. These slugs glide about on a large flat foot, chiefly at night or during rains when they are in less danger of desiccation. If attacked, they eject a thick slime that discourages birds and insects from coming closer.

Eating vegetable matter, both living and decaying, some land slugs (such as *Limax maximus* of the Olympic National Park forest in Washington state) grow to a length of 8 inches. Sea slugs lack a shell altogether, and are classified in Order Opisthobranchiata. They also lack gills and breathe by means of highly decorative plumes upon the back.

Sea slugs commonly creep over corals, sea fans, and other coelenterates, browsing on the polyps; they also crawl among seaweeds, eating the moss animals (bryozoans). One kind (*Glaucus eucharis*) has a deep blue color, and creeps along the underside of the surface film on the warm water of tropical oceans, capturing minute crustaceans and other animals as food.

SMELT, any of 13 different kinds of slender, bony, salmon-shaped fishes, with a small soft adipose fin in front of the tail, directly above the large anal fin. Smelt are fish of the Northern Hemisphere, especially Pacific Ocean coasts.

Tons of Sacramento smelt (*Spirinchus thaleichthys*) are caught annually in San Francisco Bay and the mouth of the Columbia River. The small surf smelt (*Hypomesus pretiosus*), which lives mostly close to shore, is a favorite bait for both surf fishermen and commercial operators.

The 1-foot Atlantic smelt (*Osmerus mordax*) of the American east coast was introduced into the Great Lakes in 1912 and is thriving in fresh water. The Atlantic smelt, or sparling, of Europe (*O. eperlanus*) is a valuable fish of northern waters, reaching a length of 8 inches. Order Isospondyli, family Osmeridae.

SNIPE, any of 25 different kinds of small- to medium-sized shore birds with short legs, and long beaks used for probing for small edible animals in muddy shores. They nest in arctic muskegs and freshwater marshes of all continents except Australia.

The circumpolar common snipe (*Capella gallinago*) nests over the northern United States, most of Canada, and much of northern Eurasia, but winters in the Americas from the middle United States to southern Brazil, and in the Southern Hemisphere of the Old World. The Japanese snipe (*Gallinago hardwicki*), which nests only on the northern islands of Japan, winters in New Zealand and eastern Australia, where it is called the Australian snipe. Order Charadriiformes, family Scolopacidae.

SOLE. See *Flatfish*.

SOWBUG, or slater, any of a large number of terrestrial crustaceans with a jointed oval body. On all continents, they scavenge in damp places, under fallen logs, stones, and the bark on rotting trees, eating principally decaying vegetation.

Some sowbugs, such as members of the common genus *Armadillidium*, are able to curl up into a ball when disturbed. In this position, their delicate legs and the vestigial gills with which they breathe in air are well protected by the hard armor of the body's upper surface. These particular sowbugs are often called "pill bugs."

Other kinds are unable to curl so tightly. Sometimes one that does not curl is seen to be a female carrying a batch of eggs with her, in a brood sac formed by flat projections from her legs. The young that hatch out are of the same body form as the parents. Order Isopoda.

SPARROW, or bunting, any of about 265 different kinds of 4½- to 8-inch perching birds, usually of a dark brown inconspicuous color and with a beak smaller than that of a finch. Found all over the world but most commonly in the American tropics, they generally frequent grasslands or open woodlands, hunting for seeds and insects on or near the ground. They nest on the ground or in low bushes. The snow bunting (*Plectrophenax nivalis*) and several kinds of longspurs (species of *Calcarius*) are circumpolar, nesting southward in mountain regions.

Temperate North America has about 50 different kinds of native sparrows, of which the largest is the fox sparrow (*Passerella iliaca*), 7 inches long, with a streaked breast and a reddish brown tail; it nests across Canada and in the western United States, wintering in the southern states. Its pleasant song is heard only in spring and fall, while the bird is migrating. The song sparrow (*Melospiza melodia*) is more widespread and sings much of the year; its white underparts have brown markings that fuse in the center of the breast to form a large blotch.

The white-throated sparrow (*Zenotrichia albicollis*), which nests in Canada and New England and winters in the southern United States, has a particularly sweet, clear whistle. The chipping sparrow (*Spizella passerina*), 5 inches long with a rusty stripe on the top of the head, nests near houses.

None of these native sparrows damages crops or drives away other birds as does the house sparrow (*Passer domesticus*), which was introduced into the United States in 1850, supposedly to eat insect pests. House sparrows spread to all parts of the continent, and became pests themselves. In their native northern Eurasia, they appear helpful to farmers, devouring insects and weed seeds.

Eurasia and Africa have 30 different kinds of very similar birds, which are called buntings (*Emberiza* species), and the most common sparrow of all—the chaffinch (*Fringilla coelebs*). All are primarily seedeaters, although the name seedeater is ordinarily reserved for about 30 kinds of birds in tropical America (species of *Sporophila*). Order Passeriformes, family Fringillidae.

SPRINGTAIL, any of a large number of widely distributed minute, wingless insects in which the hind-most abdominal segments (the "tail") are held in a curled position, turned forward under the more anterior abdominal segments. There the tip of the tail is held by a sort of catch, under voluntary muscular control. When alarmed, a springtail tenses its abdomen as though to straighten it out, then slips the catch. The tail strikes the surface, land or water, on which the springtail is standing, with enough force to toss the insect itself high in the air. It falls somewhere else and may be able to scurry away before being discovered.

Often large numbers of springtails scavenge for microscopic particles of food along the edge of a stream, on the water surface, giving the combined appearances of a gray-blue line ¼ inch or more in width. At the slightest disturbance, all of these insects toss themselves into the air, and the line vanishes as though by magic. Order Collembola.

SQUETEAGUE, or sea trout, or weakfish, any of several different kinds of marine bony fishes related to the croakers, with a triangular front dorsal fin and long rear dorsal fin. Squeteagues travel in schools along both the Atlantic and Pacific coasts of North America, attracting both commercial fishermen and sportsmen. The name weakfish refers to the ease with which the jaws can be torn from the head with a fisherman's hook while the fish is fighting for its life.

The Atlantic kinds attain lengths to 32 inches and weights to 17½ pounds. The closely related California sea bass (*Cynoscion nobilis*) is larger; largest is the totuava (*C. macdonaldi*) of the Gulf of California, which grows to 225 pounds. Order Percomorphi, family Sciaenidae, members of genus *Cynoscion*.

SQUID, any of about 300 different kinds of free-swimming, predatory, marine, cephalopod mollusks with 10 long arms projecting from the head end of the barrel- or cigar-shaped body. Squids are common in all oceans from the surface down to the greatest depths. They have 2 well-developed eyes, quite similar in form to those of vertebrate animals.

When disturbed, a squid gives off an inky substance that provides an underwater smokescreen and apparently dulls the sense of smell for fishes that are pursuing the squid. Squid themselves eat smaller fishes, young fishes, and crustaceans of many kinds; in turn, squid are eaten in large numbers by large fishes, seals, and toothed whales. Most squids are less than 2 feet long, but a giant squid (*Architeuthis harveyi*) of the North Atlantic attains a length of 52 feet, including both body and arms. Order Dibranchia.

SQUIRREL, any of about 280 different kinds of active rodents, mostly with bushy tails and tree-dwelling habits. They are found in most land areas except southern South America, Madagascar, Australia and New Zealand, and major deserts. Many are ground

U.S. NATIONAL PARK SERVICE
SQUIRREL

squirrels with less conspicuous tails, living underground except while hunting for food. All except the flying squirrels, which do not fly but glide by means of a parachute of skin extending between the legs of each side, are active during the day and sleep at night.

Squirrels eat seeds and fruits, as well as some insects and snails, and occasionally birds' eggs. When numerous and hungry, they may attack corn and other crop plants. In the United States and Canada, red squirrels (2 species of *Tamiasciurus*) are common in evergreen coniferous forests, whereas the gray (*Sciurus carolinensis*) and fox (*S. niger*) squirrels live among hardwoods. Gray squirrels are larger and drive away red squirrels when the two meet.

The fur of a number of larger kinds of squirrels is valuable, and their meat is delicious. In both North America and Eurasia, ground squirrels (*Citellus* species) are plains animals, whereas chipmunks (*Tamias* in eastern North America and *Eutamias* in the West as well as in Asia) inhabit brush land and growing forests. Order Rodentia, family Sciuridae.

STARFISH. See *Sea Star*.

STARLING, any of about 106 different kinds of Old World perching birds with short tails, strong beaks and legs, and stout bodies. Most of them walk, instead of hopping. Starlings are chiefly African and Oriental birds of open country, but one of the Eurasian kinds is known as the common starling (*Sturnus vulgaris*). A vigorous, 8½-inch bird with a yellow beak, black iridescent feathers, and pointed wings, it provides important control over insect pests in its native regions.

Introduced into New York around 1890, it has spread over almost the entire United States and become a major menace, descending in enormous flocks to eat cereal crops, cultivated fruits, and berries. It competes for food and nesting places with many native birds, nearly all of which are more beneficial to man than the introduced starling. In many cities, the clamor of roosting starlings and the filth from their droppings have led to campaigns to destroy these birds, never with any success. Order Passeriformes, family Sturnidae.

STICK INSECT, any of a large number of biting insects with a long slim cylindrical body, long feelers (antennae), long slender legs, and wings (if any) similar to those of grasshoppers. Most stick insects, and all of the large ones—some to a length of 10 inches—live in the Tropics.

Stick insects move very slowly, eating green leaves on shrubs and trees, and remain motionless or slightly swaying if alarmed. In this way they resemble dead sticks or twigs and are overlooked by animals that eat insects. In the middle and northern United States and southern Canada, a completely wingless stick insect (*Diapheromera femorata*) is fairly common, and grows to a length of 4 to 5 inches, larger in the female. Order Orthoptera, family Phasmidae.

STICKLEBACK, any of several small fishes of the Northern Hemisphere. The 3-spine stickleback (*Gasterosteus aculeatus*), which has 2 or 3 sharp stiff spines on its back in front of its dorsal fin, occurs in both freshwater and salt water in North America and Eurasia. The brook stickleback (*Eucalia inconstans*), which rarely exceeds 2½ inches in length, has 4 to 6 spines and is restricted to fresh waters in the northernmost United States and southern Canada, coast to coast.

In breeding season, the male stickleback builds an elaborate globular nest with a front and back door. He courts a female and induces her to lay her eggs in his nest. After fertilizing the eggs, he stands guard over them and aerates them by fanning water through them with his fins. After the eggs hatch, he tries to keep the young fish together near the nest but they soon wander off. Despite their spines, many sticklebacks are eaten by birds. Order Thoracostei, family Gasterosteidae.

STILT, either of 2 shorebirds, related to avocets, with long, slender, straight beaks and very long legs. Only flamingos have legs longer in proportion to the body. In temperate and tropical regions all over the world, the black-necked, or pied stilt (*Himantopus mexicanus*) wades with a peculiar gait, as though skating on the water. Its back is black, its belly white, and its legs blood red.

The banded stilt (*Cladorhynchus leucocephalus*) of Australia and Tasmania stands slightly taller, and is white except for a brown band across the wing; its belly is light brown, and its legs red. Stilts swim if necessary and are strong fliers. All of them migrate to the Tropics for the winter. Order Charadriiformes, family Recurvirostridae.

STOAT. See *Weasel*.

STONE FLY, any insect (more than 200 kinds in North America) with biting mouthparts, 2 pairs of similar wings held flat over the back at rest, 2 "tails" (cerci) at the end of the abdomen, and aquatic young. The adults mate soon after emerging from the water, and live only a few days. Females deposit masses of eggs in the water of streams and rivers, where they hatch into immature stone flies, called naiads or nymphs.

The naiads are carnivorous, preying upon smaller water animals found while prowling along the bottom. Each naiad has strong jaws, strong legs, visible gills in pads just behind the base of the legs, and two tails. It may need 1 to 3 years to reach full size. Both naiads and adults are favorite food of trout and other fishes. Order Plecoptera.

STORK, any of 17 different kinds of large heronlike birds with comparatively short toes, which are partially webbed, and no voice. They communicate by gestures and by clapping the beak together. Storks live in most temperate and tropical countries, but not in northern North America, New Zealand, and islands of the South Pacific. They inhabit the vicinity of marshes and rivers, where they find food consisting of frogs, lizards, fishes, and even young birds.

The white stork (*Ciconia alba*) is migratory, arriving at nesting areas from the Mediterranean to Scandinavia, departing for the winter to warm areas of Africa all the way to the Cape of Good Hope. The black stork (*C. nigra*) is a swamp bird of Europe and Asia. The adjutant birds, or marabou, storks (*Leptoptilus* species) of tropical Africa and Asia, 60 inches tall, feed on carrion and snakes and are protected as useful scavengers by Indian law.

The wood stork, often misnamed an ibis (*Mycteria americana*), of the Gulf coast of the United States and as far south as Argentina, sometimes migrates after the breeding season to both California and Canada. It is one of the most striking of the group; it stands 4 feet high, is white with black tail and wing-tips, and has long, bluish legs and a long probing bill; the head and neck of the adult are entirely bare. Order Ciconiiformes, family Ciconiidae.

STURGEON, any of 21 different kinds of large fishes whose elongated body is clad in 5 rows of platelike scales, each with a raised ridge down the center; the upper half of the tail is longer than the lower, and the snout bears 4 barbels, somewhat resembling whiskers, beside the small sucking mouth. Sturgeons are native to the Northern Hemisphere, some in the ocean but entering fresh water to spawn, others in lakes and streams for their entire lives.

The American lake sturgeon (*Acipenser fulvescens*), once plentiful in the Great Lakes, reaches a weight of 200 pounds; it has blotched, reddish sides. The common sturgeon (*A. sturio*), a marine fish found on both sides of the North Atlantic Ocean, grows to 10 feet long and a weight of 500 pounds. The largest in North America is the white sturgeon (*A. transmontanus*) of freshwaters along the Pacific coast, weighing as much as 1,800 pounds. In Eurasia, the giant is the famous beluga (*Huso huso*) of the Caspian Sea, Black Sea, and Volga River, where it is believed to attain an age of 200 years; the record for size is 28 feet long and 2,860 pounds.

All sturgeons are sluggish fish, resting on the bottom, and sucking in vegetable matter plus any animals in it from the debris around marshes and near shore. Smoked sturgeon meat is widely appreciated as a delicacy. The eggs, preserved with salt, form caviar; the best quality comes from a small Russian sturgeon, the sterlat (*A. ruthenus*), usually 2 to 3 feet long. Air bladders from sturgeons were formerly sold as transparent plastic, called isinglas. Order Chondrostei, family Acipenseridae.

SUCKER, any of about 100 different kinds of minnowlike freshwater bony fishes in which the thick-lipped mouth is set low in the head and is toothless.

The fish was named from its habit of sucking mud and organic matter from the bottom. Most are North American fishes. The commonest, the white sucker (*Catostomus commersonnii*), is 28 inches long, with soft, bony, edible flesh. Order Eventognathi, family Catostomidae.

SUNFISH, any of more than 25 different kinds of small- to medium-sized freshwater fishes and 3 of enormous oceanic fishes, which have compressed bodies that appear oval or almost circular from the side. Freshwater sunfishes are all native to North America, although they have been introduced into Europe and elsewhere to delight fishermen. They differ from perches in having the spiny and soft-rayed portions of the dorsal fin continuous or separated by no more than a narrow notch, never as entirely separate fins.

Some sunfishes, such as the pumpkinseed (*Lepomis gibbosus*) which is common in ponds and streams from Maine to Florida and the Mississippi valley, have an earlike lobe from the rear edge of the gill cover, blood red in the pumpkinseed and bright blue in some other species.

Largest is the largemouth bass (*Micropterus salmoides*), recorded at 22½ pounds and 32½ inches in length, which eats smaller sunfishes, including the bluegill (*L. macrochirus*). In the southeastern United States, two kinds of sunfishes called crappies (species of *Pomoxis*) are favorites with fishermen. All freshwater sunfishes are edible, and belong to family Centrarchidae of order Acanthopteri.

Ocean sunfishes include one (*Mola mola*) as much as 11 feet long, weighing a ton; as a young fish, it swims in the normal vertical position, but as it ages it lazily cruises with one side up, swallowing medusae and other slow animals of the sea surface. Order Plectognathi, family Molidae.

SWALLOW, any of 79 different kinds of small, slender, long-winged birds with 12 tail feathers and short, broad beaks that open widely, surrounded by stiff facial bristles. Swallows are almost cosmopolitan over land, being absent chiefly from polar regions, oceanic islands, and New Zealand. All are noted for their graceful flight, and for their regular migrations in great flocks. They feed almost exclusively on insects, which they catch on the wing.

The name swallow is often mistakenly applied to the swifts, which have 10 tail feathers and no facial bristles. The American barn swallow (*Hirundo rustica*), 7½ inches long and with a deeply forked "swallow tail," is known in Britain as "the swallow" and elsewhere in Europe as "the chimney swallow"; it builds a nest of mud and grass atop the rafters of barns.

The cliff swallow (*Petrochelidon pyrrhonota*), 6 inches long, of America from Canada to central Mexico, constructs bottle-shaped nests of mud under eaves or cliffs; those nesting at the San Juan Capistrano Mission in California have earned a reputation for returning, generally on the same date each spring. Largest of the swallows in America is the sociable purple martin (*Progne subis*), 8 inches long, which alternately soars and flies rapidly. Order Passeriformes, family Hirundinidae.

SWALLOWTAIL, any of a number of large butterflies found all over the world, in which the hind wings are abruptly extended into a "tail" as much as ½ inch long. The eggs of swallowtails are laid on plants, where they hatch into caterpillars that eat the leaves.

Generally, swallowtail caterpillars are able to repel birds by suddenly extending from the head region a pair of long soft tentacles that release a disagreeable odor and probably a bad taste. When full grown, each caterpillar spins both a button of silk in which to anchor its posterior end and an open loop of silk to give extra support to the body after it transforms into a chrysalis (pupa). Within its loop, the chrysalis remains head up, leaning back like a professional window washer into his safety belt.

Among the best-known swallowtail butterflies of America, where it is widespread except along the West Coast, is the tiger swallowtail, or lilac butterfly (*Papilio glaucus*), which has a wingspan of about 5 inches, and a caterpillar that feeds on foliage of ash, birch, cherry, and poplar; it spends the winter in the chrysalis stage, and emerges in late spring, seemingly just in time to visit lilac flowers for nectar. Order Lepidoptera, family Papilionidae.

SWAN, any of 7 different large, long-necked water birds, with webbed feet and a beak about as long as the head. All but 2 swans are white birds of the Northern Hemisphere. The black swan (*Cygnus atratus*) of Australia has a little white on the wings; the black-necked swan (*C. melanocoryphus*) of South America is white except for the black neck.

European swans include the Polish swan (*C. olor*) of Eurasia which is the domesticated species, the whooping swan (*C. cygnus*) and the smaller Bewick's swan (*C. bewicki*), both of which nest in the Arctic. The domesticated swan is often called the mute swan, although it does make several different calls. In the United States there are 2 wild species: the whistling swan (*C. columbianus*) of arctic barrens, which winters southward along the Atlantic coast and the trumpeter (*C. buccinator*) of Montana and Wyoming, which does not migrate. Trumpeter swans were on the verge of extinction when they were made a protected species, and in their sanctuary their number has begun to increase.

The legend that the swan sings before it dies—a farewell song—is not true. Formerly swans were bred for the table but they are now raised solely as ornamental birds for lakes and pools. Order Anseriformes, family Anatidae.

SWIFT, any of 67 different kinds of small, fast-flying, insect-eating birds in which the tail contains only 10, not 12, feathers, and the short beak and wide mouth have no fringe of bristles such as distinguish the swallows. Swifts are primarily tropical and subtropical birds. Even the American chimney swift (*Chaetura pelagica*) journeys to Colombia, South America, for each winter.

Swifts are usually seen in groups. Nests are placed in inaccessible places, such as the sides of rocks, chimneys, and caves and are fastened in place by the birds' saliva. The edible birds' nests of Asia, especially China, are built by small swifts, particularly *Collocalia inexpectata*; and these nests are almost entirely composed of a salivary secretion. Order Apodiformes, family Apodidae.

SWINE, any of about 9 different medium-sized, thick-skinned mammals with barrel-shaped bodies, short necks, long heads ending in a flat snout, and a 2-chambered stomach. They are native to Eurasia, Africa, and Madagascar. The Eurasian wild hog (*Sus scrofa*) was hunted for centuries for sport and meat, and to prevent it from destroying crops; later it was domesticated, and true-breeding strains were selected for smallness of tusks, large production of meat, and other qualities.

In the wild form, the young are marked with brown stripes that remain for several months after birth. The African wart hog (*Phacochoerus aethiopicus*) received its name from the large facial growths that resemble warts. In this species there is a growth of long hair down the middle of the back, and the tusks are well developed in both jaws. Order Artiodactyla, family Suidae.

SWORDFISH, a very large bony fish in which the head is prolonged into a sharp, straight projection one-third as long as the body. These fishes are widely distributed in open waters of both the Atlantic and the Pacific oceans. The body itself is cylindrical in form, tapering toward the strongly notched tail. There are no scales, the sides being naked and grayish in color. This fish has no teeth and no ventral fins, and the dorsal fin is very long, often projecting above the surface of the water when the fish is sunning itself. The maximum weight of specimens is about 800 pounds, but the average is about half that size.

The beak of the swordfish can be a dangerous weapon and there are instances on record of its having been thrust through the planking of ships,

AMERICAN MUSEUM OF NATURAL HISTORY
SWAN

so crippling them that they were forced to turn home for repairs. In feeding, the swordfish, capable of great speed, swims in among a school of fishes, lashing out from side to side with its beak, crippling or killing its food. Order Percomorphi, family Xiphiidae, specifically *Xiphias gladius*.

SWORDTAIL, a handsome freshwater fish with an extraordinary extension (the "tail") shaped like a sword, from the lower portion of the normal tail on the male fish; females are swordless. These fishes live in rivers along the Atlantic slope of southern Mexico and Guatemala. The body is shining olive-brown above, shading to blue or green on the sides, marked lengthwise and often vertically with red brown.

As a popular aquarium fish, a male swordtail will mate with 4 to 6 females, who produce living young in 6 to 8 weeks. The parents are likely to eat their own young if the 100 to 200 little fishes cannot find hiding places among tangled vegetation in the aquarium. Female swordtails are generally larger than males, and may attain a length of 4 inches. Order Cyprinodontes, family Poeciliidae, specifically *Xiphophorus helleri*.

TANAGER, any of about 200 different kinds of small- to medium-sized perching birds with a slightly downcurved conical beak that is notched in the cutting edges just before the slightly hooked tip. All live in tropical and subtropical America, except 4 that have become migratory and have spread as far north as Canada.

The best-known tanager is the handsome scarlet tanager (*Piranga olivacea*), 7 inches long, which nests from the Atlantic coast to Manitoba and Oklahoma, migrating for the winter to western South America. The male in summer is flaming red with jet-black wings and tail, but in fall and winter changes the red to olive-green shading to yellow underneath; the female resembles the winter male except that she is brownish gray where he is black.

The summer tanager (*P. rubra*), which migrates from the southern United States to Cuba, Mexico, and Central America for the winter, is slightly larger; the male is a uniform, dull red, and the female is yellowish green above, dull yellow below. In the western tanager (*P. ludoviciana*), which prefers open woodlands from the Rocky Mountains to the Pacific coast, the male is variegated yellow, black, and red; the female is undistinguished except that she has 2 yellow wing bars which are lacking in other similar birds.

The hepatic tanager (*P. flava*) nests as far north as Arizona and New Mexico, south to Guatemala. Many of the tropical tanagers belong to the genera *Tanagra* and *Tangara*, names derived from the language of the Tupi Indians of the Amazon basin. Order Passeriformes, family Thraupidae.

TAPEWORM, any of a large number of parasitic flatworms living in the digestive tract of vertebrate animals, each worm consisting of a single anchoring individual (the scolex), which holds to the wall of the intestine by means of hooks or suckers or both, and an indefinite number of flat individuals that appear to be mere segments of the tapeworm, called proglottids. The scolex individual absorbs food from the intestinal contents, and reproduces asexually, forming one proglottid after another from the free end by the process of budding.

The proglottids remain connected to one another and to the scolex for a long while, and give the appearance of a continuous ribbon, constricted at intervals where one proglottid joins the next younger or next older one. The proglottids also absorb food and grow, becoming sexually mature and mating within the intestine. Eventually each proglottid is old and full of fertilized eggs that have already developed through many embryonic stages. The old proglottid breaks free and is carried out with the feces.

The embryos hatch into larvae which can wait a few days or weeks to be swallowed by a host of another kind, such as a cow or a fish. In this secondary host, the larvae move to the muscles and become dormant. If the beef or fish flesh is eaten uncooked, the dormant larvae of the tapeworm become active and soon attach themselves to the lining of the digestive tract in the meat-eating animal (the primary host), growing there into the scolex stage that can produce a whole tapeworm. Nine different orders in class Cestoda.

TAPIR, any of 4 different large tropical mammals somewhat resembling donkeys with close-clipped fur, short tails, and a long flexible nose bearing the nostrils at the tip. The Brazilian tapir (*Tapirus terrestris*) inhabits water edges in rain forests from northern South America to Paraguay. The mountain tapir (*T. roulini*) travels in its search for vegetable food even higher than the limit of forest in the Andes. Baird's tapir (*T. bairdi*) is found northward from Ecuador through Central America into southeastern Mexico.

Largest of all is the Malayan tapir (*T. indicus*), 6 to 8 feet long, which, unlike the dull reddish or brownish black animals of the New World, is white on the back and sides. All young tapirs are striped and spotted with yellow and white. Tapirs have 3 toes reaching the ground on both the fore and hind feet. Order Perissodactyla, family Tapiridae.

TARANTULA, originally the name given to a moderately poisonous wolf spider (*Lycosa tarentula*) of Taranto in southern Italy, with a striped tan and brown body about 1 inch long and legs spreading about 2½ inches. In North America, tarantula became the name for large and relatively harmless hairy spiders (*Avicularia* and *Eurypelma* species particularly), which arrived in shipments of tropical fruit. Order Araneae.

TARPON, either of 2 different kinds of marine bony fishes with a large bony plate under the head between the two sides of the lower jaw, and a long filamentous extension from the last ray of the dorsal fin. The smaller Pacific tarpon (*Megalops cyprinoides*), which ranges from Guam to the east coast of Africa, rarely exceeds 40 inches in length.

The Atlantic tarpon (*M. atlanticus*), which is caught from Cape Cod in summer to Brazil, grows as much as 8 feet long and to 240 pounds or more. The large overlapping silver scales of such a fish are more than 3 inches across.

No fish fights harder for its freedom than a hooked tarpon; it often makes explosive leaps as much as 8 feet out of the water, 15 to 20 times in succession before becoming exhausted. At each leap, its greenish blue upper back and shining silver sides gleam in the light. Order Isospondyli, family Elopidae.

TEAL, any of about 15 different kinds of small diving ducks with particularly rapid flight. They are found in the Americas, Eurasia, Africa, Australia, New Zealand, Hawaii, and other oceanic islands. One of the world's vanishing birds is the little teal of Laysan Island (*Anas laysanensis*), which nests nowhere else. The common teal in Eurasia (*A. crecca*), 14 inches long, is Europe's smallest duck; it visits North American coasts regularly. The Hottentot teal (*A. punctata*) of Ethiopia is Africa's smallest duck.

North American teals come in several sizes: the 14-inch green-winged teal (*A. carolinensis*), which has a chestnut-brown head, nests across Canada and in the northwestern United States; the 15-inch blue-winged teal (*A. discors*), which has chalky blue patches on the wings, nests over most of Canada and the United States; and the 16-inch cinnamon teal (*A. cyanoptera*), with a cinnamon-colored head and body, nests in the western provinces of Canada and states southward into Mexico. Order Anseriformes, family Anatidae.

TENT CATERPILLAR, the destructive larval stage of a North American moth (*Malacosoma americana*) found commonly east of the Rocky Mountains. Tent caterpillars hatch in early spring from thick, crusty masses of about 200 eggs which surround the twigs of trees, particularly apple and cherry. At once the caterpillars set about spinning an unsightly protective tent of silk, into which they retire by day. At night, when birds are less active, the caterpillars walk out of their tent and feed on the foliage, often stripping a tree in a few days.

When fully grown, a tent caterpillar is about 2 inches long, with a continuous white stripe down its black back, and with blue and white spots on each side. After about 6 weeks of feeding, the larvae spin cocoons, often on the bark of the same tree, and pupate. In about 3 weeks the moths emerge, each rather heavy bodied, with a wingspread of 1¼ inches in the male to 2 inches in the female.

A related moth and caterpillar (*M. disstria*) which is widespread in forested areas of Canada, the United States, and Mexico, is often called a "forest tent caterpillar" moth, although

ANIMALS

its caterpillars produce silken carpets only—never a voluminous tent in which to hide. Order Lepidoptera, family Lasiocampidae.

TERMITE, or white ant, any of about 1,800 different kinds of insects with biting mouthparts, the thorax of the soft body broadly joined to the abdomen, and 2 pairs of similar, narrow membranous wings carried flat over the back and detached after the nuptial flight. Termites are mostly tropical, social insects, living in social communities with an elaborate system of castes and functional varieties.

Immature individuals of both sexes assist in the work of the colony, gathering and sharing food. The queen lays millions of eggs, sometimes 4,000 in a day. Many termites eat wood, which they digest with the help of single-celled protozoans in their intestines. Their damage to wooden buildings, books, and other human possessions causes enormous losses in tropical countries and, until extermination methods were improved recently, in many temperate regions of the United States.

In Africa and Australia, certain termites build huge nests, or termitaries, 20 to 40 feet high, piled up a grain of earth at a time. The earth is cemented by saliva. Order Isoptera.

TERN, or sea swallow, any of 39 different kinds of slender, gull-like seabirds 8 to 23 inches long, with slender pointed beaks, webbed, weak feet, and a pattern of feather coloration that is usually gray above and white below, with black markings on the head; some kinds are pure white.

Although all terns are migratory, the circumpolar Arctic tern (*Sterna paradisaea*), which is grayish white with a red beak and red legs, is probably the champion migrant. Most of the Arctic terns breed in the Arctic in summer, and winter in the Antarctic, 11,000 miles away. They travel more than 25,000 miles a year; many cross the Atlantic Ocean in their migration. Order Charadriiformes, family Laridae.

TERRAPIN. See *Tortoise*.

THRUSH, any of 306 different kinds of medium-sized perching birds, 8 to 12 inches long, many of them renowned for their melodious song. They are native to all temperate and tropical lands except New Zealand and some oceanic islands. Thrushes include the nightingale (*Luscinia megarhynchos*) of Europe and southwestern Asia, the song thrush (*Turdus ericetorum*) of Eurasia, the familiar and widespread North American robin (*T. migratorius*), and the smaller, more slender wood thrush (*Hylocichla mustelina*) of the eastern United States, and the widely distributed hermit thrush (*H. guttata*).

Opinion is divided as to whether the nightingale, the hermit thrush, or the shama thrush (*Kittacincla macrura*) of India has the sweetest song. All are birds of the underbrush, eating insects and fruits, and raising young whose breast feathers are spotted. Order Passeriformes, family Turdidae.

TICK, any of about 2,000 different kinds of external parasitic arthropods larger than mites, which attach themselves to vertebrate animals and suck the blood, often becoming greatly engorged before voluntarily dropping off. They are found all over the world. Immature mites have 3 pairs of legs, but add a fourth pair at the molt that brings them to mature form. Several different diseases, such as tularemia in rabbits and Texas fever in cattle, are transmitted from infected animals to uninfected ones by ticks. Order Acarina of class Arachnida.

The name tick is used also for several degenerate kinds of insects that are external parasites, such as the sheep tick (*Melophagus ovinus*) of Order Diptera, family Hippoboscidae.

TITMOUSE, any of about 65 different kinds of small, active songbirds similar to chickadees. Most are Eurasian, but several live in Africa and in America south to Guatemala. In Britain and Europe they are called tits. All are extremely energetic and trusting, as they hunt for insects in bark crevices and on foliage; they also eat some small fruits and seeds. The tufted titmouse (*Parus bicolor*) of the southeastern United States, which has a crest and is about 6 inches long, often visits feeding shelves around homes for suet, peanut butter, and sunflower seeds. Order Passeriformes, family Paridae.

TOAD, any of several hundred different kinds of amphibians that, like frogs, develop from aquatic tadpoles, have a protrusible tongue fitted for catching insects, and large hind legs fitted for leaping. Toads differ from frogs in having a rough skin, more suited for life on land far from water. Toads are common in most parts of the world except the Australasian region, living even in some deserts. Many kinds have glands in the skin that secrete an acrid or poisonous fluid, which protects them from attack. They cannot cause warts. Several orders in subclass Salientia.

AMERICAN MUSEUM OF NATURAL HISTORY
TURTLE

Tortoise 61

TOOTH SHELL, or tusk shell, any of about 200 kinds of marine mollusks that produce a slightly curved and gradually tapered conical shell open at both ends. The common tooth shell (*Dentalium entale*) found on both sides of the Atlantic Ocean below low tide in sandy bottoms attains a length of about 2 inches.

The precious tooth shell (*D. pretiosum*) of the Pacific coast of North America served until recently as a form of money and status symbol among west coast Indians; the abundant 1-inch shells had little value, but a 2-inch specimen had the buying power of a shilling, and a 3-inch shell could be owned only by a major chief, who generally wore it around his neck on a loop of woven plant fiber. In New Guinea, mountain people still use large tooth shells for personal adornment, pushed through holes made in lower lip, nose, and ear lobes.

A living tooth shell keeps the small end of its shell above the sediments of the bottom, to breathe water in and out through the hole at the end; it has no gills. The body is extended from the lower, larger opening of the shell to extend the foot—shaped like a horse's hoof—and a number of threadlike tentacles. The tentacles push among the sand particles, find and capture small bits of organic matter as food, and bring it back to the mouth. Class Scaphopoda, family Dentalidae.

TORTOISE, or turtle, any of about 265 different kinds of broad-bodied, slow-moving reptiles with horny jaws instead of teeth, and usually with some vertebrae and ribs fused to a shell-like armor consisting of an upper, convex carapace and a lower, flat plastron, which are joined at the sides. The shell protects the head, legs, and tail when these are retracted into special cavities.

Tortoises are found worldwide, except for western South America and New Zealand. Some are marine, coming ashore only to lay their eggs; others live in arid lands and deserts; most live near freshwater or frequent moist forests. Most tortoises eat both plant and animal food, including small dead animals.

Among the largest are the giant tortoises of the Galápagos Islands and islands in the Indian Ocean, where individuals attain a length of 4 feet and a weight of 400 pounds. Notable among the sea turtles are the green (*Chelonia midas*) of tropical Atlantic and Gulf of Mexico coasts, the loggerhead (*Caretta caretta*) of the Atlantic, and the hawksbill (*Eretmochelys imbricata*) of all tropic seas, which provides the best quality of horny plates from the shell, known commercially as "tortoise shell." All of these large sea turtles are sought for meat, and their eggs are collected for people to eat.

In the southeastern United States, the diamondback terrapin (*Malaclemys centrata*) was formerly raised in pens as one of the most expensive luxury foods; this turtle of muddy marshes, both brackish and salt, grows to 5½ inches long in about 9 years, then more slowly; for a while, a 7-inch terrapin brought $7 on the market, with an extra dollar for each ½ inch additional length.

Painted turtles (*Chrysemys marginata* and related species), 5 to 6 inches long, are common in freshwater ponds of eastern North America; the box turtle (*Terrapene carolina*), on the other hand, frequents open woodlands in the same area. This turtle can draw its body completely within its shell and close the ends by raising hinged portions of the plastron. Order Testudinata.

TOUCAN, any of 37 different kinds of tropical, fruit-eating birds with a beak nearly as long as the body, not including the tail. They are birds of forests and clearings from southern Mexico to Paraguay. Although the beak is strong, it is lightweight and does not make the bird awkward. Toucans use their beaks to pick fruit and in elaborate courtship displays. They fly with beak ahead, almost like woodpeckers—flapping vigorously 8 to 10 times, then gliding with wings stiffly spread. They nest in holes in trees.

The toco (*Ramphastos toco*) of the Guianas and Brazil is 25 inches long, of which 8 inches is beak and 8 inches is tail; its black plumage is set off by a white throat, red under the tail, and an orange-red, black-tipped beak. Many smaller toucans are called araçaris (species of *Pteroglossus*), and live in large flocks. In the Andes they are found to 10,000 feet elevation. Order Piciformes, family Ramphastidae.

TRAP-DOOR SPIDER, any of a number of black or brown spiders with long stout legs, on which the third pair bear a claw used in digging. They live in the western and southern United States and Latin America, and on other continents.

Most are 1 inch or more in length, and dig vertical burrows 6 inches or more deep, topped with neatly fitted trapdoors made of mud and silk. Below the doors, the spiders rest, ready to jump out and seize passing insects, then drag them back into the burrow and close the door again. New Zealand trapdoor spiders make similar lairs in the thick bark of trees. Order Araneae, family Ctenizidae, many different genera.

TROGON, any of 34 different kinds of brightly colored tropical birds with long tails or tail-covert feathers. The New World has 20 kinds from the southwestern United States to northern Argentina. Africa has 3 kinds south of the great deserts. Asia has the others, chiefly in Malaya and the islands of Sumatra, Java, and the Philippines.

The most famous trogon is the quetzal (*Pharomachrus moccino*), the national symbol of Guatemala and the name used for their coin. It is now almost extinct there. In former times the native chiefs used the long, green tail-covert feathers of the male for decorations. The bird was worshiped by the Aztecs and Mayas in the cult of Quetzalcoatl, the mythical king, part bird and serpent (coatl).

The female trogon is brownish except for green back and wings and red under the tail; the male is brilliant green on head, chest, and wings, blue on the back, and scarlet underneath. Order Trogoniformes, family Trogonidae.

TROUT, a common name for several bony fishes closely related to salmon, with soft, rayed fins and a small soft adipose fin without rays on the back behind the large dorsal fin. They have very small scales. All are excellent eating and are regarded as game fish.

The North American brook trout (*Salvelinus fontinalis*) thrives in the coldest and clearest streams, laying its eggs in December or January. Other species in North America are the lake trout (*Cristivomer namaycush*) and the salmon trout (species of *Salmo*) in the East, and the rainbow and Dolly Varden trout in the West. Sea trout is a general term for any salt-water trout that enter freshwater only to spawn.

All species belong to the Northern Hemisphere, but they have been introduced into Australia and New Zealand. Order Isospondyli, family Salmonidae.

TUBE-NOSED BIRD, any of the large or medium-sized sea birds in which the beak provides a tubular extension for the nostrils, making these breathing holes open separately almost at the tip of the beak or open together as a single hole above the tip of the beak. They include the albatrosses, shearwaters (or mutton birds), the storm petrels, and the diving petrels. All of these birds remain at sea, feeding on fishes and squids from the surface water, except during the breeding season. Order Procellariiformes.

TUNA, any of about 10 large marine bony fish, resembling the smaller but closely related mackerels in having a streamlined body that narrows to a slender stalk just before the large tail, which is almost T-shaped. Tunas are found in all oceans, and are hunted by both sportsmen and commercial fishermen; tuna flesh is valuable food.

Largest of tunas is the great bluefin (*Thunnus thynnus*), which reaches a length of 14 feet and weight of 1,800 pounds, following a migration pattern from the Tropics to far northern waters off Norway. The albacore (*T. alalunga*), which has particularly long pectoral fins, is a favorite because its meat is white.

Yellowfin tunas (*T. albacares*) of the Indian and Pacific oceans grow as much as 60 pounds in a year; those at 90-pound size are sought for canning. They feed in great schools and are netted or caught with a short line on heavy poles. Of recent years this fish has become recognized by sportsmen for its strength and fighting ability, and specimens weighing around 800 pounds have been landed by rod and reel. One of the favorite grounds for tuna fishing is off Nova Scotia. Order Acanthopteri, family Scombridae.

TUNICATE, or sea squirt, any of about 1300 kinds of soft-bodied marine animals that attach themselves to solid objects in sea water and secrete a stiffening tunic of cellulose within the skin. They are found along most seacoasts in water to 200 feet deep. Most of the space in the body of a tunicate is occupied by an enormous throat region (pharynx) of the digestive tract.

Water entering the mouth passes out through a large number of pores in the pharyngeal walls, while oxygen is exchanged for carbon dioxide and particles of food are captured in a film of mucus. The loaded mucus goes on to the intestine. If a tunicate is disturbed, it contracts suddenly, expelling water from its mouth in a forceful jet, hence the name sea squirt.

In season, tunicates develop reproductive organs and release into the sea small larvae that resemble tadpoles. Each has a pharynx with gill openings, a hollow dorsal nerve cord, and a supporting rod called a notochord in the propulsive tail.

These features indicate that tunicates are degenerate members of the same phylum to which the vertebrate animals belong. Degeneration occurs when the larva settles to the bottom, attaches itself permanently, and absorbs its tail, its notochord, its propulsive muscles, and transforms into the form of the adult. Order Ascidiacea of the chordate subphylum Urochorda.

TURKEY, either of 2 different large pheasantlike birds with naked heads. They are native to woodlands in America from Canada to Central America, where they search along the ground for food by day and roost each night in trees.

The common turkey (*Meleagris gallopavo*), a 48-inch bird of southeastern United States and Mexico, was domesticated in Mexico at least 500 years before Columbus discovered America. Spanish conquistadores introduced them into Europe, and colonists brought them to New England. The tame birds differ somewhat in appearance from the birds in a wild state. In Yucatan, British Honduras, and Guatemala, the ocellated turkey (*Agriocharis ocellata*) still runs wild; it is a 36-inch bird, which lacks the beardlike chest tuft of feathers characteristic of the male common turkey. Order Galliformes, family Meleagrididae.

TURTLE. See *Tortoise*.

VAMPIRE, any of several different kinds of blood-sucking bats in which the incisor and canine teeth are shearlike, specialized for cutting through the skin of warm-blooded animals. Vampire bats alight gently on sleeping mammals such as horses, cattle, and even man, or creep along to a vantage point from which they can use their teeth to get blood flowing. They then lap the fresh blood with the tongue.

The teeth are so sharp that often considerable blood is lost and the bat has departed before the victim becomes aware that anything has happened. Order Chiroptera, family Desmodontidae.

VIPER, any of a large number of poisonous, stout-bodied Old World snakes in which the venom is discharged through 2 erectile fangs at the front of the upper jaw. They are widespread in Eurasia and Africa, and differ from the pit vipers of America in lacking the heat-sensitive pits between eye and nostril.

The adder, or common viper (*Vipera berus*), widely distributed in Eurasia, is the only British venomous snake. Its bite rarely proves fatal. It attains a length of 25½ inches, is brown with a black zigzag line down the back, feeds chiefly upon mice and, like most vipers, is viviparous (bears young alive —not from eggs).

The puff adders (*Bitis arietans*) of Africa south of the great deserts lie in wait for rat-sized rodents, which they strike with incredible speed and then slowly pursue for the few seconds needed until the victim dies of the poison. Largest is the Gaboon viper (*B. gabunica*), nearly 6 feet long and 6 inches in diameter, which rarely bites people, even to defend itself. Order Serpentes, family Viperidae.

VOLE, or meadow mouse, a small, short-tailed rodent (*Microtus pennsylvanicus*) of orchards and pasturelands in North America. The head and body are chestnut-brown above, gray beneath, marked with black above and cinnamon color below. A vole eats approximately its own weight daily of many kinds of plants, and cuts down a great deal that it does not eat.

Since a female vole begins producing young when only a month old, and may bear 13 litters of 4 to 8 young within a year, the population can increase spectacularly if not controlled by foxes, hawks, and other predators. Voles are the basic food for most of these flesh-eaters. Order Rodentia, family Cricetidae.

VULTURE, any of 6 different carnivorous, scavenging birds of the New World, and of 4 in the Old, all capable of soaring for hours with no apparent motion of their wings. With incredibly keen eyesight, they watch from high up for carcasses of dead animals or mammals that are dying or badly injured. Circling down, they alight near the carcass, then, using their strong hooked beaks, tear it into strips small enough to swallow.

Largest is the Andean condor (*Vultur gryphus*), 52 inches long with a wingspan of 10 to 12 feet and a weight of 20 to 25 pounds; it is one of the world's largest flying birds, and is becoming increasingly rare although it nests and perches from 10,000 to 15,000 feet above sea level on inaccessible cliffs. Under stress of hunger, it descends to the plains in search of sick and dead domestic animals, and is shot by ranchers.

A somewhat similar bird, the California condor (*Gymnogyps californianus*), is threatened with extinction in its last retreat—some relatively inaccessible mountain regions of California.

In the Old World, the only vulture of comparable size is the bearded vulture, or lammergeier (*Gypaetus barbatus*), named for a tuft of bristly feathers on its chin, which has the reputation of stealing lambs over the mountains from the Pyrenees and North Africa to eastern India. However, its feet are too weak to hold a struggling animal and it ordinarily waits until other scavengers have cleaned a carcass before descending to get the bones; it can crush these or drop them on crags and pick up the pieces to get at the marrow inside.

The griffin vulture (*Gyps fulvus*), a 41-inch bird with a ruff of white feathers into which it can withdraw its bare head and neck, watches over the same area surveyed by the lammergeier for animals to die; flocks of griffin vultures stand near the burning ghats in India, waiting to feast on the remains of human corpses that are thrown into the sacred Ganges. The smaller, white, Egyptian vulture (*Nephron percnopterus*), sometimes called pharaoh's chicken, ranges all over countries bordering the Mediterranean, often staying close to villages to eat whatever meat scraps it can find.

In the New World, the turkey vulture, or turkey buzzard (*Cathartes aura*), is the common scavenger from southern Canada to Tierra del Fuego. It gets its name from the reddish color of the naked head and upper neck; its body plumage and wings are drab gray-brown, but its wingspan of 6 feet lets it soar gracefully all day. Its services as a scavenger have earned it rigorous legal protection.

The black vulture, or black buzzard, or carrion crow, or urubu (*Coragyps atratus*), is a heavier bird of smaller size, residing in the southern United States and southward to Argentina. From southern Mexico southward it competes to some extent with the king vulture (*Sarcorhamphus papa*), a 32-inch bird whose naked head and neck bear many bright colors—white, yellow, red, and black—in a pattern made more startling by the bird's white eye.

New World vultures all belong to family Cathartidae, distinguished by longitudinal instead of round nostrils, lack of a voice, beaks so weak they cannot tear flesh until it rots, slightly webbed toes, and the hind toe somewhat elevated. Old World vultures belong to family Vulturidae. All vultures are classified in order Falconiformes.

WALLABY, any of about 35 different kinds of small- and medium-sized grazing and browsing marsupial mammals similar to but smaller than kangaroos. They inhabit Australia, New Guinea, and adjacent islands, often taking refuge among boulders. Often they emerge to sunbathe, but they feed mostly at night. The many genera are classified in order Marsupialia, family Macropodidae.

WALRUS, an arctic marine mammal (*Odobenus rosmarus*), closely related to seals and sea lions, distinguished by its bristly whiskers and enormous, down-turned tusks, or canine teeth, projecting from the upper jaw. Those of the male are larger and longer and sometimes reach a length of 16 inches beyond the sockets. The generic name means tooth walking, for it was once supposed that the walrus used its tusks to help drag its heavy body along land and ice. Actually, the tusks are used by the walrus to free mollusks from the sea bottom when feeding. The female walrus has smaller tusks.

Walruses have a heavy body, deepest at the shoulders, and limbs that are adapted for swimming. They reach a length of 12 feet or more, and a weight of 2,200 pounds. They are hunted for their hides, their tusks, and their blubber that produces 25 to 30 gallons of oil from each walrus. Order Pinnipedia, family Odobenidae.

WARBLER, any of 300 different kinds of small birds, mostly dull colored, in the Old World, all members of family Sylviidae, and nearly 120 of small, mostly bright-colored birds in the New World, all members of family Parulidae. To prevent confusion, the New World warblers are now referred to often as wood warblers. The name warbler is deceptive, in that very few of them are singers of any ability. In spite of this, the warblers are among the most charming and useful citizens of our wildlife. Their insect- and larvae-destroying activities are worth millions of dollars yearly.

Widespread in Eurasia are the grasshopper warbler (*Locustella naevia*), whose song is more distinctive than its plumage; the reed warbler (*Acrocephalus scirpaceus*) of reed beds and waterside shrubbery; the sedge warbler (*A. schoenobaenus*) of similar habitats; the blackcap (*Sylvia atricapilla*) of woodlands; the garden warbler (*S. borin*) of bramble patches; the whitethroat (*S. communis*) of more open country; and the chiffchaff (*Phylloscopus collybita*) of evergreen woodlands.

Familiar warblers in North America include the black-and-white warbler (*Mniotilta varia*) that creeps around tree trunks searching for insect food in crevices; the yellow warbler or yellowbird (*Dendroica petechia*), yellowish green above and bright yellow beneath; the myrtle warbler (*D. coronata*), slate gray, with conspicuous yellow patches at the base of the tail, the crown, and on either side of the breast; the redstart (*Setophaga ruticilla*), with brilliant red wing and tail marks contrasting with its jet-black plumage; and the yellowthroat (*Geothlypis trichas*), olive above and bright yellow below, with a black mask over its face. Order Passeriformes.

AMERICAN MUSEUM OF NATURAL HISTORY
VULTURE

WASP, a member of any of several families of insects that, as adults, have biting mouthparts, 2 pairs of membranous wings of which the fore pair is much the larger, a narrow waist between thorax and abdomen, and in females and sterile workers, a well-developed stinger and poison gland at the hind end of the body.

Wasps differ from bees in having slenderer bodies and no pollen-gathering specialized apparatus on the hind legs. Some are solitary; others form colonies in which the individuals work together for the common good. Solitary wasps include the digger wasps (family Bembecidae), which excavate holes in the soil or in wood and there store insects that they have paralyzed with their stinger, as food for the maggotlike young that will hatch from their eggs.

The thread-waisted wasps (family Sphecidae) include mud daubers (genus Sceliphron), which collect spiders to fill the cells of nests built by sticking mud to beams in barns or similar places. The social wasps, chiefly members of family Vespidae, are commonly called simply wasps, or hornets.

Some wasps make a nest in the earth; others make paper nests from bits of decaying wood that they chew into a real paper pulp. In the colonies the male wasps die when winter approaches; but the females live to start a new colony in the spring. Order Hymenoptera.

WATER BOATMAN, any of a large number of aquatic insects (Corixa) ¾ inch long or less that swim actively in fresh and stagnant water, propelling themselves with oarlike hind legs. They are found all over the world. The front legs are adapted for scraping microscopic algae from leaves, stones, and other firm surfaces. Females lay top-shaped yellow eggs on submerged objects. The immature water boatmen that emerge have the same blunt, boat-shaped body as the adults, but gain wings only at the final molt when they are mature.

Water boatmen often fly to lights, as well as to colonize new bodies of freshwater, including bird baths and public fountains. The adults are eaten by many kinds of birds, and the aquatic individuals by fishes and water birds. Order Heteroptera, family Corixidae.

WATER FLEA, a small crustacean of fresh and brackish water, not more than ⅛ inch long, which appears to dance as it swims by lashing its 2 feathery antennae. Most water fleas belong to genus Daphnia. They are found all over the world.

The sides of the flattened body of the water flea are extended ventrally to provide protection for the gills and for clusters of developing eggs. For favorable parts of the year, sexual reproduction is unnecessary; females reproduce by parthenogenesis, freeing a new brood of minute young with the same body form every 7 to 11 days.

Males develop toward the end of the summer or when a pond becomes too stagnant; the fertilized eggs have a heavy shell and can survive desiccation or frost. In this dormant condition, water fleas pass periods of drought, of winter, and get carried from one pond to another in mud on the feet of wading birds. Water fleas are raised in enormous numbers by fanciers of tropical fish, as a suitable food to add to aquariums. Order Cladocera.

WATER STRIDER, or pond skater, any of a large number of insects with a compact, canoe-shaped body that support themselves on 4 long outstretched slender legs atop the surface film over ponds and streams. They are found in the Americas, Eurasia, and Africa, but not in Australasia or most oceanic islands.

Waxy hairs of microscopic size prevent the water from wetting the feet of a water strider. The insect holds its body well above the surface film as it sculls along with its middle pair of legs, riding its slight weight on the long hind legs and short front legs, which are held close together below the head.

Water striders are scavengers, investigating as possible food all objects of modest size that float up to the water film from below or that float in it after falling from above. In winter and during rain storms, most striders crawl out on the shore and hide under leaves. One that cannot often do so is the sea-going water strider (Halobates) that is common among the mangroves on quiet tropical lagoons, but ventures also far out at sea. It is believed to lay its eggs on the floating feathers dropped by sea birds. No one knows how it survives during storms. Order Heteroptera, family Gerridae.

WATER THRUSH, either of 2 short-tailed wood warblers (Seiurus), closely related to the ovenbird, which seem nervous as they teeter while walking along the edges of streams and rivers in North America and northern South America.

The northern water thrush (S. noveboracensis) is slightly smaller than the Louisiana water thrush (S. motacilla), and differs in that it has a yellowish line above the eye rather than a white one, and dark streaks on the greenish yellow breast instead of none. The northern water thrush prefers northern bogs and swamps or near quiet water as a nesting site; the Louisiana water thrush prefers flowing streams and rivers.

Both birds eat insects and crustaceans picked up along the edge of the water but, unlike the water ouzel, they do not venture into the water itself. Order Passeriformes, family Parulidae.

WAXWING, any of 3 different kinds of sleek, crested, fruit-eating, tree-dwelling birds 6 to 8 inches long, which have a yellow band across the end of the tail and red tips to the secondary flight feathers that show when their wings are folded at rest. The largest is the Bohemian waxwing (Bombycilla garrulus), found from northern Eurasia into the western United States.

The cedar waxwing (B. cedrorum) nests from coast to coast in Canada and the northern United States, flying south into Central America and the West Indies for the winter. A Japanese waxwing (B. japonica) has red-tipped wing feathers, but not the small pellets of waxy bright-red material found in the New World birds. Order Passeriformes, family Bombycillidae.

WEASEL, or stoat, any of 10 different kinds of short-legged predatory mammals so slender that they can follow a mouse to the end of its burrow or pass through a knothole into a chicken coop. They are found in North Africa, Eurasia, and America as far south as the rim of the Amazon basin. The longtailed weasel (Mustela frenata) of southernmost Canada southward into South America has brown feet even in winter when, in northern latitudes, its coat becomes completely white except for the feet and the black tip of the tail.

The ermine (M. erminea) of the northern United States, Canada, and northern Eurasia similarly has a black tip to its tail, turns white elsewhere in winter, and brown on the back in summer. Its pelt has been sought for centuries to line the robes of royalty and magistrates and, more recently, to make expensive fur coats for wealthy people.

Closely related are the two semi-aquatic minks, the European (M. lutreola) being found from Scandinavia into Siberia, and the American (M. vison) over all of North America except the southwestern states and Mexico. Unlike other weasels, minks have some webbing between their toes and a white patch on the chin; otherwise they are dark brown or black. Young minks are sometimes kept as pets and used like ferrets for hunting. Order Carnivora, family Mustelidae.

WEEVIL, or snout beetle, any of a large number of beetles, in which the forward part of the head is prolonged into the form of a snout, with the jaws at the tip. They are found all over the world, often as pests causing extensive damage to fruits and grains. With its jaws, a weevil cuts a cylindrical hole the length of its snout into fruits of many kinds, both to obtain food and to prepare a deep pit in which it can have some protection for the eggs it lays there. Order Coleoptera, family Curculionidae.

WHALE, any of about 34 different kinds of large marine mammals in which the forelimbs have the form of flippers, the hind limbs are completely concealed within the body or absent, and the tail is expanded widthways into flukes used in sculling along. Only the little white whale (Delphinapterus leucas) of shallow waters and large rivers in the Arctic, and the narwhal (Monodon monoceros)—named for the single long spirally-twisted tusk that grows straight forward from the male's head—of Arctic seas are less than 15 feet long; these two mature at 11 to 12 feet in length, and are placed in the same family (Monodontidae).

ANIMALS

Twenty other kinds of whales have teeth of some kind, and are referred to as "toothed whales." They include the gregarious pilot whales, or blackfish (species of *Globicephala*), which are harvested off Newfoundland for oil and for meat to feed foxes on fur farms; and the dreaded killer whale, or orca (*Orcinus orca*), of all seas but especially the Arctic and Antarctic, which attack in packs, often tearing even the biggest whales to pieces; these are members of family Delphinidae. Beaked whales of 14 different kinds (family Ziphiidae) and of all oceans are less famous than one of the 2 kinds of sperm whales—the cachalot (*Physeter catodon*) made familiar by Melville's *Moby Dick*; it attains a length of 60 feet, a weight of 50 tons, provides the teeth carved by sailors and called "scrimshaw," and is placed in family Physeteridae.

The whalebone, or baleen whales, which have row upon row of fringed horny plates ("whalebone") hanging from the roof of the enormous mouth, include the gray whales of the North Pacific (*Eschrichtius glaucus*), many of which migrate within sight of the California coast to calving and breeding areas along the coasts of Baja California and mainland Mexico; and 5 different "right" whales (family Balaenidae) represented in all oceans, so named because they floated and could be flensed by old-time whalers, whereas "wrong" whales—the 6 kinds in family Balaenopteridae—sank when harpooned. The latter include the largest of whales: the blue or sulphur-bottom (*Sibbaldus musculus*), to 100 feet long and 100 tons—the largest mammal that ever lived; 4 kinds of finback whales (members of genus *Balaenoptera*); and the humpback whale (*Megaptera novaeangliae*) that often swims near coasts and inlets on its migration between tropical and polar seas north and south. Whalebone whales use their strange plates to strain from the water the 1- to 2-inch crustaceans and the squids and fishes that form their food. The blubber of whales, which underlies the smooth shining skin, is rich in oil and serves both to insulate the body from losing heat too rapidly in icy water and to buoy up the whale, saving it from expending extra effort to stay near the water's surface.

All whales dive, holding their breath for many minutes. The champion diver is the sperm whale, which dives to such great depths that it sometimes is caught and drowned by becoming entangled with transoceanic telephone cables. To these depths the sperm whale plunges in pursuit of the giant squid that form its favorite food. Undigestible beaks from these squids may irritate the lining of the whale's digestive tract until it forms a cheesy material called ambergris, which is much sought as a fixative for perfumes. Order Cetacea.

WHIPPOORWILL, an American bird (*Caprimulgus vociferus*) related to the nighthawk and the European nightjar, or goatsucker, named for its loud cry that sounds like "whip poor Will" with the last syllable heavily accented. The bird is not often seen, although it is abundant in damp woods of the eastern United States. It usually rests on the ground during the day and searches for insects at early nightfall.

It is about 10 inches long and of plain colors, being grayish, much variegated with black and buff. Its bill is very broad, its mouth large (hence the genus name meaning cave mouth) and provided with a tuft of long bristles. It builds no nest but deposits its eggs on leaves or in a slight depression in the ground. Order Caprimulgiformes, family Caprimulgidae.

WHITEFISH, any of several freshwater fishes (*Coregonus*) of cool clear lakes and deep rivers in the Northern Hemisphere, distantly related to shad and herring. Whitefishes have few or no teeth, possess a pair of flaps between the nostrils, and are characteristically meaty and clad in silvery scales. They feed principally on insects and bottom animals, but come to shallow water to lay their eggs on rocks. These eggs are often gathered for sale as edible fish roe. The Great Lakes whitefish (*C. clupeiformis*) was formerly an important commercial species, attaining a length of 24 inches and a weight to 23 pounds. Invasion of the lakes by sea lampreys has ruined the fishery. Order Isospondyli, family Coregonidae.

WHITING. See *Cod*.

WIDGEON. See *Duck*.

WILDEBEEST. See *Gnu*.

WOLF, either of 2 different kinds of doglike, flesh-eating mammals, 42 to 54 inches long, with a tail 12 to 22 inches in length that is held high when the animal runs. Formerly, wolves were widespread in Eurasia and in North America from the Arctic to south of Mexico. Now the small, tawny red wolf (*Canis niger*) is restricted to a few areas of Oklahoma and Texas. The formerly widely distributed timber wolf, or gray wolf (*C. lupus*), has been restricted to parts of the United States and eastern Canada. In the northernmost parts of its range, it remains white most or all of the year. Farther south it is usually gray, sprinkled with black.

A wolf differs from other members of the genus *Canis* in its larger size, longer legs, narrower but deeper and heavier body, and wider nose pad. Wolves can be crossed successfully with some breeds of domestic dogs, especially Eskimo sled dogs. Probably the preference for sled dogs that are part wolf has continued for thousands of years, keeping the fertility high despite the fact that the domestic dog has a separate, Asian origin. Order Carnivora, family Canidae.

WOLVERINE, or glutton, a heavy-bodied weasel-like mammal with a squarish head, short legs, and bushy tail, and very dark brown except for a pale stripe along each side and across the back at the base of the tail. It inhabits the northern coniferous forest

AMERICAN MUSEUM OF NATURAL HISTORY
WOLF

near the arctic tundra of Eurasia and North America. Usually solitary, it lives in dens or burrows, emerging when hungry to seek carrion or to feed on live animals, birds' eggs and nestlings in spring, and fruits in autumn. It is notorious for its skill in robbing traps of the meat used to bait them, without getting caught despite the most ingenious devices set for that purpose.

On a full-grown wolverine, nearly 3 feet long, the fur is coarse. Yet, better than any other fur, it repels condensation of moisture in freezing weather and, for that reason, is in large demand to trim parkas and reduce the formation of frost from moisture in the breath. Order Carnivora, family Mustelidae, specifically *Gulo gulo*.

WOMBAT, either of 2 different kinds of bearlike marsupial mammals, 2 to 3 feet long, with small eyes, short legs, and chisel-like incisor teeth that continue growing like those of rodents. Wombats live in Australia and Tasmania, hiding in burrows by day and feeding on grasses and roots in the forest by night. Both the coarse-haired wombat (*Phascolomis ursinus*) and the soft-furred wombat (*Lasiorhinus latifrons*) compete with livestock, and are in danger of being exterminated by stock raisers. Order Marsupialia, family Phascolomidae.

WOODCHUCK. See *Marmot*.

WOODCOCK, either of 2 different kinds of heavy-bodied birds with extraordinary adaptations to concealment on the ground against a pattern of fallen leaves, making a strange whirring courtship flight in twilight, and probing in the soft soil of swamps for earthworms. The Eurasian woodcock (*Scolopax rusticola*), 14 inches long, migrates from temperate regions southward for the winter. The American woodcock (*Philohela minor*), an 11-inch bird known also as the timberdoodle, nests in eastern Canada and the United States, and winters in the southeastern States.

Both kinds arrive in their nesting territories in early spring, and prepare a place for their eggs on the ground close to an alder swamp, into which they lead the young as soon as these hatch out. All during the mating and nesting season, the male woodcock performs at twilight his rapid, whizzing flights, rising high into the air and descending again close to his mate. She seems so confident that her soft mottled brown feathers match her background that she will not move if approached on the nest, until actually touched.

A woodcock's beak is well adapted to probing for and catching worms and insects deep down in the soft soil of the swamp. At all times when the beak is down, the bird can see in all directions because its large eyes are positioned unusually high on its head. The flesh of woodcock is delicious, and the birds are challenging targets, for they ascend almost vertically when flushed from the thick cover of vegetation, and fly off at high speed, dodging branches in a zigzag flight path. Many gunners swear a woodcock can fly sideways. Order Charadriiformes, family Scolopacidae.

WOODPECKER, any of 210 different kinds of birds with strong, straight, pointed beaks, long extensile tongues having barbs at the tip, short legs with 2 long toes forward, 2 backward and sharp curved toenails, and tailfeathers that are stiff, strong, and pointed at the tip. Woodpeckers live on all major land areas where there are trees, except Madagascar, Australia, and the oceanic islands. They fly strongly, undulating by beating their wings 4 or 5 times in quick succession to gain altitude, then closing the wings and curving downward like a projectile until the next series of wingbeats.

Most woodpeckers perch on tree trunks and branches, clinging to the bark while propping themselves with their special tail feathers. They hammer with the beak to expose insects, then spear each on the barbed tongue. Flickers, which often stand on the ground to pick up ants, and sapsuckers, which drill for sap and also eat nuts and fruits, match their food supply by migrating regularly. Other woodpeckers rarely fly far or on a schedule corresponding to the seasons. All except the South African ground woodpecker (*Geocolaptes olivaceus*) use the beak to make nest cavities in large trees.

The largest woodpeckers, which feed on carpenter ants in large, dead standing trees, are in danger of extinction because suitable forests are getting fewer: the imperial woodpecker (*Campephilus imperialis*), a 22-inch bird with a crest in Mexico; the ivory-billed (*C. principalis*), which once made the chips fly in the southeastern United States and Cuba; and the magellanic woodpecker (*C. magellanicus*) of southern South America. The sparrow-sized woodpeckers, such as the downy (*Dendrocopos pubescens*) of North America and the lesser spotted woodpecker (*D. minor*) of Europe are much more widespread and common.

The yellow-bellied sapsucker (*Sphyrapicus varius*), an 8½-inch bird of temperate North America, and the 6 kinds of flickers (genus *Colaptes*) of America from Alaska to southern Chile are seen as transients in many regions between their nesting and wintering grounds. Two North American woodpeckers show peculiar habits, the red-headed (*Melanerpes erythrocephalus*) often pursuing insects on the wing in the manner of a flycatcher, and the California woodpecker (*Balanosphyra formicivora*) often embedding acorns in telephone poles. Order Piciformes, family Picidae.

WREN, any of 59 different kinds of small brownish birds with slender, slightly downcurved, pointed beaks, short, rounded wings, and comparatively large strong legs and feet. They fly fast, straight, and with a buzzing sound, and stand characteristically with tail upright. All but one are birds of the New World. The one (*Troglodytes troglodytes*), called the winter wren in America, is found in Eurasia from Iceland to Siberia, south to northern India and northwest Africa. The house wren (*T. aedon*), a 4½- to 5½-inch bird that nests readily in bird houses close to people, is distributed all the way from southern Canada to Tierra del Fuego.

The song of the wren is very melodious but exasperatingly repetitious and amazingly loud for so small a bird. The male is a good protector for nesting territory and young, often attacking birds much larger than itself, such as a bluebird and swallow. Most wrens live on or near the ground, feeding on insects and worms that they find in the dense underbrush. Order Passeriformes, family Troglodytidae.

YAK, or grunting ox, a long-haired, heavy-bodied, cud-chewing mammal (*Bos grunniens*) native to the high regions of Tibet. A full-grown male may be 6 feet high at the shoulder and weigh nearly a ton, with widespreading horns. Wild yaks are blackish brown with a pale mark over the eye that gives them a sleepy appearance. Domesticated yaks are more varied in color, and serve docilely as beasts of burden; they are also a source of meat and milk. Yak hair is woven into fabrics and rope, and the tails are used for fly swatters. Order Artiodactyla, family Bovidae.

YELLOWLEGS, either of 2 American shorebirds with long, yellow legs. They are seen most often on migration or near the water of coastal marshes during the winter, for their breeding territory extends in a narrow band from Alaska across the southern end of Hudson Bay to southern Labrador and Newfoundland.

The greater yellowlegs (*Totanus melanoleucus*) winter along both oceanic coasts of the United States around the Gulf of Mexico and well down into the West Indies and Latin America. The lesser yellowlegs (*T. flavipes*), which have a straight rather than an upturned beak and are 11, not 15 inches long as are the greater yellowlegs, spend the cold months around the Gulf coast and in the West Indies southward to Patagonia. In flight, these birds extend beak and long neck forward, and their legs stretch out behind. They wade about, capturing mollusks, aquatic insects, crustaceans, and some small fishes among water plants near shore. Order Charadriiformes, family Scolopacidae.

YELLOWTHROAT, an active olive-brown wood warbler with a yellow throat and a buff-colored breast, of which the male has a distinctive black mask on the face; both sexes differ from similar birds in having a whitish belly. Yellowthroats live in North America, frequenting the edges of swamps, marshes, and streams. They build a large cup-shaped nest of grasses and leaves, usually under a bush in a marsh.

The northern yellowthroat (*Geothlypis trichas*), formerly called the Maryland yellowthroat, has a loud song, *witchity-witchity-witch*, heard over most of the United States and Canada; it winters in the Gulf States, California, Latin America, and the West Indies. A Mexican bird that does not migrate, the Rio Grande yellowthroat (*Chamaethlypis poliocephala*) is larger and vireolike; the black mask of the male is so small that it does not reach beyond the eye. Order Passeriformes, family Parulidae.

ZEBRA. See *Ass*.

—Lorus J. Milne, Margery Milne

BIBLIOGRAPHY

ALLEN, GLOVER M. *Birds and Their Attributes*. Peter Smith, 1962.

BELLAIRS, ANGUS D'A. *Reptiles*. Harper & Bros., 1960.

BUCHSBAUM, RALPH M. and L. S. *Lower Animals: Living Invertebrates of the World*. Doubleday & Co., Inc., 1960.

BURTON, MAURICE. *A Systematic Dictionary of Mammals of the World*. Thomas Y. Crowell Co., 1962.

COCHRAN, DORIS M. *Living Amphibians of the World*. Doubleday & Co., Inc., 1961.

GLASS, BENTLEY, OWSEI TEMKIN, and WILLIAM L. STRAUS, JR. *Forerunners of Darwin, 1745–1859*. The Johns Hopkins Press, 1959.

HERALD, EARL STANNARD. *Living Fishes of the World*. Doubleday & Co., Inc., 1961.

MILNE, LORUS J. and MARGERY. *Animal Life*. Prentice-Hall, Inc., 1959.

PALMER, EPHRAIM LAURENCE. *Fieldbook of Natural History*. McGraw-Hill, Inc., 1949.

ROTHSCHILD, NATHANIEL MEYER. *Classification of Living Animals*. John Wiley & Sons, Inc., 1961.

STORER, TRACY IRWIN and ROBERT L. USINGER. *Elements of Zoology*. McGraw-Hill, Inc., 1961.

SUSSMAN, MAURICE. *Animal Growth and Development*. Prentice-Hall, Inc., 1960.

TEALE, EDWIN WAY. *Grassroot Jungles: A Book of Insects*. Dodd, Mead & Co., 1953.

WALKER, ERNEST P., and ASSOCIATES. *Mammals of the World*. The Johns Hopkins Press, 1964.

Plants

PLANT LIFE

All living organisms on earth are either animals or plants. The main characteristics that distinguish plants are ability to manufacture their own food from raw materials through the process of photosynthesis; general presence of chlorophyll; fixed location in their environment; and cellulose in their body structure.

These differentiating qualities are quite obvious in the higher forms of plant life. The acacia tree, for example, could hardly be confused with the giraffe that browses on its leaves. In the lower forms, however, the differences are not so clear: the molds and fungi, lacking in chlorophyll, cannot manufacture their own food and therefore must live parasitically on other plants; some plants ingest and devour insects; the algae, diatoms, bacteria, and many seaweeds move about freely and often vigorously in water, soil, and air; the slime molds are totally lacking in the characteristic plant building materials, cellulose. Yet all of these are plants.

In the very lowest orders the distinctions between plants and animals cannot be made at all, and in the realm of microbiology, plants and animals are considered as a single group of living organisms. This provides still more evidence of the common ancestry of plant and animal life.

Plants are literally vital to all animal life on earth. Without plants there would be no oxygen; without grass the grazing animals—and man—could not survive. Plants make up the staple food of mankind throughout the world, and only with great difficulty can man adapt himself to land where they do not thrive.

Even in the arctic wastes the chain of life depends on the simplest plants. The caribou and reindeers feed on lichens, a simple combination of algae and fungi; the seal, whose body furnishes the Eskimo with almost all the necessities of life, feeds on fish that feed on other fish, which in turn are all dependent on the simple protozoan plankton—floating sea plants.

METROPOLITAN MUSEUM OF ART: THE CLOISTERS
NATURAL SCIENCE in the Middle Ages was studied with a naive naturalism that often wandered into the fantastic. The unicorn in this fourteenth-century tapestry is a product of the imagination; the plants are not. Most have been identified by genus and species.

BOTANY

The branch of biology dealing with all aspects of plant life is called *botany*. It includes the study of structure, activities, distribution, origin, classification, and uses of plants.

Botany also touches on many other areas of study, some of which are *taxonomy*, or *plant systematics*, the grouping of related forms in a systematic order; *morphology*, the description of physical forms; *anatomy*, the phase of morphology dealing with structure; *histology*, the study of tissues; *physiology*, dealing with the processes, activities, and phenomena incidental to and characteristic of living matter; *cytology*, the study of the structure and physiology of individual cells; *pathology,* the description and investigation of the causes and control of diseases; *genetics,* the study of inheritance and breeding; *ecology,* the relationship of living organisms to their environment; and *paleobotany,* the study of fossilized plants and the evolution of plants.

In addition, there are several botanic specialities dealing with particular groups of plants. Some of these are *microbiology,* the study of microscopic forms of life; *bacteriology,* the study of bacteria; and such other branches of botany as *algology, mycology,* and *lichenology,* dealing with algae, fungi, and lichens, respectively.

Other related fields, once considered parts of botany but now regarded as practical sciences are *agronomy,* dealing with field-crop production; *horticulture,* dealing with greenhouse, garden, and orchard plants; and *forestry,* dealing with trees and forests.

HISTORY. The first studies of plants were primarily concerned with their magical and medicinal values; and the early stages of botany are more closely allied to myth, magic, and poetry than to the scientific method. Yet such contemporary drugs as digitalis, quinine, paregoric, and morphine had their origins in medicinal plants that for centuries have been man's pharmacological storehouse.

The first actual botanist was Theophrastus (c. 372–c. 287 BC), a pupil of Aristotle. He described and categorized plants, dividing them arbitrarily into *trees, bushes,* and *herbs.* In the first century AD Dioscorides and Pliny the Elder described many plants, stressing medical uses.

It was not until the 1500s that botany, and especially the classification of plants, became systematized. The invention of printing made possible the publication of the first *herbals,* books describing wild and cultivated plants and illustrated with woodcuts. One of the best of these herbals was written by Otto Brunfels (1488–1534), a German botanist.

Contemporary with Brunfels were Hieronymus Bock, author of *Materia Medica,* and Leonhard Fuchs (1501–1566), who wrote a glossary of technical terms, the first terminology of botany. Up to this point, attempts at systematic classification were crude at best; and the main concern of botanists was still with the medicinal virtues of plants.

Taxonomy. The need to distinguish useful plants led gradually to greater accuracy of description and eventually to an interest in *taxonomy,* the organization of the myriad plant forms in a scheme demonstrating their interrelationships.

The Italian botanist Andrea Cesalpino (1519–1603) made the first formal attempt at a methodical classification of plants. In his *De Plantis* (1583), he divided the 1,520 plants then known into 15 classes, basing his divisions on the character of the fruit. John Ray (1627–1705), an English naturalist, developed a system of natural affinities. He separated the flowering from the flowerless plants, calling them *dicotyledons* (having two seed leaves) and *monocotyledons*

NEW YORK PUBLIC LIBRARY

LINNAEUS, naturalist, physician, and philosopher, founded systematic botany.

(having one seed leaf), respectively. The same names are used today.

Linnaeus. Karl von Linné (1707–1778), the Swedish botanist who is also known by his Latin name Carolus Linnaeus, founded a system of nomenclature that was based on the characteristics of stamens and pistils; since these are the reproductive organs of the flower, the system is often called the *sexual system.* It was essentially an artificial arrangement, as Linnaeus himself knew; he considered it only a temporary method, to be used until a natural system of classification was developed.

Linnaeus also contributed much to *nomenclature,* or the naming of plants; and his *binomial method,* with one name for the *genus* and a second, qualifying word for the *species,* is universally accepted.

DARWIN was often caricatured and his ideas mocked by an angry and sceptical public.

A notable advance was made by Antoine de Jussieu (1748–1836), professor of botany at the Jardin des Plantes in Paris. The necessity for logical arrangement of the plants caused him to devote considerable time to the problem, and in his *Genera Plantarum* (1789) he outlined a plan that included the best features of Ray's and Linnaeus' systems. It was based on a close study of plant organs, made use of Linnaeus' simple definitions, and showed in general the natural relationships of plants, thus forming the basis for the natural classification predicted by Linnaeus.

Augustin de Candolle (1778–1841) showed that the natural affinities of plants must be found by a study of morphology, not of physiology.

Darwin. The most important influence on taxonomy was Darwin's theory of evolution and the origin of species by natural selection, published in 1859. "Natural" came to mean related by descent, and any classification scheme became a cross section of the course of evolution. This relationship of systematics and evolution, together with the identification and classification of new species, is the main concern of taxonomists now.

CLASSIFICATION OF PLANTS. The ordering of the more than 350,000 known forms of plants into groups of related organisms is the task of taxonomy. In the taxonomic system, every living plant form has its place in relationship to all other forms, both living and extinct.

Plants that seem to be related because of similarities in form and structure are assigned to a definite group; and smaller groups, based on some common characteristics, are formed within larger divisions. Some organisms do not fit well into any group, or perhaps they fit indifferently into several groups, for during the course of evolution all types and degrees of diversity have developed.

Nature is not concerned with the maintenance of groups, and organisms may be shifted from one group to another as taxonomic knowledge increases. The purpose of classification is to present a natural system of relationships; ideally, it aims not to create an artificial ordering but to discover the order inherent in the working of natural forces. Thus, a truly natural system of classification is also an evolutionary system, reflecting in its organization progressive differentiation of plant forms.

Logic of Classification. The logic of the taxonomic system is that of describing the order and connection of the various forms in terms of their relative similarity or, stated conversely, in terms of their progressive differentiation. Starting from the most general or inclusive group, all living organisms belong to the *Organisma;* this expresses the similarities between all animals and plants and their differences from all nonliving forms.

The next step in differentiation is that between plants and animals: all plants belong to the kingdom *Planta,* whose members share some of the properties of animals and are differentiated from them in other commonly shared properties. Differentiation continues in this fashion, with each group sharing certain characteristics with the preceding group, yet also differing from it in other characteristics.

In each case the succeeding group is a function of the preceding one and branches from it like a limb on a tree. Each limb in turn has smaller branches, and these branches give rise to even smaller ones. When a particular group has been so closely defined that there can be found no further characteristics to differentiate its members, the system is closed.

Every property of every plant in the series has a place in the system at some level. Thus, every member of the last group in each series can be placed in relation to every other plant, and organism, in the world.

As just described, the taxonomic system represents a progression from overall similarity to greater and greater differentiation, or *heterogeneity*. Viewed from the other direction, that is starting from the most differentiated unit, the same system presents a picture of greater and greater similarity, or *homogeneity*.

In order to find the position of a particular plant—for example, a white oak tree (*Quercus alba*)—in the whole taxonomic system, it is necessary to start with the particular and proceed through the more and more general groups. From this standpoint, the units of classification are ranged in order of increasing inclusiveness, from the most differentiated to the most undifferentiated.

The basic unit is the *species*, in this case *alba* (the white oak); the next step is the *genus* (plural *genera*), which for the oak is *Quercus*. (In some cases there are also types or *varieties* of species, but these are generally artificial and are not maintained in nature.) A group of closely related genera is a *family*; the oaks belong to the family *Fagaceae*, together with the chestnuts and beeches.

Families are in turn grouped in *orders*, and the *Fagaceae* belong to the order *Fagales*, which includes two other families, the birch and the beech. Groups of related orders are called *classes*, in this case the *Dicotyledoneae*, a large class of 47 orders that includes most flowering trees and many flowering plants.

The class *Dicotyledoneae*, together with the *Monocotyledoneae*, forms the important subdivision *Angiospermae*, to which belong all flowering trees and plants. The largest group within the plant kingdom is the *phylum*, and the oak is a member of the seed-bearing *Spermatophyta*.

The divisions into orders, classes, and phyla, and the groupings of the phyla into subkingdoms, has not been conclusively determined; and a number of systems are current. Many botanists hold that the *Thallophyta* as formerly constituted and the *Pteridophyta* do not represent true natural groupings; some have designated two main subkingdoms as *Thallophyta* and *Embryophyta*. Other systems propose a phylum *Tracheophyta*, which groups together all of the vascular plants.

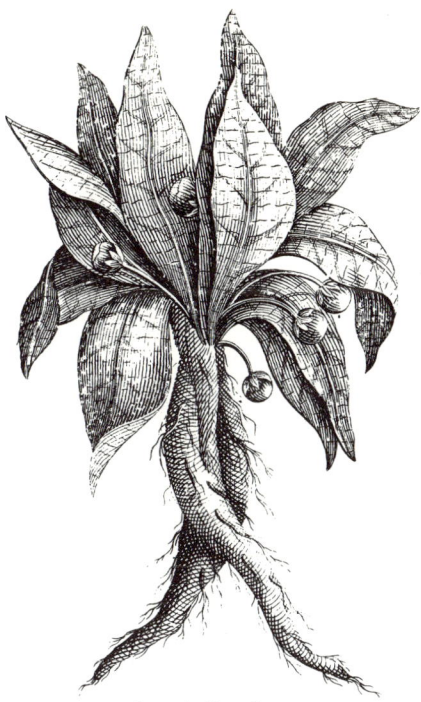

MANDRAKE, long believed to possess magical powers and credited with human attributes, was thought to shriek if uprooted.

Kingdom Planta

Phylum **Thallophyta** (simple plants without roots, stems, leaves; usually one-celled reproductive organs).
    Subdivision **Algae** (containing chlorophyll, e.g., pond scums, seaweeds).
    Subdivision **Fungi** (lacking Chlorophyll, e.g., molds, mushrooms).
Phylum **Bryophyta** (simple plants without roots, stems, leaves; many-celled reproductive organs).
    Class **Hepaticae** (live worts)
    Class **Musci** (mosses)
Phylum **Pteridophyta** (complex plants with true roots, stems, and leaves, and possessing vascular tissue, but lacking seeds).
    Class **Filicineae** (ferns)
    Class **Equisetineae** (horsetails)
    Class **Lycopodineae** (club mosses)
Phylum **Spermatophyta** (complex plants with true roots, stems, and leaves, vascular tissue, and bearing seeds).
    Subdivision **Gymnospermae** ("naked seed" plants, bearing cones, e.g., pines, spruce).
    Subdivision **Angiospermae** ("covered seed" plants or true flowering plants; e.g., grasses, maples, roses, orchids).
        Class **Monocotyledoneae** (embryo bearing one cotyledon and flower parts typically in 3's; e.g., tulips, orchids).
        Class **Dicotyledoneae** (embryo bearing two cotyledons and flower parts in 4's or 5's; e.g., roses, beans).

The classification given above, although not the most recent or the most accurate in terms of evolutionary relationships, is still common.

LIVING PLANTS

THALLOPHYTES. The phylum *Thallophyta* consists of plants possessing neither true roots, stems, nor leaves. They may be unicellular or multicellular; each type may be found in various forms.

Two divisions are recognized, algae and fungi. Algae are usually "independent," possess chlorophyll, and are able to manufacture their own food. Fungi do not possess chlorophyll and are dependent upon an outside source of carbon-furnishing food, such as the carbohydrates.

Algae. The oldest and simplest of all green plants, the *algae* range from simple unicellular organisms to complex, multicellular colonies. They vary in size from diatoms only a fraction of an inch in diameter to seaweeds 150 to 200 feet long. Although primarily water plants, algae grow all over the globe, from the ice and snow of the Arctic regions to the backs of certain turtles living in tropical regions.

While many species are attached, others constitute much of the floating life of aquatic habitats. The smaller forms especially are an important source of food for aquatic animal life. Reproduction may be effected by simple *fission* (splitting off) or by nonsexual spores that may be motile or nonmotile.

Except for the flowering plants, the algae are the most numerous and widespread of all green plants; but they are a heterogeneous group whose exact interrelationships are not known. They include over 50,000 known species, grouped under different systems in various phyla. Some of the most important types are the following:

Green algae, the *Chlorophyceae*, are those algae in which chlorophyll is conspicuous. They are more numerous than all others combined and include about 10,000 species. The more primitive forms are unicellular, and some possess whiplike motile organs (cilia) in the active state.

Reproduction is primarily by simple fission—a parent cell becoming quiescent and dividing in two. Since death of the parent cell does not occur, any cell may be immortal. Sexual reproduction also occurs when two motile cells (or gametes) fuse to form a new cell.

The simple green algae are of special interest as steps in the chain of evolution. *Euglena*, a single-celled form with one whiplike cilia, may stand at the diverging point of plants and animals. Other green algae may be ancestors of the higher plants.

Filamentous forms of the green algae are numerous; these are the typical pond scums. Green algae of various types also occur in the sea, from the many one-celled forms that constitute large parts of plankton to such complex seaweeds as *Ulva*, the sea lettuce, which consists of colonies of cells forming broad ribbons or leaflike structures.

Diatoms are peculiar unicellular algae whose cell walls are impregnated with silica and fitted together in a boxlike shape. The hard, glasslike walls persist after the death of the cells and settle to the ocean floor, forming large deposits of *diatomaceous earth*, an exceptionally fine abrasive. Much petroleum is also of diatom origin.

Blue-green algae, the *Myxophyceae*, owe their common name to the occurrence of a blue pigment along with the chlorophyll. They may occur as single cells, but colony-forming species are more common. A gelatinous sheath or extensive jelly may enclose the colony, and in stagnant water the blue-green algae may give off a disagreeable odor. There are simple algae, apparently with less organization of the cell than any other algal group. Reproduction is by simple fission.

Brown algae, the *Phaeophyceae,* show great structural complexity and include the largest of all algal forms. They are almost exclusively marine, and include common rockweed and seaweeds. Species of *Laminaria,* or kelp, occur in deeper, colder waters. On the Pacific coast a giant kelp *Nereocystis,* often grows to exceed one hundred feet in a season. Many species break loose and float with the ocean current, often in great quantities; the Sargasso Sea is named after one algae genus, *Sargassum.* Chlorophyll is present in these algae, but is masked by the occurrence of another, golden-brown pigment in the plastid.

Reproduction in the brown algae is by spores or, often, by gamete production. The common rockweeds, *Fucus,* reproduce only by sexual gametes, and their life cycle resembles that of the flowering plants. The brown algae are used for food, especially in the Orient, and supply iodine and considerable fertilizer.

Red algae, the *Rhodophyceae,* are generally red and typically marine. They may be filamentous, massive, and highly differentiated; or they may be membranous. They often require deep waters, and in regions of plentiful sunshine have been found at depths exceeding three hundred feet.

FUNGI. The second great division of the thallophytes, the *fungi,* are commonly filamentous in the vegetative condition and are distinguishable from the algae primarily by the absence of chlorophyll.

Practically speaking, fungi occur wherever organic matter exists, since one or more species may inhabit any dead or non-living material and many species attack living tissues, especially those of seed plants. The chief classes of fungi are *Phycomycetes,* *Ascomycetes,* and *Basidiomycetes;* they also include the bacteria and the slime molds.

Phycomycetes are the alga-like fungi. The vegetative plant body is a *mycelium* and consists of a greatly branched system of threads, or *hyphae,* not clearly divided into distinct cells. There are two large groups.

The first group, the *zygomycetes,* includes the common bread mold. The mold reproduces both nonsexually and sexually. Nonsexual spores are produced in structures known as *sporangia,* which are borne at the ends of specialized filaments; in sexual reproduction, hyphae cut off at their ends form cells that act as gametes, which fuse together and form a thick-walled resting spore known as the *zygospore.*

The second group, the *Oomycetes,* includes the water molds and downy mildews. Some species of water molds are parasitic; one form causes a disease of fish. The downy mildews are parasitic on seed plants, such as the grape.

Ascomycetes are fungi characterized by a saclike reproductive body that produces spores. More than 10,000 species of ascomycetes are known, and they occur in many different situations.

The *saprophytic* species (those inhabiting dead material) are found abundantly upon decaying vegetation and in or on the soil. The blue and green molds of foods, such as *penicillium,* from which the drug penicillin is made, belong to this group. It also includes a few families of fungi with large and fleshy fruit bodies, such as the edible morels and truffles. Another useful group is that of the *yeasts.*

Parasitic species are likewise numerous, and cause such plant diseases as apple scab and rose mildew.

Basidiomycetes are a class of fungi that comprises orders and families varying in both structure and habitat, but the different subclasses are all related through the possession of *basidia* (club-shaped cells) that typically bear four spores. *Rusts* and *smuts* constitute the main parasitic groups; other divisions include the vast majority of the fleshy or woody fungi, such as mushrooms. Smut fungi are most recognizable during the spore stage.

Some rust fungi exhibit an exceedingly complicated life history. The black-stem rust of wheat has one stage on the wheat and related plants and another on the barberry. The apple rust passes from the apple to the red cedar and from the red cedar back to the apple. On the host plant the fungi are ordinarily characterized by the occurrence of rusty spots; these are the beds of the fungal spores.

Woods and fields yield hundreds of fungi variously known as mushrooms, toadstools, and puffballs. They grow in the soil or on decaying logs and vegetation, and a considerable number cause heartwood or sapwood decay of trees. Among fleshy forms there are both edible and poisonous species. They vary in texture from soft, spongy forms to hard, woodlike growths; in size, they range from the microscopic to two feet across.

Bacteria. Among the fungi there are usually included the smallest plants known, the *bacteria,* or *schizomycetes.* They seem, however, to constitute an independent group, perhaps related to some of the lower algae. They are so small that they are visible to the unaided eye only when growing in colonies of many hundreds or thousands. If they were arranged end to end, it would require about 500 of these bacteria of average size to reach across the head of a pin.

Under favorable conditions, bacteria reproduce by fission at an astonishingly rapid rate. Some also produce spores at the rate of a single spore per cell; these enable them to survive hostile conditions.

Bacteria are universally found in air, water, and soil, as well as on and within all living bodies. They have harmful effects as producers of disease in plants, animals, and man, but they are also beneficial as agents of the decay that return nutrients to the soil, and as the *nitrogen bacteria* that are vital in completing the cycle of this important element. Bacteria are also the agents of many useful fermentation processes. They are used commercially in the dairy industry, in wine-making, and in the curing of tobacco.

Slime Molds. *Myxomycetes,* or *slime molds,* are organisms sometime classed as plants and sometimes classed as animals. They form a slimy mass of naked protoplasm in decaying matter in moist, warm places.

The multinucleate protoplasm moves in amoeboid fashion and can ingest solid food, a characteristic that links the slime molds closely to the animal world.

Lichens. A *lichen* consists of a fungus and an algae growing together in a *symbiotic,* or mutually helpful, relationship to form a dual colony so closely associated that the colonial composite acts as one. To a degree the fungus is parasitic upon the alga and

BETTMANN ARCHIVE

BENEATH THE FOREST FLOOR, the mushroom plant extends a network of filaments. The familiar cap, with its spore-producing gills, makes up the "fruit," or reproductive body.

FERNS have survived almost unchanged from the time 350 million years ago when they left their imprint (*left*) fossilized in the earth.

holds it captive, but the alga is thus enabled to grow in many places where it could not otherwise exist. Within the lichen, the alga multiplies vegetatively; the fungus has its characteristic spore reproduction.

Lichens commonly grow on trunks and branches of trees, on rocks, and on soil. Some are flat and leafy, and some are mosslike. Reindeer moss, really a lichen, is typical of the mosslike group. Lichens are often gray-green and are very resistant to extremes of cold and drought. In the Arctic, they sustain the vast reindeer herds.

MOSSES AND MOSSLIKE PLANTS. Members of the class *Bryophyta*, mosses and mosslike plants, constitute a considerable group of green plants higher in the scale of development than the algae, but less complex than seed plants. In some classifications they are considered the lowest members of the subkingdom *Embryophyta*, plants that form embryos. However, they lack the vascular tissues characteristic of the higher forms.

Mosses. Small, green, flowerless plants, the mosses grow erect but are usually no more than one to two inches high. They occur commonly in moist environments as miniature velvety or feathery growths carpeting the ground, growing on rocks, on the trunks of trees, and even in ponds or running water. The parts of the mosses usually visible look like those of higher plants; they have a stemlike axis with numerous leaves. But there is no true stem or root, such as characterize seed plants.

The mosses are among the most primitive of plants and have persisted almost unchanged since they arose about 300 million years ago. Because they have given rise to no other forms, the mosses are considered a terminal evolutionary group.

Liverworts. Primitive land and freshwater plants, the liverworts are closely related to the mosses. Their growth pattern is flat and branching, and they resemble some seaweeds in appearance. They are the simplest land plants surviving, and may have evolved from certain algae.

FERNS AND FERN ALLIES. The *ferns*, together with a few related families of the class *Pteridophyta*, are the remnants of a once flourishing form of plant life that dominated the earth's vegetation for years. Geologically one of the oldest groups, the ferns originated in the Paleozoic era, 350 million years ago. Giant *tree ferns* once covered the earth, and the energy they gathered from the sun and stored in their tissues is preserved in the earth's great coal deposits.

Ferns are characterized by large, divided, feather-like leaves, or *fronds*, which usually uncurl from the tip. They have short stems that often grow underground. Unlike the mosses, they have true roots. Ferns, like the higher plants, have vascular tissues that transport nutrients and water from the roots to the leaves.

Ferns are abundant on the moist, shaded, forest floor and along streams; some species, however, thrive on rocky cliffs or slopes. Geographically, these plants range from the Arctic to the equatorial jungles and rain forests, where tree ferns often reach heights of forty feet.

Alternation of Generations. Reproduction in the ferns is marked by a distinct *alternation of generations*, which involves two different forms: the first is the familiar fern plant, which has a root, stem, and leaves; the second is a thin, flat, heart-shaped plant called the *prothallium*. Prothallia produce male and female sex organs in which gametes are developed. A male gamete fuses with an egg, and

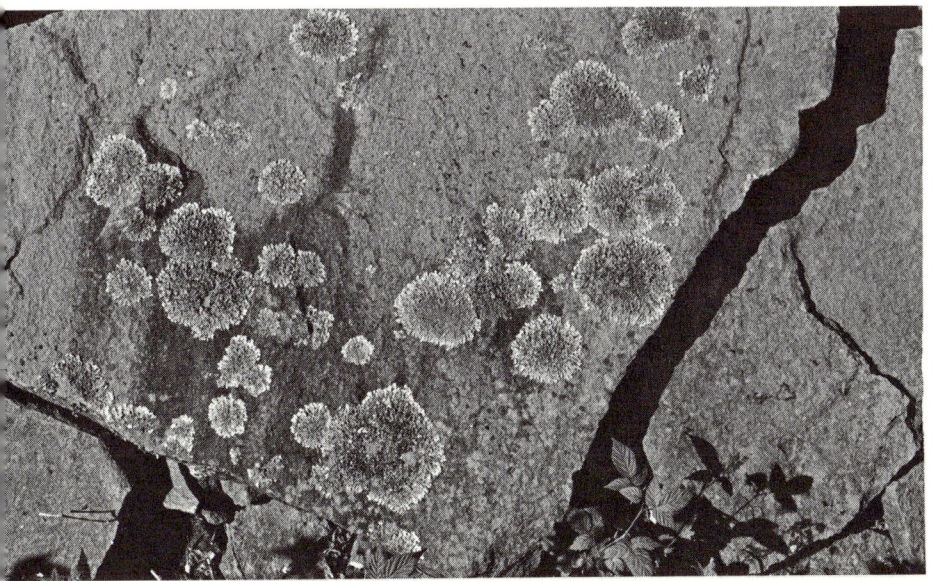

LICHENS, as enduring as the stone they cover, are among the most primitive land plants.

STAR OF BETHLEHEM, BY LEONARDO DA VINCI: ALINARI-ART REFERENCE BUREAU

THE FLOWERING PLANTS are the highest evolutionary form in the plant kingdom and the flower itself is the most effective means of reproduction evolved by any of the plants.

from the fertilized egg develops the fern plant with its roots, stem, and leaves.

On the underside of the fern's leaves there are small spore cases, or *sporangia*, which are often distributed as dots, rows, or larger masses. In these spore cases, large numbers of single-celled spores are produced; when they germinate, they give rise to the prothallia. Thus, the prothallia are *gametophytes* producing gametes, and the leafy fern is a *sporophyte* producing spores.

Club Mosses. Also called *ground pines*, club mosses are rarely more than three feet high. These relatives of the fern are neither mosses nor pines; they are small evergreen plants that have simple leaves resembling pine or hemlock needles. Sometimes they grow upright, but often they trail on the ground, where they propagate by means of *runners*, or elongations of the root stock that send up new sprouts. They also reproduce spores.

Horsetails. Only twenty-five living species of *horsetails* are known, and all of these belong to a single genus. Many extinct forms, however, have been found in fossils. Horsetails are the only surviving representatives of a group containing members that grew to over ninety feet.

Horsetails are composed of underground stems that send up tall, vertical, jointed stalks and of branches covered with scalelike leaves. These plants are also called *scouring rushes*, a name derived from the rough texture imparted by the silica they contain.

Cycads and the Ginkgo. The *cycads* are plants that resemble tree ferns in general appearance, but reproduce by means of seeds. Few in number today, they are the remains of a once dominant group which flourished in the great fern forests of the Permian age.

The *ginkgo*, also called the maidenhair tree, has fan-shaped leaflets, similar in form to those of the maidenhair fern. This leaf-form is found on no other flowering plant and the ginkgo represents a missing link between ferns and flowering plants.

SEED PLANTS. The *spermatophyta*, or seed plants, the highest division in the plant kingdom, contains all plants that reproduce by means of seeds. It includes all living trees and flowering plants. Seed plants form the dominant part of the vegetation of the earth today and thus can be considered the highest, or most successful, plant form.

Seed plants embrace two major divisions: the *gymnosperms*, or "naked seed" plants, in which the seeds lie exposed and unprotected on the cone scales, and the *angiosperms* or "enclosed seed" plants in which the seeds are borne inside a jar-shaped swelling, the ovary, located at the base of the flower pistil.

Gymnosperms. Familiar examples of gymnosperms are the pines, spruces, and other evergreen trees or shrubs with conelike fruits, known as the *Coniferae*. This group forms the great coniferous forests of the temperate zones and includes the largest plants on earth, the giant redwoods.

Vascular or woody tissues reach a high state of development in the stems and roots of conifers. The leaves of mature pines are called *needles*; they are retained for more than a year, giving rise to the name *evergreen*. These needles are highly specialized in structure and are adapted to resist extremes of cold and dryness. Morphologically they are grouped in *fascicles* (clusters) of two, three, or five needles, depending upon the species.

In the conifers the spore-bearing leaves or scales (*sporophylls*) do not constitute a flower. As the scales of the seed-bearing cones separate, the winged seeds may be seen, a pair under each scale.

In the pine, the embryo plant within the seed is surrounded by a considerable food-storage layer, called the *endosperm*, and the whole is enclosed by the seed coat, or *integument*.

Maturity of the seed is accompanied by a certain amount of drying out and by a period of inactivity, or *dormancy*. The seed remains dormant until it absorbs water, and *germination*, or sprouting, ensues. The young seedling, free of the seed coat, consists of root; bud, or *plumule;* and a whorl of long, green seed leaves, or cotyledons.

Angiosperms. The angiosperms, or true *flowering plants*, include the great majority of the familiar flowers and weeds, as well as all the trees and shrubs except the gymnosperms. The angiosperms have seeds and a complex tissue system in which vascular or woody elements attain a further advanced state of differentiation, and they exhibit the highest evolutionary development through the production of flowers.

The angiosperms, which include more than half the known plants—about 200,000 species—are subdivided into two groups. In the *monocotyledons* the young seedling bears a single seed leaf, or *cotyledon*. *Dicotyledons* bear two seed leaves, sometimes thickened, that provide reserves of organic food. Another characteristic of dicotyledons is apparent in the mature plant: the *venation*, or vein system, of the monocotyledons is parallel, as in corn; in dicotyledons it is netted, or *reticulate*, as in the rose.

There are other characteristics, of both floral parts and inner structure, that are generally distinctive of the two groups, such as the three-part flower structure of the monocotyledons, as opposed to the four or five parts that are found in dicotyledons.

Monocotyledons include such families as the grasses (*Gramineae*) which furnish the cereal grains, pasture grasses, and ornamental grasses;

tropical palms (*Palmaceae*), including the date and coconut palms; lilies and related plants (*Liliaceae*); bananas and plantains (*Musaceae*); and the highly prized orchids (*Orchidaceae*), famous both for the delicacy and variety of their waxlike flowers and for the remarkable modification in floral parts, the latter having come about in adjustment to insect pollination.

The orchids and the grasses show extreme differences in floral anatomy. The orchid flower's extreme complexity represents a high point in evolutionary development; the grass flower, also an advanced form, shows a high degree of reduction of parts, consisting of a pistil with ovary, style, and two feathery stigmas, and three stamens enclosed in scalelike leaves, or *bracts*.

Dicotyledons are nearly five times as numerous as monocotyledons; they are also regarded as geologically the older group. They have attained far greater diversity in form and have advanced to higher types of development.

Among families exhibiting less complex types of floral structure are the willows and the poplars (*Salicaceae*), which have simple flowers in spikelike branches called *catkins*. Related to the willows are other families without showy floral parts, such as the walnut-hickory family (*Juglandoceae*) and elms (*Ulmaceae*).

In a varied group of families that includes the pinks, sweet Williams, carnations (*Caryophyllaceae*), water lilies (*Nymphaeceae*), buttercups, columbines, peonies, and clematis (*Ranunculaceae*), there are many wild and garden plants. All of these have distinct petals (are *polypetalous*), and the carpels are either separate or united.

The rose family (*Rosaceae*) and the pulse family (*Leguminosae*) are closely related, and together they constitute a very considerable part of the separate-petal series of families. As a whole, the rose family is rather heterogeneous; its members include the blackberries, roses, and cherries.

In the pulse family there are several thousand species, among which are the lupines, clovers, beans, peas, and acacias. Generally the *corolla* (floral leaf) is *papilionaceous* (butterfly-like); the fruit is characteristically a pod or legume.

Among the families of dicotyledons in which the petals are united are the mints (*Labiatae*), fragrant herbs, and shrubs with flowers that are commonly two-lipped. The nightshade family (*Solanaceae*) includes the potato, tomato, eggplant, tobacco, and petunia; the flowers are prevailingly rotate, and the fruit is a *berry* (as in tomato) or a capsule (as in Jimson weed). Melons are the fruit of certain members of the gourd family (*Cucurbitaceae*).

Botanists generally agree in placing the composite family (*Compositae*) at the pinnacle of development in the plant kingdom. This is the family of sunflowers and goldenrods, asters and thistles, chrysanthemums and dahlias. It also includes lettuce, globe artichoke, and salsify. It is a huge family with perhaps 12,000 species, nearly all of which are annuals or perennial herbs; the woody members are not trees.

The outstanding characteristic of the composite family is the compact head of many flowers—some with ray flowers (as in sunflowers) and some without (as in thistles). The fruits are hard and one-seeded (*achenes*), and are often provided with a feathery appendage, or *pappus* (as in dandelions), that helps wind distribution of the seeds.

PLANT STRUCTURE

From the smallest bacteria, 1/50,000 of an inch long, to the largest angiosperm, 372 feet tall, plants are made up of *cells*, the basic units of life. The study of cell structure and function is called *cytology*.

CELLS. A typical plant cell is enclosed by the *cell wall*, which is composed primarily of cellulose and nonliving substances and gives support and form to the cell and the whole plant. The enclosed *protoplasm* is a viscous, transparent, living matter composed of water, proteins, sugars, fats, acids, and salts.

Protoplasm is differentiated into two aspects. The dark, usually round *nucleus* controls the chemical activities of the cell and bears the *chromosomes*, carriers of hereditary traits. Surrounding the nucleus is the *cytoplasm*, in which are the structures that carry on the physiological cell functions: the *plastids*, including chlorophyll-bearing *chloroplasts* that are capable of photosynthesis; the *chromoplasts*, containing red and yellow coloring; the *leucoplasts*, which build sugar into starch grains; *mitochondria*, which produce chemical regulators; *vacuoles*, liquid-filled spaces that serve as storage areas; starch grains and crystals.

TISSUES. In all multicellular plants the individual cells are organized into *tissue*. *Histology* is the study of these groups of structurally similar cells that are organized to perform physiological functions.

Embryonic Tissue. *Meristem*, or young tissue, consists of thin-walled, active cells rich in protoplasm. They are able to divide by cell division and thus to continue the growth of the organ. All other tissues are derived from meristem by differentiation or modification. *Cambium*, the layer of active growth and cell formation in stems and roots of dicotyledons, is a form of meristem.

Permanent Tissue. The new cells produced by division and differentiation of the meristematic cells become the permanent tissue of the plant. As these cells mature, they no longer reproduce by cell division but expand in size. The cell walls stretch and, in many instances, thicken; the cytoplasm thins out and the major portion of the cell interior is taken up by the enlarged vacuole. Further modifications in shape and structure occur as the cell takes its place within one of the various types of permanent tissue.

There are two kinds of permanent tissues: *simple tissues*, in which each tissue is composed of similar cells; and *complex tissues*, in which different types of cells work together as a unit to perform certain physiological functions. Most plant parts are composed of simple tissues. However, the *xylem* and *phloem*, the vital carriers of water and food, are complex tissues consisting of parenchyma, fibrous, sieve, and vascular tissues.

Parenchyma, or soft tissue, consists of mature, thin-walled, usually short cells that have attained their growth, such as the tissue of ripened fruits and the green tissue of leaves.

Collenchyma tissue consists of long cells with thick angles. In many stems it occurs as a strengthening tissue just beneath the epidermis.

Sclerenchyma, or stone tissue, consists of thick-walled usually short cells, so tightly packed that they form a hard mass, as in nutshells and the "stones" of many fruits.

Fibrous and bast tissue consists of thick-walled, elongated cells so tightly packed together that they make up wood fibers (fibrous tissue) and bark (bast tissue) of the stems of most higher plants. Bast fibers are used in ropemaking and linen making.

Sieve tissue consists of elongated, usually large cells, more or less united into tubes and having only slightly thickened walls. The name derives from the perforation of the transverse partitions between the cells in a sievelike pattern; through these perforations the protoplasm connects

DECIMATED by the caddis fly, these leaf skeletons reveal the supporting venation.

AMERICAN MUSEUM OF NATURAL HISTORY

from cell to cell. Sieve tissue occurs primarily in the young bark and is important in conveying organic food.

Vascular tissue is also tubular, but the continuity of the cavity is usually more complete than in sieve tissue. When they are young, these tubes contain protoplasm; but eventually they contain water or air. Vascular tissue occurs in the woody parts of stems and leaves.

Epidermal tissue, a single layer of cubical cells, constitutes the outer layers of leaves, young stems, and roots.

ANATOMY OF SEED PLANTS

Although the lower plants have developed quite complicated forms and structures and have adapted very successfully to a wide range of environments, the most highly differentiated and evolved structures are found in the angiosperms.

The bodies of typical seed plants are composed of four kinds of parts: *roots, stems, leaves,* and *flowers* (which in turn produce *fruit* and *seeds*). The first three structures are found also in the mosses, ferns, liverworts, and other lower forms; but flowers and their accessory products are exclusive to seed plants.

ROOTS. All living organisms, including the plants, are descended from forms which originated in the sea; and no cells, animal or vegetable, can exist without access to that most important element, water.

In the higher plants, the *root* is the vital link between the plant and its lost aquatic environment. Through its roots a plant absorbs the water that makes up most of its tissues and that it uses to carry on its life processes, as well as some oxygen and most of the mineral nutrients it requires.

Root Structure. All roots are covered at the growing tip with a *root cap* which protects the sensitive tip and serves as a boring point to push into the soil. Behind the root caps, the sides of the roots are covered with many fine *root hairs,* made up of single cells, which penetrate the soil and increase the roots' absorption.

Root Systems. The slender, branching roots of grasses, corn, and wheat are *diffuse systems* spreading over wide but relatively shallow areas. *Tap-root systems,* such as those of the carrot and beet, are made up of a single primary root that probes deeply into the soil and often is thickened to serve in food storage.

Specialized Roots. Adaptations to particular needs are the *aerial roots* of ivy and other *epiphytes* (plants that grow on other plants but are not parasitic); *prop roots* of corn and fig trees, which act as buttresses; *adventitious roots,* which drop down from the stem to lend additional support to many tropical trees; and the *aerating roots* of the cypress and mangrove, which grow above water to obtain oxygen.

STEMS. The *stem* is the part of the plant that supports the leaves and reproductive organs and supplies them with water and mineral nutrients absorbed by the roots. It also serves to carry food back down to roots and other parts for storage.

Most stems grow above the ground (*aerial stems*), but some grow below the surface (*subterranean stems*). Aerial stems are either *herbaceous* or *woody,* an important feature distinguishing groups of plants. All gymnosperms have woody stems, while those of angiosperms can be either woody or herbaceous.

It is generally believed that woody stems are the more primitive and that herbaceous stems have evolved from them. Herbaceous stems are soft and green, covered by an epidermis; they grow in length but little in diameter and are chiefly *annual* (confined to a single growing season). Woody stems are hard and are covered with a tough layer of bark. They grow considerably in diameter and are chiefly *perennial* (surviving through many growing seasons).

Woody Stems. Internally, *woody stems* are made up of two kinds of tissue, the outer *bark* and the inner *wood*; these are separated by a single layer of cells, the growing *cambium* layer. As the cambium cells divide the outer portions become differentiated into a layer of cells called *phloem,* and the inner cells form the *xylem*.

Phloem cells transport food, and the xylem cells conduct moisture throughout the plant. This formation of new cells causes a thickening in the diameter of the stem, and it is thus that the trunks of trees continue to increase in girth. The cells produced in the summer are larger and therefore lighter in color; the winter cells are smaller and appear darker.

This color differential creates the *annual rings* marking a year's growth. As a tree grows, the inner layers become clogged and loaded with tannins, resins, and gums. These make up the hard, dark *heartwood,* while the outer, more active layers constitute the *sapwood*.

Herbaceous Stems. Herbaceous stems resemble young woody stems in structure except that the xylem and phloem are arranged in clusters called *vascular bundles,* which are either scattered throughout the stem (monocotyledons) or arranged in a circle (dicotyledons). Herbaceous stems are chiefly annual, and growth is primarily in the length, not the diameter.

Buds. Buds are the growing ends of the stems of both woody and herbaceous plants and are the immature forms of leaves and flowers. *Terminal buds* provide growth at the tip of a stem or twig; *lateral buds* or *axillary buds* form side branches as well as leaves and flowers.

In annuals and tropical woody plants, the buds grow continuously; but in woody plants of temperate climates they become dormant when the plant slows its metabolism during the winter.

Subterranean Stems. *Rhizomes* are horizontal stems growing on or beneath the ground; they serve for storage of food and for reproduction. They are perennial and send up new shoots each year. *Tubers* are the enlarged tips of rhizomes; highly specialized for the storage of food, they are also, as with the potato, important means of propagation.

Bulbs, such as those of the onion and tulip, and *corms,* such as those of the gladiolus and crocus, are enlarged stem buds with overlapping leaves. They serve for storage and reproduction and as a means of carrying the dormant plant through seasons unfavorable to growth.

LEAVES. Leaves are the plant structures specialized primarily for the manufacture of food through photosynthesis. Thus, most leaves are constructed so as to provide the greatest possible surface area and are ar-

HELEN BUTTFIELD

POWERFUL ROOTS anchor the beech tree firmly in the ground while, deep in the soil, their growing tips spread out, searching for the moisture that nourishes the crown.

PLANT LIFE — Anatomy of Seed Plants

ranged so as to expose this surface to the maximum amount of sunlight.

Leaf Form. Most leaves consist of a slender stalk, or *petiole*, and a broad, expanded blade, or *lamina*. From the apex of the petiole, *veins* extend into the blade. Veins serve for mechanical support, for the transport of raw materials through the leaf, and for carrying away the products elaborated by the green cells.

Leaves vary in size from a fraction of an inch up to 60 feet, as in the palm tree. In shape they range from the long, thin blades of grass to the circular leaves of the nasturtium and water lily; there are many irregular forms also, as in the maples and oaks.

The *venation* (arrrangement of the vein) is characteristic for different kinds of plants: *net* venation in dicotyledons and *parallel* venation in monocotyledons. In *pinnate* net venation, the petiole extends as a main vein or midrib through the center of the leaf, lateral veins extending off it on each side to give a featherlike appearance; this is found in the apple and elm. In *palmate* net venation, several larger veins radiate from the apex of the petiole, as in the maple.

The leaf blade may be simple, as in the apple, or compound, consisting of *leaflets*. The leaflets may have the pinnate arrangement, as in the pea and tree of heaven; or the leaf may be palmately compound, the leaflets arranged at the end of the petiole like the fingers on a hand.

The leaves of grasses are specially modified in that, instead of a distinct petiole, the basal part of the petiole is a sheath that closely surrounds the stem. At the base of the blade there is a special growing zone, so that grass leaves continue to increase in length for long periods.

Leaves may undergo many modifications. *Bud scales* are greatly reduced leaves that overlap and protect the delicate bud tissues during cold and drought. The thick, fleshy leaves of sedum and other succulent plants store quantities of water.

Some barberry leaves are modified into *spines*; and in the pea, some of the leaflets are modified into *tendrils* that assist the plant in climbing. Very curious modifications occur in the insectivorous plants, such as the pitcher plants and Venus's flytraps; the latter's leaves are modified to attract and capture the insects that are digested by these plants.

Longevity. The leaves of most of the temperate zone plants do not continue to grow as do the grasses; they live for a single season and then fall. Such plants are *deciduous*, as opposed to the evergreens, which retain their leaves for a longer period—normally not for more than four years.

The falling of the leaves is the result of chemical changes in which the substance *auxin* plays a considerable part. In autumn, a special layer of cells, called the *abscission layer*, forms at the base of the petiole; these cells block the flow of water and nutrients. As a result, the chlorophyll decomposes, resulting in the yellow and orange pigments typical of autumn foliage. The red colors are new pigments that develop within the cells. Meanwhile, the middle cells of the abscission layers disintegrate and the leaf breaks off and falls, leaving a *leaf scar* on the stem.

Leaf Arrangement. Leaves usually are arranged on the stem in one of three ways: *spiral*, or *alternate*, one leaf at a node, the leaves forming a continuous ascending spiral on the stem, as in the apple or elm; *opposite*, two leaves that usually are directly opposite each other, as in the maple; *whorled*, three or more leaves at the same node, as in the lily.

Buds are regularly found in the *axils* of the leaves and, under favorable conditions, will grow into branches bearing leaves or flowers.

Internal Structure. In a cross section of a leaf blade, different types of tissues and cells are observed.

Epidermis.—The *upper epidermis* and *lower epidermis* each consists of a single layer of cells that covers the entire leaf surface, protecting the tissues within from mechanical injury and drying out. The epidermis, particularly the upper one, is usually covered with a waxy *cuticle*, which further prevents loss of water.

The epidermal cells are longer and wider than they are deep and, as viewed from the surface, have wavy cell outlines. Among the epidermal cells are special crescent-shaped *guard cells*, which contain chloroplasts. Between the guard cells are openings called *stomata* (singular, *stoma*). The size of these openings is regulated by the movements of the guard cells. It is through the stomata that the gaseous exchange takes place between the interior of the leaf and the air. Water vapor escapes and carbon dioxide enters for the process of photosynthesis; oxygen escapes as a product of photosynthesis or enters in connection with respiration.

Mesophyll.—Between the upper and lower epidermis there are specialized chlorophyll-bearing cells. Beneath the upper epidermis, long, narrow cells are arranged in a palisade fashion, and between these and the lower epidermis are more or less rounded or irregularly shaped cells arranged to form a loose, spongy tissue, with abundant air chambers between. These cells are largely concerned with carbohydrate manufacture.

Vascular bundles.—These are the veins of the leaves, as seen from the surface; the larger ones branch into smaller bundles, which may end in a single cell.

FLOWERS. From the standpoint of the continuation of the species, which is the only *natural* purpose, the flower and its resulting fruit and seed are the most important structures of the plant. It is for the flower's support that the entire plant is designed. The flower is the reproductive organ of the higher plants; its function is to produce the seed containing the male and female gametes that will unite in sexual reproduction and produce the new generation.

Flower Parts. The basic flower parts can be divided into four sets of structures. The outer set of parts (green in some plants) is the *calyx*, the individual leaves of which are the *sepals*. Next there is a set of showy leaves known as the *corolla*, the individual parts of which are *petals*; these are brightly colored and often secrete an aromatic and sweet substance (*nectar*) that attracts insects. Within the petals are a group of small sporophylls, the *stamens*. A stamen consists of a slender stalk (*filament*) with a pollen-bearing *anther* at its tip.

The central and last structure constitutes a united set, termed a *pistil*, that is made up of several parts, or *carpels*. Each group of carpels has an enlarged basal *ovule sac*, a terminal *stigma*, and a connecting shank known as the *style*. In the ovule sac there are differentiated ovules within which the egg gametes are produced.

The sepals and petals are known as *accessory parts* because they are not directly concerned with reproduction. The *essential parts* are the stamens (male parts) and the pistils (female parts).

Pollination. The development of the seed is preceded by the process of *pollination*. *Pollen* is produced on certain specialized structures and carried by the wind or by insects to the female structures. *Self-pollination* is the transfer of pollen within a single flower or from one flower to another on the same plant; *cross pollination* is the transfer of pollen from one plant to the female structures of another plant. There the pollen germinates,

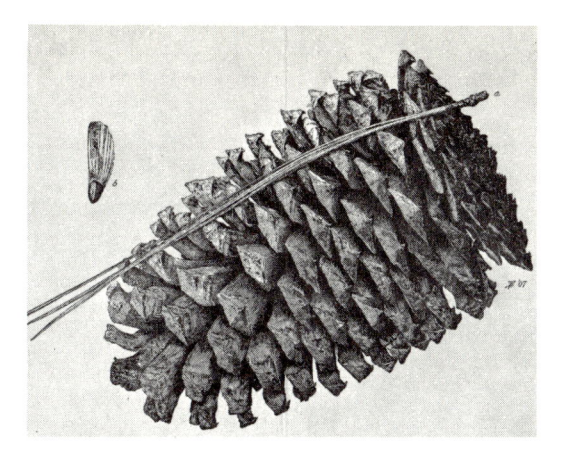

THE WINGED SEED of the Jeffrey Pine and the feathery seed of the dandelion are two examples of highly efficient seed dispersal; these need merely the air and the wind.

giving rise in a short time to male gametes that fuse with the female gamete. The latter develops into the embryo plant that, surrounded by protective structures, becomes the seed.

SEEDS AND FRUITS. The *seed* develops from the ovule and consists of the young embryo plant with its surrounding nutritive and protective tissues. The seeds are enclosed in the ovary during their development; the fully developed ovary with its adjacent parts constitutes the *fruit*.

Seeds. The seed consists of a *seed coat*, usually tough and partly impervious to the water that is necessary for germination; an *embryo*, the miniature plant that develops from the fertilized egg, or *zygote*; and the *endosperm*, or food-storage tissue that nourishes the germinating plant or seedling.

Effective seed dispersal is vital to the angiosperms because the parent plant is not mobile; seeds must be widely scattered to provide optimum conditions for germination and growth. Most of the striking characteristics of seeds and fruits are adaptations that aid dispersal: by wind, as in the wings of the maple seed and plumes of the dandelion; by spines and burrs that adhere to animals, as in the cockleburs; by floating, as in the coconut; or by the fleshy fruits of such plants as apples and cherries, which are eaten by animals and thus have their seeds distributed.

Fruits. There are several different kinds of fruits.

Fleshy fruits.—Soft and pulpy at maturity, *fleshy fruits* include the *berries* (grape, tomato, orange, squash); the *drupes* (cherry, peach, olive); and the *pomes* (pear, apple).

Dry fruits—Dry and hard at maturity, dry fruits fall into two types. Those that split open at maturity are the *dehiscent* fruits and include *follicle* (milkweed); *legume* (pea); and *capsule* (iris, lily). Fruits not splitting open are *indehiscent*: *achene* (buckwheat, sunflower); *caryopsis*, or grain (cereals); *samara*, or winged (maple, ash, elm); and *nut* (oak, chestnut).

Structural differences.—Fruits are called *simple* when they develop from a single or a compound ovary within the flower. If there are several separate carpels in the flower, an *aggregate* fruit is formed; in the raspberry there is an aggregation of many drupes. A *multiple* fruit arises when the fruits developed from separate flowers remain united, as in the mulberry and pineapple.

PLANT PHYSIOLOGY

ABSORPTION OF WATER AND NUTRIENTS. Active living plants contain a high percentage of water, and every growing plant must in some way be in contact with a water supply. While the seaweeds and floating algae are surrounded by water, the land plants have had to develop specialized structures, the roots, to penetrate the soil in search of moisture.

In such complex plants the cell walls are in close contact; and thus, although the leaf cells may be many feet from the absorbing roots, the distribution of water is so perfect that there is indirect water contact with the soil through long chains of tissue cells.

Each cell takes its water from some other cell or conducting vessel nearer the constant supply. Unless a plant contains a quantity of dead tissue, as in trees or shrubs, the water content is usually 75 percent to 80 percent of its weight.

Chemical Nutrients. Plants contain the chemical elements carbon, hydrogen, oxygen, nitrogen, phosphorus, sulfur, potassium, calcium, magnesium, and iron. Carbon, hydrogen, and oxygen enter into the composition of the carbohydrates as starch, cellulose, and dextrins. Proteins contain these same three elements, plus nitrogen, and minute traces of phosphorus and sulfur. In addition to these ten elements, minute traces of copper, manganese, boron, and zinc have been found to be necessary for plant growth.

Carbon, in the form of carbon dioxide, and oxygen are obtained mainly from the air; the other elements, usually in the form of nitrates, phosphates, and sulfates, are obtained in solution from the soil.

Absorption and Conduction. All the elements except carbon and oxygen, as well as the vital water molecules in which these elements are dissolved, must somehow be absorbed by the roots and carried, sometimes hundreds of feet, upward through the stem or trunk to the leaves. This task, which is actually an extraordinary and complex chemical and physical process, begins in the single-celled root hairs.

The walls of the root-hair cells are made up of *semipermeable membranes* that permit the passage of liquids from a less dense to a more dense solution, a process known as *osmosis*. Since the protoplasm inside the cells is of greater density than the water outside, the root cells absorb water; the cells become *turgid* from the increasing water content, and *root pressure* then forces the water up into the stem. However, this force is not strong enough to raise water more than a few inches off the ground.

The force that moves the nutrient-laden water up to the leaves is actually a form of suction and results from the plant's loss of water vapor through its leaves (*transpiration*). Thus, the actual force that draws the water upward is the great absorptive capacity of the dry, waterless air surrounding the plant.

Transpiration. The water and mineral nutrients absorbed by the roots are conducted through the xylem to the leaves, where they are utilized in food production. A large proportion of water absorbed is there transpired through millions of small pores, or *stomata*, on the leaf surfaces, which open or close according to the water pressure in surrounding cells.

PHOTOSYNTHESIS. *Photosynthesis* is the unique process of green plants in which they manufacture not only their own food, but also the food for all higher organisms. The raw materials are carbon dioxide from the air and water from the soil; the energy for the process is obtained from sunlight.

Photosynthesis takes place in the chlorophyll-bearing part of the living cells. Since most green cells are found in the leaf, the latter is the principal site of photosynthesis. The chief product synthesized is sugar; oxygen is given off.

Leaves are thin, broad, expanded structures and thus expose a large surface for the absorption of sunlight. The carbon dioxide necessary for photosynthesis enters the leaf through the same pores that function in transpiration, the stomata. The number of stomata varies greatly in different plants. Sometimes they are confined to one surface of the leaf; in other cases they are found on both.

FOOD STORAGE AND DIGESTION. The sugar manufactured in the leaves and other green portions of the plant may be stored temporarily in the form of starch. Most of it is soon transported to other parts of the plant, where it is utilized for building up the plant tissues. Some of it is used in the synthesis of proteins, which are manufactured in any living plant cell; the nitrogen for the proteins is derived from salts absorbed through the roots.

The legumes, such as peas and clover, are able to utilize the free nitrogen of the air through the presence of certain bacteria, called *nitrogen-fixing bacteria*, that develop characteristic nodules on the roots of these plants.

Much of the organic material manufactured during the growing season is stored as carbohydrates, fats, and proteins in the seeds and fruits, tuber, and roots. Upon the return of growing conditions, the plant utilizes this stored material; but, before it can do this, it must change it from an insoluble form to a soluble form for transportation. This is the process of *digestion* and is carried out by means of enzymes.

RESPIRATION. The plant must have a supply of energy in order to carry on the various life processes. This energy

HELEN BUTTFIELD

SUNLIGHT AND AIR surround the growing, green leaf. Within the leaf, the mysterious processes of life are carried on; these include: respiration, transpiration, and the chemical transformations of photosynthesis.

Plant Physiology

PUSHING UP through the dead leaves in the forest, the young mayapple will break free, expanding in a delicate umbrella. Tendrils uncoiling toward the light exemplify every plant's constant growth.

comes from the breaking down of the complex organic compounds within the cell; most of these breakdowns are associated with *respiration*.

It is a common mistake to confuse photosynthesis and respiration. Respiration is the same in green plants, nongreen plants, and animals. The chief end product of respiration is carbon dioxide, but one of the end products of photosynthesis is oxygen.

ASSIMILATION. The final conversion of carbohydrates, fats, and proteins into living material (protoplasm) is called *assimilation*, a process whose inner working still eludes the scientists' grasp. Very little is known except that assimilation can take place only where life already exists.

Since assimilation is the process by which living, organic protoplasm is created out of nonliving, inorganic materials, the problem of its mechanics is very close to the mystery of life itself.

STIMULUS AND RESPONSE. One of the basic characteristics of living matter is a property known as *irritability*. It is this that enables living protoplasm to be stimulated by outside forces and to respond to them, either positively or negatively. Without this capacity to respond to outside stimuli, no organism could live and grow. Although plants are less sensitive than animals in some respects, there are many stimuli to which they respond quickly and intensely.

Tropisms. In general, the most important stimulus to almost all plants is light, and their response to it is called *phototropism*. If a sunflower seedling, for example, is illuminated from one side, the stem will bend and the plant grow toward the source of light. This bending is the result of the concentration of auxin, a growth-stimulating hormone, on the side of the stem away from the light. Since the cells on that side grow more rapidly they force the stem to bend gradually toward the light. *Mimosa pudica* and certain other legumes close their leaves when they are placed in darkness and expand them when moved to the light.

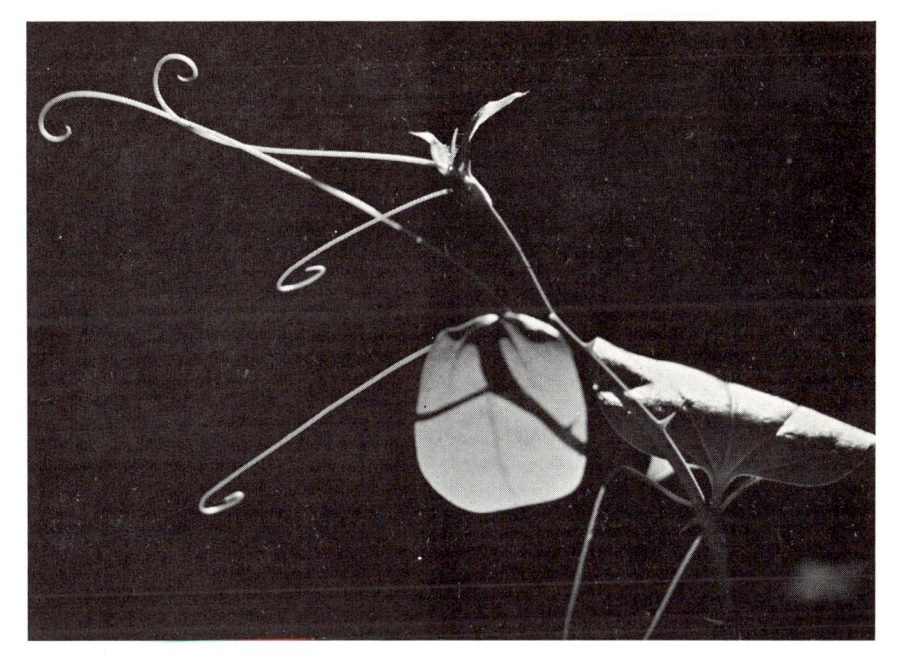

Another important though invisible force is the pull of the earth itself. If a seedling is laid horizontally in the dark, the stem will grow upward and the root will bend and grow downward; both growths are in response to the influence of gravity and are, respectively, negative and positive forms of *geotropism*. Roots are also sensitive to the closeness of water and will grow toward it; this is known as *hydrotropism*.

Other Motions. Movements called *turgor movements* are responses of certain plants to light, temperature, and touch, and are usually more rapid than the tropisms. The leaves of clover fold up at night in *sleep movements;* the leaves of the mimosa will fold and droop on being touched; and the specialized leaves of the Venus's flytrap are extremely sensitive to contact, closing to entrap any insect that lights on them.

Photoperiodism. A recent development in physiology is the discovery of *photoperiodism*, the effect of the daily duration of light exposure on reproductive activity. Some plants are *short-day* plants that require brief periods of light in order to reach the flowering stage; others are *long-day* plants and flower only when they are exposed to long periods of light.

PLANT GROWTH. Growth is a familiar characteristic of all living organisms and a vital one for plants, for, unlike animals, when plants cease to grow, they will soon die. Growth is closely related to movement, which is obvious in the slow upward growth of the young seedling, less apparent in the steady spiraling motion made by growing shoots and even by roots.

Germination. Within each seed is a dormant embryo plant, conceived and nurtured on the parent plant, then dispersed and arrested in its growth until it finds the conditions necessary to renew its activity. Primary among these conditions are warmth and water, although other factors will also affect the chances of germination. Most seeds are able to withstand fairly long periods of inactivity before germinating—some up to 2,000 years, as in the case of certain lotus seeds.

When water permeates the hard seed coat, it permeates the cells, expanding their length up to one hundred times. The root of the sprouting plant emerges, the cells growing actively at the tip. Behind the tip, the cells elongate rapidly, continually increasing the length of the root.

As soon as the cells in any zone cease elongating, root hairs develop to establish the vital connection with the soil and water. The same elongation takes place in the stem until the young seedling is formed. Further growth requires new cells produced by cell division, which takes place in the *meristematic zone* at the tip of both stem and root.

Growth Regulation. The hormone *auxin*, present in the growing tips, has been shown to control growth in the young stem and root. This growth is precisely regulated, for each plant has a certain pattern that it must follow. Buds are formed and the leaves set out at exact and regular intervals, and modifications of the various parts are controlled to produce the proper structures when and where they are needed.

Growth rate, as well as form, is a function of the specific inheritance of the plant and of the favorableness of the environment. The bamboo grows with great rapidity, the oak and the bristlecone pine with extreme slowness; the maximum relative-growth rate of each is highest with adequate sunlight, warmth, moisture, and soil nutrients.

Every structure, organ, or individual plant has growth characteristics peculiar to itself and different requirements as to growth conditions. Therefore, some plants grow primarily in the spring or in midsummer; some grow in all seasons.

—Helen Buttfield

PLANTS

ABACÁ, an important plant native to the Philippine Islands, cultivated for the long strong fibers in its leaves. Known as Manila hemp, the fibers are 6 to 12 feet in length and are used in better grades of rope and cable because they wear well and do not easily jam or kink in pulleys.

Abacá bears 12 to 20 clusters of leaf stalks, each 15 to 25 feet tall, from which large, undivided leaves rise. It requires a warm, damp climate and deep, rich soil. Attempts to introduce its culture into other tropical islands and into America have largely failed. Family: Banana (Musaceae); genus and species *Musa textilis*.

ACACIA, a large genus consisting of about 500 different kinds of woody shrubs and trees, found mostly in warm climates throughout the world. Acacias have pinnately compound or featherlike leaves, clusters of small, yellow or white flowers, and, usually, long, sharp thorns. Those of Australia are called wattles. An African species yields gum arabic. An Indian species, called cutch, provided the original dye for khaki cloth. Family: Pea (Leguminosae).

ACANTHUS, a genus consisting of about 25 different kinds of handsome, thorny shrubs native to the tropics and subtropics of the Old World. Their leaves are usually broad, shiny, and deeply notched.

Acanthus flowers are in spikes, generally white, purple, or red. They are familiar because they were the models used by the ancient Greeks and Romans for decorative designs on architectural columns. In Christian painting and sculpture the acanthus leaf often symbolizes heaven. Family: Acanthus (Acanthaceae).

ACONITE, any of about 75 different kinds of hardy, perennial herbs found in mountain regions of the North Temperate Zone. They have palmate leaves, ornamental, yellow or purplish-blue flowers, and a dangerous poison in all parts. The uppermost sepal is helmetlike, giving these plants the common name of monkshood.

The European yellow aconite is called wolfsbane; it is cultivated as a garden plant and for medicinal purposes. The drug derived from it can be used in small doses as a sedative for certain respiratory and cardiac ailments. Family: Buttercup (Ranunculaceae); genus *Aconitum*.

AGAVE. See *Century Plant*.

AGERATUM, or flossflower, a genus of about 30 different kinds of tropical American herbs with opposite leaves and flowers in small, tassel-like, clustered heads. *A. mexicana*, the most easily grown as a border plant, is usually blue, but it may be white or rose-colored. Family: Daisy (Compositae).

AGRIMONY, any of about 10 different kinds of coarse, perennial herbs native to temperate regions of Eurasia, North America, Brazil, and South Africa. The pointed and toothed leaflets on the pinnately compound leaves are generally of several sizes on a single leaf. Small, yellow flowers grow in stiff spikes at the top of the 2- to 4-foot stems and develop seeds enclosed in a spiny bur. Family: Rose (Rosaceae).

AKEE, or vegetable brain, a tropical African tree that grows to 40 feet; its fruit, which is straw-colored to magenta, is also called akee. The fruit is about 3 inches long and encloses 3 shiny, spherical seeds to which are attached a corresponding number of spongy, ivory-white arils.

At exactly the correct stage of ripeness, the arils can be cooked to make a delicious vegetable with a nutty flavor. At any other stage, the whole fruit is deadly poisonous. Cultivation of the akee is forbidden in the United States, but it is a favorite food tree in Jamaica and some other Caribbean areas. Family: Soapberry (Sapindaceae); genus and species, *Blighia sapida*.

ALDER, any of about 20 different kinds of small, deciduous trees with toothed leaves and conelike fruits, most of which are native to the North Temperate Zone, although some are found south along the Andes. Alders usually grow in swamps and along the edges of streams.

The alder's wood is soft and unsuited for construction purposes, but has been used for turning and in making charcoal. Yellow, red, and brown dyes are obtained from the wood, and the bark is a source of tannin. Family: Birch (Betulaceae); genus *Alnus*.

ALFALFA, or lucerne, one of the world's leading forage plants for cattle, probably native to southwestern Asia or southeastern Europe, but now grown extensively in the United States. Its roots grow very deep, helping the plant to resist drought.

Alfalfa leaves have a high content of protein, and they can be dried to form an alfalfa meal. The flowers are small, purple, and followed by a twisted pod resembling a snail shell. Family: Pea (Leguminosae); genus and species, *Medicago sativa*.

ALLIGATOR PEAR. See *Avocado*.

ALLSPICE, or Jamaica pepper, or pimento, a small evergreen tree of the West Indies with fragrant, leathery leaves; the spice that is made from its fruits, which are picked unripe and cured by artificial heat, is also called allspice. The flavor seems to combine and suggest those of cinnamon, clove, and nutmeg. Jamaica and Grenada are the most important sources of allspice. Family: Myrtle (Myrtaceae); genus and species, *Pimenta officinalis*.

ALMOND, a small tree native to central Asia, but now cultivated extensively around the Mediterranean and in California for its seeds, which resemble those of a peach and develop similarly inside a stony covering coated with a soft flesh and outer skin. The blossoms of the almond are beautiful, suggesting those of the peach and cherry trees, to which the almond is related.

Bitter almonds are often used for flavoring extracts; at one time they were the chief source of the poison called prussic acid, which is chiefly hydrocyanic acid. Sweet almonds are used in candy and desserts; horticultural varieties are hard-shelled, soft-shelled, and paper-shelled. Family: Rose (Rosaceae); genus and species, *Prunus amygdalus*.

ALOE, a genus consisting of about 200 different kinds of shrubby or treelike perennial plants with succulent leaves in dense rosettes either at the ground or the ends of the branches. They are native chiefly to South Africa, particularly to the Karroo deserts, where local people have learned to use them to make tonics, purgatives, and dyes. Family: Lily (Liliaceae).

ALYSSUM, a genus containing about 100 different kinds of herbs native to Europe and west-central Asia, mostly with fragrant, white or yellow flowers in clusters. Sweet alyssum (*A. maritimum*) is a favorite border plant, bearing white flowers most of the summer; golden alyssum (*A. saxatile*), known also as goldentuft, blooms profusely in early spring. Family: Mustard (Cruciferae).

AMARANTH FAMILY (Amaranthaceae), a group of about 800 different species in 64 genera, chiefly plants of tropical regions. Some are cultivated as decorative plants; others are noxious weeds. See *Cockscomb*, *Pigweed*, and *Tumbleweed*.

AMARYLLIS, or belladonna lily, a bulbous plant native to South Africa, now cultivated widely outdoors in warm, moist countries and indoors elsewhere for the annual cluster of large, bell-shaped flowers it produces at the top of a tall stalk. The name amaryllis is sometimes given to related plants from tropical America, which produce similar stalks of flowers before any

BURPEE SEEDS
AMARYLLIS

leaves appear. Family: Amaryllis (Amaryllidaceae); genus and species, *A. belladonna.*

AMARYLLIS FAMILY (Amaryllidaceae), a group of about 1300 different species in 90 genera, many of them highly adapted for survival in arid parts of tropical and subtropical regions. See *Amaryllis, Century Plant, Narcissus, Rose of Sharon, Sisal, Snowdrop,* and *Tuberose.*

ANEMONE, a genus of about 100 different kinds of perennial herbs, mostly from the North Temperate Zone, but some from the Andes. They produce divided leaves from the base of the plant and showy flowers with sepals but no petals.

The delicate, starlike flower of the wood anemone, or windflower *(A. quinquefolia),* is characteristic of early spring in North American forests. The European pasque-flower *(A. pulsatilla)* and American pasque-flower *(A. patens)* bloom before the leaves expand. The blood-red poppy anemone *(A. coronaria)* grows in the open on rocky ground all around the Mediterranean Sea. Family: Buttercup (Ranunculaceae).

ANISE, an aromatic herb of eastern Mediterranean countries, raised for its seeds and the oil that can be obtained from them. The seeds are used for flavoring in condiments, candy, and cheese, and for making a liqueur. The oil is helpful in hiding the unpleasant flavor of medicines and in adding fragrance to soap and some perfumes. The leaves can be used for seasoning and garnishing. Family: Carrot (Umbelliferae); genus and species, *Pimpinella anisum.*

APPLE, any of a large number of different horticultural varieties of fruit trees native to the North Temperate Zone. The greenish-gray, oval leaves grow thickly on the spreading branches, making a pleasant shade tree. In early spring it bears small clusters of beautiful, 5-petaled blossoms that are white, tinged with pink.

The fruits ripen in summer. Each is round, reddish or yellow outside, with a central core that is star-shaped in cross section. Named varieties have been developed according to the flavor of the fruits (from sweet to sour), the color, the keeping and cooking qualities, and the normal range of sizes. Family: Rose (Rosaceae); genus and species, *Pyrus malus.*

APRICOT, a small fruit tree native to central Asia but now grown in mild, temperate climates throughout the world. The oval, orange-colored fruit has a flavor similar to that of the related peach and plum. Apricots require careful handling because they bruise easily. They are used fresh, dried, and canned. Family: Rose (Rosaceae); genus and species, *Prunus armeniaca.*

ARAUCARIA FAMILY (Araucariaceae), a group of 37 different species in 2 genera, all evergreen, coniferous trees and shrubs, mostly of the South Temperate Zone, where they are often the dominant and most valuable native timber trees. The kauri pine *(Agathis australis)* of New Zealand is important for lumber and also for Manilacopal resin, used in paints and varnishes.

The monkey puzzle tree *(Araucaria araucana)* of Chile is widely cultivated in warm countries as a curiosity because of its short, stiff leaves, which completely cover the branches. See also *Norfolk Island pine.*

ARBOR VITAE, literally "tree of life," a small or medium-sized, cone-bearing, evergreen tree of eastern North America from Tennessee to Canada, producing small, flat, soft leaves pressed close to the stems and hiding them. Family: Cypress (Cupressaceae); genus and species, *Thuja occidentalis.*

ARBUTUS, or ground laurel, or mayflower, or trailing arbutus, a creeping plant with oval, hairy, evergreen leaves and clusters of fragrant, white

T.H. EVERETT
ARBUTUS

or pink blossoms in early spring. It grows in light, sandy loam, but is becoming extinct or rare in many areas of New England and the eastern United States where it was formerly common because people often tear out the plants when they pick the flowers.

Arbutus is also a genus consisting of about 20 kinds of evergreen shrubs and trees native to western North America (such as the madroño, *A. menziesii,* which yields timber), Central America, and Mediterranean countries. Family: Heath (Ericaceae); genus and species, *Epigaea repens.*

ARNICA, a genus containing about 18 different kinds of perennial herbs, found in temperate and mountainous regions in Eurasia and North America, including mountain tobacco *(A. montana),* which has large, yellow heads of flowers. The roots and leaves of several species yield an extract used in liniments for sprains and bruises. Family: Daisy (Compositae).

ARROWHEAD, any of about 40 different kinds of marsh plants that produce ribbon-shaped leaves under water and arrowhead-shaped leaves in air. A leafless stalk bears whorls of white flowers, each with 3 white petals. American Indians and the Chinese, as well as other people in both hemispheres where arrowhead is native, dig the fleshy, tuberous roots as a source of starchy food. Family: Water plantain (Alismataceae); genus *Sagittaria.*

ARROWROOT, any of a number of distantly related and unrelated plants with large, tuberous, underground stems from which a nutritious starch similar to sago can be extracted. According to tradition, arrowroot starch is particularly easy to digest, and, therefore, is a good food for infants and invalids.

West Indian arrowroot *(Maranta arundinacea)* is a member of the arrowroot family (Marantaceae); East Indian arrowroot *(Curcuma angustifolia)* is a member of the ginger family (Zingiberaceae); Queensland arrowroot *(Canna edulis)* is a tropical American member of the canna family (Cannaceae); Portland arrowroot, from the European cuckoo-pint *(Arum maculatum),* is a member of the arum family (Araceae); Hawaiian arrowroot, or pia, is from a Polynesian, liliaceous plant *(Tacca pinnatifida)* of family Taccaceae; and Florida arrowroot, or Seminole bread, or coontie, is from a member *(Zamia floridana)* of the cycad family (Cycadaceae).

ARTICHOKE, a herbaceous plant with long, prickly leaves and an upright stem 2 to 3 feet high, bearing heavy heads of white- or violet-colored flowers, each head surrounded by edible, fleshy, green bracts. Native to Mediterranean countries, the artichoke is widely cultivated (particularly in Tunisia and California) as a source of edible bracts, which are cooked as a vegetable. The so-called Jerusalem artichoke *(Helianthus tuberosus)* is a sunflower with edible, tuberous roots. Family: Daisy (Compositae); genus and species, *Cynara scolymus.*

ARUM FAMILY (Araceae), a group of about 1500 species in 105 genera, mostly of tropical regions, including plants of marshes, woodland herbs, climbing shrubs, and perching plants with aerial roots. Although the roots, stems, and leaves vary so greatly, the flowers are clustered on a cylindrical stalk (the spadix) partly surrounded by a prominent and brightly colored, leaflike bract (the spathe). See *Arrowroot, Calla lily, Jack-in-the-pulpit, Skunk cabbage,* and *Taro.*

ASH, any of about 65 different kinds of trees 50 to 125 feet high when mature, with opposite leaves that are pinnately compound and flowers that are followed by winged seeds called samaras or ash-keys. Native to north temperate regions, ash trees are valued for shade and as a source of strong, lightweight wood. Several are grown and harvested commercially, the wood used particularly for oars, baseball bats, and tool handles. The inner bark from some yields a dyestuff. The Mediterranean flowering ash (*Fraxinus ornus*) is unusual because of its showy, white petals; most European species and all those native to North America lack petals, making the flowers inconspicuous. Family: Olive (Oleaceae); genus *Fraxinus*.

ASPARAGUS, a large genus of about 300 different kinds of herbaceous plants in which the true leaves are mere scales on the green stems at the places where short, green side-shoots, called phylloclades, arise and serve in photosynthesis. All are native to the Old World particularly Africa.

One kind of asparagus (*A. Officinalis*) is cultivated for its edible young stems; when these are permitted to grow they appear feathery and produce either yellow-green, bell-shaped flowers bearing pollen, or less conspicuous, smaller flowers that mature to red berries containing seeds. Florists raise asparagus-fern (*A. plumosus*) and a related, thorny species they call smilax. (*A. asparagoides*) and use as a hardy decorative material that can be added to floral bouquets. Family: Lily (Liliaceae).

ASPEN. See *Poplar*.

ASPHODEL, any of about 12 different hardy, stemless, herbaceous plants with fleshy roots, long, gray-green leaves, and tall clusters of white or yellow flowers. They are native to warmer parts of Europe and Asia, and figure prominently in Greek mythology because they were regarded as flowers of the dead. The asphodel referred to by Shakespeare and other poets of England and France is believed to have been the related daffodil. Family: Lily (Liliaceae); genus *Asphodelus*.

ASTER, a genus composed of about 600 different kinds of tall, hardy perennials native to North America, where they are particularly abundant, and to Eurasia and Africa. They characteristically bloom in autumn, bearing flowers in starlike heads varying in color from white to pink, violet, and purple. The wild aster of Britain has been hybridized with several kinds form North America to produce the handsome horticultural Michaelmas daisy, which blooms as late as Michaelmas (September 29). Family: Daisy (Compositae).

AVOCADO, or alligator pear, a medium-sized tree of the West Indies and tropical America, with thick, oval, evergreen leaves and clusters of small, greenish flowers. The avocado can be used as a shade tree, or trimmed low in cultivation so that its fruits are easy to pick. The fruit is about the size of a large pear, green or purple outside, with a thick, soft, greenish-yellow, oily pulp around a single, large, central seed.

The pulp is eaten alone or used in salads. The seeds yield a black dye. Oil from the fruit can be used in soaps and in oil lamps. While avocados are taken for granted because they are so

U.S. DEPARTMENT OF THE INTERIOR
AZALEAS

common in the American tropics, they are prized as a delicacy in temperate regions. Family: Laurel (Lauraceae); genus and species, *Persea americana*.

AZALEA, any of a large number of deciduous shrubs in the vast genus *Rhododendron*, native to arctic and north temperate regions, and to tropical mountains as far south as New Guinea and Australia. The leaves are small, smooth-edged, oval, and dull-green; the flowers fragrant, funnel-shaped, and white, yellow, pink, or flame-colored. Many horticultural varieties have been developed, but the wild flame azalea (*R. calendulaceum*) of the Appalachians, and the rhodora (*R. canadense*) are highly esteemed. Family: Heath: (Ericaceae); genus *Rhododendron*.

BABY'S BREATH, a fine-stemmed, narrow-leaved plant with feathery stalks of tiny pink or white flowers, characteristic of limy soil and native to Eurasia. It is widely cultivated as a perennial in gardens, where it grows to 1 to 3 feet, and is used in decorative bouquets. Family: Pink (Caryophyllaceae); genus and species, *Gypsophila paniculata*.

BACHELOR'S BUTTON. See *Cornflower*.

BALD CYPRESS, a swamp tree of the southeastern United States, that grows in water or waterlogged soil; air reaches its roots through blunt, porous, upward projections called cypress knees. Attaining a height of 150 to 170 feet, the tree sheds all of its needles in autumn and grows new needles in spring. Like the larch, the dawn redwood, and a few other conifers it is deciduous. Its wood is hard and especially valuable for shingles. Family: Bald cypress (Taxodiaceae); genus and species, *Taxodium distichum*.

BALD–CYPRESS FAMILY (Taxodiaceae), a group of about 16 species in 9 genera, all but one native to the North Tem-

perate Zone; the exception is found in Tasmania. All are trees or shrubs with needle-like or scalelike leaves and woody cones. See *Bald cypress*, *Cedar*, and *Sequoia*.

BALM, an aromatic, perennial herb with lemon-scented, paired leaves, growing 1 to 2 feet high and producing clusters of almost white flowers all summer. Native to Eurasia, it has been adopted as a garden plant and has escaped from cultivation to grow on roadsides and open woodlands. Family: Mint (Labiatae); genus and species, *Melissa officinalis*.

BALM OF GILIAD. See *Poplar*.

BALSA, or corkwood, a small tree of the West Indies, Central America, and northern South America, with palmately compound leaves, white flowers as much as 6 inches across, and the lightest wood known. The wood is used for airplane floats, for such rafts as the *Kon-Tiki*, and for model-making. Family: Bombax (Bombacaceae); genus and species, *Ochroma lagopus*.

BALSAM, or garden balsam, an erect, branching, annual herb 1 to 2½ feet in height, with succulent, pale-green branches, narrow, finely-toothed leaves, and short-stalked flowers in pastel colors ranging from white to deep crimson. Native to humid mountain valleys in northern India, it has been planted widely in gardens of temperate zones. The most popular variety is double-flowered. Family: Jewelweed (Balsaminaceae); genus and species, *Impatiens balsamina*.

BALSAM FIR. See *Fir*.

BAMBOO, any of about 200 different kinds of tall grasses bearing leaves at well-marked joints, between which the strong stems are hollow. They form dense thickets in tropical and subtropical countries, or clamber, vinelike, over trees, forming impenetrable tangles. Tallest is the giant bamboo (*Dendrocalamus giganteus*) of India and Malaysia, which attains a height of 120 feet.

Most widely cultivated is a smaller bamboo (*Bambusa vulgaris*) of Madagascar and tropical Asia, used to build bridges, houses, pipelines, and supports for climbing crops (such as beans and yams), and to make utensils of many kinds. Young bamboo shoots are cut as food for people in various countries; they are also a major part of the diet of gorillas in the Congo. Family: Grass (Gramineae).

BANANA, a tall, treelike, herbaceous plant of the Old World tropics, sometimes growing to more than 30 feet, with leaves 5 to 20 feet long. As each upright stem matures, it forms a terminal cluster of flowers that becomes pendant. As each spathelike bract of the flower bud opens, it exposes about a dozen flowers; the fruits from these ripen as a "hand" of bananas. Thus a single stem of bananas at the harvesting stage supports many hands, with the greener fruit closer to the remains of the bud. Additional stems from the same root system perpetuate the life of the plant after each stem load of fruits matures and the stem dies. Cultivated bananas have no seeds and must be propagated from cuttings of the root system. Bananas are second only to coconuts as commercial products of tropical countries. Family: Banana (Musaceae); genus and species, *Musa sapientum*.

BANANA FAMILY (Musaceae), a group of about 150 species in 5 genera, widely distributed in the tropics. Most are large herbs, often treelike, with broad leaves and a flower cluster that opens between spathelike bracts. It includes the famous traveler's-tree (*Ravenala madagascariensis*) of Madagascar, the decorative bird-of-paradise flowers (*Strelitzia* species) of South Africa, the handsome baliser (one of about 50 species of *Heliconia*), which is the national flower of Trinidad, and the various kinds of bananas. See *Abacá* and *Banana*.

BANEBERRY, any of about 12 different kinds of perennial herbs of the North Temperate Zone, growing 1½ to 2 feet tall, with coarsely toothed, compound leaves. The sepals drop from the small, fuzzy, white flowers as soon as they open. The flower clusters are soon followed by bright-red or waxy-white, poisonous berries on conspicuous red stalks. A Eurasian species (*Actaea spicata*) and 2 in North America (*A. alba* and *A. rubra*) are called herb Christopher. Family: Buttercup (Ranunculaceae); genus *Actaea*.

BANYAN TREE. See *Fig*.

BAOBAB, or cream-of-tartar tree, any of about 10 different kinds of tropical, deciduous trees with enormously thick trunks to 30 feet in diameter. They are native to open savannas of continental Africa, Madagascar, and northern Australia. During prolonged dry seasons in Africa, elephants sometimes use their tusks to break through the bark of baobab trees to get at the moist, pulpy interior. The inconspicuous flowers are followed by a gourdlike fruit with a woody shell and a soft, edible, slightly acid pulp. These fruits offer a generous supply of food where monkeys can get at them and are known as monkey bread. Family Bombax (Bombacaceae); genus *Adansonia*.

BARBERRY, any of about 175 different kinds of thorny shrubs native to the North Temperate Zone, particularly Asia and the Andes. Japanese barberry (*Berberis thunbergii*), which has smooth-edged leaves, simple spines, and rather dry, plump, scarlet fruit scattered along its spreading stems, is used as a prickly hedge.

The fruit of the European barberry (*B. vulgaris*), in which many of the leaves are reduced to triple or branching spines, is borne in clusters at the tips of the branches; cultivation of this plant is prohibited in many states where wheat cultivation is important because it is the alternate host for the fungus disease known as wheat rust. A native American barberry (*B. canadensis*), which does not grow in Canada, produces fruit in flat clusters on stiff stems as much as 3 feet tall. Family: Barberry (Berberidaceae).

BARBERRY FAMILY. (Berberidaceae), a group of about 300 species in 10 genera, all perennial herbs and shrubs of the North Temperate Zone. See *Barberry*, *Mayapple*, and *Oregon grape*.

BARLEY, an annual grass native to Asia but now cultivated throughout the world for its grain. The individual seeds are small, and, like wheat, are produced in heads among stiff, projecting hairs; they contain no gluten and cannot be made into raised bread. Flat bread and porridge can be made of this cereal, however, and these have been customary foods in North Africa and the Near East since at least 5000 BC.

In North America, barley is raised chiefly as a food for stock animals, for use in the manufacture of malt beverages, as a breakfast cereal, and as baby food. Malt is sprouted barley seeds. Family: Grass (Gramineae); genus and species, *Hordeum vulgare*.

BASSWOOD. See *Linden*.

BAYBERRY, or candleberry, or wax myrtle, any of several different kinds of densely branching shrubs with aromatic, leathery foliage, fragrant bark, and small berries that yield wax when boiled in water. The bark is sometimes used in astringents and tonics; the wax is commonly made into candles. Family: Bayberry (Myricaceae); genus *Myrica*.

BAYBERRY FAMILY (Myricaceae), a group of about 40 species in 2 genera, all aromatic shrubs or trees of temperate and subtropical regions. They include sweet fern (*Comptonia aspleni-folia*) of eastern North America, sweet gale (*Myrica gale*) of bogs in northern and temperate Eurasia and North America, as well as bayberry. See also *Bayberry*.

BAY-RUM TREE. See *Myrtle*.

BEAN, any of a large number of different erect or climbing plants with small, white, purplish, scarlet, or yellow flowers that are followed by elongated pods containing several somewhat flattened seeds. Usually the leaves are compound, consisting of 3 leaflets. The broad bean (*Vicia faba*) of the Old World is generally dried and ground up with peas and lentils, and made into soup or porridge.

Lima beans (*Phaseolus limensis*) and kidney beans (*P. vulgaris*) are from the New World and are regarded as vegetables; while still in their green, immature pods, they can be cooked as snap beans or string beans. Soybeans (*Glycine soja*), which have long been eaten by Asian peoples, from Manchuria to Japan, are now cultivated extensively as food for livestock and as a source of useful oils. Family: Pea (Leguminosae).

BEAR GRASS, any of a number of different North American, liliaceous plants with grasslike leaves and a conspicuous cluster of flowers borne on a tall, upright stalk. The name is given to several species of *Yucca* in the Gulf States and deserts of the Southwest, to some of the aloe-like sotols (*Dasylirion*) of Texas and Mexico, to camass or quamash (*Camassia*), which grows from edible bulbs in western North America, and to plants (*Xerophyllum tenax*) of western mountainsides that bear baton-like heads of creamy-white, fragrant flowers. Family: Lily (Liliaceae).

BEDSTRAW, any of about 300 different kinds of weak-stemmed, sprawling, flowering herbs found in most temperate regions, all with square stems, leaves in whorls, and clusters of small, white, yellow, or purple flowers.

Those varieties with minute hooks on the stems and leaves show resistance to crushing. This feature, and their pleasant fragrance, have made them favorite materials with which to stuff mattresses. Family: Madder (Rubiaceae); genus *Galium*.

BEECH, any of 10 different kinds of symmetrical, deciduous trees native to temperate parts of the Northern Hemisphere, generally with ash-gray bark that is so smooth that it tempts people to carve their initials into it. In medieval Germany, beechwood boards were inscribed with runes and symbolic charms. Today, the water-resistant, fine-grained wood of beech trees is valued for furniture, flooring, and tool handles because it does not split easily.

Some kinds of beech attain a height of 100 feet, with silky, oval leaves that bear coarse teeth along the sides; the flowers are small with both staminate and pistillate flowers on the same tree. Prickly husks open to drop the beechnuts, which are small,

BANANAS

triangular, with a rich, delicate flavor. Beechnuts and acorns from oaks were formerly referred to as the mast, which was important for fattening hogs. In the Southern Hemisphere related trees called Antarctic beech (*Nothofagus* species) form large forests. Family: Beech (Fagaceae); genus *Fagus*.

BEECH FAMILY (Fagaceae), a group of about 600 species in 6 genera, many of them important timber trees. Half of the species are oaks. Equally famous, although far fewer, are the beeches and chestnuts of the North Temperate Zone. South America, New Zealand, Australia, Tasmania, and the East Indies have comparable forests of Antarctic beech trees (*Nothofagus*), including the myrtle tree (*N. cunninghami*) of Australia, which yields valuable timber. See *Beech, Chestnut,* and *Oak*.

BEET, a biennial herb native to northern Europe, where for centuries it has been cultivated for both its luxuriant tops and its straw-yellow, enlarged roots, which develop in the first year of growth. The tops can be cooked as potherbs; a favorite variety is called Swiss chard. A different variety with red instead of yellow roots appeared in the 16th century, and has been propagated widely in Britain and Anglo-America.

Sugar beets, which have a higher than normal concentration of sucrose in the roots, were developed in the late 18th century as a source of refined table sugar. In its second year the beet plant produces a new whorl of leaves and a tall branching stem bearing flower clusters and a large number of small seeds. Family: Goosefoot (Chenopodiaceae); genus and species, *Beta vulgaris*.

BEGONIA, a genus of tropical flowering plants containing more than 800 different kinds, most numerous in northern South America. The individual flowers are often showy, but always either pistillate or staminate, although both types may be included in the same cluster. The ovary bears winglike extensions, which remain conspicuous on the capsule.

Many kinds and horticultural hybrids are also cultivated for their handsome leaves, which may be shiny with wax or fringed with long hairs, and for their flowers. Some have fibrous roots, and others have tuberous or bulbous roots. Family: Begonia (Begoniaceae, which includes four other small genera of similar plants).

BELLADONNA, or deadly nightshade, a coarse herb growing 2 to 5 feet tall from a thick, perennial root, with large, smooth-edged leaves and dull-purple, solitary flowers that are followed by plump berries that range in color from purple to black when ripe. Native to Europe, it has escaped from cultivation in other temperate lands. It is the source of the poisonous alkaloid atropin. Crude extracts of this substance from the roots and stems were formerly used in Europe by actresses who wished to make

T.H. EVERETT
BEGONIA

their eyes appear more attractive by chemically dilating their pupils. The purified extract can be used to relieve pain, particularly in spasms. Family: Potato (Solanaceae); genus and species, *Atropa belladonna*.

BELLADONNA LILY. See *Amaryllis*.

BERGAMOT, a small tree of southern Europe and Asia Minor, with leaves and flowers resembling those of orange trees and small, lemon-yellow fruits shaped and formed like oranges, but yielding a fragrant, essential oil used in the manufacture of perfumes, cosmetics, and liqueurs. Wild bergamot (*Monarda fistulosa*, of the mint family, Labiatae) is an entirely different fragrant herb of North America, bearing terminal clusters of lilac-colored, pink, or white flowers. Family: Rue (Rutaceae); genus and species, *Citrus bergamia*.

BIGONIA FAMILY (Bignoniaceae), a group of about 750 species in 110 genera, chiefly tropical shrubs, trees, or woody creepers (lianas). Included are some of the world's most beautiful flowering trees, such as the species of *Jacaranda* native to Brazil and the West Indies, which have showy, blue or purple flowers, and the African tulipan or flame-tree (*Spathodea campanulata*).

The sausage trees (*Kigelia* species) of tropical Africa and Madagascar, which produce elongated, woody fruits on long stalks, and the calabash tree (*Crescentia cujete*) of tropical America, which bears huge, spherical, hard-shelled fruits on its trunk and branches, are among the most unusual. See *Calabash tree, Catalpa,* and *Trumpet creeper*.

BINDWEED, or wild morning-glory, any of several different trailing, herbaceous vines from perennial roots, native to Eurasia but now widespread as weeds on roadsides and vacant land in temperate North America. It clambers on other plants, winding around them and spreading its spear-shaped leaves and pink to white, bell-shaped flowers in the sun. Family: Morning-glory (Convolvulaceae); genus *Convolvulus*.

BIRCH, any of about 40 different kinds of woody plants of arctic, alpine, and temperate areas of the Northern Hemisphere, with saw-edged leaves that open after pollen has been distributed from long, staminate catkins and caught from the wind by shorter clusters of pistillate flowers. Arctic and alpine birches are often mere shrubs, but in the Temperate Zone the species include many graceful, trees as much as 70 feet tall.

The bark is conspicuously marked with crosswise, narrow slits (lenticels) and may be white, gray, brown, black, or red, according to the species. From canoe, or paper, birch (*Betula papyrifera*) of Canada and the northern United States, Indians cut the bark to make coverings for canoes and wigwams. Today white birch is grown as an ornamental tree.

The aromatic bark of the black birch (*B. lenta*) of eastern North America yields oil for wintergreen. The sap of others can be used instead of maple sap to produce a sweet syrup or the raw material for birch beer. Family: Birch (Betulaceae); genus *Betula*.

BIRCH FAMILY (Betulaceae), a group of about 105 species in 6 genera, all deciduous shrubs and trees with simple leaves and flowers in pendant catkins. See *Alder, Birch, Hazel,* and *Hornbeam*.

BIRTHWORT FAMILY (Aristolochiaceae), a group of about 400 species in 6 genera, 300 of them in *Aristolochia* (including *A. durior*), most of which are tropical, twining shrubs and perennial herbs. Wild ginger (*Asarum canadense*) of eastern North America is a woodland wild flower with a few kidney-shaped leaves shading peculiar, globular, chocolate-brown flowers growing at ground level. See *Dutchman's pipe*.

BITTERROOT, a low-growing, perennial herb of western North America, with starchy, edible roots, small, succulent leaves, and large, pink- or rose-colored flowers close to the ground. The roots were eaten by the Indians and early white colonists. It is the state flower of Montana. Family: Purslane (Portulacaceae); genus and species, *Lewisia rediviva*.

BITTERSWEET, either of 2 different types of woody vines bearing simple, ovate leaves and small, conspicuous fruits. One, the nightshade (*Solanum dulcamara*) of temperate Eurasia, which has been introduced and become widespread in other parts of the world, bears small clusters of pink or violet flowers, followed by bright-red, poisonous berries. It is a member of the Potato Family (Solanaceae).

The other, known also as wax-work, is a climbing plant (*Celastris scandens* of the eastern United States or *C. orbiculatus* from eastern Asia) with inconspicuous clusters of greenish flowers at the tips of side branches.

In autumn, the ivory-colored coverings of the fruits split open and drop off, exposing brilliant scarlet or crimson seeds in a tight, spherical cluster. It is a representative of the Staff-tree Family (Celastraceae).

BLACKBERRY, any of 20 or more different kinds of thorny brambles of North America, with stalked leaflets in the compound leaves, and raspberry-like, edible fruits borne in terminal clusters. The canelike, arching stems grow 5 to 6 feet high and usually bear fruit in their second or third year. Family: Rose (Rosaceae); genus *Rubus*.

BLACK-EYED SUSAN, or yellow daisy, a handsome, North American wildflower, 1 to 2 feet tall, bearing a flower head the center of which is composed of numerous tiny, brown flowerets closely packed, surrounded by gay, yellow petals of flowers that have lost their reproductive parts. It thrives in dry fields, blooms from June to September, and is the state flower of Maryland. Family: Daisy (Compositae); genus and species, *Rudbeckia hirta*.

BLACK HAW, or sweethaw, or stagbush, a coarse shrub or small tree growing 15 to 40 feet tall, with spreading branches, oval leaves that turn bright red in autumn, and clusters of white flowers in April or May. Native to eastern North America, it is used as a decorative tree. Family: Honeysuckle (Caprifoliaceae); genus and species, *Viburnum prunifolium*.

BLADDERWORT, any of about 250 different kinds of carnivorous water plants found throughout the world but most varied in South America and the East Indies; they are always found in sluggish streams and ponds.

The submerged leaves, which are finely divided, bear bladder-like traps 1/8 to 1/4 inch long, with hinged doors that swing inward suddenly, sucking small animals into the interior where they are held and digested. Bladderwort produces upright stems bearing white or yellow flowers, which are pollinated by flying insects. Family: Bladderwort (Lentibulariaceae); genus *Utricularia*.

BLADDERWORT FAMILY (Lentibulariaceae), a group of about 260 species in 6 genera, mostly carnivorous plants growing in moist places in the North Temperate and South Temperate zones and on mountains of tropical America. See *Bladderwort* and *Butterwort*.

BLEEDING HEART. See *Dutchman's-breeches*.

BLOODROOT, a delicate, herbaceous, perennial flower of woodlands in eastern North America, which produces an upright stem with a single, circular leaf tightly rolled around the single flower bud. The leaf opens in early spring; the flower expands its 8 to 12 white petals and lasts only a day or two. All parts of the plant contain an orange-red juice. Indians formerly gathered the thick, underground stems of bloodroot to obtain the juice for use as warpaint and basket dye. Family: Poppy (Papaveraceae); genus and species, *Sanguinaria canadensis*.

BLUEBELL, any of a number of low-growing plants with blue, bell-shaped flowers, particularly the widespread harebell (*Campanula rotundifolia*, of the bellflower family, Campanulaceae) of temperate Eurasia and North America, which bears one flower at the nodding tip of each of its hairlike stems, and has been made famous in poetry and prose as the "bluebell of Scotland." The name bluebell is also given to the European wood hyacinth (*Scilla nonscripta*) and the grape hyacinth (*Muscari botryoides*, both of the lily family, Liliaceae).

In New Zealand the name bluebell is used for some kinds of tuftybells (*Wahlenbergia*, a large genus of the bellflower family). In North America, bluebells may be the Virginian cowslip (*Mertensia virginica*, of the borage family, Boraginaceae), the American brooklime (*Veronica americana*, of the figwort family, Scrophulariaceae), the Jacob's ladder (*Polemonium reptans*, of the phlox family, Polemoniaceae), or the leatherflower (*Clematis crispa*, of the buttercup family, Ranunculaceae).

BLUEBERRY, any of a number of different kinds of shrubby plants of wide distribution, bearing small, bell-shaped, pink or white flowers and blue-black berries, which are usually edible and often confused with those of the related huckleberry. Many horticultural varieties have been developed from the highbush blueberry (*Vaccinium corymbosum*) of dry uplands in eastern North America, which yield large crops of berries with a delicious flavor, highly esteemed when eaten fresh, dried, frozen, or canned. Family: Heath (Ericaceae); genus *Vaccinium*.

T.H. EVERETT
BOUGAINVILLEA

BLUEBONNET. See *Lupine*.

BLUEGRASS, any of several different pasture grasses with a bluish color on the upright stems (culms). In North America, bluegrass is generally either Kentucky bluegrass (or junegrass, or speargrass, *Poa pratensis*), which is native to subarctic meadows and moist slopes in Eurasia and North America but grows well in Kentucky and other regions, or Canada bluegrass (or wiregrass, *P. compressa*), which is native to Eurasia but is now widespread in North America. Unrelated grasses are given the same name in Australia and New Zealand. Family: Grass (Gramineae).

BOMBAX FAMILY (Bombacaceae), a group of about 140 species in 22 genera, all trees of the tropics, often of vast girth or with enormous buttresses. See *Balsa*, *Baobab*, and *Kapok*.

BONESET, any of several different related American herbs with a stout, hairy stem growing 2 to 5 feet tall and bearing wrinkled, saw-edged leaves and clusters of flowers in shaggy heads; the flowers are usually greenish-white or pale pink. The Indians used extracts from the flowers and leaves in treating ague and fevers. Family: Daisy (Compositae); genus *Eupatorium*.

BORAGE, a coarse, hairy, annual or biennial herb native to Europe, where it is cultivated as a source of nectar for bees. It has been introduced and become widespread in many other temperate areas of the world, and is noted for its clear, blue flowers. Family: Borage (Boraginaceae); genus and species, *Borago officinalis*.

BORAGE FAMILY (Boraginaceae), a group of about 2000 species in 100 genera, widely distributed, mostly herbs, commonly with simple, smooth-edged leaves covered with rough, bristly hairs. See *Bluebell*, *Borage*, *Forget-me-not*, and *Heliotrope*.

BOSTON IVY, a hardy, deciduous, woody vine native to China and Japan that climbs by means of branching tendrils with expanded, adhesive pads at the tips. Its long-petioled, simple leaves turn red or orange in autumn and usually fall before the petioles do, exposing clusters of dark purple fruits.

Introduced into New England and Canada, the plant provides wall covering in places where English ivy is killed by cold. A close relative in eastern North America is the Virginia creeper (*Parthenocissus quinquefolia*) with compound leaves consisting mostly of 5 leaflets. Family: Grape (Vitaceae); genus and species, *Parthenocissus tricuspidata*.

BOUGAINVILLEA, a genus of South American vines that bear flowers in groups of 3, surrounded by 3 purple or red conspicuous bracts. A Brazilian species (*B. spectabilis*) is cultivated in warm countries as a decorative covering for walls. Family: Four-o'clock (Nyctaginaceae).

BOUNCING BET, or soapwort, an attractive, perennial herb with a sturdy, smooth stem, smooth, oval leaves, and clusters of pink or white flowers. Native to Europe, it has become a roadside weed in North America. Colonial housewives crushed its leaves into water to produce a lather possessing some of the qualities of a soap solution. Family: Pink (Caryophyllaceae); genus and species, *Saponaria officinalis*.

BOX, a popular evergreen shrub native to western and southern Europe, cultivated in many temperate and cool climates as a hedge plant. It grows slowly to a height of 16 feet, producing small, oval leathery leaves so close together that they provide privacy and a screen from the wind. The flowers are inconspicuous. The pale yellow wood is very hard and sometimes used for wood engraving and for making wind instruments. Family: Box (Buxaceae); genus and species, *Buxus sempervirens*.

BOX ELDER. See *Maple*.

BRACKEN, or brake, any of several kinds of tall, coarse ferns growing 2 to 14 feet tall, their fronds divided into 3 branches and bearing spore cases underneath the edges. Found throughout the world, particularly in dry, rocky pastures, these ferns can be dug up to extract a solution used as a bitter beverage or for tanning from their thick, underground stems. Family: Polypody (Polypodiaceae); genus *Pteridium*.

BRAZIL NUT, a tree that grows in moist soil along river banks in northern South America, where it attains a height of 100 to 150 feet, and bears huge, oval, leathery leaves, creamy-white flowers, and large, globular pods containing 18 to 24 wedge-shaped, oily seeds, each in a hard seed coat. The seeds, called brazil nuts, are flavorful and edible, and yield an oil used by watchmakers and artists, as well as by native people for fuel in lamps. Family: Brazil nut (Lecythidaceae); genus and species, *Bertholletia excelsa*.

BRAZIL–NUT FAMILY (Lecythidaceae), a group of 315 species in 18 genera, all tropical trees with simple leaves clustered at the ends of the branches. Included is the strange cannonball tree (*Couroupita guianensis*) of northern South America and the West Indies, which bears large rust-colored, woody, seed-filled capsules on short, twisted side branches extending from the main trunk; it is a source of good timber. See also *Brazil nut*.

BREADFRUIT, a tropical tree with thick, oval leaves that are deeply indented around the edge. Native to the South Pacific islands, where it rarely grows to more than 40 feet tall, the breadfruit is valued for its large, spherical, green fruits, each pebbled on the outside and full of a starchy pulp that is edible when baked or fried. A sticky substance that oozes from wounds in the bark can be used as birdlime or to seal the seams of small boats. Strong bast fibers can be removed from the inner bark and woven into tapa cloth. The wood itself can be used to build houses or canoes. First described by Capt. James Cook, breadfruit was introduced into the West Indies as food for Negro slaves by Capt. William Bligh after an expedition to Tahiti aboard the famous ship *H.M.S. Bounty*. Family: Mulberry (Moraceae); genus and species, *Artocarpus incisa*.

BRIDAL WREATH. See *Spiraea*.

BROCCOLI. See *Mustard*.

BROOM, any of several related plants with long, slender, stiff, green branches, small leaves, and showy, yellow flowers resembling those of a sweet pea. Scotch broom (*Cytisus scoparius*), which is native to Britain and temperate parts of Europe, has been introduced into North America, South Africa, and New Zealand, where it grows well. A medicine made from the foul-tasting twigs and seeds has been used as a diuretic.

Other plants to which the name broom is applied include several kinds of gorse (*Genista* and *Ulex* species) of Europe, western Asia, and north Africa. Family: Pea (Leguminosae).

BROOMCORN, a tall coarse, annual sorghum native to warm parts of Eurasia, but cultivated in America since colonial days. It has escaped from cultivation. It raises jointed stems either 4 to 6 feet tall (dwarf variety) or 10 to 14 feet tall (standard variety), which bear long leaves and terminate in a brushlike cluster of inconspicuous flowers. After the seeds have ripened the long "broom straws" of the flower cluster are gathered and used to make brooms and brushes. Family: Grass (Gramineae); genus and species, *Sorghum vulgare technicus*.

BRUSSELS SPROUTS. See *Mustard*.

BUCKEYE. See *Horse chestnut*.

BUCKTHORN, any of about 100 different kinds of woody shrubs, mostly from the North Temperate Zone. They include some that attain a height of 12 feet, with black bark, small, scalloped leaves, tiny 4-petalled, yellowish-green flowers, and blue-black berries which yield a purgative juice and a pigment used by painters. Most buckthorns have thorny branches.

Dried bark of the western North American *Rhamnus purshiana* is called *cascara sagrada* (sacred bark), and is the source of a mild laxative. Family: Buckthorn (Rhamnaceae); genus *Rhamnus*.

BUCKTHORN FAMILY (Rhamnaceae), a widely distributed group of about 550 species in 45 genera, all tree or shrubs with simple leaves and flowers that, strangely, have stamens that are opposite to the petals instead of alternate with them. Several kinds are valued for their fruits, as well as for drugs or ornamental planting. See *Buckthorn* and *Jujube*.

BUCKWHEAT, an annual herb with a slender, jointed stem, 2 to 3 feet tall, bearing heart-shaped leaves and clusters of small, white, pink, or purplish-red flowers. Although the plant is not a grass, the ripened seeds are regarded as a cereal crop.

Cultivated for many centuries in the Orient, buckwheat was introduced into Europe and then into North America where it is grown in the northeastern United States as a food for cattle and poultry, or made into a flour for griddle cakes. Buckwheat honey has a distinctively dark color, and a strong flavor. Family: Buckwheat (Polygonaceae); genus and species, *Fagopyrum sagittatum*.

BUCKWHEAT FAMILY (Polygonaceae), a group of about 800 species in 32 genera, mostly herbs of the North Temperate Zone, but including also some shrubs, climbing vines, and trees. They are encountered as small trees on tropical beaches, for example, the sea grape (*Coccoloba uvifera*), which has edible fruits; or as coralvine (*Antigonum leptopus*) of Mexico and Central America, which climbs trellises or tall trees and bears a profusion of pink flowers. See *Buckwheat*, *Dock*, *Rhubarb*, and *Sheep sorrel*.

BULRUSH, any of about 200 different kinds of grasslike herbs with narrow leaves in 3 rows that provide a sheath for the triangular stem. Widely distributed, they are plants of shallow water or wet soil, particularly characteristic of bogs, marshes, and wet moorland in areas where the climate is cool. The end of the stem bears many flowers in a clublike cluster. The "bulrushes" of which the floating cradle of the infant Moses was made

T.H. EVERETT
BUCKTHORN

were probably *Iris* because bulrushes do not grow in Egypt, whereas *Iris* leaves are still used for such purposes along the Nile. Family: Sedge (Cyperaceae); genus *Scirpus*.

BUNCHBERRY, a low-growing herb of cool, damp woodlands in northeastern North America, producing 4 to 6 oval leaves above which a slender stalk bears 4 to 6 conspicuous, white bracts resembling petals around the central cluster of inconspicuous green flowers. When ripe, the clustered scarlet berries are edible. Family: Dogwood (Cornaceae); genus and species *Cornus canadensis*.

BURDOCK, a coarse biennial herb native to temperate Eurasia but now widespread as a weed in North America. In its first year it produces broad, wavy-edged leaves, and stores nourishment in a sturdy root. The following year it raises a branched, leafy stem with flowers opening in heads from July until the first frost arrives in the fall.

Hooked bristles cover the flower heads, which have pink or purplish florets packed tightly together, converting the cluster of ripened seeds into a bur that catches on to clothing or the fur of passing animals. New burdocks grow along paths, fences, and walls where the burs are scratched free or fall. Family: Daisy (Compositae); species chiefly *Arctium lappa*, the great burdock, *A. minus*, the common burdock, and *A. nemorosum*, or hybrids among these.

BURNING BUSH. See *Euonymus*.

BUTTERCUP, or crowfoot, any of about 300 different kinds of wildflowers with tough, green, branching stems 3 to 30 inches tall, bitter juice, small, deeply-cut leaves, and cup-shaped flowers, generally golden-yellow and intensely reflecting. They are found in wet areas of cool and temperate regions, in the Arctic, north temperate, and alpine areas of the Americas and New Zealand. The Mt. Cook lily (*Ranunculus lyalli*) has large, white flowers and is the national flower of New Zealand. Family: Buttercup (Ranunculaceae); genus *Ranunculus*.

BUTTERCUP FAMILY (Ranunculaceae) a group of about 1500 species of herbs, vines, or shrubs in 5 genera, common to both the North Temperate and South Temperate zones. See *Aconite, Anemone, Baneberry, Bluebell, Buttercup, Clematis, Columbine, Hellebore, Hepatica, Larkspur, Marsh marigold, Peony,* and *Woodbine*.

BUTTERFLY BUSH, a decorative, tall, branching herb of northwest China, with showy clusters of small, lilac-colored flowers that attract butterflies and other insects. Widely introduced as a garden plant, it thrives in sunny, warm climates. Family: Logania (Loganiaceae); genus and species, *Buddleia alternifolia*.

BUTTERFLY FLOWER, a tall, herbaceous plant native to Chile but widely introduced into gardens for its lacy, fernlike leaves and varicolored flowers, each of which has small, winglike petals suggesting those of a butterfly. Family: Potato (Solanaceae); genus and species, *Schizanthus pinnatus*.

BUTTERFLY WEED. See *Milkweed*.

BUTTERNUT. See *Walnut*.

BUTTERWORT, any of about 40 different kinds of small, herbaceous plants that grow in wet soil. They are prevalent in the North and South Temperate zones and the mountains of tropical America.

Thick oblong leaves arise in a rosette close to the ground; first they capture and then they digest insects that alight and are caught on the sticky surface. Small clusters of violet-like flowers, generally blue or purple, are borne on an upright stalk, which is about 4 inches tall. Family: Bladderwort (Lentibulariaceae); genus *Pinguicula*.

BUTTONWOOD. See *Plane-tree family*.

CABBAGE. See *Mustard*.

CACAO, a small tree native to Central America and northern South America, with a thick trunk that grows to 40 feet, spreading branches with a downy covering, leathery, oval leaves that hang downward, and inconspicuous, pink flowers on cushion-like projections from the trunk; the large fruits, 10 to 14 inches long and 5 inches in diameter, are dark purplish-red on the outside, and have 25 to 50 purple seeds embedded in a mucilaginous, pink pulp.

The seeds, or cocoa beans, can be removed by hand, cured by fermentation, and dried. Later they can be ground and processed to make cacao powder and chocolate. Cacao orchards that provide the world with chocolate have always been planted with a cover of taller trees to provide the necessary shade; this is particularly true of tropical Africa. Family: Sterculia (Sterculiaceae); genus and species, *Theobroma cacao*.

CACTUS FAMILY (Cactaceae), a group of about 1700 species in 120 genera, originally from the New World, most with fleshy stems armed with spines and bristles, leaves that drop off without expanding, and large flowers followed by a fleshy berry. Many are cultivated for their unusual form and handsome flowers. Prickly-pear (*Opuntia* species), barrel cactus (*Ferocactus* species), Christmas cactus (*Zygocactus truncatus*) from Brazil, and organ-pipe cactus (*Cereus marginatus*) are among the forms that have attracted widespread attention. See *Night-blooming Cereus* and *Saguaro*.

CALABASH TREE, a small tree native to tropical America, with opposite leaves on its small branches but with flowers extending from the bark of large branches and the trunk. The fruits develop as much as 12 inches in diameter, with a hard rind. Native people clean out the central pulp and seeds, thus creating a woody calabash that can be used to carry liquids or as a drinking utensil. Family: Bignonia (Bignoniaceae); genus and species, *Crescentia cujete*.

CALCEOLARIA, or slipperwort, a genus containing about 200 different kinds of herbaceous, perennial plants native to America from Mexico to Tierra del Fuego, growing 1 to 2 feet tall, bearing oval leaves and usually, yellow flowers with red markings, each flower with a large, saclike, lower lip and a small, erect, upper lip. Family: Figwort (Scrophulariaceae).

CALENDULA. See *Pot marigold*.

CALLA LILY, a cultivated South African herbaceous plant with thick, starchy, horizontal, underground stems and green, upright stems bearing large, white, flower-like spathes around a bright yellow spadix of minute flowers. A golden calla (*Zantedeschia elliottiana*) has white-spotted leaves and a yellow spathe.

The name calla is actually that of the genus of a related but small-flowered water arum (*Calla palustris*), which is native to the bogs and marsh edges of the North Temperate Zone. Family: Arum (Araceae); genus and species, *Zantedeschia aethiopica*.

CALTROP, any of more than 20 different kinds of Eurasian, African, and American perennial herbs and shrubs with opposite, leathery leaves, the inconspicuous flowers of which produce hard fruits with sharp, rigid spines. These fruits, called caltrops, may puncture the tires of bicycles and automobiles as well as wound the feet of man and animal; *Tribulus terrestris*, which is a native weed from the Mediterranean to Tibet that has been introduced and become widepsread elsewhere, is therefore called puncture weed.

In the Middle Ages arms makers used the caltrop fruit as a model for a metal device with 4 sharp spikes equally spaced in radial directions; one of these spikes always pointed

U.S. DEPARTMENT OF THE INTERIOR
CACTUS

upward no matter how the device rested, thus readily maiming a horse or man who stepped on it. Family: Caltrop (Zygophyllaceae); genera *Tribulus* and *Kallstroemia*.

CALTROP FAMILY (Zygophyllaceae), a group of about 250 species in 27 genera, chiefly plants of warm regions, all with opposite leaves. Several kinds are grown as ornamental, and some are useful trees. Bean capers (*Zygophyllum fabago*) of Asia Minor yield buds than can be pickled for use as a condiment. See *Caltrop, Creosote bush,* and *Lignum vitae.*

CAMELLIA, a genus of Asian shrubs with glossy, pointed, slightly toothed, evergreen leaves and waxy, roselike flowers, 3 to 7 inches in diameter, ranging in color from red to white. Of the 80 different species, many are cultivated widely in temperate areas as house plants.

C. sinensis, native to the area from Japan to India, is raised on plantations to yield young twigs and partly opened leaves that are cured, dried, and later steeped to yield a tea. Tea bushes or tea trees can naturally attain a height of 30 feet, but they are usually pruned to a height of 3 to 5 feet to enable workers to reach more easily the young growth that is to be picked. Family: Tea (Theaceae).

CAMOMILE, or chamomile, any of several related branching herbs with pinnately dissected leaves and solitary, terminal heads of small, daisylike flowers. These plants have long been gathered or cultivated for their aromatic foliage and young stems, which are the source of a drug used to induce perspiration and to inhibit muscular spasms. Some species are grown as decorative garden plants. Family: Daisy (Compositae); genera *Anthemis* and *Matricaria*.

CAMPHOR. See *Cinnamon.*

CANDYTUFT, any of about 30 different kinds of herbaceous, branching, stiff plants with toothed or deeply cut, narrow leaves and showy white or crimson flowers in which the lowest 2 of the 4 petals are larger than the others. The first species introduced as low-growing garden plants were annuals from Candia on the island of Crete; hence the name candytuft. Others that are now widely cultivated are evergreen perennials, produced primarily in Mediterranean countries. Family: Mustard (Cruciferae); genus *Iberis*.

CANNA, a genus of about 60 different kinds of tropical American plants that comprise a separate family. Many are cultivated for their large, sheathing leaves, which are green, bronze, or red, and for their terminal clusters of red, white, or yellow flowers in which the conspicuous parts are 1 to 5, petal-like, modified stamens. The underground stem of *C. edulis*, from Central America, is starchy and edible and known as Queensland arrowroot. Family: Canna (Cannaceae).

CANTALOUPE. See *Melon.*

CANTERBURY BELL. See *Bellflower.*

CAPE JASMINE. See *Gardenia.*

CAPER, any of about 350 different kinds of shrubs and small trees found in warm climates, some climbing by means of tendrils from the axils of the simple leaves. The showy flowers have 4 sepals, 4 petals, and numerous stamens. The flower buds of a Mediterranean species called capers (*Capparis spinosa*) are dried for use as seasoning; the plants are cultivated for this purpose. Family: Caper (Capparidaceae); genus *Capparis*.

CAPER FAMILY (Capparidaceae), a group of about 700 species in 46 genera, all tropical or subtropical herbs, shrubs, or trees. One kind, the Spiderflower (*Cleome spinosa*) of tropical America, is a widespread, cultivated, garden ornament, named for its extraordinarily long, projecting stamens. See also *Caper.*

CARAWAY, an erect, biennial herb with aromatic, pinnately compound leaves, and white or pink flowers in clusters, producing small seeds with a distinctive flavor. The plants are cultivated in many temperate countries.

Plants were introduced from Europe to obtain seeds that are dried and added as flavoring to bread, cheese, candy, soups, and sauces. An oil extracted from the seeds is used in soaps and perfumes. Family: Carrot (Umbelliferae); genus and species, *Carum carvi*.

CARDAMOM, an East Indian herb with elongated, sheathing leaves and a stem growing to 10 feet, topped by a spike of white-striped, purple flowers that are followed by 3-cornered pods containing aromatic, brown, white-lined seeds. Cultivated for its seeds, particularly in Ceylon, India, and Latin America, cardamon is the source of medicinal substances with stimulant and purgative qualities as well as the preferred source of a spice that is added to curries.

The name cardamom (or cardamon or cardamum) is also given to alternate spices from a related plant, *Anomum cardamon*, of Java. Family: Ginger (Zingiberaceae); genus and species, *Elletaria cardamomum*.

CARDINAL FLOWER. See *Lobelia.*

CARNATION. See *Pink.*

CAROB. See *Locust.*

CARROT, or Queen Anne's lace, a biennial, herbaceous plant with finely divided leaves and flat-topped clusters of small white flowers. It is native to Europe but has been introduced and become widespread as a weed all over the world.

A cultivated variety, with a large, edible, yellowish or reddish-orange root from its first year of growth, is valued as a food because of its high content of vitamin A and minerals. Family: Carrot (Umbelliferae); genus and species, *Daucus carota*.

CAMELLIA

CARROT FAMILY (Umbelliferae), a group of about 2900 species in 125 genera, represented on all continents but most numerous in the North Temperate Zone. Most are biennial or perennial herbs with aromatic leaves, the stalks of which enclose the stems, and with flat-topped clusters of flowers (umbels). See *Anise, Caraway, Carrot, Celery, Dill, Fennel, Parsley, Parsnip,* and *Poison hemlock.*

CASCARA SAGRADA. See *Buckthorn.*

CASHEW, a small tree native to the American tropics, with alternate, simple leaves, clusters of 5-part flowers, and distinctive fruits called cashew apples, each with a large, pearlike, fleshy portion below which a hard-shelled seed, called a cashew nut, projects. The cashew apple is edible; the seeds can be made edible by roasting to destroy a poisonous, irritating compound and break the shells. Family: Sumac (Anacardiaceae); genus and species, *Anacardium occidentale*.

CASSAVA, or manioc, or yuca, either of 2 kinds of erect, slender, woody plants of tropical America, with stems growing to 9 feet tall and bearing large leaves that are deeply notched into 3 to 7 long, narrow, spreading lobes. The fleshy underground stems, which may be 3 feet long and 9 inches in diameter, are dug up, purified of any bitter poisonous substances present, and converted into either a flour from which a flat bread can be made or into a pudding known as tapioca.

These foods are produced from cultivated cassava plants; they provide a poor diet but are the principal sources of nutritional calories in many parts of Latin America, tropical Africa, and from Malaya through the East Indies and the South Pacific islands. Family: Spurge, (Euphorbiaceae); genus and species, *Manihot esculenta* (bitter) and *M. palmata* (sweet).

CASTOR-OIL PLANT, or palma Christi, a tropical perennial shrub or small tree of Africa and Asia, which reaches a

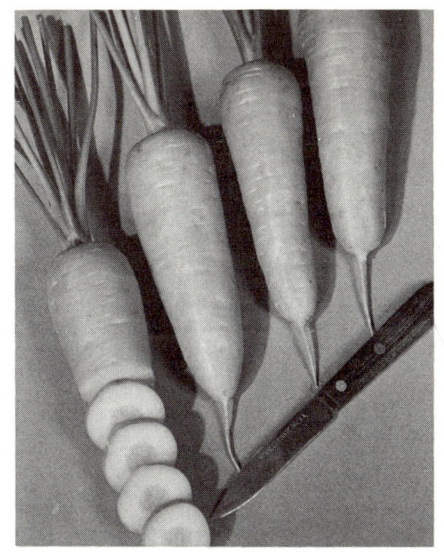

CARROTS

height of 30 to 40 feet, with palmately compound, bronze-green leaves, small flowers in loose clusters, and spiny capsules that contain poisonous, mottled seeds.

The castor-oil plant grows quickly and produces fruits even in temperate climates, where it is killed by winter frosts and can therefore be cultivated only as an annual. Castor oil can be extracted from the seeds; it is used as a violent laxative and as a fine lubricating oil. Family: Spurge (Euphorbiaceae); genus and species, *Ricinus communis*.

CATALPA, a genus comprised of 10 different trees of East Asia and eastern North America, including the West Indies, several of which have been introduced and become widespread beyond their native areas for their attractive, large, heart-shaped, mostly opposite leaves; their tall, open clusters of 2-lipped, frilled flowers; and their useful wood. They produce drooping, cylindrical pods 6 to 20 inches long for which the trees are often called Indian beans or cigar-trees. Family: Bignonia (Bignoniaceae).

CATNIP, an aromatic, perennial herb native to Eurasia, with an erect, square stem, opposite, pointed, serrate, velvety leaves, and terminal whorls of white, purplish, or blue-tinged flowers. Introduced and widespread in most temperate parts of the world, it was long valued as the basis of a catnip tea used for colic and colds. Cats are attracted by the odor of the fresh or dried aerial parts of the plant. Family: Mint (Labiatae); genus and species, *Nepeta cataria*.

CATTAIL, any of 12 different perennial herbs found in marshes all over the world, with starchy, horizontal stems in water-soaked soil and erect, sword-shaped leaves partially sheathing upright stems that end in club-shaped spikes of minute flowers. The top of the spike consists of staminate flowers which soon drop off, leaving a naked length of stem beyond the clustered, pistillate flowers, which have a furry appearance. The single genus is in a family by itself. Family: Cattail (Typhaceae); genus *Typha*.

CAULIFLOWER. See *Mustard*.

CEDAR, in the strict sense, any of 4 different kinds of handsome, evergreen, coniferous trees native to Eurasia, where 3 are becoming rare because of the excessive harvesting of the fragrant wood. Only the deodar (*Cedrus deodara*) in its native Himalayan forests is not yet seriously threatened.

The famous cedar of Lebanon (*C. libanotica*) is represented today by a few dwindling forests in Turkey and scattered trees introduced elsewhere. The Cyprus cedar (*C. brevifolia*) is threatened in addition by goats and fires. The Atlantic cedar (*C. atlantica*), which was once widespread in Algeria and Morocco, is now scarce.

All cedars have rather short, sharp needles arranged in spirals on spurlike side branches; they shed their winged seeds when the ovulate cones disintegrate, dropping their scales and leaving only the central supporting stem attached to the branch.

Many unrelated coniferous trees with fragrant wood belonging to genera *Chamaecyparis* (North American), *Juniperus* (North Temperate), *Libocedrus* (Pacific coasts), *Thuja* (North American and East Asian), and *Widdringtonia* (African, in the cypress family, Cupressaceae), and *Cryptomeria* (Japanese, in the baldcypress family, Taxodiaceae), are commonly referred to as cedars. Family: Pine (Pinaceae); genus *Cedrus*.

CELANDINE, a European biennial herb 1 to 2 feet tall, with a sprawling, brittle stem, deeply notched, alternate leaves, and odorless, yellow flowers; its yellow juice, which stains skin and clothing, contains a dangerous poison. Family: Poppy (*Papaveraceae*); genus and species, *Chelidonium majus*.

CELERY, a biennial herb native to Europe but widely cultivated for its fleshy petioles, which are eaten raw or cooked, and for its seeds, which are dried for use as a condiment. It has fibrous roots, a very short stem, and deeply divided leaf blades. When allowed to flower, it produces small blossoms in flat topped clusters. Family: Carrot (Umbelliferae); genus and species, *Apium graveolens*.

CENTURY PLANT, any of about 230 different kinds of succulent-leaved plants of arid and semiarid areas from northern South America to the southern United States. Most have stems that remain very short and produce an ever greater whorl of thick sword-shaped leaves until a critical amount of nourishment has been accumulated. Then, during a month or two of rapid growth, the stem extends upward to a height of as much as 20 feet, displaying a large cluster of fragrant, yellow, tubular flowers. After blooming, the plant develops seeds and sometimes suckers, but the leaves and main stem die. Originally believed to require a century to bloom, century plants normally need 20 years or less. Many are cultivated for the strong fibers in their leaves, which include henequen (from *Agave fourcroydes*), sisal (from *A. sisalana* and *A. letonae*), istle (from *A. lophantha* and *A. funkiana*), Mauritius hemp (from *Fourcroya gigantea*), cabuya (from *F. cabuya*), and fique, the fibers of which are used in making Colombian coffee bags (from *F. macrophylla*). Family: Amaryllis (Amaryllidaceae); genera *Agave* and *Fourcroya*.

CHARD. See *Beet*.

CHERIMOYA. See *Custard apple*.

CHERRY, any of several trees of the North Temperate Zone with small, smooth, oval leaves usually finely toothed around the edge, beautiful clusters of fragrant, white or pinkish flowers, and edible fruits with a soft pulp and a central, armored seed.

Some, such as the black cherry (*Prunus serotina*) of eastern North America, attain a height of 100 feet and are sought after for their hardwood. Others such as the sweet cherry (*P. avium*) of southern Europe and the sour cherry (*P. cerasus*) of Asia, are appreciated for their fruit. Still others, such as the flowering cherry (*P. serrulata*) of Japan, are planted for their spring flowers and attractive foliage; the small and rather tasteless fruits are left for the birds. Family: Rose (Rosaceae); genus *Prunus*.

CHESTNUT, any of 10 different kinds of shrubs and trees of the Northern Hemisphere, bearing alternate leaves that are coarsely serrate and have conspicuously straight side veins. The staminate flowers are borne in cream-colored, loose catkins; the pistillate flowers are small but produce 2 or 3 nuts grouped in a leathery bract, which opens to release them.

Best known is the Spanish or Italian chestnut (*Castanea sativa*) of the Mediterranean region, with large, edible nuts, sold freshly roasted on street corners in many large cities. The American chestnut (*C. dentata*), of the eastern United States and Canada, was formerly important as a timber and nut tree, but it has almost been exterminated by a fungus blight that still prevents it from becoming reestablished. Family: Beech (Fagaceae); genus *Castanea*.

CHICKWEED, any of about 200 different kinds of frail, quick-growing, herbaceous perennials of temperate regions, rarely more than 8 inches tall, with small, oval leaves in pairs at swellings on the slender stems, and with solitary or clustered white flowers bearing 5-notched petals. Both flowers and seeds are produced throughout the spring and summer. Family: Pink (Caryophyllaceae); evenly divided between genera *Stellaria* and *Cerastium*.

CHICORY, or succory, a perennial herb of the Mediterranean region, now cosmopolitan as a weed. The lower leaves are oval, the upper leaves on the stiff, flowering stems are very small and bractlike, and the flower heads are 1½ inches across and composed entirely of strap-shaped florets in varying shades of blue.

In Europe the long, heavy taproots are dug up, dried, and pulverized to make a substitute for coffee or to adulterate the coffee. The blanched lower leaves can be used for salads. A close relative, the endive (*Cichorium endiva*), has frilly, bitter, edible leaves. The endive is cultivated largely for use in salads. Family: Daisy (Compositae); genus and species, *Cichorium intybus*.

CHINABERRY, or bead tree, or pride of India, a fast-growing, spreading tree native to eastern Asia and northern Australia but introduced widely. It has alternate, pinnately compound leaves, large clusters of fragrant, purplish flowers, which are followed by nearly spherical, yellow fruits ½ inch in diameter. The thin pulp soon dries over the armored seed, producing a "bead." Family: Mahogany (Meliaceae); genus and species, *Melia azedarach*.

CHOCOLATE. See *Cacao*.

CHRISTMAS BERRY, a shrub or small tree native to California and used there in place of holly for Christmas decorations. Growing 5 to 25 feet high, the tree has pale, aromatic bark, glossy, serrate, evergreen leaves, loose clusters of white flowers, and bright red berries which are edible, pleasant tasting, and ripen during the coldest part of winter. Family: Rose (Rosaceae); genus and species, *Heteromeles arbutifolia*.

CHRISTMAS ROSE. See *Hellebore*.

CHRYSANTHEMUM, a genus of about 150 different kinds of annual and perennial herbaceous plants of the Northern Hemisphere and Africa, some of which are attractive weeds, and others of which are cultivated for their handsome flowers. All have notched or pinnately divided leaves and flattened flower heads.

The oxe-eye daisy or whiteweed (*C. leucanthemum*) of Eurasia is now almost cosmopolitan in temperate regions. The East Asian species (particularly *C. morifolium*) were cultivated in early times, leading Japan to adopt a stylized chrysanthemum with 16 florets as its national emblem; horticultural varieties include many in which all florets are strap shaped and twisted, the flower heads as much as 10 inches across and in many colors. Family: Daisy (Compositae).

CINCHONA. a genus of perhaps 40 different kinds of trees native to mountain slopes from Peru northward to Costa Rica, with red bark, spreading branches, opposite, ovate leaves, and open clusters of pink flowers. The fruit is a capsule that opens to release its many seeds. Known since about 1630 as a source of an anti-malarial drug, quinine, cinchona trees have been cultivated in India and Java; the latter country is the principal commercial producer of the drug itself, which is extracted from the bark, called Peruvian bark. Family: Madder (Rubiaceae).

CINERARIA, the florist's name for a herbaceous perennial plant from the Canary Islands, with large, ovate leaves, short, branching stem, and large, daisy-like flowers with purple disc florets and white, red, or purple ray florets. *Cineraria* is a genus of South African herbs and low shrubs with thistle-like flowers. Family: Daisy (Compositae); genus and species, *Senecio cruentus*.

CINNAMON, a small evergreen tree native to Ceylon, but cultivated in China, tropical America, Florida, and California for the inner bark of its young shoots and branches, which yields a popular flavoring, cinnamon. The tree itself has large, ovate, paired leaves, loose clusters of malodorous, greenish flowers, and small, fleshy fruits. Oil can be extracted from the fruit and leaves as well as from the bark, but only the light, yellowish-brown bark can be powdered as a spice; the spice has a sweet, warm taste from the aromatic oil it contains.

A closely related tree native to Formosa, Japan, and China (*Cinnamomum camphora*) is now cultivated in California, Texas, and Florida as a shade tree, a windbreak, and a source of gum; it is the principal source of camphor, which is distilled from young shoots or old trees cut into chips. Family: Laurel (Lauraceae); genus and species, *Cinnamomum zeylanicum*.

CITRON, a small evergreen tree with irregular branches, large, oval leaves, and bluish blossoms. It is native to India, China and Southeast Asia but is cultivated chiefly in southern Europe, primarily for its greenish-yellow lemon-shaped fruits, 5 to 6 inches long; the fruit rind is candied and the juice used as a beverage or concentrated to a syrup. An oil extracted from citron leaves is used in making perfume. Family: Rue (Rutaceae); genus and species, *Citrus medica*.

CLEMATIS, a genus containing about 230 different kinds of vines and climbing shrubs with opposite compound leaves the petioles of which are tendril-like and curl around supports. The flowers of all lack petals but have 4 showy sepals and many stamens. Represented on most continents in areas with cool summers, the genus is best known in eastern North America as virgin's bower, or old-man's-beard (*C. virginiana*), which has feathery plumes attached to the many seeds in each cluster of a flower. Family: Buttercup (Ranunculaceae).

CLOVER, any of about 300 different kinds of herbaceous plants native to temperate and subtropical regions, bearing palmately compound leaves with 3 to 5 leaflets, and round heads of tiny, closely packed, white, pink, or purplish flowers. Bees make some of the most delicious honey known from their nectar. Clovers are valuable forage plants for livestock, and are often grown as part of a rotational sequence for soil improvement. Family: Pea (Leguminosae); genus *Trifolium*. See also *Sweet clover*.

CLOVE TREE, a tropical evergreen tree with large oval leaves, native to the East Indies, where it grows to a height of 50 feet. It is cultivated near the seacoasts and on tropical islands of South America, the West Indies, and Africa, particularly Zanzibar. It is pruned as a low shrub from which the buds of the clustered, crimson flowers can easily be picked in order to be dried and used as spice cloves. Each tree yields from 5 to 75 pounds of cloves annually.

The spice is used for making candy and clove liqueur, and for flavoring. Oil of cloves, extracted by distillation, is used in medicine, soaps, and perfumes. Family: Myrtle (Myrtaceae); genus and species, *Eugenia aromatica*.

CLUB MOSS, any of about 180 different kinds of creeping herbaceous plants found almost all over the world, with upright stems clad in evergreen and bractlike leaves, bearing spore cases either among the leaves or clustered to form the club-shaped ends of the vertical stems. The spores are carried by wind, and can germinate in moist soil into ½-inch, carrot-shaped plants with sex organs. Fertilized eggs in these develop into the club moss.

Because of a fancied resemblance, various club mosses are known as staghorn evergreen, ground pine, ground fir, and ground cedar. Few grow more than a foot tall, and most live in moist forests. Family: Club moss (Lycopodiaceae); genus *Lycopodium*.

COCA, a small shrub of mountain slopes in Bolivia and Peru, with straight branches growing to a height of 8 feet, bearing small, oval leaves distinctly marked with a transparent area on each side of the midrib; the small, white flowers are followed by small, black berries. The native people have learned to pluck the leaves as soon as each is stiff enough to break when bent, to dry them, and to keep them dry. The product, which resembles tea

BURPEE SEEDS

CINERARIA

CORN

leaves, is chewed by Indians at work or on long journeys, dulling hunger and fatigue and apparently giving them strength and endurance; or it is marketed as a source of the drug cocaine, which is used as a local anesthetic in surgery. Coca belongs to a genus of about 200 different species native to the American tropics, many of which contain smaller amounts of cocaine. They form a small family. Family: Coca (Erythroxylaceae); genus and species, *Erythroxylum coca*.

COCKSCOMB, a low-growing, herbaceous plant of tropical Asia, widely cultivated in temperate gardens as an annual because, about its long, pointed, green leaves, it produces a monstrous flower head suggesting a rooster's comb. The flower head is sometimes as wide as the plant is tall and consists of crimson, orange, or creamy-white flowers at the ends of multiple stalks that grow in a fan-shaped bundle. Family: Amaranth (Amaranthaceae); genus and species, *Celosia aristata*.

COCOA. See *Cacao*.

COFFEE, any of about 45 different kinds of small trees with paired, oval, shining, evergreen leaves and clusters of fragrant, white flowers from which, after about 7 months, crimson, cherry-like fruits develop, each containing 2 flat seeds known as coffee beans.

Native to Arabia and tropical Africa, particularly Ethiopia and Madagascar, a few species have been intensively cultivated for their beans in Ceylon, Java, and elsewhere in the East Indies, as well as in Brazil, Cuba, Central America, and Colombia. These beans are cured and dried and later ground and brewed to make a mildly stimulating beverage containing caffeine. Family: Madder (Rubiaceae); genus and species, *Coffea arabica*.

COFFEE TREE. See *Kentucky Coffeetree*.

COLUMBINE, any of about 50 different kinds of graceful, perennial herbs of the Northern Hemisphere, with long-stalked palmately compound leaves and large, showy flowers at the end of the branches; each flower has 5 sepals and 5 long-spurred petals that secrete nectar. Family: Buttercup (Ranunculaceae); genus *Aquilegia*.

COREOPSIS, a genus that comprises about 115 different kinds of weak-stemmed herbs ranging from 12 to 15 inches tall, mostly native to North America but found also in Africa and Hawaii. They produce a few narrow leaves and many long-stalked, yellow or pink, daisy-like flowers. Several species are cultivated as ornaments in temperate gardens. The most notable is an annual, *C. calliopis*, the ray florets of which are red, maroon, or yellow.

The name tickseed is given to many species, particularly *C. major* of eastern North America, because the small, flat fruits have tiny hooks that cause them to adhere to fur and clothing. Family: Daisy (Compositae).

CORN, or Indian corn, or maize, an erect, herbaceous, annual grass native to mountainous tropical America, domesticated by the Indians and developed horticulturally into many diverse genetic strains, chiefly for the fruits (called kernels) borne in a tight spiral (the cob) within a sheath of spathe-like leaves (the husk), from the end of which the long, threadlike filaments (the silk) extend. Pollen from a terminal cluster of stamens (the tassel) is carried by the wind, pollinating each of the separate, clustered, pistillate flowers from which the kernels develop.

Various strains of corn grow 2 to 30 feet tall; the chief food varieties are dent, flint, flour, pod, pop, and sweet corn. Corn stalks, with their partly sheathing, elongated, coarse leaves are cut for storage and fermentation in farm silos. They are used to provide winter food for livestock. Family: Grass (Gramineae); genus and species, *Zea mays*.

CORNEL. See *Dogwood*.

CORNFLOWER, or bluebottle, or bachelor's button, a slender annual herb of southern Europe, now common in gardens throughout the temperate zones. It grows 1 to 2 feet tall, with small, grayish leaves and fringed, trumpet-like flower heads containing many blue, pink, or white florets. Family: Daisy (Compositae); genus and species, *Centaurea cyanus*.

COTTON, any of several different cultivated, annual, branching, erect herbs of tropical and subtropical regions, with alternate, 3-lobed leaves, and large, showy, creamy flowers that turn red on the second day after opening. The fruit is a globular capsule, called a boll, filled with fluffy fibers attached to the flattened seeds.

Wild cotton grows more than 15 feet tall, but domesticated species are short to facilitate picking the ripe bolls, from which the fibers are removed for use in making textiles and the seeds for the extraction of a commercial cottonseed oil. Family: Mallow (Malvaceae); genus *Gossypium*.

COTTONWOOD. See *Poplar*.

COWPEA, or black-eyed pea, a sprawling, herbaceous plant native to tropical Asia, now cultivated in warm parts of Europe, North America, and Africa for its edible seeds, which may be eaten fresh or dried for storage and later soaked before cooking.

The plant itself is a twining annual with 3-part leaves and a few purplish flowers; it produces pods growing to 12 inches long, with kidney-shaped seeds, each usually with a black spot around the point of attachment. Family Pea (Leguminosae); genus and species, *Vigna sinensis*.

COWSLIP. See *Marsh marigold* and *Primrose*.

CRABGRASS, a coarse, annual European grass, now almost cosmopolitan on cultivated land and wasteland in temperate regions. It has a creeping stem, rough, hairy leaves 2 to 10 inches long, and radiating spikes of minute, grayish-yellow flowers that produce red or purple seeds. In some parts of Europe crabgrass is raised as forage for livestock. Family: Grass (Gramineae); genus and species, *Digitaria sanguinalis*.

CRANBERRY, either of 2 closely related, slender, creeping, shrubby plants with alternate, leathery, small, evergreen leaves which are dark above and paler below, the edges curving downward. The plants have up to 10 nodding, pink or white, bell-shaped flowers on each branch, followed by red, spherical fruits that float on water. Cranberries grow on boggy or peaty soil, along swamp edges, and on floating bogs.

The small-berried species is found across Eurasia and North America, and at higher elevations in the south; the larger-berried North American species is cultivated in artificial bogs that can be flooded at harvest time. The fruits are used for canning, preserving, and in baking. Family: Heath (Ericaceae); genus and species, *Vaccinium oxycoccus* (small-fruited) and *V. macrocarpon*.

CRAPE MYRTLE, an Oriental shrub or small tree with paired, oval, glossy, green leaves and showy, open clusters of lavender-colored flowers, often called "lilac-of-the-South" in the southeastern United States, where it is commonly planted as an ornament. Family: Loosestrife (Lythraceae); genus and species, *Lagerstroemia indica*.

CREOSOTE BUSH, a tough, perennial shrub of deserts in Mexico and the adjacent United States, growing 3 to 4 feet tall, with gray stems marked with black paired leaflets at the end of each petiole; after a rainfall, it produces yellow flowers.

Few animals will eat the foliage or stems because of the strong, tarry odor, even though the creosote-bush is one of the few types of vegetation that has adopted well to conditions of extreme chronic drought. Family: Caltrop (Zygophyllaceae); genus and species, *Larrea tridentata*.

CRESS, any of several different kinds of small, perennial herbs that grow prostrate or buoyed up by running water, with hot-tasting leaves sought as ingredients for salads, or as a garnish or seasoning. They can be cultivated for home use in tubs or frames that hold water. If allowed to flower, all produce small clusters of white or yellow blossoms, each with 4 petals.

The most common kinds are the European watercress (*Nasturtium officinale*), the garden cress or peppergrass (*Lepidium sativum*) from Mediterranean countries, the wild peppergrass (*L. virginicum*) from North America, which has been introduced into Europe, and the winter cress (*Barbarea verna*), from the North Temperate Zone. Family: Mustard (Cruciferae).

CROCUS, a genus of about 70 different kinds of bulbous, herbaceous plants, most of which are native to the Mediterranean region. They blossom in early spring before extending their narrow, stiff, white-lined, green leaves, a characteristic that makes them attractive as ornaments. A fall-flowering species (*C. vernus*) is harvested in Spain for the stigmas of its blossoms, which yield saffron dye.

The name autumn crocus, or meadow saffron, is given to an unrelated bulbous plant (*Colchicum autumnale* of the lily family, Liliaceae) that produces flowers in autumn after its leaves of the year have shriveled and disappeared; its bulbs and seeds are the source of the poisonous alkaloid colchicine, which is used in medicine and horticulture. Family: Iris (Iridaceae).

CROTON, a genus that comprises about 600 different kinds of tropical shrubs native to the Old World and the New, many of them with handsomely mottled leaves in shades of green, yellow, and dark red, usually with long, terminal spikes of small flowers, the staminate flowers commonly nearer the tip of the same spike than the pistillate ones. An Asian species (*C. tiglium*) yields croton oil, which is a strong purgative. The cascarilla (*C. cascarilla*) of the Bahamas and Florida yields a bark known as Eleuthera bark or cascarilla bark and is used to make a tonic and an incense. Family: Spurge (Euphorbiaceae).

CUBEB. See *Pepper.*

CUCUMBER, a trailing annual, herbaceous plant that probably originated in Asia south of the Himalayas, but is now cultivated throughout the world for its edible fruits. The hairy stem bears 3-lobed leaves and bell-shaped, yellow flowers on short stalks; the green, fleshy, oblong fruit is eaten fresh, cooked, or pickled. A close relative from the West Indies (*Cucumis anguria*) bears prickly, small fruits called gherkins. Family: Gourd (Cucurbitaceae); genus and species, *Cucumis sativus*.

CURRANT, any of a small number of branching, shrubby perennials with smooth stems, round, scalloped leaves, clusters of small, yellowish or purple flowers, and, later, similar clusters of red, black, striped, or white berries. Cultivated in many temperate countries are the Eurasian red currants (*Ribes rubrum* and *R. vulgare*) and Eurasian black currants (*R. nigrum*); they bear edible fruits that can be eaten raw, cooked, or preserved. The fruits of the golden currant (*R. aureum*) of the western United States are regarded as less important than their bright yellow, fragrant blossoms, which are unusual because they are tubular rather than bell-shaped. Family: Saxifrage (Saxifragaceae); genus *Ribes.*

CUSTARD APPLE, a small, West Indian tree with large, leathery leaves and solitary, nodding flowers bearing 3 sepals and usually 6 petals, as well as numerous stamens and separate pistils. The fleshy fruits of the separate pistils unite as they ripen, often becoming very large.

Introduced into many other parts of the tropics, custard apples are cultivated for their fruits, which are too soft to ship, and are generally eaten with a spoon. Related trees from the American tropics, yielding different but delicious fruits, include the sweetsop or sugar apple (*Annona squamosa*), the soursop (*A. muricata*), and the cherimoya (*A. cherimolia*), all used in making drinks, ices, jellies, and preserves. Family: Custard apple (Annonaceae); genus and species, *Annona reticulata.*

CUSTARD-APPLE FAMILY (Annonaceae), a group of about 850 species in 80 genera, chiefly woody plants—shrubs, vines, or trees—with aromatic, simple leaves. See *Custard apple* and *Papaw.*

CYCAD, any of about 100 different kinds of woody shrubs and trees widely distributed in the tropics and subtropics, with thick, slow-growing stems that have a very large pith, alternate, pinnately compound, leathery, evergreen leaves, and separate staminate and ovulate cones, the seeds often brightly colored and with a fleshy covering.

Many cycads are palmlike, two kinds (*Macrozamia* species) in eastern Australia growing to a height of 60 feet. The "palms" of hotel lobbies in many parts of the world are actually either *Cycas revoluta* of southeastern China and southern Japan or *Dioon edule* of Mexico. The seeds of the latter are starchy and can be ground into an edible meal.

The pith of the sago palm (*Cycas circinalis*) of the East Indies yields sago starch, which is almost indistinguishable from that of many true palms (family Palmaceae). In Florida, the Seminole Indians dug the heavy, short, underground stems of the native cycads (chiefly *Zamia floridana*), called coonties, as a source of starchy flour. Family: Cycad (Cycadaceae).

CYCLAMEN, a genus of 13 different kinds of herbaceous, perennial plants native to southern Europe and Asia Minor, with leathery, kidney-shaped leaves on long stalks, and nodding flowers with reflexed petal lobes, white, rose, pink, or purple in color. One species (*C. persicum*) is cultivated in greenhouses and homes of northern Europe and North America for its flowers. Family: Primrose (Primulaceae).

CYPRESS, any of 12 different kinds of evergreen, coniferous trees native to warm parts of the Northern Hemisphere. All grow tall, with tiny leaves less than ¼ inch long, closely pressed to the branchlets, and small cones composed of less than 20 cone scales. None tolerates hard frosts or extended cold weather.

The funeral cypress (*Cupressus funebris*) of China, which grows like a tall, dark green column with branches that hang down and are said to "weep," is planted in cemeteries in many warm countries. Family: Cypress (Cupressaceae); genus *Cupressus.*

CYPRESS FAMILY (Cupressaceae), a group of about 140 species in 15 genera, all shrubs or trees with scalelike or needlelike leaves and mature cones that are dry and woody or fleshy and berry-like. See *Arbor vitae, Cedar, Cypress,* and *Juniper.*

DAFFODIL. See *Narcissus.*

DAHLIA, a genus of perennial plants native to Mexico and Central America, including about 9 different kinds, of which one, *D. pinnata*, is grown widely as an ornamental garden flower. The wild plant grows 2 to 6 feet tall and bears compact heads of red flowers, each with a yellow center.

More than 10,000 horticultural varieties have been developed in every color except blue. Although many of the varieties produce seeds that will germinate, the named kinds are usually grown from the tuberous roots, which have buds at the stem end. Family: Daisy (Compositae).

DAISY, any of a number of different plants that produce flat flower heads surrounded by a radiating row of white petals. The lawn daisy (*Bellis perennis*), a stemless little plant that produces 1-inch flower heads on 2- or 3-inch slender stalks from spring until autumn is widespread in Britain and has been introduced by Europeans into many parts of North America, Asia, and New Zealand. A field full of tall, white daisies usually consists of the ox-eye, marguerite, or whiteweed (*Chrysanthemum leucanthemum*) of Eurasia, which has become a pasture weed in Canada and the United States.

The Shasta daisy, with flower heads up to 4 inches in diameter, is a hybrid developed by Luther Burbank chiefly from the smaller *Chrysanthemum maximum* of the Pyrenees. Daisy-like flowers also open on more than 125 different kinds of daisy-bushes (*Olearia*) in New Zealand, Australia, and New Guinea, where these shrubs often form thickets. Family: Daisy (Compositae).

DAISY FAMILY (Compositae), the largest family of flowering plants, with more than 20,000 species in 950 genera, widely distributed and including shrubs and a few trees as well as herbs. All are easy to recognize by their flower heads, in which many florets are attached side by side to the broad end to the stalk and surrounded by a row of bracts called an involucre. See *Ageratum, Arnica, Artichoke, Aster, Black-eyed Susan, Boneset, Burdock, Camomile, Chicory, Chrysanthemum, Cineraria, Coreopsis, Cornflower, Dahlia, Daisy, Dandelion, Edelweiss, Elecampane, Everlasting, Gaillardia, Golden glow, Goldenrod, Guayule, Hawkweed, Ironweed, Joe-Pye weed, Lettuce, Marigold, Mayweed, Pot marigold, Ragweed, Safflower, Sagebrush, Salsify, Sunflower, Tarragon, Thistle, Wormwood, Yarrow*, and *Zinnia*.

DANDELION, or blowballs, a common weed of lawns introduced from Europe and now kept widespread in the United States by its light-weight fruits, each with a terminal tuft of silky hairs that catches the wind. The bright yellow flowers are borne on tall, hollow stalks that rise from a flat rosette of leaves; the leaves, which are toothed along the edges, have led to the name dandelion (*dents-de-leon*, "lion's teeth").

Europeans commonly gather the leaf rosettes and boil them as potherbs, or collect the flowers and extract their sugar as the basis of dandelion wine. Family: Daisy (Compositae); genus and species, *Taraxacum officinale*.

DASHEEN. See *Taro*.

DEVIL'S–PAINTBRUSH. See *Hawkweed*.

DEWBERRY. See *Blackberry*.

DILL, a biennial herb of southern Europe and North Africa, originally cultivated in Asia Minor, India, and North America for its seeds, but more recently for its immature flower clusters and leaves as well. From all these an extract called dill herb oil can be obtained for use in flavoring. Like caraway and anise extracts, it apparently reduces gas in the human digestive tract. Family: Carrot (Umbelliferae); genus and species, *Anethum graveolens*.

DOCK, any of several coarse weeds of Eurasia, now widespread, each a perennial with a long, stout taproot, broad, ruffled leaves, and a stem 1½ to 3 feet tall, topped by clusters of small, green flowers. They grow on poor, acid soil, where other plants do not find enough nourishment, and provide some food for livestock. In Eurasia the young shoots are used as a vegetable. Mexican tanner's dock (*Rumex hymenosepalus*) yields canaigre, an extract used in tanning hides. Family: Buckwheat (Polygonaceae); genus *Rumex*. See also *Burdock*.

DODDER, any of about 160 different kinds of rootless, leafless, non-green, parasitic vines that grow as annual plants, twining around the stalks of other vegetation. They are native to most temperate and tropical countries. At intervals along the yellow, red, or white, threadlike stems are short suckers that extend into the tissues of the host plant and absorb nourishment. The pink flowers generally appear in small clusters from July to September, and are followed by capsules of minute, ripe seeds that travel as impurities among seeds of crop plants. Family: Morning-glory (Convolvulaceae); genus *Cuscuta*.

DOGBANE, any of about 25 different kinds of herbaceous perennial plants native to the North Temperate Zone, with paired, simple leaves on branching stems 1 to 4 feet tall, and small clusters of pinkish-white, bell-shaped flowers. Family: Dogbane (Apocynaceae); genus *Apocynum*.

DOGBANE FAMILY (Apocynaceae), a group of about 1300 species in 300 genera, widely distributed but best represented in the tropics. They include trees, shrubs, tropical woody vines, and herbs, all with milky sap and simple, smooth-edged leaves. Some yield drugs, latex, tannins, and other valuable substances, whereas others are valuable chiefly as ornaments. Frangipani or temple tree (*Plumeria rubra*), native to tropical America, is grown for its perfumed, clustered flowers. See *Dogbane, Indian Hemp, Oleander*, and *Periwinkle*.

DOGTOOTH VIOLET, or dog's-tooth-violet, any of several similar and related fawn lilies with a pair of mottled, basal leaves, producing in early spring a nodding, single flower at the top of a slender stalk. The Eurasian dogtooth violet (*Erythronium denscanis*) has a red or purple flower. The eastern North American area has a yellow violet, adder's-tongue (*E. americanum*), and a white one (*E. albidum*). A rosy-pink dogtooth violet (*E. propullans*) is native to Minnesota. Family: Lily (Liliaceae); genus *Erythronium*.

DOGWOOD, any of about 40 different kinds of shrubs and trees with simple leaves, native to the North Temperate Zone and to tropical mountains. Their small but often conspicuous fruits remain after the leaves drop in autumn, providing winter food for birds. The widespread red osier dogwood (*Cornus stolonifera*) forms thickets that may be identified by the many smooth, red stems and, in autumn, white or lead-colored fruits; its flowers are inconspicuous.

The flowering dogwoods, small trees in which the flower clusters are conspicuous because of the 4 to 7 white or colored, petal-like bracts associated with them, include the Cornelian cherry (*C. mas*) of central and southern Europe and western Asia, the western dogwood (*C. nuttallii*) of British Columbia to California, and the eastern dogwood (*C. florida*) of eastern North America, including eastern Mexico. Family: Dogwood (Cornaceae); genus *Cornus*.

DOGWOOD FAMILY (Cornaceae), a group of about 125 species in 18 genera found in temperate areas in the Northern and Southern hemispheres, including the higher slopes of tropical mountains. They are woody undershrubs, shrubs and trees with simple leaves. See *Bunchberry, Dogwood*, and *Tupelo*.

DOUGLAS FIR, a tall, straight tree of western North America, with flattened needles on short stalks and pendant cones 2 to 4 inches long, which are unique because every cone scale is accompanied by a 3-pronged bract that projects half an inch or so beyond the scale. When the leaves drop off the stem is smooth, as in a true fir; the cones, however, remain attached until after the seeds have been dispersed, whereas those of a true fir disintegrate to release the seeds.

Douglas fir grows to a height of 221 feet, and is the leading timber tree in America today, yielding about a quarter of the lumber produced in the United States and Canada. Family: Pine (Pinaceae); genus and species, *Pseudotsuga taxifolia*.

DUTCHMAN'S–BREECHES, a woodland wildflower of northeastern North America, with delicate, green leaves and slender stalks 5 to 10 inches high, bearing rows of small, heart-shaped, spurred, white or pink flowers shaped somewhat like the ballooning breeches once worn by Dutch peasants.

Closely related are the bleeding heart (*Dicentra spectabilis*) of China and Japan, which is cultivated in gardens because of its rosy-red and pink flowers, and the squirrel corn (*D. canadensis*), named for the yellow, tuberous knobs on its buried, horizontal stems. Family: Fumitory (Fumariaceae); genus and species, *Dicentra cucullaria*.

DUTCHMAN'S–PIPE, a woody, climbing vine native to eastern North America, from Pennsylvania to Georgia and Alabama, now widely cultivated for its smooth, heart-shaped leaves and its clusters of showy flowers, each resembling a Dutch pipe. The showy part is the calyx, for petals are lacking. Family: Birthwort (Aristolochiaceae); genus and species, *Aristolchia durior*.

EBONY, any of several related trees of equatorial Africa and tropical Asia, the intensely hard, black, heartwood of which can be given a high polish. India and Ceylon are the principal sources for *Diospyros ebenum*, which attains a height of 100 feet, and has oblong leaves, fragrant, yellow flowers, jet-black bark, and almost white sapwood surrounding the valuable heartwood. Family: Ebony (Ebenaceae); genus *Diospyros*.

EBONY FAMILY (Ebenaceae), a group of 325 species in 5 genera, all shrubs or trees with simple, smooth-edged, leathery leaves. They are most numerous in Southeast Asia but are widely represented in tropical and subtropical regions. See *Ebony* and *Persimmon*.

EDELWEISS, an alpine plant with narrow, wooly, white leaves and flowers with many separate heads, which are clustered so close together that insects can walk from one to the next, obtaining nectar and pollinating the blossoms. Native to high peaks in the European Alps, where it is endangered by excessive picking, it is now cultivated in gardens in many temperate parts of the world. In cultivation it sometimes grows to 6 feet. Family: Daisy (Compositae); genus and species, *Leontopodium alpinum*.

EGGPLANT, a bushy, annual plant native to northeastern India, domesticated and cultivated in warmer parts of Eurasia, North America, Australia, and New Zealand for the pendant, oblong, edible fruits, which may be purple, yellow, or white. The stems are spiny, the leaves large and lobed, and the flowers are violet-colored. Family: Potato (Solanaceae); genus and species, *Solanum melongena*.

ELDER, any of about 20 different kinds of shrubs and trees native to temperate and tropical lands, with pinnately compound leaves and flat clusters of tiny flowers that are followed by juicy fruits, each containing 3 tiny, armored seeds.

The fruits of the European elder (*Sambucus nigra*), native to western Asia and North Africa and to Europe, and of the common American elder (*S. canadensis*) in eastern Canada and the United States are eaten by birds unless they are harvested. The berries are made into elderberry pie or used as the basis of elderberry wine. Family: Honeysuckle (Caprifoliaceae); genus *Sambucus*.

ELECAMPANE, or horseheal, a tall, coarse herb of Eurasia, with large, egg-shaped tubers on the roots, and 4-inch heads of daisy-like flowers bearing golden-yellow petals around the rim and disc florets that change in color from yellow to tan as they mature.

The root tubers yield a medicinal agent rich in the carbohydrate inulin, with a warm, bitter taste and an odor suggestive of that of camphor. Family: Daisy (Compositae); genus and species, *Inula helenium*.

ELEPHANT'S EAR. See *Begonia*.

ELM, any of about 30 different kinds of trees native to the North Temperate Zone and the mountains of tropical Asia, bearing simple leaves that are oblique at the base and winged fruits with the seed at the center. The American elm (*Ulmus americana*) develops a wide-spreading crown, making it a valuable shade tree. It rises to a height of 160 feet with a top 75 feet across; the wood is so cross-grained that it can hardly be split.

The slippery elm (*U. rubra*) of the eastern United States has a mucilaginous inner bark that has been used medicinally. Like the European elm or the English elm (*U. campestris*), and the Chinese elm (*U. parvifolia*), it is a lesser tree but is immune to the fungus infection known as the Dutch elm disease, which is destroying the New England elms. Family: Elm (Ulmaceae); genus *Ulmus*.

ELM FAMILY (Ulmaceae), a group of nearly 160 species in 15 genera, all shrubs or trees with simple leaves that are native to the North Temperate Zone and mountains of tropical Asia. See *Elm* and *Hackberry*.

BURPEE SEEDS
EGGPLANT

ENDIVE. See *Chicory*.

EUCALYPTUS, or gum trees, a genus of tall trees including about 600 different kinds native to Australia, New Guinea, and the adjacent islands. The leaves are usually narrow and pendant, casting little shade. The sepals and petals drop from the flowers as they open, exposing a tuft of stamens that are commonly bright red, gold-tipped, and attractive to pollinating insects. The fruits are hard and dry.

A fast-growing eucalyptus, the Australian bluegum (*E. globulus*), has been introduced in many temperate areas as a windbreak and as a quick source of wood. It grows to a height of 50 feet in about 5 years. Tallest is the gum tree (*E. regnans*) of eastern Australia, which attains a height of 326 feet and a diameter of 25 feet at chest height. Oil of eucalyptus, used medicinally for colds and bronchial infections, is extracted from the young twigs and leaves of several different kinds. Family: Myrtle (Myrtaceae).

EUONYMUS, a genus of shrubs and trees native to the Northern Hemisphere and Australia, with about 100 different species, many of them evergreen. All have spreading branches, pointed, serrate leaves, open clusters of drooping, purple flowers, and seeds covered by bright orange or red arils, which are exposed in autumn when the fruit capsule breaks open.

The European spindle-tree (*E. europaeus*) and the burning-bush or wahoo (*E. atropurpureus*) of eastern North America are often raised as ornamental shrubs or trees partly because their leaves turn a rich purplish-red in autumn before dropping; they grow to 25 feet tall. The winged spindle-tree (*E. alatus*) also displays such rich fall coloring; it is native to eastern Asia and has corky, winglike projections from its branches. Family: Staff tree (Celastraceae).

EUPHORBIA, a large genus of latex-bearing plants native to subtropical and warm, temperate parts of Africa and America. Most have succulent, spiny stems, simple leaves, and tiny flowers in large, nectar-producing glands.

Of the 1600 different kinds, the most widely cultivated are the poinsettia (*E. pulcherrima*) of Mexico and Central America, the flower clusters of which are made conspicuous by an open whorl of adjacent, bright red or white leaves, and the prickly crown-of-thorns (*E. splendens*) of Madagascar, often planted as a hedge; the latter bears a succession of slender stems from its woody branches, holding 2 or 4 scarlet "flowers," each of which is a diminutive cluster.

Africa south of the Sahara has tree euphorbias, which resemble organ-pipe cacti, and have adapted in a similar way to store water in arid highlands. Family: Spurge (Euphorbiaceae).

EVENING PRIMROSE, any of about 100 different kinds of American herbs found from the Arctic to Patagonia. Most bear bright butter-yellow or white flowers that open late in the day and close again permanently the following dawn, often changing to a pink or magenta color as they fade.

Hawkmoths are attracted by scent to serve as pollinators. The seeds have a thin membrane that catches the wind; in this fashion any gust can distribute them widely. The root and upper foliage of some kinds are edible. Family: Evening primrose (Onagraceae); genus *Oenothera*.

EVENING-PRIMROSE FAMILY (Onagraceae), a group of about 650 species in 20 genera, widely distributed, growing as herbs, shrubs, or trees with simple leaves. See *Evening primrose, Fireweed, Fuchsia,* and *Godetia*.

EVERLASTING, any of several different kinds of annual plants the dried blossoms of which have a strawlike texture; they retain their color and form and can be displayed as decorations throughout the winter.

The flower heads, cut before they open fully, are often hung upside down to be dried and then dyed in assorted colors. This custom presumably began with the wild immortelle (*Helichrysum orientale*) of Asia and Africa, which is cultivated in southern Europe, but it has also been followed with the Australian *Waitzia* and the North American species of *Anaphalis, Antennaria,* and *Gnaphalium*. Family: Daisy (Compositae).

FENNEL, a stout, aromatic, perennial herb native to Europe, bearing leaves that are divided into threadlike projections from the midrib, flat heads of yellow flowers, and slender seeds about ¼ inch long. The young leaves are sometimes eaten as salad greens, and the seeds used as a relish or as the source of a fragrant oil used in perfumes and soaps. Introduced into North America, it has sometimes become a troublesome pasture weed. Family: Carrot (Umbelliferae); genus and species, *Foeniculum officinale*.

FIG, any of about 800 different kinds of tropical and subtropical shrubs and trees, which have a palatable, milky juice in their alternately arranged leaves and produce a unique, pear-shaped, inverted receptacle enclosing tiny flowers that produce small fruits. The edible part of the fig is the fleshy receptacle, which may be eaten raw, fresh, dried, cooked, or preserved, or may be used as the base from which wine and other alcoholic beverages are made.

The commercial fig is the product of a 20-foot tree *(Ficus carica)* of western Asia, now cultivated in all Mediterranean countries and the United States; its fruits vary in color from white to yellow, purple, and black. The India-rubber plant *(F. elastica)* of India and Java, which was formerly a commercial source of rubber, is now widely cultivated as a house plant with glossy, oblong leaves.

The peepul tree, or botree *(F. religiosa),* which is sacred to Gautama Buddha, is planted outside Buddhist shrines, providing shade, a useful lac, and an extract useful in tanning leather. The banyan tree *(F. benghalensis)* of the East Indies supports its outspread, heavy limbs on strong, adventitious roots that grow down to the soil and become thick; a single tree can extend itself in this way over a broad area. Family: Mulberry (Moraceae); genus *Ficus.*

FIGWORT, any of about 150 different kinds of coarse herbs native to the North Temperate Zone, found especially in Asia, with a 4-sided stem, mostly opposite leaves, and a loose, terminal cluster of flowers shaped like those of the snapdragon. The flowers are usually greenish, purple, or blood-red. Fleshy knobs on the horizontal, underground stems of some species were once believed to be evidence that the plants could be used to cure fig-warts and scrofula. Family: Figwort (Scrophulariaceae); genus *Scrophularia.*

FIGWORT FAMILY (Scrophulariaceae), a group of about 2600 species in 200 genera, represented on all continents, mostly herbs and low shrubs with simple leaves and bilaterally symmetrical flowers, the 5-part corolla typically 2-lipped. Included are the imperial tree *(Paulownia tomentosa)* of China and Japan, which grows 40 feet tall with large, heart-shaped leaves and clusters of white flowers; the louseworts *(Pedicularis* species), which are partially parasitic on tree roots; and the paintbrush *(Castilleja* species), chiefly of western North America, in which the upper leaves and bracts near the inconspicuous flowers are brightly colored in orange and red. See *Bluebell, Calceolaria, Figwort, Foxglove, Mullein, Snapdragon,* and *Veronica.*

FILBERT. See *Hazel.*

FIR, any of about 40 different kinds of coniferous, evergreen trees native to Eurasia and North America, which release their winged seeds when their upright cones disintegrate. Balsam firs, particularly the North American

BURPEE SEEDS
FORGET-ME-NOT

Abies balsamea, yield a fragrant resin from numerous "blisters" on the trunk that is used in medicine. With the exception of the noble fir *(A. nobilis)* of the northwestern United States and adjacent Canada, the firs are less valuable than the spruces for lumber; young firs are favored as Christmas trees. Family: Pine (Pinaceae); genus *Abies.*

FIREWEED, or great willow herb, a perennial, herbaceous plant of cool, temperate, and arctic-alpine parts of the Northern Hemisphere, where its lightweight, hair-tufted seeds germinate on cleared and burned-over land, leading to a conspicuous stand of stout stems 5 to 7 feet tall; these stems are generously clad in narrow, green leaves shaped like those of the willow, and end in a conspicuous, elongated cluster of magenta or pink flowers. Family: Evening primrose (Onagraceae); genus and species, *Epilobium angustifolium.*

FLAX, a slender, upright, herbaceous plant native to Eurasia, with almost grasslike leaves and few branches. At the tip of each branch it produces a delicate, violet-blue flower with petals that spread about ¾ inch across. The seeds, from which linseed oil is extracted, ripen in globular capsules.

To obtain fibers to be made into linen thread, the plants are harvested when the seeds are not yet fully ripe; at this stage, the fibers in the stems are at their best for removal and working. Weaving linen from flax plants is one of man's oldest technical achievements. Today, most of the fibers are from the Soviet Union and Europe from Poland to France. Family: Flax (Linaceae); genus and species, *Linum usitatissimum.*

FORGET-ME-NOT, or scorpion grass, any of about 300 different kinds of low herbs of temperate regions, some of which are supposed to have curled clusters of flower buds suggestive of a scorpion's upturned tail, and others to have leaves resembling mouse-ears, thus inspiring the generic name *Myosotis.* The European forget-me-not *(M. scorpioides)* has been widely introduced as a decorative plant for flower borders, where its small, pink buds open into pale blue blossoms; when it escapes from cultivation, it thrives in its normal surroundings—partly shaded banks of shallow streams as well as other wet places. Family: Borage (Boraginaceae).

FORSYTHIA, or golden bells, a genus with just 4 species of shrubs native to temperate parts of Eurasia, but now widely cultivated for their arching stems on which bright yellow flowers open before the leaves expand in spring. The 4-pointed petals diverge symmetrically from the rim of a bell-like throat. The pointed leaves have saw-teeth along the edges, and are arranged alternately along the stems. Family: Olive (Oleaceae).

FOUR-O'CLOCK, or marvel of Peru, a handsome herb with opposite leaves and clustered, trumpet-shaped flowers that open petal-like sepals with amazing regularity about four o'clock every afternoon, stay open through the night, and close again around sunrise. In its native Peru and in warm parts of the United States, four-o'clock is a perennial, whereas in temperate regions it is cultivated as a garden annual. Family: Four-o'clock (Nyctaginaceae); genus and species, *Mirabilis jalapa.*

FOUR-O'CLOCK FAMILY (Nyctaginaceae), a group of about 250 species in 28 genera, mostly herbs or woody plants of the tropics and subtropics, in which the floral parts seem reversed: the 5, united sepals are petal-like, the petals are absent altogether, and the imitation corolla is backed by green, sepal-like bracts. See *Bougainvillea* and *Four-o'clock.*

FOXGLOVE, any of about 25 different kinds of tall herbs of the Old World from the Canary Islands to central Asia, growing to a height of about 5 feet, with scattered, ovoid leaves and a tall spike of yellow, white, pink, or purple, spotted, tubular flowers that hang like inverted bells. *Digitalis purpurea* from western Europe has been widely introduced as an ornament, and is the principal source of the powerful heart stimulant digitalis. Family: Figwort (Scrophulariaceae); genus *Digitalis.*

FREESIA, a genus composed of 3 different kinds of herbaceous plants native to South Africa that grow from bulbs and produce an upright stem with small leaves and linear clusters of trumpet-shaped, fragrant flowers varying in color from white to cream, yellow, rose, and lavender. They are raised as house plants in many countries. Family: Iris (Iridaceae).

FRITILLARY, or checkered lily, any of about 50 different bulbous herbs of the North Temperate Zone, which produce nodding clusters of bell-

GAILLARDIA

shaped flowers the petals of which are checkered or spotted. Among the most handsome species cultivated as an ornament is the crown imperial (*Fritillaria imperialis*) of Iran. Family: Lily (Liliaceae); genus *Fritillaria*.

FUCHSIA, a genus of shrubs and trees, chiefly from Central and South America, with about 75 different species, including 2 in New Zealand. The plants have dark green, paired, oval leaves and funnel-shaped, pendant flowers on slender stalks. The sepals are usually a different color from the petals, providing such striking color contrasts as red and blue, red and cream, or scarlet and green. The plumlike fruits contain red seeds.

Many ornamental fuchsias are found in outdoor gardens of warm regions or grown as house plants in colder climates. They are often of hybrid origin. Family: Evening primrose (Onagraceae).

FUMITORY, a leafy-stemmed, branching, annual plant of Mediterranean countries, now cultivated in the United States and elsewhere in warm temperate parts of the world that escapes from cultivation into waste ground. The dense spikes of small, spurred, irregular, purplish flowers are followed by cylindrical capsules, each with a single seed. The name refers to the odor of the roots when they are first pulled from the soil. Family: Fumitory (Fumariaceae); genus and species, *Fumaria officinalis*.

FUMITORY FAMILY (Fumariaceae), a group of about 425 species in 19 genera, widespread in the North Temperate Zone and in South Africa. All are weak, smooth herbs with a watery sap and bilaterally symmetrical flowers. See *Dutchman's-breeches* and *Fumitory*.

FURZE. See *Gorse*.

GAILLARDIA, or blanket flowers, a genus of stiff, herbaceous wildflowers comprising 12 different kinds native to the western United States, all growing 2 to 3 feet tall, with a few oval, notched leaves and conspicuous flower heads, the red or yellow ray flowers of which form a bright halo around a golden center. Several have been developed by horticulturalists as garden flowers, which are popular because they bloom until late autumn. Some are annuals and others perennials. Family: Daisy (Compositae).

GARDENIA, a genus of about 100 different woody shrubs native to the Old World tropics, with broad, simple, opposite, evergreen leaves, and attractive, regular flowers. The fruits are bright orange and as much as 1½ inches long in cultivated gardenias such as the cape jasmine (*G. jasminoides*) of China, so named because the first plants brought to England came from the Cape of Good Hope.

Bearing fragrant, white or yellow flowers that have a waxy texture and last a long time, gardenias have become popular greenhouse plants in cool places; in warm regions, such as southeastern United States, they bloom outdoors and are used for decorative hedges. Family: Madder (Rubiaceae).

GARLIC, a strong-smelling, small onion native to southern Eurasia, with spearlike leaves rising from a hard bulb that reproduces itself as it grows, providing additional small bulbs (called cloves) within the tough outer skin. Cultivated for use as a flavoring, garlic has been introduced into many regions and has escaped from cultivation to roadsides and fields.

Along with such related plants as wild garlic (*Allium oleraceum* from Europe and *A. canadense* from eastern North America) and European field-garlic (*A. vineale*), it has become a hazard in pastures because cows tend to eat it, thus spoiling the taste of their milk. Family: Lily (Liliaceae); genus and species, *Allium sativum*.

GENTIAN, any of about 500 different kinds of herbaceous plants of temperate, cool, and especially alpine regions all over the world. They bear single or clustered, showy flowers late in the growing season. Most have deep, purplish-blue flowers, but some (particularly in the Andes) have pink or red, and a few have yellow flowers.

Several kinds are known as closed or bottle gentians because the petals of their deep, tubular corollas never spread; bumblebees force their way into these flowers to get nectar and attend to pollination. Gentian seeds are small, winged, and wind-distributed.

Those of the fringed gentian (*Gentiana crinita*) of moist woodlands from Maine to Minnesota and southward have had so little chance to ripen in recent years because people pick the flowers, that the plant is facing extermination. The flowers are lovely azure, urn-shaped blossoms with fringed edges that turn down. Because it is an annual in the southern parts of its range and a biennial in the northern parts, the fringed gentian depends for survival upon producing seeds from each flower.

The roots of the yellow gentian (*G. lutea*) of southern Europe and Asia Minor yield a drug formerly used as a tonic. Many other gentians produce a dye called gentian violet, which can be extracted and used in treating various skin and respiratory infections. Family: Gentian (Gentianaceae); genus *Gentiana*.

GENTIAN FAMILY (Gentianaceae), a group of about 800 species in 70 genera, widely distributed, some in the Arctic and on high mountains. All have opposite, simple leaves and clusters of regular flowers. The petal tips of the flowers uncurl as the bud opens.

A very different related plant is the water snowflake, or floating heart. Twenty different varieties of this plant grow in shallow ponds and slow-flowing streams, their heart-shaped leaves floating like waterlily pads on the surface; water snowflakes are often cultivated in garden pools and large aquaria. See also *Gentian*.

GERANIUM, a name applied widely and without discrimination to herbaceous plants of two related genera. About 300 of them are known as cranesbills (*Geranium*) from the shape of the fruit, and 250 are known as storksbills (*Pelargonium*).

Cranesbills have 5 similar petals without sepal extended in the form of a hollow spur. The upper 2 petals of storksbills are smaller, larger, or bear different markings, and the sepal behind these is extended into a long, hollow spur that is joined for its whole length to the flower stalk. Cranesbills include the wild geranium (*G. maculatum*) of eastern North American meadows, thickets, and woodlands, and the herb Robert (*G. robertianum*), found on gravelly shores and rocky woodlands of much of North America, Eurasia, and North Africa.

The hardy house plant known as geranium, which survives in poor soil with little attention as long as it gets warmth, sun, and an occasional watering, is a storkbill developed horticulturally, primarily from a South African ancestor; most are aromatic, with stiff stems, luxuriant, round, or nearly heart-shaped leaves, and large heads of red, rose, pink, yellow, or white, irregular blossoms.

The essential oil extracted from leaves and stems of *Pelargonium* is called geranium oil and is used in perfumes. Family: Geranium (Geraniaceae).

GESNERIA FAMILY (Gesneriaceae), a group of about 1200 species in 85 genera, most of them tropical and subtropical herbs with opposite leaves. A number are widely enjoyed as ornamental plants for house or greenhouse. Cape primrose (*Streptocarpus* species) is native to South Africa and Madagascar.

African violet (horticultural varieties from 3 species of *Saintpaulia*), native to East Africa, propagates

PLANT TYPES

MOREL MUSHROOM

AIRPLANT BLOSSOM

BEAR GRASS

BARLEY FIELD

DWARF BANANA

HEDGEHOG CACTUS

BARCO

PAPAYA

FLOWERS

ZINNIA

LOTUS

CLEOME (CASPER PLANT)

WATER LILY

SINGLE CHRYSANTHEMUM

COSMOS

PETUNIA

FLOWERS

PHOTOS BAUMAN/LOOK

GLADIOLUS

DAHLIA

HELIOTROPE

PHLOX

JAPANESE CHRYSANTHEMUM

ROSES

TREES

TWO CROWN SHAPES OF AMERICAN ELM
WILLIAM HARLOW FROM NATIONAL AUDUBON SOCIETY

NORWAY MAPLE
ARTHUR W. AMBLER FROM NATIONAL AUDUBON SOCIETY

REDWOOD
DENNIS BROWN FROM NATIONAL AUDUBON SOCIETY

ASPENS
RICHARD PARKER FROM NATIONAL AUDUBON SOCIETY

easily from leaves in water. The Brazilian gloxinia (*Sinningia*) is similar in many ways, although with much larger flowers and a need for an annual period of inactivity. See also *Gloxinia*.

GILLYFLOWER. See *Stock* and *Wallflower*.

GINGER, a herbaceous perennial of tropical and subtropical Asia, generally a cultivated species with alternate, narrow, grasslike leaves along an upright, reedy stem rising from a fleshy, underground rhizome (horizontal stem), which also produces slender stalks topped with clusters of flowers.

The cultivated species is no longer found wild; it is believed to have been adapted by early man in tropical Asia. The spice ginger is made from the rhizomes, which may be scrubbed, dried, and then ground, or cooked while fresh and then candied.

In North America, an unrelated perennial herb (*Asarum canadense* and other species of the birthwort family Aristolochiaceae) is called wild ginger; it has an aromatic rhizome that produces 2 kidney-shaped, furry leaves and a bell-shaped flower without petals, which is purple inside and green outside. Family: Ginger (Zingiberaceae); genus *Zingiber*, particularly *Z. officinale*.

GINGER FAMILY (Zingiberaceae), a group of about 1400 species in 47 genera, chiefly tropical, perennial herbs with fleshy, underground stems and 2-ranked leaves or whorls of basal leaves. Several yield valuable spices. Others are outstandingly beautiful, such as the brilliant torchflowers (*Hedychium* species) native to Madagascar and Southeast Asia, and the shellflower (*Alpinia speciosa*) of the East Indies. See *Arrowroot*, *Cardamom*, and *Ginger*.

GINKGO, or maidenhair tree, an erect, generously branching Oriental tree that attains a height of 60 to 80 feet and bears clusters of fan-shaped leaves on short, woody spurs rising from the main branches. The staminate trees produce stamens in clusters resembling catkins. The ovulate trees form ovules in pairs on short spurs and, later, seeds that appear plumlike, with a fleshy outer covering over an inner stony layer. When ripe, the fleshy covering decomposes, emitting a fetid odor.

Staminate trees are therefore preferred for ornamental planting. They are hardy and grow well in cities, despite soot, exhaust fumes, and pavement reaching to within a few inches of the trunk on all sides. The single species (*Ginkgo biloba*) is a "living fossil," with no wild representatives known. It has been perpetuated by Oriental monks in temple grounds. Fossil ginkgoes have been found in many parts of Eurasia and North America. Family: Ginkgo (Ginkgoaceae).

GINSENG, any of about 6 different kinds of herbaceous, woodland plants of tropical and eastern Asia and temperate North America, growing 1 to 4 feet high, with alternate compound leaves and flat or globular clusters of small, yellow flowers that produce scarlet, fleshy fruits.

The Chinese have long considered the fleshy roots a valuable medicine and pay a high price for those of the Manchurian species (*Panax schinseng*) and a lower price for the kind native to eastern North America (*P. quinquefolius*). Family: Ginseng (Araliaceae); genus *Panax*.

GINSENG FAMILY (Araliaceae), a group of about 800 species in 65 genera, most abundant in tropical America and Southeast Asia, all with 5-part, small flowers in clusters that are flat-topped or spherical. It includes the devil's club (*Echinopanax horridus*), a dangerously spiny shrub native to western North America from California to Alaska, and the rice-paper tree (*Tetrapanax papyrifera*) of Formosa, from which rice-paper is made. See *Ginseng*, *Ivy*, and *Spikenard*.

GLADIOLUS, a genus of bulbous plants with narrow, linear leaves and spikes of large, stemless, irregular, trumpet-shaped flowers. In addition to the 250 different species native to Africa and southern Europe, many horticultural varieties have been developed. They are propagated by natural division of the bulbous corms and produce large flowers that are white, yellow, pink, rose, purple, or combinations of more than one color. Family: Iris (Iridaceae).

GLOXINIA, a low-growing, tuberous, Brazilian herb with large, thick, hairy, deeply-veined, spreading leaves and large, bell-shaped flowers. Cultivated as a decorative house plant, it has developed horticultural varieties with red, rose, pink, or white flowers, rather than the violet-colored flowers characteristic of the wild plants. Family: Gesneria (Gesneriaceae); genus and species, *Sinningia speciosa*.

T.H. EVERETT
GINKGO

GODETIA, a genus of herbaceous plants native to western North America, with about 25 different species of which one, called summer's darling or farewell-to-spring (*G. amoena*), bearing large, satiny petals ranging in color from white to deep red, is widely cultivated as a garden ornament. Family: Evening primrose (Onagraceae).

GOLDEN BELL. See *Forsythia*.

GOLDEN CHAIN. See *Laburnum*.

GOLDEN GLOW, a coarse, perennial, garden plant developed by horticulturalists from a flower of eastern North America. Golden glow has spherical heads of golden-yellow disc florets 2 to 4 inches across and hardly any, or no ray florets. Family: Daisy (Compositae); genus, species, and named variety, *Rudbeckia lacinata hortensis*.

GOLDENROD, any of about 90 different kinds of perennial herbs, one native to Britain and parts of Europe, one to the Azores, a few found in temperate Asia and South America, and the vast majority in North America where they brighten forest, field, and roadside with feathery sprays of small flowers, usually golden-yellow but sometimes white or greenish in color.

They are flowers of late summer and autumn, some of them growing on rough, hairy stems 7 feet tall that bear many small leaves all the way up. Family: Daisy (Compositae); genus *Solidago*.

GOOSEBERRY, a low-growing, spiny shrub, sometimes 3 feet tall, native to North Africa and much of Europe, producing 3-lobed leaves, small, pale yellow blossoms in loose clusters, and spherical, shiny fruit with minute seeds. Cultivated varieties, with edible green or purple fruit, are raised in cool parts of Europe, North America, South Africa, New Zealand, and Australia. The fruit is eaten raw or used in cooking and in making preserves. Family: Saxifrage (Saxifragaceae); genus and species, *Ribes grossularia*.

GOOSEFOOT FAMILY (Chenopodiaceae), a group of about 1400 species in 102 genera, widely distributed but especially well represented in arid and salty or alkaline areas. They include annual and perennial herbs, shrubs, and some small trees, often with fleshy enlargements on the stems where leaves are attached or where leaves would have been attached had the stem not been leafless.

Glasswort, or samphire (*Salicornia* species), are fleshy, leafless herbs of seacoasts, often changing in color from bright green to brilliant red in autumn. See *Beet*, *Lamb's-quarters*, *Pigweed*, *Saltbush*, *Spinach*, and *Tumbleweed*.

GORSE, or furze, or whin, any of about 20 different kinds of spiny, woody shrubs; its green spines are modified leaves. It is native to Europe and North Africa, but has been widely introduced as a soil-binding plant, a hedge, and a source of young growth appealing to sheep and other livestock. It is also grown for the large, yellow, fragrant flowers that precede the conspicuous brown pods. Family: Pea (Leguminosae); genus *Ulex*.

GOURD, a fleshy fruit with a thick, firm, outer part (the rind) surrounding a more fibrous, soft part (the pulp) in which the seeds are embedded; also, the plant that produces such a fruit. Most are members of the gourd family (Cucurbitaceae) and are usually vines native to Africa or warm and temperate parts of the Northern Hemisphere.

Some gourds are raised for their fruits, others as ornaments, and still others to be dried, cleansed of their pulp, and made into drinking vessels, dishes, and musical instruments.

GOURD FAMILY (Cucurbitaceae), a group of about 850 species in 100 genera, mostly tropical and subtropical prostrate or climbing herbs with tendrils that appear along the length of the stems. Many are cultivated for food or for their decorative value. See *Cucumber, Gourd, Melon, Pumpkin, Squash,* and *Vegetable sponge.*

GRAPE, any of about 60 different kinds of woody vines mostly native to temperate parts of the Northern Hemisphere. The spherical fruits are also called grapes. The grape plant or grapevine bears simple, heart-shaped leaves, and climbs by means of tendrils that are highly adapted terminal buds growing out of side branches that lack leaves. The flowers are small, green, and generally hairy; the fruits are small or large, seeded or seedless, tart or sweet, green, red, blue, or greenish-white in color.

Grapes may be eaten raw, dried as raisins, or used in fermentative processes to make many kinds of wine. Until the 1600s, almost the only grape in cultivation was the one that was domesticated in prehistoric times in southern Europe and Asia Minor. Its culture was introduced into America before the value of the American species was recognized.

The principal species used are the European *Vitis vinifera* and the North American *Vitis labrusca,* as well as numerous hybrids and horticultural varieties. Family: Grape (Vitaceae); genus *Vitis.*

GRAPE FAMILY (Vitaceae), a group of about 600 species in 11 genera, native to the tropics, subtropics, and some temperate regions, chiefly climbing shrubs with terminal buds that become tendrils, requiring the stem to continue growth by an apparent bend as the axillary bud extends into a new branch. The flowers are clustered and produce berries.

Among cultivated plants in this family are the trailing begonia (*Cissus discolor*) of Java and the peppervine (*Ampelopsis arborea*) of the southern United States. See *Boston ivy, Grape,* and *Woodbine.*

GRAPEFRUIT, a small tree with large, ovate leaves and fragrant, white flowers, discovered first in the West Indies and probably derived from the pummelo or shaddock (*Citrus grandis*) of Southeast Asia. The fruits of the grapefruit grow in clusters of 5 to 15, and include among the varieties developed by horticulturalists a number of thin-skinned and seedless types differing considerably from the original stock. The fruit is eaten fresh, canned, or made into juice. Family: Rue (Rutaceae); genus and species, *Citrus paradisi.*

GRAPE HYACINTH, any of about 40 different kinds of small, bulbous plants with bladelike leaves and clusters of bell-shaped flowers at the top of upright stems. The clusters suggest bunches of blue, white, or yellow grapes. Native to Mediterranean Europe, they have been introduced widely as decorative plants used in flower borders and rock gardens. Family: Lily (Liliaceae); genus *Muscari.*

GRASS FAMILY (Gramineae), a very large family with about 4500 species in 500 genera, the most widely distributed of vascular plants. Many have the ability to lie dormant during protracted droughts.

They have colonized prairies, plains, savannas, campos, pampas, steppes, and veldts, and are a source of food for grazing animals, a great variety of seed-eating birds, and rodents. They have fibrous roots, typically hollow stems, and parallel-veined leaves. Their flowers are clustered and so specialized that only the stamen and pistil seem to correspond to parts of flowers in other plant families.

See *Bamboo, Barley, Bluegrass, Broomcorn, Corn, Crabgrass, Millet, Oat, Pampas grass, Reed, Rice, Rye, Sorghum, Sudan grass, Sugarcane, Timothy,* and *Wheat.*

GROUND IVY, or gill-over-the-ground, a delicate but prolific creeping and trailing plant with a square stem, round or kidney-shaped leaves on short petioles, and clusters of blue or yellow flowers. It is native to Europe but has been introduced into many parts of the world and has escaped from cultivation to become a weed. Family: Mint (Labiatae); genus and species, *Glechoma hederacea.*

GROUNDNUT. See *Peanut.*

GROUND PINE. See *Club moss.*

GUAIACUM. See *Lignum Vitae.*

GUAVA, a small tree with square stems, opposite leaves, fragrant, white flowers with four petals, and mildly acid, yellow fruits about the size of a hen's egg. Native to the West Indies, it is now cultivated extensively in the southern United States, North Africa, Malaya, and China. The pinkish flesh of the fruit is too soft to withstand transportation, but it is eaten raw where grown or made into jams and jellies. Family: Myrtle (Myrtaceae); genus and species, *Psidium guajaba.*

GUAYULE, a branching shrub with luxuriant, silvery leaves, native to the North American southwest, and now cultivated in Texas and Mexico for its latex, which contains solid particles suitable for extraction and manufacture into a valuable rubber.

When about 4 years old the whole plant is pulled up, dried, crushed, and immersed in water. The particles that have been suspended in the cell sap then float to the top and can be skimmed off. Between 150 and 200 million pounds of this material are used annually. Family: Daisy (Compositae); genus and species, *Parthenium argentatum.*

GUNNY. See *Jute.*

GUTTA-PERCHA. See *Rubber.*

GYPSOPHILA. See *Baby's-Breath.*

HACKBERRY, any of about 60 different small trees of the Northern Hemisphere, with elmlike leaves and plumlike fruits. The bark of the most widespread species in eastern North America (*Celtis occidentalis*) is silvery and deeply grooved into a checkered pattern. The wood is soft, easily broken by strong windstorms and accumulations of sleet, but useful for making boxes, baskets, and some kinds of furniture.

Hackberries are often planted as windbreaks and as shade trees in the southern United States. Family: Elm (Ulmaceae); genus *Celtis.*

HAREBELL. See *Bluebell.*

HAWKWEED, any of perhaps 2000 different kinds of herbaceous perennial plants of temperate and cool climates in the Northern Hemisphere, the Andes, and South Africa. Most have hairy, simple leaves in a whorl close to the ground and hairy, upright stalks bearing one or more flower heads. All of the florets in each head bear strap-shaped corollas, which are commonly orange, yellow, or scarlet. Many are noxious weeds that reproduce by seeds and runners. Family: Daisy (Compositae); genus *Hieracium.*

BURPEE SEEDS

GOURDS

HAWTHORN, any of perhaps 1000 different kinds of woody shrubs and small trees of the North Temperate Zone with alternate leaves that are deeply cut into lobes, prominent spines on the stems, and clusters of pink or white flowers that open in spring. The flowers are followed by small, red, yellow, blue, or black, apple-like fruits called haws. Family: Rose (Rosaceae); genus *Crataegus*.

HAZEL, any of 8 different shrubs and small trees of the North Temperate Zone, with oblong to round leaves that are folded lengthwise in the bud, drooping catkins of staminate flowers, budlike, pistillate flowers with conspicuous red stigmas in early spring, and hard-shelled seeds released from leaflike bracts that develop around the ripening fruit.

The seeds of the European hazel (*Corylus avellana*) are produced commercially by orchards in Italy, Turkey, Spain, and the state of Oregon for sale as filberts. A filbert differs from the hazelnuts of other species in that it is larger but shows no distinctive difference in shape, texture, or taste. Family: Birch (Betulaceae); genus *Corylus*.

HEATH, any of about 500 different tough, branching shrubs and trees of Europe, southwestern Asia, and South Africa, with small, white, pink, or purple, cuplike flowers, and 4-chambered capsules that open to release small seeds. A great many heaths are characteristic of moorlands. The tree heath (*Erica arborea*) of the Mediterranean region grows to a height of 65 feet and furnishes brierwood for briar pipes. Family: Heath (Ericaceae); genus *Erica*.

HEATH FAMILY (Ericaceae), a group of about 1900 species in 70 genera, almost all woody shrubs and trees. The heath constitutes the characteristic vegetation of moors, many mountain slopes and swamps in temperate and subarctic lands, and the higher slopes of tropical mountains. See *Arbutus, Azalea, Blueberry, Cranberry, Heath, Heather, Huckleberry, Madroña, Manzanita, Mountain laurel, Pipsissewa, Rhododendron,* and *Wintergreen*.

HEATHER, or ling, a low-growing evergreen shrub native to Greenland, Europe, and western Asia but now introduced into eastern North America and covering large areas of moorland. The leaves are minute, overlapping, and in opposite pairs. The small pink, purple, or white flowers generally arise on one side of the stem or its branches, near the tip. The bright color is in the calyx, which overlaps and hides the small corolla.

In true heaths (*Erica*), on the other hand, the calyx is small and the corolla shows the color. Family: Heath Ericaceae); genus and species, *Calluna vulgaris*.

HELIOTROPE, any of about 250 different kinds of herbs, vines, shrubs, and small trees, chiefly native to tropical South America, but found also in warm parts of Eurasia and North America. All have simple leaves and

T.H. EVERETT
HELIOTROPE

funnel-shaped or tubular flowers with flaring petals borne in spikes. Many horticultural varieties of the cherry pie (*Heliotropium arborescens*), native to Ecuador and Peru, are cultivated for their perfumed flowers. Family: Borage (Boraginaceae); genus *Heliotropium*.

HELLEBORE, any of about 22 different kinds of evergreen plants native to southern Europe, with glossy, palmately compound leaves, and showy, cup-shaped flowers that lack petals but have white, pink, or purple sepals. The powdered roots of some have been used in medicine as a sedative and in agriculture as an insecticide.

A cultivated ornamental plant is the Christmas rose or black hellebore (*Helleborus niger*), which blooms in winter and often pushes its rather stiff, 2-inch flowers through the snow. Each flower has 5, widely spreading, white, petal-like sepals and numerous golden stamens. Family: Buttercup (Ranunculaceae); genus *Helleborus*.

HEMLOCK, any of 12 different coniferous, evergreen trees characteristic of forests in China, Japan, and North America, but not native to Europe or other continents. The needles are flat, with 2 white lines beneath, and are arranged on the 2 sides of drooping branches. Tan colored cones grow on the under-sides of the branches and release winged seeds.

The eastern hemlock (*Tsuga canadensis*) of North America grows well in the shade of hardwood forests and is valuable for the tannins in its bark. Western hemlock (*T. heterophylla*) of the Pacific Northwest is a much larger, stronger tree, rising to about 260 feet, and yielding inportant timber, as well as bark that is rich in tannins. Family: Pine (Pinaceae); genus *Tsuga*. See also *Poison hemlock*.

HEMP, an erect or twining annual plant native to Asia, growing 3 to 18 feet high, with 3 to 7 narrow, toothed leaflets on each of its palmately compound leaves. The inner bark is valuable for its tough fibers, which are made into twine, rope, canvas, and sailcloth. Resin extracted from hairs on the stem and leaves contains a mixture of narcotic compounds responsible for the drug effects obtained from smoking the dried unextracted plant materials, known as marijuana, hashish, or charas. Hemp seeds are used for feeding cage birds and as the source of a commercial oil resembling linseed oil. Family: Hemp (Cannabinaceae); genus and species, *Cannabis sativa*.

HEMP FAMILY (Cannabinaceae), a small group of 3 species in 2 genera, often included in the Mulberry family (Moraceae). The genus *Cannabis* has only one species, hemp (*C. indica*). See *Hemp* and *Hop*.

HENEQUEN. See *Century Plant*.

HEPATICA, or liverleaf, a small genus of woodland wildflowers blooming in early spring in the North Temperate Zone. Each plant consists of a basal whorl of 3-lobed leaves on slender, hairy petioles and, in season, a number of white, pink, or lavender flowers with many stamens but no petals, the petal-like sepals providing the color.

There are two species native to eastern North America; one, *H. triloba*, is native to Eurasia but not to the British Isles. Family: Buttercup (Ranunculaceae).

HERB CHRISTOPHER. See *Baneberry*.

HIBISCUS, or rose mallow, a genus of herbs, shrubs, and small trees native to tropical and subtropical countries, with large, showy flowers. One (*H. rosasinensis*), known as rose of China, or shoeblack plant, or shoeflower, has almost become a symbol of the tropics because of its wide cultivation as a decorative hedge plant. Its blossoms collapse permanently at the end of a day. They contain a black dye that makes them suitable for polishing and cleaning black shoes.

More than 1000 horticultural varieties of the hibiscus plant with distinctive names and petals of many colors and forms have been developed.

Among the 200 other species of the genus, the Asian rose of Sharon (*H. syriacus*) with 3-lobed leaves and cup-shaped, red flowers is commonly planted as an ornamental shrub; okra, or gumbo, or bandakai (*H. esculentus*), which probably originated in northeastern Africa, is cultivated extensively in tropical West Africa, southeastern United States, Turkey, and India for its edible, partly ripened capsules, which are mucilaginous unless properly cooked. Family: Mallow (Malvaceae).

HICKORY, any of several kinds of trees native to eastern North America and Southeast Asia, with large, shiny, pinnately compound leaves, trunks 60 to 160 feet tall, tough, close-grained wood, and small flowers in separate clusters, the staminate flowers in yellow, tassel-like catkins and the pistillate flowers in stiff spikes. The leathery coverings of the fruits crack open, releasing the armored seeds, which fall to the ground.

Some species are shagbark or shellbark hickories; these shed their old bark in long, flat strips that loosen gradually and curl slightly away from the trunk. Others are more smooth-barked, marked only by deep surface furrows. Most have edible kernels in the seeds. The pecan *(Carya pecan)* grows to a height of 150 feet, and yields the best nuts of any member of the group; a native of the Mississippi Valley, the Southwest, and into Mexico, it is now cultivated in large orchards in Georgia and adjacent states. Family: Walnut (Juglandaceae); genus *Carya*.

HOLLY, any of about 280 different kinds of shrubs and trees with alternate, simple leaves and small clusters of regular flowers that are followed by berry-like fruits containing several nutlets. They are widely distributed, although Europe has only one, *Ilex aquifolium*: a small tree with very hard wood, leathery, glossy, evergreen leaves, and bright red fruits that remain in place until mid-winter. The European holly was used in pagan rituals, and later found a place in Christmas ceremonies.

An American holly *(I. opaca)* with prickly leaves that are only slightly less glossy than those of the European holly is used for Christmas purposes in the New World, although fruits develop only on the pistillate trees when they are near the fruitless staminate trees. Some hollies, such as black alder *(I. verticillata)* of swamps in the eastern United States, are deciduous. Others are appreciated because their prickly leaves contain caffeine and can be brewed into the popular beverage, *yerba maté*, or Paraguay tea (from the South American evergreen shrub *I. paraguariensis*). Family: Holly (Aquifoliaceae); genus *Ilex*.

HOLLYHOCK, a tall, biennial herb with large wrinkled leaves on an erect stem that grows 5 to 6 feet high, producing an ascending progression of saucer-shaped flowers in white, pink, yellow, lavender, and even a violet so dark that it seems black. Native to the Balkans, the plant was brought to western Europe by returning Crusaders and adopted as a stately garden flower. In Egypt its leaves are sometimes cooked as a vegetable. Family: Mallow (Malvaceae); genus and species, *Althaea rosea*.

HONEYDEW MELON. See *Melon*.

HONEY LOCUST. See *Locust*.

HONEYSUCKLE, any of about 180 different kinds of erect or climbing shrubs with opposite, simple leaves and paired flowers that are bilaterally symmetrical and often both fragrant and supplied generously with nectar. Native to the Northern Hemisphere, they include several shrubs that have been introduced widely and cultivated for their flowers and, in some cases, the evergreen cover the climbing species provide over unwanted native vegetation. Family: Honeysuckle (Caprifoliaceae); genus *Lonicera*.

T.H. EVERETT
HONEYSUCKLE

HONEYSUCKLE FAMILY (Caprifoliaceae), a group of about 275 species in 18 genera, chiefly native to the Northern Hemisphere, mostly trees or shrubs, but many climbing vines, all with opposite leaves and clustered flowers. It includes the twinflower *(Linnaea borealis)*, found in the far north of both Eurasia and North America. See *Black haw, Elder, Honeysuckle, Viburnum,* and *Woodbine.*

HOP, a perennial climbing vine of Eurasia, with rough stems 15 to 20 feet long, coarse, lobed leaves, staminate flowers on some plants and pistillate flowers on others. The pistillate flowers are enclosed by green bracts (the "hops" of brewers) which bear yellow, dustlike grains of a bitter substance used to give flavor and sparkle to beer. Family: Hemp (Cannabinaceae); genus and species, *Humulus lupulus*.

HOREHOUND, a perennial herb with a square stem, opposite, hairy, silvery leaves, and clusters of small, white flowers in the leaf axils. Native to the Mediterranean countries from the Canary Islands to western Asia, it has been cultivated and naturalized elsewhere for an extract used in candies and in syrups designed to treat colds and coughs. Family: Mint (Labiatae); genus and species, *Marrubium vulgare*.

HORNBEAM, any of about 20 different small trees of the North Temperate Zone, with gray bark, hard wood, drooping branches, oval, serrate leaves that turn orange in autumn, and separate clusters of staminate and pistillate flowers in catkins. The small, one-seeded fruits are winged. Family: Birch (Betulaceae); genus *Carpinus*.

HORSE CHESTNUT, a handsome, deciduous tree attaining a height of 60 feet, with opposite, palmately compound leaves. The leaflets are wedge-shaped and toothed along the edges. Pyramidal clusters of creamy flowers are followed by prickly fruits that open to release large, inedible seeds resembling chestnuts.

Native to the Balkans and the Caucasus, the horse chestnut is cultivated widely as an ornamental tree. Relatives from South America and the North Temperate Zone include the buckeyes of California, the north central states, and the southeast. The light wood of these trees is used for paper pulp and the manufacture of artificial limbs. Family: Horse chestnut (Hippocastanaceae); genus and species, *Aesculus hippocastanum*.

HORSERADISH, a perennial herb native to Eurasia, growing to about 2 feet in height, with narrow leaves, clusters of white flowers, and white, fleshy roots that are edible and used as a condiment. The plant is now widely cultivated and used to give flavor to relishes. Family: Mustard (Cruciferae); genus and species, *Armoracia rusticana*.

HORSETAIL, any of about 25 different kinds of perennial rushlike herbs with hollow, jointed stems. They have neither leaves nor flowers and are found throughout the world except in the Australasian region. Most are less than 3 feet tall, but the *Equisetum giganteum* of the West Indies and tropical South America may attain a height of 36 feet.

Several species are native to both Eurasia and North America, such as the scouring rush *(E. hyemale)*, the stems of which are so harsh because of the siliceous material they contain that poineers and peasants have used them to scour pots, floors, and other surfaces. All horsetails develop terminal clusters of spore cases. The spores germinate on suitable moist surfaces and grow into small, special plants bearing the sexual reproductive organs. Fertilized eggs from these grow into the familiar herbs. Family: Equisetaceae; genus *Equisetum*.

HUCKLEBERRY, any of about 40 different kinds of shrubs 1 to 6 feet tall, with smooth, oval, leathery leaves, white or pink, bell-shaped flowers, and clusters of glossy, black berries containing 10 minute, hard seeds. Native to the Americas, they are often confused with blueberries *(Vaccinium)*, which have somewhat less acid berries and no armor around the seeds. Family: Heath (Ericaceae); genus *Gaylussacia*.

HYACINTH, any of about 30 different kinds of hardy, bulbous herbs native to Mediterranean countries and South Africa. They are cultivated widely for their early spring flowers, which are fragrant, bell-shaped, white, pink, blue, or violet, and grow in tall, compact clusters that precede the stiff, bladelike leaves.

The name is also given to some related plants of other genera, such as the wood hyacinth *(Scilla non-scripta)* of the Old World, and the wild hyacinth *(Camassia scilloides)* of eastern North America. Family: Lily (Liliaceae); genus *Hyacinthus*. See also *Grape Hyacinth*.

HYDRANGEA, a genus containing about 80 different species of woody shrubs native to the North Temperate Zone. They attain a height of 8 to 20 feet, and bear large, paired leaves and round heads composed of globular flowers. The Oriental species (*H. paniculata*) is the most common ornamental species, with flowers ranging from white to pink and blue. The wild hydrangea (*H. arborescens*) of eastern North America attains a height of 10 feet and grows mostly on wet soils rich in lime. Family: Saxifrage (Saxifragaceae).

ICE PLANT, a succulent, low-growing plant of South Africa, with leaves densely covered with small, bladder-shaped hairs that glisten like ice crystals. Grown as a ground cover, rather than for its small white or pink flowers, the plant is cultivated extensively in southern California and elsewhere. It does not tolerate hard frosts.

The juice of the plant can be used as a diuretic and demulcent. In Spain the ashes of its leaves and stems are often added to the mixture used in making glass. Family: Carpetweed (Aizoaceae); genus and species, *Mesembryanthemum Crystallinum*.

INDIAN HEMP, a widespread North American perennial herb with a milky juice in tough stems 2 to 4 feet tall. It has paired, oval leaves, and bell-shaped, white or greenish flowers in terminal clusters. Indians used the fibers of the inner bark for making rope. Family: Dogbane (Apocynaceae); genus and species, *Apocynum cannabinum*.

INDIAN PIPE, a colorless, saprophytic plant of moist woodlands in North America. It lives on dead vegetable matter in the soil with the help of a fungal partner. The upright stems are covered with waxy, white scales, and they terminate at a height of 4 to 10 inches in a nodding, white, cylindrical flower. The stem and flower turn black when picked. As the seeds ripen, the stem straightens, shrivels, and turns blackish-brown, holding an upright capsule. Family: Pyrola (Pyrolaceae); genus and species, *Monotropa uniflora*.

INDIAN TOBACCO. See *Lobelia*.

INDIAN TURNIP. See *Jack-in-the-pulpit*.

INDIGO, a shrubby plant native to the East Indies. The blue dye obtained by fermenting and oxidizing the juice from the odd-pinnate leaves of this plant is also called indigo. Cultivation of indigo for the dye industry was formerly a major occupation in India and other warm parts of Asia and South America, but operations virtually ceased when cheaper synthetic dyes became available. Family: Pea (Leguminosae); genus and species, *Indigofera tinctoria*.

IRIS, a genus of about 200 different species found in the North Temperate Zone, all with grasslike or sword-shaped leaves, usually growing from a fleshy underground stem. The flowers have 3 showy sepals which turn down (called by horticulturalists "the falls") while 3 similar petals turn up ("the standards"); the 3 branches of the style on the pistil are often petal-like, arching over the stamens.

Many species, hybrids between species, and horticultural varieties are cultivated for their flowers. The Florentine iris (*I. florentina*), with white flowers, is probably the model for the French emblem, the fleur-de-lis ("flower of the lily"). The dried and powdered roots of this and a few other European irises, known as orris root, are used to give an imitation violet fragrance to perfumes, tooth pastes, and other cosmetics. Family: Iris (Iridaceae).

IRIS FAMILY (Iridaceae), a group of about 1500 species in 58 genera, native to all but the coldest regions, mostly herbaceous plants with storage organs in underground stems or roots, and sword-shaped or grasslike leaves rising from the base. Their flowers differ from those of lilies and related families in having only 3 stamens instead of 6. See *Crocus, Freesia, Gladiolus,* and *Iris*.

IRISH MOSS, or carrageen, a soft seaweed growing attached to rocks at moderate depths along North Atlantic coasts, where it is often torn loose and cast ashore in vast quantities by winter storms. Although technically a red alga, it may be green, yellow, purplish, or brown.

When gathered, washed, and dried in the sun, it can be pulverized to make a flourlike material of some food value. Soaked in water, it becomes mucilaginous and is used to give body to soups and desserts such as blancmange, or to medicines such as cough mixtures. Family: Gigartina (Gigartinaceae); genus and species, *Chondrus crispus*.

IRONWEED, any of about a dozen North American, rough-stemmed, coarse, herbaceous perennials growing as high as 10 feet, with many alternate, narrow, pointed leaves and clusters of purplish-red or white flowers that resemble thistle heads without prickles. They produce prodigious numbers of seeds, and spread quickly over neglected or overgrazed land, offering little that attracts livestock but providing abundant nectar for honeybees.

Some of their relatives in Africa are valuable timber trees. These are perhaps the largest representatives of the family. Family: Daisy (Compositae); genus *Vernonia*.

IVY, or English ivy, a vigorous climbing plant native to temperate Eurasia, with dark glossy, oval or 5-lobed, evergreen leaves, yellowish flowers, and clusters of black berries. It clings by means of short, aerial roots penetrating small cavities in wood or stone surfaces.

Garlands of ivy were used in ancient Greece to decorate statues of Dionysus or Bacchus, and became a symbol of those establishments where wine was sold by the glass. Later, ivy-clad walls became a mark of institutions of learning. Introduced into the New World, ivy forms an attractive ground cover in the southern United States, but is often killed by winter cold in northern states and Canada.

The name ivy is commonly given to other creeping and climbing plants. Family: Ginseng (Araliaceae); genus and species, *Hedera helix*. See *Boston Ivy, Poison Ivy,* and *Woodbine*.

JACK-IN-THE-PULPIT, or Indian turnip, any of several herbaceous, woodland plants of temperate North America, bearing one or more palmately compound leaves. It has a single flower cluster with a spathe extended into a flaplike hood (the "pulpit") around the central column (the spadix, or "Jack") bearing the tiny staminate and pistillate flowers.

The thick, short, underground stem is made acrid by a sap containing needle-like crystals of poisonous calcium oxalate, which the Indians removed with boiling water to obtain an edible food. Family: Arum (Araceae); genus *Arisaema*.

JAPONICA, or flowering quince, a popular Oriental ornamental shrub. It has spreading spiny branches 3 to 6 feet tall, glossy leaves, scarlet or orange flowers blooming early in the year, and 2-inch, globular, hard fruits rich in pectin and suitable for making into a jelly. Family: Rose (Rosaceae); genus and species, *Chaenomeles lagenaria*.

JASMINE, any of about 200 different erect or climbing shrubs native to all continents except Africa and Australasia. Several are cultivated in warm, temperate, and tropical countries for their attractive and fragrant white or yellow starlike flowers borne on climbing, slender stems among delicate, pinnately compound leaves. The fresh flowers are used to make perfume. Dried flowers are often added to tea in China and Japan.

JACK-IN-THE-PULPIT

The name jasmine is often given to the unrelated yellow jessamine (*Gelsemium sempervirens* of the strychnine family, Loganiaceae), an evergreen vine with clustered, golden flowers native to swamps in the southeastern United States. Family: Olive (Oleaceae); genus *Jasminum*.

JEWELWEED, or touch-me-not, or snapweed, any of several herbaceous plants of the North Temperate Zone, with hollow, juicy stems 2 to 5 feet tall, oval leaves, and clusters of pendant, orange flowers shaped like those of the snapdragon but with a spur formed by the extended calyx.

The fruits are explosive capsules that shatter when ripe, scattering the pellet-like seeds over a radius of several feet. Sparkling drops of water often adorn the leaves in the early morning, giving them the name of jewelweed. Family: Jewelweed (Balsaminaceae); genus *Impatiens*.

JIMSONWEED, or thorn apple, a malodorous and dangerously poisonous coarse annual native to the Asian area between India and the Caspian Sea. It is now almost cosmopolitan as a rank weed growing to 5 feet, with broad leaves toothed around the margin and white, trumpet-shaped flowers that are followed by a prickly, ovoid seed capsule. The sweet-tasting seeds are deadly poisonous; all other parts of the plant are almost equally dangerous. Family: Potato (Solanaceae); genus and species, *Datura stramonium*.

JOE-PYE WEED, a herbaceous perennial of eastern North America with oval, serrate leaves whorled around its thick stems; the stems are 3 to 10 feet tall and bear flat-topped clusters of pink or purple flowers. It was named after Joe Pye, a traveling Indian medicine man of New England, who advertised a tonic made from this plant. Family: Daisy (Compositae); genus and species, *Eupatorium purpureum*.

JONQUIL. See *Narcissus*.

JUDAS TREE. See *Redbud*.

JUJUBE, a shrub or small tree of southern China and the East Indies, attaining a height of 20 to 50 feet, with alternate leaves, hooked spines, and plumlike fruits about the size of olives. These fruits are known as jujubes or Chinese dates. It has been introduced into the southern United States as an ornamental tree, but preserved jujubes are still imported from Mediterranean countries and Japan. Family: Buckthorn (Rhamnaceae); genus and species, *Zizyphus jujuba*.

JUNIPER, any of about 60 different kinds of shrubs and trees native to the North Temperate Zone, with scale-like or needle-like, evergreen leaves and one-seeded, fleshy cones known as juniper berries. Oil of juniper, extracted from these cones, is used medicinally as a diuretic, and commercially in the manufacture of varnish and the flavoring of gin.

Eastern red cedar (*Juniperus virginiana*) provides long-lasting posts, railroad ties, and wood for making lead pencils, but because it is an alternate host for the fungus causing apple rust, some states prohibit the planting of this tree near apple orchards. Western juniper (*J. occidentalis*) grows at moderate altitudes in the mountains of western North America, sometimes reaching the age of 2000 years. Family: Cypress (Cupressaceae); genus *Juniperus*.

JUTE, or gunny, the fiber from the inner bark of either of two East Indian shrubs, which are raised as annuals and grow 6 to 12 feet tall. They are planted so close together that they produce almost no branches. The fiber is used for cheap twine, cording, burlap, bagging, oakum, and strong wrapping paper. Family: Linden (Tiliaceae); genus and species, *Corchorus capsularis* and *C. olitorius*.

KAFIR CORN. See *Sorghum*.

KALE. See *Mustard*.

KAPOK, or silk-cotton tree, a tropical American tree of moderate height, with large, 5-lobed leaves; a heavy, ridged trunk; bark studded with conical, blunt spines; bell-shaped flowers; and pods full of fluffy, silky fibers that can be separated from the seeds.

These fibers are water-resistant, buoyant, elastic, but not useful for spinning. Kapok trees are cultivated extensively in Java, Malaysia, Ceylon, and the Philippine Islands to obtain the fibers. The fibers are used to stuff mattresses, life-preservers, and pillows, and for the manufacture of wallboard, ceiling insulation, and even bathing suits. The oil from kapok seeds is used in foods and soap. Family: Bombax (Bombacaceae); genus and species, *Ceiba pentandra*.

KENTUCKY COFFEE TREE, a deciduous, hardwood tree of the southeastern United States, growing 50 to 100 feet. It has rough, scaly, reddish-gray bark; twice pinnately compound leaves; terminal clusters of white flowers; and pods containing black seeds, which were used by the colonists as a substitute for coffee beans. The hard wood is useful for fence posts. Family: Pea (Leguminosae); genus and species, *Gymnocladus dioica*.

KOHLRABI. See *Mustard*.

KUDZU, a hairy, twining vine native to southeastern Asia. It has luxuriant foliage and clusters of purple flowers. In the United States it has been planted as a decorative porch vine capable of climbing 60 feet or more, and in the southern states, as a soil binder to control erosion on slopes. Family: Pea (Leguminosae); genus and species, *Pueraria lobata*.

KUMQUAT, any of 6 different Asian shrubs 6 to 8 feet tall, with glossy, green, simple leaves, fragrant, white flowers, and fruits the size of an olive resembling miniature oranges. The fruits may be eaten raw or preserved, and are now the basis for the cultivation of kumquats in the southern United States. Family: Rue (Rutaceae); genus *Fortunella*.

LABURNUM, a genus consisting of 3 different kinds of small European and western Asian trees with dark 3-parted leaves and pendant sprays of bright yellow flowers. *L. anagyroides* is cultivated for Easter decorations and as the principal source of the alkaloid cytisine, used in medicine. Golden chain (*L. vulgare*), is popular in the southern United States for decorative outdoor planting. The wood of all of these trees is used in fine cabinet work. Family: Pea (Leguminosae).

LACQUER TREE, or varnish tree, any of several unrelated trees from which substances can be extracted for the production of lacquer or varnish. Most notable is a small tree of China and Japan, with handsome, pinnately compound leaves that turn orange-red in autumn. A mildly toxic latex can be obtained from these trees by slashing the bark on the trunk or stripping the bark from branches less than an inch in diameter. The viscous latex turns black upon exposure to air.

Chinese workmen who have become immune to its irritating effect upon the skin paint the blackened latex on boxes, trays, and other objects, and later smooth the coating with a stone tool to produce a handsome, high luster. The practice began in prehistoric times and reached the greatest perfection during the Ming dynasty (1364–1644 AD). Family: Sumac (Anacardiaceae); genus and species, *Rhus vernicifera*.

LADY'S SLIPPER, any of about 30 different kinds of perennial, woodland orchids of the North Temperate Zone, with coarse, fibrous roots, broad, pleated leaves that clasp the stem, and mostly solitary, showy flowers atop a tall stalk. The lower lip (labellum) of the corolla resembles the toe part of a shoe or moccasin, inspiring the other common names of shoeflower or moccasin flower.

The lady's slipper flower may be white, pink, purple, yellow, brown, orange, or red, plain or attractively mottled. The large yellow lady's slipper (*Cypripedium pubescens*) is often grown in shady gardens. Family: Orchid (Orchidaceae); genus *Cypripedium*.

LAMB'S-QUARTERS, an annual plant native to western Asia but now cosmopolitan as a weed of roadsides and neglected land, growing as a straight stem to 1 to 9 feet, with narrow, serrate leaves and sprays of greenish-white flowers. In Eurasia the green portions of young plants are sometimes cooked and eaten. Family: Goosefoot (Chenopodiaceae); genus and species, *Chenopodium album*.

LARCH, any of about 10 different kinds of needle-leaved trees of the North Temperate Zone, bearing deciduous needles in clusters of 10 or more, and small cones from which winged seeds are distributed by the wind. All larches produce useful wood.

The European larch (*Larix decidua*) is the source of a yellow resin called Venice turpentine, used in lithography. The American larch (*L. laricina*), known also as the tamarack or hackmatack, grows in cold bogs across the continent from Alaska to New England. Family: Pine (Pinaceae); genus *Larix*.

LARKSPUR, any of about 200 different kinds of herbaceous plants found in the North Temperate Zone, with palmately lobed or divided leaves and an upright, sturdy stem growing to 2 to 7 feet. The stem is topped by a graceful cluster of handsome flowers, each with the top sepal prolonged into a spur that is hollow and surrounds similar extensions from the top 2 petals. The 5 sepals and 2 or 4 petals are all petal-like, in blue, purple, pink, pale yellow, white, or blended colors.

Horticulturists reserve the name larkspur for annuals and use the generic name for perennials. Many wild larkspurs are poisonous to cattle. Family: Buttercup (Ranunculaceae); genus *Delphinium*.

LAUREL, or sweet bay, a handsome tree of Mediterranean countries, with aromatic, glossy, evergreen leaves, yellow flowers, and purple fruits resembling cherries. Wreaths and coronets were made with its leafy branches as a traditional sign or honor for the winners in Greek games.

A similar and related tree, California laurel (*Umbellularia californica*), found in forests of California and Oregon and growing to a height of 80 feet, yields hard wood used a great deal in cabinetry. Family Laurel (Lauraceae); genus and species, *Laurus nobilis*. See *Mountain laurel*.

LAUREL FAMILY (Lauraceae), a group of about 1100 species in 45 genera, chiefly shrubs and trees with aromatic bark, aromatic, smooth-edged leaves, and clustered flowers, native to tropical and subtropical regions.

Some varieties such as the greenhart (*Nectandra rodioei*) of northern South America and the stinkwoods (*Ocotea* species) of South Africa, grow very slowly and produce exceedingly hard, strong wood.

Other varieties, such as the camphor-tree (*Cinnamomum camphora*) native to Formosa, Japan, and south China, and the cassia-bark tree (*C. cassia*) of southern China, rank along with cinnamon as a source of valued extracts and flavorings. See *Avocado, Cinnamon, Laurel, Sassafras,* and *Spicebush*.

LAVENDER, a low-growing, perennial, evergreen shrub of temperate Eurasia, with narrow, grayish-green leaves, and tall spikes of pale lilac-colored flowers. Both leaves and flowers are clad in fine hairs among which are glands containing a fragrant oil.

Fresh flowers are quite often used commercially to make lavender perfumes and other cosmetics; dried leaves and flowers are used in the manufacture of toiletries.

Southern France and Scotland have become centers of the lavender industry, although the plant itself is cultivated extensively as a garden ornament in North America. Family: Mint (Labiatae); genus and species, *Lavandula officinalis*.

LEEK, a slender, bulbous plant native to the Near East but now widely introduced and cultivated for its tasty, slender, cylindrical bulb and soft succulent leaves, which are milder than those of an onion. When it is allowed to mature it produces a cluster of white or pink flowers. Leeks are used commonly in the Old World and the New as a relish, a condiment, and to add flavor to soups. Family: Lily (Liliaceae); genus and species, *Allium porrum*.

LEMON, a low-growing, evergreen tree of Southeast Asia, 10 to 12 feet tall, with glossy, oval leaves and fragrant, white flowers. Its yellow, acid fruit is rich in citric acid and vitamin C. Cultivated for thousands of years in Asia and in warm parts of Europe, it is now grown extensively in subtropical America. The glandular rind of the fruit is frequently candied, preserved, or used in grated form to add a distinctive flavoring to foods. Family: Rue (Rutaceae); genus and species, *Citrus limon*.

LENTIL, an annual branching herb of the Mediterranean region, 6 to 18 inches tall, the pinnately compound leaves ending in climbing tendrils, the blue or white pealike flowers followed by small pods each containing 2 lens-shaped, gray or red seeds. The plant is cultivated extensively in the Old World for its edible seeds, which are made into soups and porridges. Family: Pea (Leguminosae); genus and species, *Lens culinaris*.

LETTUCE, an annual plant probably native to Asia Minor, cultivated for at least 2500 years as the most popular of salad ingredients. Until the Middle Ages, only the loose-leaved variety was known. Left to grow, it produces a stem 2 to 3 feet tall, topped by small clusters of white- or cream-colored flowers in which every floret is strap-shaped. Head lettuce, which was a new horticultural variety in the 1500s, is now generally preferred to leaf lettuce. Another variety is Cos, or romaine lettuce, with spoon-shaped leaves that have a broad midrib; it was first discovered on the Greek island of Kos. Lettuce contains important vitamins and minerals but virtually no food energy. Family: Daisy (Compositae); genus and species, *Lactuca sativa*.

LICORICE, a herbaceous perennial plant native to Europe, with pale green, pinnately compound leaves, a stem about 3 feet tall, and purple flowers resembling those of peas and beans. It is cultivated extensively in southern Europe for its fibrous roots, from which a sweet black extract can be obtained for use in candies, soft drinks, and in flavoring medicines and tobacco.

A related plant, wild licorice (*Glycyrrhiza lepidota*), found widely in the plains and pasturelands between Mexico and central Canada, has sweet-tasting roots that yield their flavor when chewed. Family: Pea (Leguminosae); genus and species, *Glycyrrhiza glabra*.

LIGNUM VITAE, any of 6 different tropical American trees with extremely hard, heavy wood, pinnately compound leaves, blue, 5-petalled flowers, and seeds in capsules. Most grow to 15 to 30 feet and yield a gum (guaiacum) used in the treatment of rheumatic and skin diseases. The wood of the *Guaiacum officinale*, native to Forida, the West Indies, and northern South America, is the hardest and heaviest of commercial woods. Family: Caltrop (Zygophyllaceae); genus *Guaiacum*.

LILAC, any of about 25 different kinds of woody shrubs with thick, oval, paired leaves and clusters of white or purplish, 4-petalled flowers, which usually emit a strong and characteristic pleasant fragrance. Native to temperate Eurasia, lilacs are cultivated extensively in North America; many horticultural varieties have been developed, chiefly from *Syringa vulgaris* of southeastern Europe. Syringa is also the common name of an unrelated, different plant. Family: Olive (Oleaceae); genus *Syringa*. See also *Mock orange*.

LILY, in the strict sense, any of about 60 different kinds of herbaceous, perennial, bulbous plants of the North Temperate Zone, with upright stems, scattered or whorled, narrow, sessile leaves, and large, trumpet-shaped flowers, the 6 petal-like parts of which curve back upon themselves to display the inner surface.

Easter lilies are usually either the white-trumpet lily (or Bermuda lily, *Lilium longiflorum*) of Japan, which blooms in late March and early April, or they are the very similar madonna lily (*L. candidum*) of southern Europe, which flowers from late April through May. Handsome markings on the inner surface of the flower are features of the golden-banded lily (*L. auratum*) of the Orient and of the

BURPEE SEEDS
LEEKS

various tiger lilies with nodding blossoms, such as the Turk's-cap lily (*L. superbum*) of the eastern United States. Family: Lily (Liliaceae).

LILY FAMILY (Liliaceae), a group of more than 4,000 species in about 250 genera, widely distributed, mostly perennial herbs with a storage organ in the shortened stem, horizontal underground stem, or enlargement of the roots. Generally the flowers are regular, with a 6-parted display of petals and petal-like sepals, and a united ovary of 3 parts that ripens to form a capsule or a berry. See *Aloe, Asparagus, Asphodel, Bear grass, Bluebell, Dogtooth violet, Fritillary, Garlic, Grape hyacinth, Hyacinth, Leek, Lily, Lily of the valley, Mariposa lily, Onion, Rose of Sharon, Smilax, Solomon's seal, Trillium, Tulip,* and *Yucca*.

LILY OF THE VALLEY, either of 2 similar, small, perennial herbs of the North Temperate Zone, with freely spreading horizontal stems, scattered, oblong, upright leaves, and slender, one-sided sprays of small, fragrant, nodding, bell-shaped flowers which are followed by red, poisonous berries that contain a few seeds.

The North American species (*Convallaria montana*) is native to woodlands in the southern Appalachians; the European species (*C. majalis*) has been widely introduced and has become naturalized. Family: Lily (Liliaceae); genus *Convallaria*.

LIME, a small evergreen tree native to the East Indies, with glossy, oval, evergreen leaves, fragrant, white flowers, and small, greenish-yellow, acid fruits, the juice of which is used in beverages and for flavoring. Limes are cultivated throughout Mexico, the West Indies, parts of southern Florida, and southern Europe. Family: Rue (Rutaceae); genus and species, *Citrus aurantifolia*.

LINDEN, or basswood, any of 12 different fast-growing trees of the North Temperate Zone, with soft wood, heart-shaped leaves, and fragrant, creamy-white flowers in small clusters at the tip of pendant stalks to which a green, oval bract is attached for much of the length.

Bees obtain a large amount of nectar from basswood flowers, and the wood is often used in the manufacture of beekeeper's supplies, furniture, woodenware, charcoal, and paper pulp. Family: Linden (Tiliaceae); genus *Tilia*.

LINDEN FAMILY (Tiliaceae), a group of about 400 species in 41 genera, mostly tropical shrubs and trees with simple, alternate leaves and clustered regular flowers. The linden tree and jute are chief among those that grow in temperate regions. See *Jute* and *Linden*.

LITCHI, a genus of a single species (*L. chinensis*). It is a handsome evergreen tree with large, pinnately compound leaves, small flowers, and oval or spherical fruits slightly more than an inch in diameter, each with a leathery skin, a pink pulp, and a central seed. When dried, the skin becomes wrinkled, brown, and brittle; the pulp becomes somewhat like that of a raisin. Cultivated extensively in the Far East since prehistoric times, its origin is uncertain. The tree is rarely raised in the western world. The fruits, dried or preserved and known as litchi nuts (also spelled lychi or leechee), are imported as expensive luxuries. Family: Soapberry (Sapindaceae).

LIVE–FOREVER. See *Orpine*.

LIVE OAK. See *Oak*.

LOBELIA, a genus of about 250 different kinds of herbs, shrubs, and treelike plants widely distributed in tropical and temperate regions. All have tubular flowers with 2 upturned upper petals and 3 lower petals forming a sort of lip.

Several kinds of lobelia with showy blossoms have been cultivated and developed horticulturally as garden plants. These include the shrubby little blue lobelia (*L. erinus*) of South Africa, used as an edging for flower beds in the Northern Hemisphere, and the cardinal flower (*L. cardinalis*) native to meadows and freshwater shores in eastern North America, its stem 2 to 4 feet tall topped by an open cluster of scarlet flowers.

Colonists in the eastern parts of North America found the Indians drying and smoking the leaves of another native kind (*L. inflata*), now known as Indian tobacco. It has large, oval leaves, small, blue flowers, and inflated capsules, and contains at least one alkaloid that is poisonous if taken internally.

In the Old World, lobelias include extraordinary species, such as the tree lobelia (*L. keniensis*) of high, misty mountain slopes in equatorial Africa, which produces leafy stems 10 to 15 feet tall, from which sturdy flower spikes rise another 6 to 8 feet. Family: Lobelia (Lobeliaceae).

LOCOWEED, any of several different kinds of bushy, herbaceous plants of the western United States and adjacent parts of Canada and Mexico. The plants are sometimes eaten by starving livestock. Within a few months, however, the animals develop symptoms of poisoning, such as an inability to drink or eat; these symtoms are usually soon followed by death. This effect has been attributed to at least 8 species of genus *Astragalus* and 3 of *Oxytropis*. Family: Pea (Leguminosae).

LOCUST, any of several different trees with pinnately compound leaves and flowers resembling those of peas. The flowers are followed by seed pods that turn brown and release the seeds. The name was originally given to the carob tree (*Ceratonia siliqua*) of the Mediterranean region, the unripened pods of which are edible and called St. John's bread. Its seeds may have been the original weights of "carats" used by jewelers. Black locust (*Robinia pseudoacacia*), a valuable timber tree of eastern North America which is now planted in many other parts of the world, grows to a height of 80 feet, producing very hard, durable wood and drooping clusters of showy, white flowers. Its branches bear pairs of sharp spines.

The honey locust (*Gleditsia triacanthos*) attains a height of 140 feet, its branches and bark armed with stiff spines that fork repeatedly. Its pods are filled with a sweet natural gum that children like to chew. Family: Pea (Leguminosae).

LOGANBERRY, a hybrid bramble produced from a cross between the western dewberry (*Rubus ursinus*) of California and the widespread red raspberry (*R. idaeus*). It was discovered in 1881 by Judge J. H. Logan and named for him (*R. loganobaccus*). It thrives in the northwestern United States, producing large fruits resembling purplish raspberries; it has not been grown with as much success elsewhere in the United States. Family: Rose (Rosaceae).

LOGANIA FAMILY (Loganiaceae), a group of about 800 species in 32 genera, including herbs, shrubs, climbing vines, and trees, all native to tropical and subtropical regions and most with opposite, simple leaves. It includes the Carolina, yellow jessamine (*Gelsemium sempervirens*), sometimes erroneously called jasmine, which is grown as a porch vine and is the state flower of South Carolina. See *Butterfly bush* and *Nux vomica*.

LOGWOOD, a small Central American tree with peculiarly ribbed bark, thorny branches, pinnately compound leaves, and almost symmetrical, 5-petalled, yellow flowers. Its dark red heartwood yields a valuable dye called haematoxylon, which can be used to dye felt, woolens, and silk a permanent black, purple, blue, or red color. An astringent extract from the wood is also used in medicine. Family: Pea (Leguminosae); genus and species, *Haematoxylon campechianum*.

LOOSESTRIFE FAMILY (Lythraceae), a group of about 475 species in 23 genera, widely distributed but most numerous in tropical America, including herbs, shrubs, and trees with simple, smooth-edged leaves, usually paired or in whorls, and flowers in which sepals, petals, and stamens all arise from the rim of a tubular part.

The henna plant *(Lawsonia inermis)*, a small shrub native to countries from northern Australia to India and East Africa, has shoots and leaves that yield the orange-red dye used for religious purposes and personal adornment.

The 25 kinds of loosestrife *(Lythrum)* are slender herbs with pink or magenta flowers, often giving their color to great areas of low, wet ground where they grow to 3 feet and bloom in mid-summer. The name loosestrife is also used for yellow-flowered herbs *(Lysimachia* species of the primrose family, Primulaceae). See also *Crape myrtle*.

LOQUAT, a small, Oriental, evergreen tree with large, oblong leaves, rust-colored underneath; fragrant, white flowers; and acid, yellow fruits shaped like miniature pears. In cultivation the tree grows to 10 to 12 feet, blossoms in autumn, and produces its fruits in spring. The fruits can be eaten raw, cooked, or preserved. Orchards of loquats have been established in California and the Gulf states. Family: Rose (Rosaceae); genus and species, *Eriobotrya japonica*.

LOTUS, any of several aquatic plants of the Old World as well as their close relatives in America. The pink-flowered, sacred lotus of China, Tibet, and India *(Nelumbo nucifera)*, like the yellow-flowered lotus *(N. lutea)* of the West Indies and the eastern United States, usually raises its circular leaves and flowers out of the ponds and quiet streams in which it grows.

The Egyptian lotuses include one with blue flowers *(Nymphaea caerulea)* and one with white *(N. lotus)*; the latter is the floral emblem of Egypt. In both, the leaves ordinarily float on the water surface and the flowers extend little, if at all, on exposed stalks. The mythical lotus tree, which yielded fruits reputed to cause forgetfulness of all responsibilities, may have been the jujube. Family: Water-lily (Nymphaeaceae). See also *Jujube*.

LUFFA. See *Vegetable sponge*.

LUPINE, any of about 100 different kinds of herbaceous plants native to North America and Europe, with palmately compound leaves and tall, upright spikes of pealike flowers. The flowers of the lupine are usually blue, but they may also be white, yellow, red, or purple.

Many lupines contain poisonous substances in their foliage, flowers, and seed pods, causing loss of life to deer and livestock that eat them in times of extreme hunger. The bluebonnet *(Lupinus subcarnosus)* is the state flower of Texas. Family: Pea (Leguminosae); genus *Lupinus*.

MADDER, a perennial herb native to Eurasia, with a thick root, a slender stem bearing repeated whorls of leaves, and small clusters of yellow flowers which are followed by fleshy berries. Until 1869, madder was cultivated extensively for the dye alizarin, which could be extracted from its roots. The discovery of a cheap way to synthesize the dye from coal tar put an end to the industry.

When animals eat madder, the coloring becomes concentrated in their bones, claws, and beaks, and these parts of their bodies become orange-red. Madder dye was used to give color to many mummy cloths found in old Egyptian tombs. Family: Madder (Rubiaceae); genus and species, *Rubia tinctorium*.

MADDER FAMILY (Rubiaceae), a group of more than 5,000 species in 400 genera, chiefly of tropical and subtropical regions, all with smooth-edged, opposite leaves with large stipules, clustered, regular flowers, stamens attached to the petals, and the corolla attached to the ovary.

They include the delicate Eurasian herb *(Rubia tinctorium)* from which madder dye ("turkey red") was formerly obtained, the low-growing bluets *(Houstonia caerulea)* of North America, the partridgeberry *(Mitchella repens)* of North American woodlands, the shrubby buttonbush *(Cephalanthus occidentalis)*, and the many kinds of shrubby gardenias from the Old World, of which the fragrant-flowered ancestor for most cultivated varieties is the Chinese *Gardenia jasminoides*. See *Bedstraw, Cinchona, Coffee, Gardenia, Madder*.

MADROÑA, or madroño, either of two closely related evergreen shrubs or trees of western North America, growing to 125 feet, with smooth, red bark that peels in strips, large, glossy leaves that are white below, edible, orange-red fruits called "madrona apples," and a fine-grained wood that can be made into a superior grade of charcoal which is ideal for use in gunpowder. Family: Heath (Ericaceae); genus and species, *Arbutus menziesii* (Pacific coast) and *A. xalapensis* (northwest Mexico).

MAGNOLIA, a genus of about 20 different species of decorative shrubs and trees native to eastern Asia and North America, with aromatic bark, large, fragrant, waxy, white, yellow, or rose-colored flowers as much as 12 inches in diameter, and cone-shaped clusters of fruits. A hybrid between two Chinese species is cultivated in the northern United States and Europe for its flowers, which open in spring before the leaves.

The large-flowered magnolia *(M. grandiflora)*, native to the southern states and the state flower of both Louisiana and Mississippi, is an evergreen tree growing to 70 feet, with handsome, dark green, glossy leaves and lemon-scented, creamy flowers 8 inches or more across. A smaller evergreen, the sweet bay *(M. virginiana)*, is native to swamplands in the southeastern states, which are then known as "bay-lands." Although it attains a height of only 15 feet, its thick, short trunk is used to make wooden bowls and utensils. Family: Magnolia (Magnoliaceae).

MAGNOLIA FAMILY (Magnoliaceae), a group of about 100 species in 10 genera, all woody shrubs or trees with simple, alternate leaves and, usually, large, showy flowers in which the receptacle is elongated beyond the petals, bearing first a spiral of many stamens and then a spiral of carpels which mature and convert the floral cluster into a large, aggregate fruit. See *Magnolia* and *Tulip tree*.

MAHOGANY, any of several related tropical trees that produce a valuable hard, red-brown wood suitable for cabinetmaking. Most highly esteemed is *Swietenia mahogani,* native to the West Indies and Central America, and cultivated in Florida and India.

Mahogany has compound leaves resembling those of the honey locust, clusters of small flowers, and large, dull brown, pearshaped fruits. African mahogany *(Khaya senegalensis)*, Indian mahogany *(Toona ciliata)* of India and northern Australia, and Philippine mahogany *(T. calantus)* are similar. Family: Mahogany (Meliaceae).

MAHOGANY FAMILY (Meliaceae), a group of about 1000 species in 50 genera, chiefly tropical shrubs and trees with compound leaves and clustered, regular flowers. It includes the West Indian cedar *(Cedrela odorata)*, which provides the fragrant wood used in cigar boxes and is supposedly insect-repellent. See *Chinaberry* and *Mahogany*.

MAIDENHAIR TREE. See *Ginkgo*.

MAIZE. See *Corn*.

MALLOW, any of about 30 different kinds of Eurasian and north African herbs, many of them annuals and biennials. Most have alternate lobed leaves, pink, white, or blue flowers, and flattened fruits commonly called cheeses, which are enclosed in 2 or 3 tough, leaflike bracts rather than the 6 to 9 bracts of the closely related marshmallow and hollyhock.

The high mallow *(Malva sylvestris)* and round-leaved mallow *(M. rotundifolio)* have been introduced into North America and other continents, escaping from cultivation to become roadside weeds. Family: Mallow (Malvaceae); genus *Malva*.

MALLOW FAMILY (Malvaceae), a group of about 1500 species in 82 genera, widely distributed but most numerous in tropical America. Whether they appear as herbs, shrubs, or trees, they have simple, alternate leaves and, in each regular flower, a central column of stamens beyond which the style and stigma protrude. See *Cotton, Hibiscus, Hollyhock, Mallow,* and *Marshmallow*.

MANDRAKE, a herbaceous plant of southern Europe and northern Africa, with a thick taproot that is often forked equally, suggesting a human torso with legs. The short stem bears a tight whorl of spreading, ovate leaves, and a single, purplish flower. Many ancient superstitions developed in relation to this plant, including the claim that it shrieked when pulled from the ground.

Dried, powdered mandrake root was used to increase fertility in women and as an emetic, purgative, and mild narcotic throughout Europe and the Orient. The name mandrake is sometimes applied to the American mayapple *(Podophyllum peltatum)*. Family: Potato (Solanaceae); genus and species, *Mandragora officinarum*.

MANGEL–WURZEL. See *Beet*.

MANGO, a small tree of the East Indies, growing to 50 feet, with glossy, oval leaves, sprays of yellow flowers, and large, pear-shaped, green fruits with a delicious, yellow pulp around a central, flattened seed. The fruit of the wild mango is smaller and less palatable than that of horticultural varieties now in cultivation in most tropical and subtropical countries. The roasted seeds are occasionally eaten. Family: Sumac (Anacardiaceae); genus and species, *Mangifera indica*.

MANGROVE, any of several different low-growing trees of tropical and subtropical shores, which grow in shallow sea water and form dense thickets. Red mangrove *(Rhizophora mangle)* of tropical America and West Africa has opposite leaves, and multi-branched aerial roots that grow downward from spreading branches.

The seeds germinate while still attached to the parent plant and fall free only after developing a long, dagger-shaped root and a terminal bud from which leaves can quickly spread. Black mangrove *(Avicennia nitida)*, an unrelated tree of the vervain family (Verbenaceae), generally grows in water-soaked soil, and gets air to its roots through upright, pencil-sized, leafless stems that grow upward for 4 to 6 inches until exposed.

The white mangrove *(Laguncularia racemosa)* of tropical America and Africa, and button mangrove *(Conocarpus erecta)* of the same regions, are members of the combretum family (Combretaceae); their bark is often harvested as a source of tannin. Family: Mangrove (Rhizophoraceae).

MANILA HEMP. See *Abacá*.

MANIOC. See *Cassava*.

MANZANITA, a stiff, branching, evergreen shrub native to the Pacific coast of North America, where it forms dense thickets or contributes to the harsh chaparral vegetation of arid areas. It produces smooth leaves, white or pink flowers, and brown fruits resembling small apples. The bark is conspicuously reddish or chocolate-brown. Family: Heath (Ericaceae); genus and species, *Arctostaphylos pungens*.

MAPLE, any of about 150 different kinds of trees and shrubs of the Northern Hemisphere and of moun-

BURPEE SEEDS
MARJORAM

tains in Java and Sumatra, all with paired leaves and paired, winged fruits (samaras) commonly known as maple keys. Many are tall trees with palmately lobed, simple leaves on long stalks and valuable hardwood. In early spring they yield a slightly sweet sap that can be boiled to make syrup or maple sugar.

Most valuable are the sugar maple *(Acer saccharum)* of the northeastern United States and adjacent Canada, which attains a height of 120 feet, and the slightly smaller sycamore maple *(A. pseudoplatanus)* of central Europe and Asia Minor. Faster growing and with softer wood are the Norway maple *(A. platanoides)* of Eurasia, and the silver maple *(A. saccharinum)* and red maple *(A. rubrum)* of eastern North America.

Box elder *(A. negundo)* of eastern Canada and the northeastern United States, which, peculiarly, has pinnately compound leaves, is a still weaker tree, growing best in wet woodlands and near streams. The largest assortment of maples is native to Japan. In autumn the foliage of most maples undergoes a spectacular change in color through all shades from yellow and orange to deep red. Family: Maple (Aceraceae); genus *Acer*.

MARGUERITE. See *Daisy*.

MARIGOLD, any of about 20 different kinds of daisy-like, herbaceous plants native to the New World from Argentina to the southern United States, with aromatic, dissected leaves and orange-red flower heads firmly supported by a cluster of green bracts. The two kinds cultivated most widely are the tall, straight-stemmed "African" species *(Tagetes erecta)* and the dwarf "French" marigold *(T. patula)*, both originally from Mexico. The related pot-marigold *(Calendula officinalis)* of Mediterranean Europe, Asia Minor, and North Africa was formerly used for flavoring and raised widely as a potherb. Now it is cultivated as an ornament which produces flowers much of the summer; each flower head is large and orange-gold. Family: Daisy (Compositae); genus *Tagetes*.

MARIPOSA LILY, any of about 40 different kinds of bulbous herbs of western North America, with narrow leaves and tulip-like flowers handsomely marked with colorful spots on white, red, yellow, or lilac petals. A mariposa lily, *Calochortus nuttalii*, is the state flower of Utah. Family: Lily (Liliaceae); genus *Calochortus*.

MARJORAM, any of several related aromatic, perennial herbs native to the Mediterranean coasts. They are widely cultivated and have also escaped from cultivation to grow naturally along roadsides. They have square stems, paired, oval leaves, and either short clusters of purple flowers *(Origanum, especially O. vulgare)* or grayish leaves and white flowers *(Majorana hortensis)*. Family: Mint (Labiatae).

MARSHMALLOW, an erect perennial herb of temperate Eurasia and North Africa, growing to 4 feet, with oval leaves and delicate, pink flowers. Formerly its roots were gathered and used in the manufacture of a sweet, white confection which is now produced artificially from cane syrup. Family: Mallow (Malvaceae); genus and species, *Althaea officinalis*.

MARSH MARIGOLD, a perennial herb of eastern North America, growing in wet places, producing glossy, kidney-shaped leaves on hollow stalks, and, usually, bright yellow flowers in spring. Young leaves and stems of the marsh marigold are eaten as greens. The whole plant is often called cowslip. Family: Buttercup (Ranunculaceae); genus and species, *Caltha palustris*.

MATÉ. See *Holly*.

MAYAPPLE, an erect perennial herb of eastern North America, with a long, branching root, umbrella-shaped leaves on tall, stout stalks, and solitary, nodding, waxy, white flowers followed by oval, yellow, fleshy fruits.

The fruits are the least poisonous part of the plant. The roots are the most dangerous part because they contain several toxic materials; these poisons have been used in primitive medicine. Mayapple is sometimes known as the American mandrake, or wild jalap. Family: Barberry (Berberidaceae); genus and species, *Podophyllum peltatum*.

MAYFLOWER. See *Arbutus*.

MAYWEED, or dog fennel, a branching perennial herb native to Eurasia and North Africa, now widespread as a weed, with pinnately dissected leaves emitting a strong, unpleasant odor, and yellow-centered, white-rayed flower heads an inch in diameter resembling daisies. The leaves were formerly employed in preparing a tea used in treating colic. The garden camomile (*Anthemis nobilis*) is a closely related plant with a pleasant odor; a tea from its foliage was once used as a blood purifier. Family: Daisy (Compositae); genus and species, *Anthemis cotula*.

MEDLAR, a small, branching tree native to Eurasia and much cultivated in Europe for its globular fruits, which resemble crab apples and have a tart flavor in the freshly-ripened, gritty pulp. When they are killed by the frost and partially decayed, the unpreserved fruits have a better flavor. Family: Rose (Rosaceae); genus and species, *Mespilus germanica*.

MELON, a prostrate vine, or the large, spherical, or egg-shaped fruit, with a thick, fleshy rind and a fibrous, seed-filled center. The term is generally used to describe all horticultural varieties of the muskmelon (*Cucumis melo*) of tropical Asia and Africa, such as cantaloupes, cassaba melons, honeydew and Persian melons, and rock melons, and the varieties of the watermelon (*Citrullus vulgaris*) of tropical Africa, including the citron, or preserving melon. Insects carry pollen from the starlike, yellow, staminate flowers to the similar pistillate flowers on the same hairy prickly stems, partially concealed below large, round leaves.

Cantaloupes have an orange pulp and a hard skin raised in ridges, often in a netlike pattern. Cassaba melons are large, round, and smooth-skinned, with a rich, creamy pulp; they mature late and are often called winter muskmelons. Honeydew melons are oval in shape, ivory to white externally, with thick, green, sweet flesh. Rock melons, or European cantaloupes, are hardly grown in the United States and Canada; they are small, with a tough skin raised in high ridges, and a comparatively shallow, orange-red flesh.

Watermelons, which were cultivated in Egypt in ancient times, have a thick, green or green and white rind surrounding a sweet red pulp, and may weigh 50 pounds or more when mature; the pulp is eaten raw, the rind pickled, and the seeds sometimes enjoyed as if they were thin-shelled nuts. Family: Gourd (Cucurbitaceae).

MESQUITE, any of about 30 different kinds of tropical and subtropical thorny trees and shrubs native to arid regions and most conspicuous in the American Southwest, South America, and Hawaii where, after locally heavy rains, the seeds germinate and send down extremely long roots. The taproots attain a depth of as much as 60 feet, reaching underground supplies of water that other plants have failed to reach. Wherever mesquite grows into unstunted trees 40 to 50 feet tall, there is water within 40 feet of the earth's surface.

The branches bear decidous, twice pinnately compound leaves, and spikes of odorous, greenish-yellow flowers followed by yellow or brown seed pods. The pods of the common mesquite (*Prosopis juliflora*) are long and straight; those of the screw bean (*P. pubescens*) are twisted into spirals. The seeds are eaten by Indians and Mexicans, and the foliage by livestock. As fodder, mesquite provides an inadequate diet and symptoms of a fatal deficiency develop in cattle that continue to eat virtually no other foods for a few months. Family: Pea (Leguminosae); genus *Prosopis*.

MIGNONETTE, any of about 50 different kinds of small, herbaceous plants native to arid areas around the Mediterranean Sea and Asia. They have small, alternate leaves and spikes of fragrant flowers with tufts of brownish stamens on the upper petals. Beekeepers sometimes plant mignonette as a nectar-producing plant that gives a pleasant flavor to the honey made by their bees.

Two Mediterranean species have become roadside weeds in the New World, one (*Reseda alba*) with white flowers and the other (*R. lutea*) with yellow flowers. Horticulturalists have developed larger, greenish flowers in the common mignonette (*R. odorata*), which has broad leaves and grows very close to the earth, forming a dense blanket over the soil or providing attractive edgings for bower beds. Family: Mignonette (Resedaceae); genus *Reseda*.

MILKWEED, any of about 90 different kinds of perennial herbs native to America and Africa, with erect stems, opposite or whorled leaves, an abundant milky juice that may contain poisonous substances. The clustered, small flowers have 5 petals that turn backward, exposing pairs of pollen masses linked by peculiar fibers that catch onto the legs of insects. Weak insects are often caught, whereas strong bees and butterflies carry the paired masses of sticky pollen and often accomplish cross-pollination. A pollinated flower develops into an inflated pod that splits along one side to release flat seeds, each with a tuft of satiny, white hairs that catch the wind.

The common milkweed (*Asclepias syriaca*) of eastern North American fields and roadsides, which was accidentally introduced into Asia Minor and later spread through much of Eurasia, has purple-pink or brownish-pink blossoms. Butterfly weed (*A. tuberosa*) of North America is often cultivated in gardens for its bright orange flowers. Family: Milkweed (Asclepiadaceae); genus *Asclepias*.

MILKWEED FAMILY (Asclepiadaceae), a group of about 1700 species in 100 genera, mostly tropical, perennial herbs or shrubs (including climbing vines), usually with a milky sap, simple, paired, smooth-edged leaves, and clustered flowers. It includes the strange carrion flowers (*Stapelia* species) of South Africa, which resemble cacti in their succulent green stems and reduced leaves. See *Milkweed* and *Waxflower*.

MILKWORT, any of about 500 different kinds of herbaceous and shrubby plants native to Eurasia and Africa, with bitter-tasting, simple leaves and attractive, irregular flowers in which the conspicuous parts are two petal-like sepals; of the five sepals, only these two are red, white, blue, or yellow instead of green.

According to superstition, a decoction made from the leaves of the common milkwort (*polygala vulgaris*) would induce more production of milk in nursing mothers. Seneca snakeroot (*P. senega*) of eastern North America is the source of an irritant drug. Family: Milkwort (Polygalaceae); genus *Polygala*.

MILLET, any of a number of different grasses cultivated in the Orient for more than 5,000 years, and generally regarded as the "poor man's cereal" although the nutritional quality of the grains is higher than that of rice as it is eaten. Common, or proso, millet (*Panicum miliaceum*) is cultivated in the Soviet Union, whereas little millet (*P. miliare*) is the favorite in India; both are members of the huge genus of panic grasses.

Italian millet (*Setaria italica*), grown in the Near East and China, is a foxtail grass. Pearl millet, known also as cattail millet (*Pennisetum glaucum*), is favored in parts of India and in the Sudan. More distantly related grasses include finger millet (*Eleusine coracana*) and broomcorn millet (*Sorghum vulgare technicus*), which are popular in Africa and India.

All millets yield grains that can be used to thicken soups or mixed with wheat to make a bread flour that will rise when baked. In North America and much of Europe millets are cultivated chiefly for poultry feed. Family: Grass (Gramineae).

MIMOSA, a genus of tropical and subtropical trees, shrubs, vines, and herbs containing about 350 species native to America, Africa, and Asia.

MIGNONETTE
T.H. EVERETT

All have feathery, pinnately compound leaves, white or pink flowers in fuzzy, globular clusters, and seeds in bivalved pods. The sensitive plant (*M. pudica*), a roadside weed in tropical America, has become famous because its leaflets and leaves fold quickly when touched. Family: Pea (Leguminosae).

MINT, any of about 15 different kinds of aromatic herbs native to the Northern Hemisphere, with square stems, opposite leaves, and clusters of blue, pink, or white flowers. Several are cultivated for the volatile oil that can be extracted from the leaves. It is used to flavor candies and to give a pleasing odor to perfumes and soaps.

Whole, fresh leaves of peppermint (*Mentha piperita*) are often added to beverages or chopped and cooked gently to make a sauce for meat. Spearmint (*M. spicata*) has become most famous as a flavoring for chewing gum. European pennyroyal (*M. pulegium*) and an American substitute, mock pennyroyal (*Hedeoma pulegioides*), are also used to flavor foods. Family: Mint (Labiatae); genus *Mentha*.

MINT FAMILY (Labiatae), a group of about 3200 species in more than 200 genera, widely distributed but most numerous in Mediterranean countries, chiefly herbs with square stems and opposite leaves but sometimes shrubs, climbing vines, or trees. The epidermal cells secrete aromatic oils and the flowers are clustered, usually with a 2-lipped corolla and the 4 stamens of different lengths—2 long and 2 short. See *Balm, Catnip, Ground ivy, Horehound, Lavender, Marjoram, Mint, Oswego tea, Rosemary, Sage, Self-heal,* and *Thyme*.

MISTLETOE, any of more than 1000 different kinds of herbaceous and shrubby parasitic plants, principally of tropical regions, growing at the expense of trees to which the mistletoes are attached by modified roots called haustoria. Most have opposite or whorled, simple leaves on branching stems, small, green or colored flowers, and a sticky covering over the seeds. Birds that pick the small fruits have difficulty swallowing the sticky seeds and scrape them off on tree branches to which the seeds adhere while germinating.

European mistletoe (*Viscum album*) grows on many trees, especially apple, and was used in pagan ceremonies. The magic attributed to the mistletoe is the source of the custom of kissing under the plant at Christmas time. In the New World the plant used for this purpose is the American mistletoe (*Phoradendron flavescens*) of the eastern United States. Family: Mistletoe (Loranthaceae).

MOCK ORANGE, a hardy European shrub that grows to 6 to 12 feet, with brown bark, oval leaves about 4 inches long, and large, sweet-scented, white or cream-colored flowers that open late in spring. Often called a "syringa" because its stems were made into pipe stems, it is not related to the lilac (*Syringa*). The state flower of Idaho, known there only as the syringa, is *Philadelphus lewisii*. Family: Saxifrage (Saxifragaceae); genus and species, *Philadelphus coronarius*.

MONKSHOOD. See *Aconite*.

MORNING GLORY. See *Bindweed*.

MORNING-GLORY FAMILY (Convolvulaceae), a group of about 1200 species in 50 genera, chiefly climbing herbs and woody vines of the tropics, but including shrubs and trees, some of which are thorny and adapted for arid conditions. See *Bindweed, Dodder,* and *Sweet potato*.

MOUNTAIN ASH, a small North American tree with pinnately compound leaves, clusters of creamy flowers that produce bunches of orange-scarlet berries, and soft, weak wood. Its flowers and fruits are decorative, and attract bees and fruit-eating birds. Moose and deer often eat the leaves and young twigs. Closely related is the Eurasian rowan (*Sorbus aucuparia*). Neither tree commonly grows taller than 30 feet and both live best in cool climates protected from the wind. Family: (Rosaceae); genus and species, *Sorbus americana*.

MOUNTAIN LAUREL, a small evergreen shrub of eastern North America, with leathery leaves and beautiful clusters of rose-pink flowers. It is the state flower of Pennsylvania. A close relative is sheep laurel or lambkill (*Kalmia angustifolia*), which is poisonous to young sheep. Family: Heath (Ericaceae); genus and species, *Kalmia latifolia*.

MULBERRY, any of about 12 different kinds of small trees native to the North Temperate Zone, which have leaves of many different shapes (oval, notched, and lobed) on the same tree, and clusters of small flowers followed by very sweet fruits. Most favored for eating raw, cooked, or preserved are the black fruits of black mulberry (*Morus nigra*), native to western Asia. Red mulberry (*M. rubra*) of the eastern United States also produces edible fruits as well as wood that is resistant to decay. White mulberry (*M. alba*) of China is raised to provide leaves on which silkworms can feed. Family: Mulberry (Moraceae); genus *Morus*.

MULBERRY FAMILY (Moraceae), a group of about 1000 species in 73 genera, all with a milky juice and alternate, smooth-edged leaves. Most are plants of tropical and subtropical regions and many are important for their edible fruits. It includes the breadfruit (*Artocarpus altilis*), a tall tree with large, deeply lobed leaves and hard, spherical fruits that can be eaten baked, boiled, or fried, and the jackfruit (*A. heterophyllus*); both are from Southeast Asia but are widely cultivated in the tropics.

One of the fast-growing pioneer trees in tropical America is the trumpet tree (*Cecropia peltata*), which harbors fierce, biting ants in hollow spaces reached through small holes in the axils of the leaves. See *Breadfruit, Fig, Mulberry, Osage orange,* and *Paper mulberry*.

MULLEIN, any of about 260 different kinds of tall, biennial herbs of the temperate parts of Eurasia, many now introduced and naturalized elsewhere. Best known is the common mullein (*Verbascum thapsus*) which, in its second year, raises an upright stem 2 to 7 feet tall above large, hairy, whorled lower leaves. On this stem a succession of flowers open, each for a single day. The plant is sometimes called flannel leaf or feltweed because of the felty texture of the leaves. Family: Figwort (Scrophulariaceae); genus *Verbascum*.

MUSKMELON. See *Melon*.

MUSTARD, any of several related annual, biennial, and sometimes perennial herbs native to Eurasia, where they have been cultivated for thousands of years as a source of small, round seeds producing a pungent oil. The plants themselves have stiff, branching stems 1 to 6 feet tall, and loose clusters of yellow flowers, each with 4 petals about ½-inch long. Young plants (mustard greens) are cooked as a slightly bitter potherb in some regions.

Black mustard (*Brassica nigra*), a hairy plant with black seeds, is the principal source of the mustard seeds that are dried and pulverized for use as a condiment in Europe, excluding the British Isles, and as the major ingredient of mustard in North America. White mustard (*B. hirta*), a rough plant with less hair and pale gray seeds, is preferred in Britain and many former British colonies for its "hotter" flavor. Small amounts are blended with black mustard powder and starch to make the mixture milder to suit the tastes of inhabitants of the New World.

Rape (*B. rapa*) is an annual with leaves that clasp the stems. Now known only in cultivation, rape is raised as a forage crop as well as for

BURPEE SEEDS
MORNING GLORY

its seeds, which yield rape oil (useful as a food, lubricant, and lamp fuel). Its seeds are also used as bird food. The closely related turnip (*B. napus*), like the rutabaga (*B. napobrassica*), stores a great amount of food in a swollen root during its first year of growth, and is cultivated as a root crop for human use and as fodder for livestock.

Chinese cabbage (*B. pekinensis*), sometimes called celery cabbage or pe-tsai, grows in a lettuce-like head of tightly wrapped, edible leaves. The inner leaves are white, crisp, and tasty. It has been raised as a salad green and vegetable in China since the first century AD and has been introduced into the United States.

Ordinary cabbage (*B. oleracea*) has been developed horticulturally from a wild Eurasian cliff plant to include the varieties known as cabbage (*B. oleaceae capitata*), eaten raw, cooked, or slightly fermented and salted as sauerkraut; kale (*B. oleracea acephala*), a headless variety with curly leaves; kohlrabi (*B. oleracea gongolodes*), which has a turnip-like enlargement of the stem just above the ground; Brussels sprouts (*B. oleracea gemmifera*), which has tight edible buds 1 to 2 inches in diameter clustered on the thick stalk; broccoli (*B. oleracea italica*), with narrow, long, erect leaves around a large, round-topped cluster of flower buds; and cauliflower (*B. oleracea botrytis*), which produces an edible head of misformed but delicately flavored, white flower stalks and buds. Family: Mustard (Cruciferae); genus *Brassica*.

MUSTARD FAMILY (Cruciferae), a group of about 2500 species in some 350 genera, mostly native to the North Temperate Zone, particularly to Mediterranean countries. All are herbs with alternate, simple leaves. Flowers with 4 sepals and 4 petals, 4 long stamens and 2 short ones around a pistal mature to become a pod that opens to release its seeds. See *Alyssum, Candytuft, Cress, Horseradish, Mustard, Peppergrass, Radish, Shamrock, Shepherd's purse, Stock,* and *Wallflower.*

MYRTLE, any of about 75 different kinds of tropical and subtropical shrubs and trees with glossy, green leaves and white or faintly pink flowers that are followed by small, black, fleshy berries. The classical myrtle (*Myrtus communis*), from which wreaths were fashioned as crowns for victorious athletes, is a strong-scented ornamental shrub native to the Mediterranean region but now grown as a hedge in the southern United States.

Myrtle wood is fine grained and useful in turning fine gunstocks. An oil extracted from the leaves has medicinal value. Various parts of the plant, all pleasantly strong smelling, are used for perfumes and cosmetics. Family: Myrtle (Myrtaceae); genus *Myrtus.* See also *Crape Myrtle.*

MYRTLE FAMILY (Myrtaceae), a group of about 3000 species in 80 genera, all shrubs or trees of warm climates, most numerous in America and Australia, with leathery, simple leaves

BURPEE SEEDS
NARCISSUS

dotted with glands containing volatile oils, and regular flowers usually in clusters. Among members of this family are many of the tall timber trees of Hawaii, New Zealand, Australia, and the East Indies, including not only members of the huge genus *Eucalyptus,* but also of *Metrosideros, Leptospermum, Melaleuca,* and *Callistemon* (bottlebrush ; for most of these, only local common names have been developed. See *Allspice, Clove tree, Eucalyptus, Guava, Myrtle, Pomegranate.*

NARCISSUS, a genus of bulbous Eurasian herbs with slender leaves and white or yellow flowers on tall stalks, each flower with a 6-part perianth opening to display a ruffled disc- or trumpet-shaped crown. Cultivated all over the world as early spring garden flowers, several of the 40 different species have become well known.

The common name narcissus is usually restricted to *N. incomparabilis,* in which the crown is well developed and edged in reddish-orange, while the rest of the flower is white. The poet's narcissus (*N. poeticus*) has a much smaller crown, making the white perianth itself the most conspicuous part of the blossom.

The daffodil (*N. pseudo-narcissus*) bears solitary flowers on each stalk; its yellow fragrant blossom has a prominent crown of the same color. Jonquils (*N. jonquilla*) have clustered, pale yellow, fragrant flowers and crowns that are small and somewhat flattened. The polyanthus narcissus, or Chinese sacred lily (*N. tazetta*) produces a flat-topped cluster of yellow or white flowers with small crowns. Family: Amaryllis (Amaryllidaceae).

NASTURTIUM, a weak-stemmed, clambering herb of South America, now cultivated in gardens on many continents. It has circular leaves with stalks attached at the center, and with handsome, spurred, irregular flowers. The 5 petals of the flower may be yellow, scarlet, or maroon. All parts of the plant, including the seed capsules, have a pleasant, pungent aroma, which can be used to add flavor to salads. Pickled seed pods are sometimes used as a garnish for meat.

Dwarf horticultural varieties of nasturtium grow only a few feet tall, whereas others climb by sensitive leaf stalks to a height of 20 feet or more. The similar and closely related canary-bird flower (*Tropaeolum peregrinum*) is also cultivated for ornamental purposes. Watercress (genus *Nasturtium* of the mustard family, Cruciferae) is unrelated. Family: Nasturtium (Tropaeolaceae); genus and species, *Tropaeolum majus.*

NECTARINE. See *Peach.*

NETTLE, any of a number of related plants belonging to several genera native to most continents, and notable for the intensely irritating effect of a toxic material contained in stiff glandular hairs on the leaves. These hairs break after penetrating skin and release the irritant, which causes acute but usually temporary itching. Yet the young plants of some species are gathered and cooked as edible greens, and the roots of a few are harvested as a source of a lasting yellow dye.

Many nettles have strong stem fibers, but preparation for textile use is often difficult. Chinagrass, or ramie (*Boemeria nivea*), of Southeast Asia, yields the toughest and silkiest fiber known. Nettletree (*Laportea gigas*) of Australia grows to a height of 90 feet. A close relative, the wood-nettle (*L. canadensis*), is a perennial herb of eastern North America, growing no more than 3 feet tall.

Most famous of the nettles are the cosmopolitan members of genus *Urtica,* of which more than 30 species are known. Some are annuals easy to eradicate by cutting off the tops before their inconspicuous greenish flowers produce seeds, and others annuals that must be dug out or killed with herbicide chemicals. Family: Nettle (Urticaceae).

NIGHT-BLOOMING CEREUS, any of several climbing cactus plants with stems ribbed lengthwise, supporting themselves by means of aerial roots. They open solitary, huge, creamy, fragrant flowers as much as a foot in diameter for an hour or two in late evening, only to close them permanently before dawn. These cacti are native to the southwestern United States, Mexico and Central America, and the West Indies. Horticultural varieties and hybrids have been developed, partly from a spectacular wild species (*Cereus grandiflorus*). Family: Cactus (Cactaceae).

NIGHTSHADE, loosely, any of 1700 different kinds of herbs, shrubs, and trees of tropical and temperate regions classified in genus *Solanum* of the potato family (Solanaceae). Specifically, either the common Eurasian nightshade (*Solanum nigrum*), which is now almost cosmopolitan as a prostrate or erect herb with small clusters of white flowers followed by bunches of poisonous black berries, or the bittersweet (*Solanum dulcamara*).

Enchanter's nightshade, 9 different north temperate and arctic plants growing from underground stems, is unrelated (genus *Circaea* of the evening-primrose family, Onagraceae); it produces paired leaves and short upright clusters of small white or pink flowers which are followed by similar clusters of dry fruits with hooked bristles that travel as burs. See also *Bittersweet*.

NORFOLK ISLAND PINE, an evergreen coniferous tree native to South Pacific islands, now widely introduced in warm climates or grown indoors in tubs for its symmetrical whorls of branches bearing luxuriant, short, needle-like leaves. Family: Araucaria (Araucariaceae); genus and species, *Araucaria excelsa*.

NUTMEG, an evergreen tree native to the Molucca Islands in the East Indies, now cultivated in the West Indies and tropical America. It grows 50 or 60 feet tall and has simple, oval leaves and tiny sprays of bell-like flowers that are either staminate or pistillate.

The flowers produce a peachlike, fleshy fruit of which the central seed is eggshaped and enclosed in a waxy, red membrane. The flesh of the fruit is preserved to be eaten as a candy, or made into a jelly. The membrane, which turns yellow, is dried for sale as the spice mace; the seed is grated or ground as the spice nutmeg. Family: Nutmeg (Myristicaceae); genus and species, *Myristica fragrans*.

NUX VOMICA, a medium-sized tree native to India and Ceylon and cultivated elsewhere in the tropics, with shining, oval leaves, clusters of greenish flowers, and globular, white fruits about the size of an orange. The bark, often called false Angostura bark, yields a bitter tonic. The green seeds embedded in the fruit are the principal source of the poisonous alkaloid strychnine. Family: Logania (Loganiaceae); genus and species, *Strychnos nux-vomica*.

OAK, any of about 300 different kinds of hardwood trees, native to the North Temperate Zone and islands of the South Pacific, with simple leaves and separate staminate and pistillate flowers. The staminate flowers are clustered in pendant, loose catkins; the pistillate flowers are solitary or in small groups close to the stem. The fruits are acorns, borne in a cup.

They mature in one year on members of the white-oak group, which bear round-lobed leaves and include the widespread Eurasian brown oak or English oak (*Quercus robur*), the only oak in Britain, and such American trees as the eastern white oak (*Q. alba*), Californian white oak (*Q. lobata*), post oak (*Q. Stellata*), bur oak (*Q. macrocarpa*), and overcup oak (*Q. lyrata*). The acorns take 2 years to ripen and usually germinate in the third year on members of the red-oak group, which have sharp-pointed lobes on the leaves and include the American trees known as red oak (*Q. rubra*), black oak (*Q. velutina*), water oak (*Q. nigra*), pin oak (*Q. palustris*), and willow oak (*Q. phellos*). Many of these trees grow to a height of 100 to 170 feet, and produce valuable lumber. They often hold their dead leaves far into the winter, although by then the handsome autumn colors have faded to a dull brown.

In the southeastern United States a valuable evergreen oak (*Q. virginiana*) is known as live oak. A much smaller evergreen oak of Mediterranean countries, growing only about 40 feet tall, is the cork oak (*Q. suber*), from which the light, spongy, bark can be stripped in thick sheets about once every 9 years to be made into the cork products of commerce. Some cork trees are grown in the United States, but the world's major cork supply comes from Portugal and Spain. Family: Beech (*Fagaceae*); genus Quercus.

OAT, an annual grass native to temperate regions of the Old World, cultivated in Eurasia for thousands of years as a forage plant, as a cereal for human use, and as food for horses. The plant grows 3 to 5 feet tall, with thin, narrow, long leaves beyond which the stem continues upward, arching over because of the weight of the many grains, each of which is surrounded by chaffy bracts. Family: Grass (Gramineae); genus and species, *Avena sativa*.

OKRA. See *Hibiscus*.

OLEANDER, a small evergreen shrub or tree 7 to 15 feet tall, with narrow, stiff leaves and sprays of attractive flowers in colors ranging from white to rose. Native to the Orient and southern Europe, the oleander has been cultivated for ornamental purposes for many years in warm parts of both hemispheres, often as a hedge, though all parts of the plant are poisonous if eaten. Family: Dogbane (Apocynaceae); genus and species, *Nerium oleander*.

BURPEE SEEDS
OXALIS

OLIVE, a small evergreen tree native to warm, semiarid areas of Eurasia and North Africa, cultivated for thousands of years and introduced into western North America, South America, and Australia as a source of fruits (olives) and oil. A branch from an olive tree, with its dull, willow-like, gray-green leaves, has long been regarded as a symbol of peace.

Olive flowers are shining-white, clustered, and followed by small, egg-shaped, plumlike fruits which turn black as they ripen. Olives are bitter and inedible until treated with lye and given time to ferment under careful control. Olive oil is obtained from pressed, ripe olives. Family: Olive (Oleaceae); genus and species, *Olea europaea*.

OLIVE FAMILY (Oleaceae), a group of about 500 species in 22 genera, all shrubs, climbing vines, or trees of tropical and warm temperate climates with opposite leaves and clusters of regular flowers, usually with just 2 stamens. See *Ash*, *Forsythia*, *Jasmine*, *Lilac*, *Olive*, and *Privet*.

ONION, a biennial herbaceous plant native to southwestern Asia, but now widely cultivated for the pungent flavor in its succulent leaf bases, which form a bulblike enlargement just below ground level. In its second year an onion plant produces a tall, upright stalk with a cluster of inconspicuous, white flowers from which the seeds may germinate before being shed from the fruits.

Horticultural varieties of large size, or flattened instead of spherical shape, or red instead of white color, or sweeter and less "hot" flavor are raised on every continent and are often known as Bermuda or Spanish onions, although the seed may be imported from the Canary Islands. Closely related are the chive (*Allium schoenoprasum*), the leek (*A. porrum*), and the shallot (*A. ascalonicum*) from Mediterranean countries, cultivated widely as flavoring for salads, stews, and cooked meats. Family: Lily (Liliaceae); genus and species, *Allium cepa*.

ORANGE, any of a number of closely related, small trees native to southern Asia, yielding some of the world's most important fruits. The unpruned trees may grow to 35 feet, with glossy, oval, evergreen leaves on short stalks that bear a narrow wing along each side. The fragrant, white flowers are followed by spherical fruits composed of 10 to 12 fleshy sections surrounding the seeds, enclosed in a tough rind beset with oil glands.

The rind may be dried or candied, or its oil may be removed for separate uses as bitter flavoring. Orange pulp is particularly rich in vitamin C, and is commonly crushed to make a nourishing beverage that can be frozen or concentrated for later use. Whole oranges are made into marmalade. For this use, the sour, or Seville, orange (*Citrus aurantium*) is often preferred; it is native to Malaysia, but much cultivated in Spain. The sweet orange (*C. sinensis*), native to China and Southeast Asia, has been horticulturally developed to produce the seedless navel orange (introduced from Brazil and cultivated extensively in California), and the Washington and Valencia oranges. The Temple orange is believed to be a hybrid between the sweet orange and the mandarin orange or tangerine (*C. reticulata*), a native of the Philippines and Southeast Asia; its rind is removed with special ease, making it a luxury fruit, raised extensively in the Gulf States. Family: Rue (Rutaceae); genus *Citrus*.

ORCHID FAMILY (Orchidaceae), an immense group of about 15,000 different species in 450 genera, often regarded as the most highly developed of all the monocotyledonous plants. Widely distributed, those of all arctic regions and most temperate regions are terrestrial, whereas the majority in tropical regions are perching plants (epiphytes) that perch on forest tree branches and bark. All family members are perennial herbs, the terrestrial ones with thickened roots, the perching ones with aerial roots specialized for absorbing water and with the stem swollen at the base to form a water-storage organ called a pseudobulb. The flowers are bilaterally symmetrical, often very showy, solitary or in clusters, with the lowest (innermost) of the 3 petals generally larger and often extended to form a spur or sac.

The fruit is a capsule containing a large number of exceedingly minute seeds that have almost no store of food and, hence, are dependent upon germinating soon after they ripen.

Lady's slippers (genus *Cypripedium*) of North Temperate woods have showy, solitary flowers, whereas the showy orchis (*Orchis spectabilis*) of eastern North America and many of its relatives produce spikes of smaller blossoms. Of the tropical perching orchids, the American species of genus *Cattleya* are especially favored for corsages because of their large size and handsome colors.

A climbing orchid, with glossy, oval leaves, is the vanilla plant (*Vanilla fragrans*) native to Mexico, and cultivated in the West Indies and Asia for its long, slender fruit capsules, which can be cured and from which the flavoring vanilla can be extracted. Artificial vanilla is now available at lower cost from other plant sources.

OREGON GRAPE, a small shrub native to the Pacific coast of North America, growing to about 5 feet, with spiny, compound leaves and clusters of yellow flowers followed by dark berries resembling grapes. Its flower is the state flower of Oregon. Family: Barberry (Berberidaceae); genus and species, *Mahonia aquifolia*.

ORPINE, or live-forever, an erect, perennial, succulent herb native to Eurasia. It is cultivated in rock gardens around the world for its 1- to 4-inch thick, tooth-edged leaves and its 15-inch fleshy, gray-green stems bearing clustered, white, purple, pink, or yellow flowers. Named live-forever because of the long survival of separated parts of the plant, which take root if given an opportunity, it was kept on hand during the Middle Ages for its supposed value in promoting the healing of wounds. It is a member of a genus containing about 500 species, known generally as stonecrops, of which *Sedum acre*, with its creeping, succulent, evergreen leaves and yellow, starlike flowers, is widely grown in gardens. Family: Orpine (Crassulaceae); genus and species, *Sedum telephium*.

ORPINE FAMILY (Crassulaceae), a group of about 1300 species in 33 genera, widely distributed but primarily found in arid regions of the Mediterranean, the American Southwest, and south-central Asia. Many are cultivated in rock gardens for their novel, often cactuslike shapes. Jade plant (*Crassula arborescens*) is a treelike member of a large genus.

Cigarette plant (*Kalanchoe verticillata*), and various kinds of life plants (*Bryophyllum* species) from the Old World tropics produce new small plants with leaves and roots in the notches of their leaves; they drop these smaller leaves to the ground as an asexual mode of reproduction. Other members of the family are known as hen and chickens because of their ability to produce new plants on short runners, thus covering the ground with close-set rosettes of fleshy leaves; live-forever or houseleek (*Sempervivum tectorum*) of southern Europe has this characteristic. See also *Orpine*.

ORRIS ROOT. See *Iris*.

OSAGE ORANGE, or bowwood, a sprawling, thorny tree 30 to 60 feet tall, native to the region between Texas and Missouri, the home of the Osage Indians. It has glossy, green leaves, staminate and pistillate flowers on separate trees, and hard, round, inedible, yellow fruits formed by the joining together of the receptacles, floral parts, and ripened ovaries of several adjacent flowers. The bark yields yellow, tan, orange, gold, and olive-colored dyes, and the wood has the strength and flexibility needed for the construction of bows for archery, tool handles, posts, and woodenware. Family: Mulberry (Moraceae); genus and species, *Maclura pomifera*.

OSIER. See *Willow*.

OSWEGO TEA, or bee balm, a perennial herb native to eastern North America, with a square stem that grows to about 3 feet, opposite, fragrant, pointed leaves, and shaggy clusters of showy, red flowers. A close relative of wider distribution in the United States and Canada is the taller, lavender-flowered, wild bergamot (*Monarda fistulosa*). Family: Mint (Labiatae); genus and species, *Monarda didyma*.

OXALIS, a genus of about 850 different species of small, perennial herbs with delicate stems filled with sour juice, small, clover-like leaves, and solitary or clustered regular flowers with 5 petals that may be pink, lavender, yellow, or white and that generally close at night and in dull weather, as do the leaflets of the compound leaves. Known generally as wood sorrels, they are widely distributed, but are most numerous in South Africa, on the slopes of the Andes, and in wet parts of Central America and Mexico. Those native to North America and Europe are often marketed in pots as shamrocks at St. Patrick's Day celebrations. Family: Oxalis (Oxalidaceae).

OYSTER PLANT. See *Salsify*.

PALM FAMILY (Palmaceae), a group of about 1500 different species in 200 genera, mostly thick-stemmed, unbranched, evergreen trees topped by a cluster of large, simple, palmate leaves (in fan palms) or pinnately compound leaves (in feather palms).

Palms have enormous economic importance in tropical and warm, temperate climates for almost every part of the tree is useful. Dead leaves are used to thatch the roofs of native houses; strips from fresh leaves are woven into mats, baskets, and wall panels; buds and many kinds of palm fruits are edible and nutritious, or yield raw materials for making sugar, wine, cosmetics, and waxes; whole trunks and strips cut lengthwise from the trunks provide valuable building materials; and fibers from the leaves are made into textiles, clothing, and hats. Door mats in countries far from the tropics are commonly composed of fibers known as coir, made from the husks of coconuts and called coco mats.

Fan palms include the cabbage palm (*Sabal palmetto*), which attains a height of 80 feet on the higher ground of some of the isolated areas in the Florida Everglades, and the prostrate scrub palmetto (*Serenoa repens*), found in neglected pastures from the Carolinas to Texas. The clambering fan palms of the Old World tropics include the *Raphia ruffia* of Madagascar, the extraordinarily long leaves of which are a source of strong raffia fiber, and the sago palms (*Metroxylon rumphii* and *M. laeve*) of the East Indies, the pith of which yields sago starch. The largest known seeds are those of a fan palm, the double coconut (*Lodoicea sechellarum*) of the Seychelles, which in the husks weigh 30 to 40 pounds and take 10 years to ripen.

The coconut palm itself (*Cocos nucifera*) is a feather palm, thriving close to salt water, rising 60 to 100 feet, producing large fruits in clusters with each seed covered by a thick, buoyant husk as well as a hard shell, and containing a layer of nutritious "meat" surrounding a cavity filled with a juice called coconut milk. The dried meat is copra, a principal product of tropical coasts, which is made into soap, coconut oil, and animal food.

Other feather palms of great economic value include the date palm (*Phoenix dactylifera*) of tropical Africa and Asia, which yields edible fruits, date sugar, and structural materials, as well as shade under the equatorial sun; the oil palm (*Elaeis guineensis*) of West Africa, cultivated extensively in the East Indies and tropical America, which yields fruits from which palm oil is extracted for use in soaps, medicines, and industry; and the betel palm (*Areca catechu*) of Southeast Asia, which produces egg-sized fruits that are generally harvested before they ripen. The husk is torn off and the mottled seed boiled, sliced, and dried in the sun for sale as "betel nut." More than 300 million people enjoy chewing betel nut, which is prepared for consumption by wrapping a small piece in a leaf of the betel pepper (*Piper betle*), along with a pellet of lime, and perhaps a pinch of some aromatic spice.

Still another feather palm is the royal palm (*Roystonea regia*) of Florida and Cuba, the smooth, gray, columnar trunks of which are greatly admired along public avenues.

PALMETTO. See *Palm Family.*

PALOVERDE, any of 3 related, small, spiny, desert trees of the North American southwest, with stiff branches, green, smooth bark, delicate, pinnately compound leaves that drop as soon as drought returns after a period of rain, and clusters of small, bright, yellow, 5-petalled flowers. Family: Pea (Leguminosae); genera and species, *Cercidium floridum, C. torreyanum*, and *Parkinsonia aculeata*.

PAMPAS GRASS, the common name given to an ornamental, tall, reedlike grass (*Cortaderia argentea*), native to mountainous country in southern Brazil and Argentina. It is cultivated in California for the decorative effect produced by its massed, coarse, basal leaves, its waving, fluffy plumes of flowers, and its 6-to-12-foot-high seeds. A similar grass with the same name (*Gynerium argenteum*) forms natural hedges along water courses in the pampas of southern South America. Family: Grass (Gramineae).

PANSY. See *Violet.*

PAPAW, or pawpaw, any of 8 different kinds of shrubs or small trees native to southeastern and eastern North America, all with large, feather-veined, pointed leaves and solitary flowers where the leaves of the previous year joined the stems.

The dull purple flowers are followed by large, pulpy fruits containing several seeds, each enclosed within a fleshy part called an aril. The pulp of the common papaw (*Asimina triloba*) is sweet and edible in autumn, but all other parts of the tree give off an unpleasant odor when bruised. Family: Custard-apple (Annonaceae); genus *Asimina*.

PAPAYA, a tall, herbaceous plant of tropical America that grows to a height of 25 feet, with a crown of large, palmately lobed leaves on long stalks and clusters of yellow flowers high on the main stem followed by huge, ovoid, melon-like fruits weighing 15 to 20 pounds.

Each papaya fruit contains a thick, orange pulp surrounding a fibrous center filled with spherical black seeds. The ripe pulp has the consistency of muskmelon. Its distinctive, pleasant flavor is greatly appreciated in salads or as a breakfast fruit. An enzyme in papaya leaves is pepsin-like, and is used to tenderize meats. Family: Papaya (Caricaceae); genus *Carica*, particularly *C. papaya*.

PAPER MULBERRY, a small, attractive tree native to Southeast Asia and the Pacific islands, but cultivated in subtropical parts of the United States as well. It has evergreen, ovate leaves that give dense shade, small clusters of flowers followed by mulberry-like fruits, and a fibrous bark that is used throughout the tree's native range to make tapa (bark cloth) for decorative material and clothing. Family: Mulberry (Moraceae); genus and species, *Broussonetia papyrifera*.

PAPRIKA. See *Pepper, Red.*

PAPYRUS, a long-stemmed, reedlike sedge native to northeastern Africa, growing to 15 feet, the 3-ranked, narrow leaves and triangular stems of which are topped by an umbrella-shaped cluster of minute flowers borne on a radiating array of fine stalks. The ancient Egyptians cut the pith of this marsh plant into long strips, arranged them into layers, and soaked and pressed them to form long sheets and rolls of writing material.

Papyrus is grown in warm parts of Europe and the United States as a decorative plant. Closely related is the umbrella plant (*Cyperus alternifolius*) of Madagascar and the Mascarene Islands, raised as a house plant for its clumps of 3 to 10 stems, 1 to 3 feet tall, which bear whorls of rough, blade-like leaves arranged like the ribs of an umbrella. Clusters of greenish flowers appear at the tops of the stems in winter. Family: Sedge (Cyperaceae); genus and species, *Cyperus papyrus*.

PARSLEY

PARSLEY, a low-growing, biennial herb of southern Europe, widely cultivated for its bright green, finely-divided leaves, which are used as a garnish and seasoning, and for the small, hard, paired fruits, which at the end of its second year, ripen from umbrella-like clusters of small, yellowish green flowers.

Parsley seeds can be used as a seasoning, and an oil from the seeds can be used as a medicine. One variety, Harburg parsley, has a thick root eaten as a vegetable. Family: Carrot (Umbelliferae); genus and species, *Petroselinum crispum*.

PARSNIP, a biennial, herbaceous plant that stores food in a thick taproot during its first year and produces a stem 2 to 5 feet tall with many compound leaves and flat-topped clusters of yellow flowers in its second year.

Native to Europe, it is used as a winter fodder for cattle and as a food for man. It is harvested after a killing frost at the end of the first growing season destroys the exposed parts and induces the formation of sugar from the starch in the underground root. Family: Carrot (Umbelliferae); genus and species, *Pastinaca sativa*.

PASQUEFLOWER. See *Anemone.*

PASSIONFLOWER, any of about 400 different kinds of tropical climbing vines, most of them native to western South America. They generally have simple, alternate leaves and a succession of paired flowers along the stem, each flower with a peculiar ring of petal-like parts growing out of the tubular support of the stamens. The common passionflower (*Passiflora caerulea*) from Brazil, which is widely cultivated in warm countries, has flowers colored blue, purple, and white, followed by peach-sized berries. A delicious beverage can be prepared from the pulp.

A passionflower with 1-inch yellow blossoms (*P. lutea*) and another (*P. incarnata*) with 3-inch, white and purple flowers are native to the southern United States. Brazilian and West Indian species with particularly large fruits are often cultivated and called granadillas. Fruits of *P. quadrangularis*, or giant granadillas, may be 10 inches long. Family: Passionflower (Passifloraceae).

PEA, any of 6 different related kinds of perennial herbs, mostly native to the Mediterranean region, with pinnately compound leaves, some leaflets modified to form tendrils used in climbing, and with characteristic bilaterally symmetrical flowers in which the lowest 2 petals join to form a pouch (keel). The fruits are straight pods containing a single row of spherical seeds.

Garden peas (*Pisum sativum*) have been cultivated for at least 1,000 years in Eurasia as a vegetable and as stock food. Often the whole pea plant is plowed under as "green manure" to enrich the soil. The living roots accomplish a great deal in this respect because they bear nodules in which bacteria use atmospheric nitrogen to produce nitrogenous substances nourishing to the pea plant and others in the same earth. Family: Pea (Leguminosae); genus *Pisum*.

PEA FAMILY (Leguminosae), a huge group with about 13,000 species in some 550 genera, probably the second largest family of plants, including herbs, shrubs, climbing vines, and trees. Many are thorny and most have nodules on their roots containing nitrogen-fixing bacteria. All produce a pod of some kind as the fruit. See *Acacia, Alfalfa, Bean, Broom, Clover, Cowpea, Gorse, Indigo, Kentucky coffee tree, Kudzu, Laburnum, Lentil, Licorice, Locoweed, Logwood, Lupine, Mesquite, Mimosa, Paloverde, Pea, Peanut, Redbud, Sandalwood, Shamrock, Sweet clover, Sweat pea, Tamarind, Tonka bean tree, Tumbleweed, Vetch, Wattle tree, Wisteria*, and *Yellowwood*.

PEACH, a small, many-branched tree easily injured by frost, native to southern China and introduced first in Europe and then the southern United States. Many varieties have been developed and some with more attractive flowers than others, producing larger fruits with special features, for instance, "freestone" instead of "clingstone" flesh.

All have simple leaves, attractive, pink, 5-petalled flowers, and edible fruits with a juicy flesh outside an armored, central seed. Smooth-skinned nectarines differ from most other varieties of peach, which have a downy or velvety covering over the fruit. Family: Rose (Rosaceae); genus and species, *Prunus persica*.

PEANUT, a sprawling, annual, herbaceous plant native to Brazil, with pinnately compound leaves and bright yellow flowers, which give rise to pods on long stalks. The ripening pods bend downward, enter the earth, and mature hidden in the soil. The peanut commonly eaten is not a nut, but the dried seed of this plant.

It has been known in South America since prehistoric times and cultivated in Africa for more than 400 years. In Africa it is known as groundnut or goober. The green parts are made into hay for livestock and the seeds are eaten raw, boiled, roasted, in cakes and candies, or crushed into peanut butter and peanut oil. Family: Pea (Leguminosae); genus and species, *Arachis hypogaea*.

PEAR, a small Eurasian tree with glossy, pointed, wavy-edged leaves, white flowers, and sweet, sometimes gritty, ovoid fruits. Dwarf trees are preferred for cultivation, because the fruits can be harvested easily.

Among the varieties, the Bartlett has a sweet fruit, the Seckel or sugar pear, a small, hard, sweet fruit, and the Kieffer pear, a coarse fruit with less flavor but a firmness that lasts into winter. The closely related sand pear (*Pyrus sinensis*) of China and Japan is often used as a strong root upon which to graft fruit-bearing tops of more desirable kinds of pears. Family: Rose (Rosaceae); genus and species, *Pyrus communis*.

T.H. EVERETT
PEACH

PECAN. See *Hickory*.

PEEPUL, or pipal. See *Fig*.

PELARGONIUM. See *Geranium*.

PENNYROYAL. See *Mint*.

PEONY, any of several different kinds of herbaceous perennials with deeply divided leaves on long stalks. All except the wild peony (*Paeonia browni*) of mountains in the Pacific states are native to Eurasia.

About 700 named varieties have been developed from the European common peony (*P. officinalis*) hybridized with the Chinese and Siberian white peony (*P. albiflora*). These are remarkable for the size of their flowers, the "doubleness" through development of extra petals instead of stamens, and the variety of colors ranging from white to pink to red to magenta.

Tree peonies, which produce an upright, woody stem 3 to 6 feet tall and flowers of a particularly satin-like texture as much as 12 inches across, have been developed from the moutan peony (*P. suffruticosa*) of eastern Asia through hybridization with a closely related species (*P. lutea*). In colonial times extracts from the roots of common peonies were used as a nerve tonic. Family: Buttercup (Ranunculaceae); genus *Paeonia*.

PEPPER, the most valuable spice in commerce today, produced from the fruits of a climbing, woody vine native to India. It has stems reaching 20 to 30 feet above the ground, ovate leaves, and spikes of inconspicuous flowers followed by yellowish-red, globular berries, each about ¼-inch in diameter, with a single seed (the peppercorn) covered by a thin pulp. Unripe fruits are gathered, dried, and ground whole to produce black pepper, whereas ripe fruits are dried, peeled, and soaked in water to free the seeds which are ground to make white pepper.

Cultivated in the Orient since ancient times, pepper became so important to the traders of the 1400s that they explored the world, seeking a shorter route to tropical India to obtain the spice. Pepper is still produced in Indonesia, India, and Thailand, as well as in some parts of Africa and tropical America.

A related plant, the betel pepper (*Piper betle*) of the East Indies provides the fresh leaves chewed with dried fragments of betel nut. Another East Indian relative is cubeb (*P. cubeba*), a woody, climbing shrub the aromatic, bitter berries of which are dried and used in remedies for respiratory ailments. Family: Pepper (Piperaceae); genus *Piper*. See also Palm Family.

PEPPER FAMILY (Piperaceae), a group of about 1400 species in 12 genera, chiefly herbs and shrubs of the tropics with stems jointed or swollen where the leaves arise and with the inside conducting tissue more or less scattered.

The flowers are clustered in spikes and produce small, fleshy fruits with a single, central seed. Most of the species are members of the large genus *Piper* and of the genus *Peperomia*, of which several among the 500 species are cultivated as house plants for their handsome foliage. See also *Pepper*.

PEPPERGRASS, or pepperwort, any of about 130 different kinds of annual herbs widely distributed in temperate regions, with branching stems to 2 feet high, curly, notched leaves, and ascending clusters of small, white flowers. The foliage is edible and has a "hot" taste, which has led to the cultivation of one species (*Lepidium sativum*) from Mediterranean countries as garden cress. It has escaped from cultivation in many regions and become a weed. Family: Mustard (Cruciferae); genus *Lepidium*.

PEPPERIDGE. See *Tupelo*.

PEPPERMINT. See *Mint*.

PEPPER, RED, a woody shrub native to tropical America, perennial in warm climates, but grown as an annual where frost occurs in winter. The leaves are generally pinnately compound; the flowers are small, solitary, and followed by a hollow berry with a thick rind containing many small, flat seeds. Cultivated by the Indians, the plant was discovered by Spanish explorers and introduced into Europe, where the sweet, or bell, pepper was developed horticulturally to be eaten green or ripe (red). Paprika is made from dried, ripe, bell peppers.

Another mild variety is the Spanish sweet pepper, known as pimento. The smaller, "hotter" varieties are used in making chili and tabasco sauce as condiments. Cayenne pepper is made from the dried, ground fruits of the Guinea pepper (*Capsicum annuum*) and the spur pepper (*C. fastigiatum*). Peppers are rich in vitamin C and have a variety of medicinal uses. Family: potato (Solanaceae); genus and species, *Capsicum frutescens*.

PEPPER TREE, an evergreen tree native to America from Mexico to Chile, with graceful, drooping branches bearing pinnately compound leaves, clusters of small, whitish, staminate or pistillate flowers, but not both on the same tree, and bright red or rose-colored firm fruits, each with a central armored seed. It has been introduced into Florida and California, where winters are mild, as an ornamental and hedge tree capable of growing 20 to 50 feet tall. Family: Sumac (Anacariaceae); genus and species, *Schinus molle*.

PERIWINKLE, or running myrtle, a perennial, trailing plant with glossy, dark, paired, evergreen leaves and solitary, purplish-blue flowers. Native to the Old World from western Europe to Asia Minor, it has been widely introduced into temperate lands as a ground cover thriving in shady areas. A tropical relative (*Vinca rosca*) from Madagascar tolerates greater summer heat but is susceptible to winter cold. Family: Dogbane (Apocynaceae); genus and species, *Vinca minor*.

PERSIMMON, any of several different shrubs and small trees, native to the Northern Hemisphere, that grow to 50 feet and produce simple, leathery, smooth-edged leaves, bark splitting into a pattern of squares, and staminate flowers on separate trees from the pistillate flowers.

The flowers are followed by spherical, orange-brown fruits, resembling tomatoes and as much as 3 inches in diameter. The flesh is sour until touched by frost and completely ripe. The cultivated persimmon (*Diospyros kaki*) of Japan comes in seedless as well as seeded varieties; it is grown in the Pacific states as well as in the Orient. The wild persimmon of the southern United States (*D. virginiana*) and the date plum (*D. lotos*) of China also produce edible fruits. Family: Ebony (Ebenaceae); genus *Diospyros*.

PE-TSAI, or Chinese cabbage. See *Mustard*.

PETUNIA, a genus of tropical American, herbaceous annuals with weak, hairy, stems 6 to 24 inches tall, smooth, oval leaves, and fragrant, trumpet-shaped, ruffled flowers of white, purple, violet, or mixed colors. Most frequently cultivated as a garden flower in the United States are the Argentinian purple petunia (*P. violacea*), the white petunia (*P. axillaris*), and hybrids between these and other species. Family: Potato (Solanaceae).

PHLOX, a genus of about 50 different kinds of annual and perennial herbs, one species of which is native to northeastern Siberia. The others are native to North America. They produce stiff stems, narrow, stalkless leaves, and clusters of white, pink, red, purple, or mottled flowers in which the corolla is 5-lobed with a slender tube expanded into a flat display.

Many cultivated annual varieties are horticultural forms of the Texan species (*Phlox drummondii*), with red or purple blossoms. Dwarf phlox, chosen as a rock-garden ornament, is generally the moss pink or ground pink (*P. subulata*) of eastern North America; it has tiny tufted leaves and clusters of magenta, pink, or lilac flowers that open early in the spring.

A taller related plant is wild sweet william (*P. maculata*), about 2½ feet tall, with clusters of pink or purple flowers. It is native to stream edges and rich woodland soil in eastern North America. Family: Phlox (Polemoniaceae).

PIGNUT. See *Hickory*.

PIGWEED, any of several related herbaceous plants, chiefly annuals of almost cosmopolitan distribution as weeds, flowering inconspicuously late in the summer, and belonging to genera *Chenopodium* (especially the European *C. lanceolatum* and *C. paganum*), *Cycloloma* ("American winged pigweed") and *Axyris* ("Russian pigweed," of the goosefoot family, Chenopoliaceae), and *Amaranthus* (especially the cosmopolitan *A. hybridus* and *A. retroflexus* of the amaranth family, Amaranthaceae).

PIMENTO, or Pimiento. See *Pepper, Red*.

PIMPERNEL, a low spreading herb native to Europe, with small, oval leaves and solitary, scarlet, white, or blue petals united at the base and closing in dull weather and at night; hence the popular English name "poor man's weatherglass." The many-seeded capsules contain fruits resembling peppercorns, which has led to the introduction of this plant along most coasts of the world and in fields a long distance inland. Family: Primrose (Primulaceae); genus and species, *Anagallis arvensis*.

PINE, any of about 90 different kinds of evergreen coniferous trees with needles of two types: one borne singly in spirals around stems, the other in bundles of 2 to 5 enclosed in papery sheaths at the base. The needles, ranging from 1 to 24 inches long, may be retained on the tree from 2 to 8 years according to the species.

Among 5-needle pines, the most valuable for timber are the North American white pine (*Pinus strobus*), found east of the Rockies and as far south as Guatemala; the western white pines (*P. monticola*) of the North American Pacific coast; and the sugar pine (*P. lambertiana*) of California and Oregon, which attains a height of about 250 feet and produces cones 20 inches or more in length.

Three-needle pines include the western yellow pine (*P. ponderosa*) and the longleaf pine (*P. palustris*) of the American southeast, a valuable source of turpentine and resins. Included among the 2-needle pines are the important Scotch pine (*P. sylvestris*) of northern Eurasia, the lodgepole pine (*P. contorta*) of western North America, and the stone pine (*P. pinea*) of Mediterranean countries, which yields edible seeds called pignolias.

Edible pine seeds, known as piñon nuts, were gathered as winter food by American Indians in the southwest, chiefly from the nut pine (*P. edulis*) and the singleleaf pine (*P. monophylla*), which has solitary leaves. Family: Pine (Pinaceae).

PINE FAMILY (Pinaceae), a group of about 210 species in 9 genera, all coniferous trees with winged seeds, yielding more lumber than any other family of plants. See *Cedar, Douglas Fir, Fir, Hemlock, Larch, Pine, Spruce*.

PINEAPPLE, any of 5 different spiny plants native to tropical America, with a basal rosette of long, stiff, saw-edged, and sharp, pointed leaves among which the stem eventually grows upward to terminate in a cluster of inconspicuous greenish or purple flowers. The ovaries join together as they ripen, forming one multiple fruit from each flower cluster.

Often the stem continues for a short distance between the ovaries and beyond the multiple fruit to bear a short cluster of harsh, stiff, green leaves. *Ananas sativa* has been developed to yield juicy, large, sweet fruits, weighing from 3 to 20 pounds, which are cut from the plant with the terminal tuft of shorter leaves still in place.

About three-quarters of all edible pineapples and pineapple products are raised and produced in the Hawaiian Islands; additional large plantations have been established in Puerto Rico and other parts of the West Indies, and in Malaysia. Wild

BURPEE SEEDS
PETUNIA

pineapple, or pinguin (*Bromelia pinguin*), from tropical America forms almost impenetrable tangles along the edges of rain forests and yields a valuable fiber from its leaves. It is sometimes grown in the tropics as a fruitbearing plant or as an ornament. Family: Pineapple (Bromeliaceae); genus *Ananas*.

PINEAPPLE FAMILY (Bromeliaceae), a group of about 1500 species in 65 genera, all but one species native to America. Most are short-stemmed, often with stiff, fleshy leaves in a rosette which holds rain water. Included are the most conspicuous perching plants of the tropical rain forests. They are epiphytes, frequently called "air plants" because they take no nourishment from the tree branches on which they grow. See *Pineapple* and *Spanish moss*.

PINK, any of almost 300 different kinds of low-growing or sprawling perennial herbs native to Eurasia and Africa, with narrow, paired, grasslike leaves and showy, fragrant flowers the 5 petals of which are conspicuously notched or "pinked" at the outer edge. Many are cultivated as garden flowers or have escaped to become widespread on other continents to which they were introduced.

The garden or grass pink (*Dianthus plumarius*) commonly has flowers almost 2 inches in diameter. The carnation (*D. caryophyllus*) produces solitary blooms of larger size; horticultural varieties are often double in size. Sweet william (*D. barbatus*), with a flat-topped cluster of flowers the petals of which usually have a line of color across, has long been a favorite of English gardeners. Family: Pink (Caryophyllaceae); genus *Dianthus*.

PINK FAMILY (Caryophyllaceae), a group of about 1800 species in 80 genera, all herbs with simple, opposite leaves and flowers with notched ("pinked") petals. See *Baby's breath*, *Bouncing Bet*, *Chickweed*, and *Pink*.

PINK, GROUND. See *Phlox*.

PIPSISSEWA, or prince's pine, a small, perennial herb of dry woodlands in the northern parts of the North Temperate Zone. Its extensive horizontal, creeping, underground stems give rise to short, upright stems bearing thick, glossy, evergreen leaves and loose, terminal clusters of white flowers with waxy, concave petals and expanded filaments on the stamens. Family: Heath (Ericaceae); genus and species, *Chimaphila umbellata*.

PISTACHIO, a tree native to the Mediterranean countries, growing 25 feet tall with compound leaves and producing three leaflets and olive-like fruits containing an edible green seed, much prized for its delicate flavor. A close relative from the same region is the terebinth tree (*Pistacia terebinthus*), which yields Chian turpentine, the only oily resin of this kind not obtained from a conifer. Family: Sumac (Anacardiaceae); genus and species, *Pistacia vera*.

POINSETTIA

PITCHER PLANT, any of several insectivorous plants with pitcher-like leaves that hold rainwater in which insects drown, are digested, and soluble products absorbed as nitrogenous nourishment for the plant. Native to bogs and swamps in the New World are the members of the pitcher-plant family Sarraceniaceae, including 7 or more (genus *Sarracenia*) in eastern North America, 1 (genus *Darlingtonia*) in northern California and southern Oregon, and 4 (genus *Heliamphora*) in high mountains of Venezuela and the Guianas.

In the tropics of Asia and of Australia, particularly in the jungles of Borneo and adjacent parts of the East Indies, are 66 members of the monkeycup family, Nepenthaceae, all in genus *Nepenthes*. These are herbs or climbing shrubs with pitchers at the ends of the leaves or climbing tendrils. An Australian pitcher plant (*Cephalotus follicularis*), found in marshes of Western Australia, is the sole member of family Cephalotaceae; only its lower leaves form insect-catching pitchers.

PLANE-TREE FAMILY (Platanaceae), a group of 8 different kinds of trees in a single genus (*Platanus*), native to the Northern Hemisphere, with massive trunks growing to 170 feet tall; tough wood; broad, deciduous leaves with 3 pointed lobes; leaf stalks concealing the axillary buds; and pendant clusters of minute flowers that mature into spherical heads of small, pyramidal, brown fruits.

The plane tree (*P. orientalis*), which is native to Eurasia, from the Mediterranean to the Himalayas, is widely planted along city avenues for its pleasant shade. Like the sycamore tree (*P. occidentalis*) of eastern North America and the California sycamore (*P. racemosa*), the plane tree has a thin, brittle bark which scales off in large patches leaving chalky white or yellow areas, as though the tree had been painted for camouflage purposes.

PLANTAIN FAMILY (Plantaginaceae), a group of about 200 species in 3 genera, almost all members of the cosmopolitan genus Plantago and chiefly weeds of temperate areas. They have fibrous roots, rosettes of thick, long leaves, short stems, and spikes of tiny, greenish or white flowers atop slender stalks 8 to 10 inches tall.

The common broad-leaved plantain (*P. major*) is found in lawns, and its seeds are eaten by birds. The narrow-leaf plantain or buckhorn (*P. lanceolata*) tends to crowd out valuable grasses in meadows and pastures. The name plantain is also given to certain tropical bananas that are cooked before being eaten.

PLUM, one of several related small trees native to Asia, with smooth, oval, saw-edged leaves, close-grained wood frequently used for cabinet work, a bitter sap containing cyanides, clusters of white flowers that open early in the year (sometimes before the leaves), followed by smooth-skinned, fleshy fruits containing a single, smooth, armored seed.

Damsons, greengages, and prune plums are varieties of the common plum (*Prunus domestica*) which has been grown extensively for its fruit in Europe and North America. Prunes, or dried plums, include certain varieties developed for cultivation in California, or those from a West Indian tree (*P. occidentalis*).

Also cultivated in the United States are the native American wild plum (*P. americana*), the hardy Canadian black plum (*P. nigra*), and the Japanese plum (*P. salicina*). Family: Rose (Rosaceae); genus *Prunus*.

POINSETTIA, a small tree of tropical America with large, jagged-edged leaves and similar brilliant leaves in irregular whorls near the tips of the branches, radiating from under the strange small flowers; these are borne in cuplike clusters, each with one pistillate and several staminate flowers. Reaching the peak of display before Christmas and lasting well through the holiday season, poinsettias are cultivated for sale as indoor decorations; the cut ends of the stems should be dipped in boiling water or sealed with paraffin or flame to prevent the loss of the milky juice.

There are a number of related herbaceous plants that are native to the southeastern United States. Among these is painted leaf (*Euphorbia heterophylla*), which has a splash of orange-red across the stalk end of its green leaves, near its terminal clusters of equally inconspicuous flowers. Family: Spurge (Euphorbiaceae); genus and species, *Euphorbia pulcherrima*.

POISON HEMLOCK, an erect, perennial herb native to southern Europe, introduced and well established in eastern North America, Mexico, South America, and elsewhere, and growing to 5 feet tall. Only the lower leaves are long-stalked but all leaves are twice pinnately compound. The small flowers are borne in umbrella-like clusters to 3 inches across followed by paired, small, dry fruits. The thick root might easily be mistaken for a parsnip. All parts of the plant, and especially its seeds, are deadly poisonous. A cupful of poison hemlock juice was a standard dose for suicide or execution of prisoners in ancient Greece. Family: Carrot (Umbelliferae); genus and species, *Conium maculatum*.

POISON IVY, an erect shrub or climbing, woody, perennial vine with deciduous, compound leaves of 3 oval leaflets, the middle one larger than the lateral ones, but all bearing a few small teeth along the sides. Small, greenish flowers in clusters are followed by hard, gray, globular berries.

All of the plant, including the underground horizontal stems and roots, is poisonous, causing the affected skin or stomach lining to swell and blister. Highly susceptible people react from contact with domestic animals that have walked through poison ivy plants in underbrush, or from smoke from fires in which poison ivy plants are burning. The active agent is urushiol, an oily substance.

Similar effects are caused by related poison sumac (*Rhus vernix*), of eastern North America, and poison oak (*R. diversiloba*), of California. Family: Sumac (Anacardiaceae); genus and species, *Rhus radicans*.

POKEWEED FAMILY (Phytolaccaceae), a group of about 125 species in 17 genera, chiefly herbs and woody perennials of the American tropics and subtropics. The most familiar of them in the United States and Canada is the pokeweed or pigeonberry (*Phytolacca americana*). It has a large, poisonous root from which a stout, smooth stem grows upward each spring bearing drooping, large leaves pointed at each end, and short spikes of petal-less flowers, each with 5 white or pinkish, petal-like sepals.

By midsummer, elongated loose clusters of plump, black berries ripen, their enclosed seeds probably distributed by birds that are immune to the poison. All parts of the plant are poisonous, except young shoots under 4 inches long in the spring; these may be cooked and eaten after the root is removed. They taste much like asparagus. Pokeweed is found along roadsides and in wasteland.

POLYPODY FAMILY (Polypodiaceae), a group of more than 7000 species in about 170 genera, most with compound leaves rising from large underground stems. They are the largest family of ferns.

The family includes the fern (*Onoclea sensibilis*) of eastern North America and eastern Asia, the fronds of which are very sensitive to frost; the Christmas fern (*Polystichum acrostichoides*) of North America, which is evergreen; the spleenworts (*Asplenium* species) and the maidenhair ferns (*Adiantum* species) of temperate and tropical regions; and the large staghorn (*Platycerium* species) of Australia, Southeast Asia, and Africa, which is a handsome perching plant often displayed in greenhouses of temperate regions. See *Bracken* and *Walking fern*.

POMEGRANATE, a small tree native to northern India and Afghanistan, cultivated throughout the Orient and in parts of Europe and the United States, with glossy leaves and short-stalked, bell-like, scarlet flowers which are followed by orange-red, fleshy fruits about the size of an orange, with a thick, leathery rind surrounding a delicious, juicy, acid pulp containing many large seeds. The sirupy beverage made from the pulp of pomegranates is called grenadine. Family: Myrtle (Myrtaceae); genus and species, *Punica granatum*.

POMELO. See *Grapefruit*.

POND LILY. See *Water lily*.

POPLAR, any of about 40 different kinds of quick-growing trees native to the North Temperate Zone, with soft wood and thin bark, used commonly for fuel and paper pulp. Their broad, triangular leaves on long flattened stalks flutter in the breeze, and turn golden-yellow in autumn.

Drooping catkins of staminate or ovulate flowers are borne on separate trees and appear in spring before the leaves. The seeds are dropped when ripe and carried by the wind which catches on the cotton-like fibers extending from the seed covering.

These trees were frequently planted along streets and avenues until city planners discovered how quickly the roots invade and clog sewers. The European white poplar (*Populus alba*), the leaves of which have a feltlike coating of white hairs beneath, the gray poplar (*P. canescens*), and the columnar Lombardy poplar (*P. nigra italica*) were introduced into America.

Native American types include the widespread quaking aspen (*P. tremuloides*), the balsam poplar (*P. balsamifera*) of Canada, the cottonwood (*P. deltoides*) of eastern states, and the black cottonwood (*P. trichocarpa*) of the Pacific coast from California to Alaska, which attains a height of 225 feet. Family: Willow (Salicaceae); genus *Populus*.

POPPY, any of nearly 200 different kinds of related herbaceous annuals and perennials native to the Northern Hemisphere, South Africa, and Australia, about 100 of them in the large genus *Papaver*. Most have deeply-cleft, hairy leaves, a milky juice, and long stalks supporting hairy, nodding, egg-shaped flower buds from which the green sepals drop off when the 4 to 6 or more thin, white or colorful petals open.

On opening, the flower turns upright, exposing its many stamens and flat-topped crown formed by the union of the stigmas. The crown then becomes the top of the seed capsule. When ripe, the capsule opens 4 to 20 small pores, through which the seeds are shaken free.

The Oriental poppy (*P. orientale*) produces large, orange or scarlet flowers as much as 10 inches in diameter; the Iceland poppy (*P. nudicaule*), which is native to all the arctic lands, is a dwarf plant with delicate petals to 2 inches across in pastel shades ranging from white to pink, or yellow. The common European poppy (*P. dubium*) and the opium poppy (*P. somniferum*) of Mediterranean countries are cultivated far beyond their native regions.

The opium poppy is grown for the milky juice that can be collected from the unripe capsules. Although a dangerous narcotic when smoked, it is also a valuable medicine when prepared in various forms such as laudanum, morphine, paregoric, and codeine. All of these are sedatives capable of relieving acute pain, but also habit-forming. The California poppy (*Eschscholtzia californica*) is the state flower of California; it produces silvery foliage and cup-shaped, orange or yellow flowers. Family: Poppy (Papaveraceae).

POPPY FAMILY (Papaveraceae), a group of about 250 species in 28 genera, mostly of the Northern Hemisphere, chiefly herbaceous plants with showy, solitary flowers and a milky or colored sap. See *Bloodroot, Celandine*, and *Poppy*.

PORTULACA. See *Purslane*.

POTATO, a branching, herbaceous plant native to western South America, with pinnately compound leaves on a stem 1 to 2 feet high and small, white or purple flowers that produce bitter, yellow, seed-filled berries. The fibrous roots produce underground stems with fleshy, swollen tips (tubers) that are starchy and edible.

Potato plants are generally propagated from pieces of tubers which have buds ("eyes") that grow into leafy stems. Over 600 varieties have developed. Family: Potato (Solanaceae); genus and species, *Solanum tuberosum*.

POTATO FAMILY (Solanaceae), a group of about 2200 species in 85 genera, principally in tropical and temperate regions of Central and South America. Included are herbs, shrubs, climbing vines, and trees, with clustered flowers distinguished by a 5-parted, wheel- or tubular-shaped corolla.

The very stiff and spiny Kaffir thorn (*Lycium afrum*) of South Africa, used for hedges and as a lionproof temporary fence around cattle pens is a close relative of the widely cultivated matrimony vine (*L. halimifolium*), a climbing shrub with purple flowers and orange berries native to Asia. Chinese lantern (*Physalis alkekengi*) and gooseberry tomato (*P. peruviana*) have their fruits concealed within paper-thin bracts resembling Oriental paper lanterns.

See *Belladonna, Butterfly flower, Eggplant, Jimsonweed, Mandrake, Nightshade, Pepper (red), Petunia, Potato, Salpiglossus, Tobacco,* and *Tomato*.

POT MARIGOLD, a large annual herb native to Mediterranean countries, with simple, pointed leaves to 5 inches long, the leaf base more or less clasping the stout, straight, somewhat hairy stem. The leaves and terminal flower heads, which have orange-yellow ray petals around a darker center, are cultivated for use as potherbs. Horticulturalists have developed many varieties with larger and more decorative flowers. The dried flowers have been used as a laxative, a healing agent for wounds, and a kidney stimulant. Family: Daisy (Compositae); genus and species, *Calendula officinalis.*

PRIMROSE, any of about 500 different kinds of low-growing perennial herbs native to the Northern Hemisphere, particularly to mountainous or northern regions. The simple leaves are mostly in a basal whorl, above which hairy stalks raise flat-topped clusters of flowers with fringed petals that are white, yellow, rose, red, or lavender.

Many primroses are grown as garden ornaments or house plants, particularly those that bloom early in the spring, such as the Eurasian cowslip (*Primula veris*), the European primrose (*P. vulgaris*) of Mediterranean countries, and the horticultural hybrid known as polyanthus (*P. polyantha* or *P. variabilis*). Family: Primrose (Primulaceae); genus *Primula.*

PRIMROSE FAMILY (Primulaceae), a group of about 800 species in 28 genera, widely distributed but most numerous in the North Temperate Zone. They are almost all perennial herbs with opposite or whorled leaves, and flowers with the 5 petals united and the 5 stamens opposite the petals producing capsules. See *Cyclamen, Pimpernel, Primrose,* and *Shooting star.*

PRIVET, any of about 50 different kinds of shrubs with dark, oval, small leaves, clusters of fragrant, white flowers at the ends of the branches, followed by black berries. Several kinds tolerate trimming and pruning, even into artistic shapes, and remain evergreen except where the winter weather is severe.

The common privet (*Ligustrum vulgare*) of the Mediterranean region is a favorite in Europe as a hedge plant. "California" privet (*L. ovalifolium*) is native to Japan. Family: Olive (Oleaceae); genus *Ligustrum.*

PRUNE. See *Plum.*

PUMPKIN, a trailing vine native to America, with a prickly stem, dark green, 3- or 4-lobed leaves, large, yellow, bell-shaped flowers, and huge, globular, dull-orange fruits with vertical ribs, the white seeds of which are in a fibrous pulp surrounded by a medium-hard rind.

Cultivated by the Indians as a vegetable, the pumpkin can be eaten boiled, baked, canned, crushed, or used for livestock food. Pumpkins are popular for use on Halloween at which time they are hollowed out and carved as jack-o'-lanterns. A burning candle is placed inside the pumpkin and glows through the translucent rind.

Horticultural varieties of economic value are the summer squash (*Cucurbita pepo condensa*), of many different shapes, and the yellow-flowered gourd (*C. p. ovifera*). Family: Gourd (Cucurbitaceae), genus and species, *Cucurbita pepo.*

PURSLANE, or pussley, a trailing, succulent herb of tropical America, now almost cosmopolitan as a weed except in Mexico, India, China, and France, where it is cultivated and sold as a salad green or potherb.

The smooth, fleshy stem is green, branched, easily broken, and supports successive whorls of fleshy leaves that are rounded at the tip and break readily from the stem. The inconspicuous yellow flowers, ¼ inch across, open for a few hours in early morning, are pollinated by insects, and close permanently, soon to be followed by small seed capsules that shed ductlike, flattened seeds. The seeds survive hard winters, permitting the purslane to grow as an annual in cold climates; it reproduces readily from fragments of stem and leaves.

Closely related succulent plants widely cultivated in rock gardens and flower beds include the garden purslane or rose moss (*Portulaca grandiflora*), native to South America, which opens to the sun large, cup-shaped flowers with rose, red, or orange petals. Family: Purslane (Portulacaceae); genus and species, *Portulaca oleracea.*

PUSSY WILLOW. See *Willow.*

PYROLA FAMILY (Pyrolaceae), a group of 70 species in 10 genera, chiefly of the North Temperate Zone and Arctic, either perennial evergreen herbs or non-green plants nourished by the decay of vegetable matter in the soil. See *Indian pipe, Snow plant,* and *Wintergreen.*

QUEEN ANNE'S LACE. See *Carrot.*

QUINCE, a small shrub or tree growing to 15 feet, native to central Asia, with crooked branches bearing downy, oval leaves and white or pink flowers, followed by hard, fragrant, acid, yellow fruits. Widely introduced and cultivated for the fruit, quince trees are hardy and deciduous, their fruits inedible raw but esteemed for making jelly and as a source of pectin for marmalade. The seeds are coated with a mucilaginous substance used in making cosmetics. The related flowering quince (*Chaenomeles lagenaria*), or "japonica," is a cultivated, ornamental shrub from Japan, with spiny branches, handsome rose or orange flowers opening very early in spring, and edible fruits. Family: Rose (Rosaceae); genus and species, *Cydonia oblonga.*

RADISH, a small, herbaceous annual, probably of Asiatic origin, cultivated as a vegetable by the Chinese for over 3000 years, widely adopted for the pungent flavor of its enlarged edible roots, red, white, gray, or black in color, from which coarse, lobed leaves arise in a basal whorl. Late in the summer the stem grows upward, bearing erect clusters of pink, 4-petalled flowers, which are followed by short pods full of black, spherical seeds. Family: Mustard (Cruciferae); genus and species, *Raphanus sativus.*

RAFFIA. See *Palm.*

RAGWEED, any of about 20 different kinds of coarse herbs native to America and Africa, usually with deeply lobed or dissected leaves and inconspicuous, greenish flowers the fine pollen of which is windblown, causing allergic symptoms of "hay fever" in many people. Several species are widespread weeds in grain fields, growing as annuals but with hardy seeds that often live several years before germinating. Family: Daisy (Compositae); genus *Ambrosia.*

RAMIE. See *Nettle.*

RAPE. See *Mustard.*

RASPBERRY, any of several related kinds of thorny shrubs with arching, woody branches bearing toothed, compound leaves, white flowers, and edible red, black, purple, yellow, or white fruits formed as aggregates from many separate pistils on the same finger-shaped receptacle. Unlike blackberries, raspberries are easily separated from the receptacle. They can be eaten raw or cooked, and are preserved. Wild raspberries are commonly called thimble berries.

The most common cultivated kinds are the red raspberry (*Rubus idaeus*) of Eurasian and North American north country, the blackcap raspberry (*R. occidentalis*) of eastern North America, and the decorative, pink-flowered, fragrant, flowering raspberry (*R. odoratus*) of eastern North America. Family: Rose (Rosaceae); genus *Rubus.*

REDBUD, a small tree native to eastern North America, with heart-shaped leaves and clusters of small, pealike, magenta flowers, followed by oblong, flat pods that are winged along the upper edge.

The redbud is cultivated in many parts of the country for its decorative value because its flowers open before the leaves in early spring. The redbud is the American counterpart to the similar Judas tree (*Cercis siliquastrum*) of Mediterranean countries. Family: Pea (Leguminosae); genus and species, *Cercis canadensis.*

BURPEE SEEDS
RADISHES

REDWOOD. See *Sequoia*.

REED, an almost cosmopolitan grass growing from branching, horizontal, under-ground stems, from which stout, hollow, upright stems rise to 10 or 15 feet, clad in wide, flat leaves to 2 feet long and topped with sprays of rose, lavender, or silvery flowers partly hidden among long bristles.

The horizontal stems growing in swampy or marshy areas catch decaying vegetable matter and sediments and help make new land. Some roofs in Europe are thatched with reeds.

The related giant reed (*Arundo donax*) of southern Europe, which grows in clumps to 15 feet high, has strong stems that are often used for fishing poles and said to be of bamboo; hard, dry, thin pieces from the stem are used in making musical reed instruments. Family: Grass (Gramineae); genus and species, *Phragmites communis*.

RHODODENDRON, a genus of about 850 different kinds of shrubs native to arctic and north temperate regions and to tropical mountains southward through New Guinea to Australia. They have simple leaves, smooth edged or toothed, and showy flowers in clusters from terminal buds. Most of the deciduous species are called azaleas.

Several of the evergreen rhododendrons are cultivated. Some have been horticulturally developed into many varieties. The rosebay, or great laurel rhododendron (*R. maximum*) is the state flower of West Virginia; the western rhododendron (*R. californicum*) is the state flower of Washington. Family: Heath (Ericaceae). See also *Azalea*.

RHUBARB, or Pie plant, a herbaceous perennial native to Central Asia, with thick, horizontal, underground stems from the ends of which coarse, triangular, wrinkled leaves grow on long, green, pink, or red stalks. The leaves and underground stems are poisonous, but the leaf stalks are edible, acid but sweet, and are commonly used in cooking.

A related species (*Rheum officinale*), which is native to China and Tibet, is the source of a root extract used in Oriental medicine for indigestion and diarrhea for over 4000 years. Family: Buckwheat (Polygonaceae); genus and species, *Rheum rhaponticum*.

RICE, an annual grass, probably native to Southeast Asia, usually cultivated in shallow ponds ("paddies") in warm parts of the Orient and the United States, but raised on drier land in Latin America with smaller yields of fruit (grain). Rice grows 2 to 6 feet tall, with narrow leaves and terminal clusters of inconspicuous flowers that produce the fruits.

When ready for harvesting, the water is drained from the paddy, the plants cut, threshed to free the fruits, and the grains polished to remove the seed coats. The product becomes edible when boiled in a little water. About 90 percent of the world's rice is grown in the Orient.

RUBBER TREE
UNITED NATIONS

A related plant, wild rice (*Zizania aquatica*) of the North American marshes, is an important food for water birds. Indians formerly beat out the grains into their canoes as they paddled among the rice plants; now it is a delicacy highly prized in modern cooking. Family: Grass (Gramineae); genus and species, *Oryza sativa*.

ROSE, any of about 150 different species, as well as an immense number of horticultural varieties of erect or climbing shrubs with pinnately compound leaves, the stalks of which are expanded into large, leaflike stipules where they join the stem; to a European the large stipules distinguish a briar (*Rosa*) from a bramble (*Rubus*, raspberries and blackberries), which has small stipules.

Roses usually have thorny stems and bear single or double flowers that are generally fragrant, ranging in color from white to yellow, pink, and many shades of red. The fruits, called hips, are enclosed within a fleshy receptacle and are edible. Rose petals, too, may be candied and eaten.

Roses, particularly the damask rose (*R. damascena*), are cultivated on a large scale in Bulgaria as the source of a rich perfume known as attar of roses, and of a rose oil.

Roses are native to the northern temperate regions and to the tropical mountains; many species, particularly from Eurasia, have been developed to produce flowers of outstanding beauty, such as the named varieties of tea roses (*R. fragrans* and *R. odorata*) of China, the multiflora rose (*M. multiflora*) of China and Japan, the sweetbriar (*R. eglanteria*) of western Asia, the cinnamon rose (*R. cinnamomea*), and the Scotch rose (*R. spinosissima*) from all across Eurasia into the British Isles. Family: Rose (Rosaceae); genus *Rosa*.

ROSE FAMILY (Rosaceae), a large group of about 3200 species in some 115 genera, widely distributed but particularly numerous in the North Temperate Zone. They include herbs, shrubs, and trees with alternate leaves and flowers in which the corolla is attached to the rim of a short tube that bears the numerous stamens. See *Agrimony, Almond, Apple, Apricot, Blackberry, Cherry, Christmas berry, Hawthorn, Japonica, Loganberry, Loquat, Medlar, Mountain ash, Peach, Pear, Plum, Quince, Raspberry, Rose, Serviceberry, Spiraea,* and *Strawberry*.

ROSEMARY, a fragrant shrub with square stems and small, simple, opposite leaves, native to arid coasts of Mediterranean countries, but cultivated in other regions for the pungent, warm taste which the leaves and young stems add to foods and medicines. The small flowers are unusual in having just 2 stamens. They are sometimes gathered to add a distinctive character to perfumes. Family: Mint (Labiatae); genus and species, *Rosmarinus officinalis*.

ROSE OF CHINA. See *Hibiscus*.

ROSE OF SHARON, any of several unrelated plants, including the meadow saffron (*Colchicum autumnale* of the lily family, Liliaceae), narcissus (*Narcissus* of the amaryllis family, Amaryllidaceae), a creeping, succulent plant (*Hypericum calycinum* of the mangosteen family, Guttiferae), and the shrubby Oriental mallow (*Hibiscus syriacus*), which grows 10 to 20 feet tall, with saw-edged, sharp-pointed, oval leaves and wide-open, bell-shaped flowers in a white, purple or rose color, resembling those of hollyhocks. See also *Hibiscus*.

ROWAN. See *Mountain Ash*.

RUBBER PLANT. See *Fig*.

RUBBER TREE, Brazilian or Pará, a tropical forest tree 60 to 100 feet tall, with long-stalked leaves, green flowers in highly specialized clusters partially surrounded by an enlarged receptacle, and with dry capsules full of small seeds.

Amazon Indians long ago learned to cut the bark to collect the milky juice (latex) from the vertical tubes, and to use the latex to make rubber balls for games. Rubber trees are set out in vast plantations, particularly in Southeast Asia and, to a lesser extent, in Africa.

Many other unrelated plants of different plant families also yield latex that can be converted into special kinds of rubber. These include the gutta-percha (*Palaquium gutta*), a Malaysian tree of the sapodilla family (Sapotaceae); the India-rubber plant (*Ficus elastica*), a small tree of India and Java now cultivated indoors for ornamental purposes; the guayule (*Parthenium argentatum*), a low-growing herb native to the southwestern United States, resembling a small sunflower, and a Russian dandelion (*Taraxacum kok-saghyz*), both of the daisy family (Compositae); and various members of the mulberry (Moraceae) and dogbane (Apocynaceae) families.

Family: Spurge (Euphorbiaceae); genus and species, *Hevea brasiliensis*.

RUE, a strongly scented shrub native to southern Europe and Asia Minor, now introduced widely and widespread, with a woody stem 1 to 2 feet high bearing notched, bitter leaves and clusters of yellow flowers. An oil extracted from its leaves was formerly regarded as a valuable medicine.

Meadow rue is unrelated. It includes any of about 10 different herbs (*Thalictrum* species, of the buttercup family, Ranunculaceae) that grow to 7 feet, with dissected leaves and plumelike clusters of flowers in which the white, yellow, or rose-colored sepals are the most conspicuous parts. Family: Rue (Rutaceae); genus and species, *Ruta graveolens*.

RUE FAMILY (Rutaceae), a group of about 1300 species in 140 genera, most abundant in Australia and South Africa, but well represented in other tropical and temperate regions. They include herbs, shrubs, and trees, usually with compound leaves dotted with glandular spots containing an aromatic oil, and with clustered flowers in which the stamens are attached at the base or on the rim of a peculiar, elevated extension of the stalk (receptacle). See *Bergamot, Citron, Grapefruit, Kumquat, Lemon, Lime, Orange,* and *Rue*.

RUSH, any of about 225 different kinds of herbaceous plants native to most countries, with narrow, grasslike leaves on stiff, upright, slender stems rising from a creeping, horizontal, buried stem; inconspicuous flowers are borne atop the tallest stems. Many rushes are marsh plants; the most widespread is the common rush (*Juncus effusus*), which also forms dense stands in wet meadows.

In Japan mats are made from rush stems. In Europe rush stems 3 to 4 feet high are collected to be made into chair seats, baskets, and rope. The pith from the thickest stems could be removed, soaked in tallow, and used for lampwicks or "rush lights." Family: Rush (Juncaceae); genus *Juncus*.

RUTABAGA. See *Mustard*.

RYE, a hardy, annual grass, probably native to southern Europe and Asia Minor, cultivated as a cereal in southeastern Europe for at least 2000 years. It grows 7 to 10 feet tall, with ribbon-like leaves and long, bearded spikes of flowers.

The straw is useful in making hats, paper, packing, and mattress stuffing. The grains can be ground to make flour for black bread, mixed with wheat flour to make a softer rye bread, or used as the base for rye whiskey.

Rye is often sown as a cover crop or grown to be plowed under as a green manure. Wild rye or lyme grass (*Elymus arenarius*) of northern Eurasia and North America is a related plant that grows well on bare sand and is often used to anchor sand dunes or bared soil. Family: Grass (Gramineae); genus and species, *Secale cereale*.

SAFFLOWER, an annual herb native to the East Indies but cultivated extensively in warm parts of North Africa, India, southern Europe, and the United States. It grows 1 to 3 feet tall, with prickly leaves and heads of bright orange, daisy-like flowers. In the Old World it is raised mostly for the pale red dye that can be obtained from the flowers, and which is used for rouge and for coloring silks. An oil used in cooking and in drying paints and varnishes can be extracted from its seeds.

The safflower plant is sometimes called bastard saffron or false saffron because a drug can be obtained from its dried flowers and used medicinally in place of the drug saffron. Family: Daisy (Compositae); genus and species, *Carthamus tinctorius*.

SAFFRON. See *Crocus*.

SAGE, any of about 550 different kinds of herbaceous and shrubby plants native to temperate and tropical countries and to all continents, usually with square stems 1 to 2 feet tall, paired leaves, and clusters of blue, purple, scarlet, pink, or white flowers.

Garden sage (*Salvia officinalis*) is a European perennial that is cultivated widely in the United States as well. Its aromatic leaves are dried and used to flavor sausages, cheeses, and dressings; in addition, a tea, which served as a tonic, was formerly brewed from its leaves. The showy scarlet sage (*S. splendens*), native to Brazil, is a tropical annual with spikes of vivid scarlet, 2-lipped flowers; it is commonly grown as a garden plant. Family: Mint (Labiatae); genus *Salvia*.

SAGEBRUSH, any of several different shrubs of arid areas in the southwestern United States and Mexico, with stiff branches 1 to 12 feet tall, notched, silvery leaves, and sprays of yellow flowers resembling small daisies. The common sagebrush (*Artemisia tridentata*) is the state flower of Nevada. Sagebrush is eaten to a limited extent by cattle and sheep and is used as an emergency fuel. Family: Daisy (Compositae); genus *Artemisia*.

SAGO PALM, any of several different true palms or palmlike cycads from the pith of which an edible starch can be obtained. See *Cycad* and *Palm*.

SAGUARO, a giant tree cactus native to the Arizona-Sonoran desert of the American southwest. Largest of all cacti, it grows to 60 feet, the spiny, fluted, columnar trunk sometimes supporting 1 or more armlike side branches, each of which may be crowned at the tip with waxy white, yellow-centered, night-blooming flowers that produce pear-shaped, edible fruits. Family: Cactus (Cactaceae); genus and species, *Cereus giganteus*.

SALPIGLOSSIS, a genus of branching herbs native to Chile, with branching stems growing to 2 feet, alternate pointed leaves, and large, trumpet-shaped flowers from which a tongue-like stamen protrudes. One of the 5 species (*S. sinuata*) is called painted tongue and is commonly cultivated in gardens of the Temperate Zone for its velvety night-opening flowers of white, yellow, or red, which are often marked with brilliantly colored veins; for these qualities it has sometimes been described as the "orchid of hardy annuals." Family: Potato (Solanaceae).

SALSIFY, or oyster plant, a herbaceous biennial native to southern Europe, with smooth-edged, grasslike leaves and a thickened, edible, tapering taproot that is creamy-white and has an oyster-like flavor when cooked. In its second year the plant produces an upright stem that grows to 3 feet and is topped by large, solitary heads of purple, daisy-like flowers. Family: Daisy (Compositae); genus and species, *Tragopogon porrifolius*.

SALTBUSH, any of several different kinds of herbaceous or woody shrubs adapted for living conditions on alkaline and arid soils, primarily in Australia and the American southwest.

Saltbushes have gray-green leaves with a salty taste, attain a height of as much as 10 feet, and bear clusters of separate staminate and pistillate flowers, in some instances on the same plant. The most widespread American species (*Atriplex argentea*) has been introduced into wasteland as far east as Ohio and westward to the Pacific coast. Family: Goosefoot (Chenopodiaceae); genus *atriplex*.

SALVIA. See *Sage*.

SANDALWOOD, any of a number of unrelated tropical trees with close-grained, fragrant wood, used for incense, boxes, and fine furniture.

Most important of these is white sandalwood (*Santalum album*) of India and Malaysia; its wood is used for funeral pyres, powdered to form, with colored solutions, a paste that is used for caste marks, carved for decorative purposes, or processed to yield a fragrant oil. Red sandalwood (*Lingoum santalinus,* of the pea family, Leguminosae) from the East Indies is less valuable. Family: Sandalwood (Santalaceae); genus, chiefly *Santalum*.

SAPODILLA, or naseberry, a small tree of tropical America that grows to 60 feet and bears stiff, evergreen leaves, white flowers, and reddish-brown berries the size of oranges, with a dark yellow, juicy pulp. On large plantations, particularly in Yucatan, the milky latex from the bark, called chicle, is tapped, collected, and used in makng chewing gum. Family: Sapodilla (Sapotaceae); genus and species, *Achras zapota*.

SAPODILLA FAMILY (Sapotaceae), a group of about 600 species in 40 genera, almost all trees with a milky sap, alternate simple, leathery, smooth-edged leaves, and stamens in 2 or 3 whorls. The outer stamens are modified and become petal-like and sterile. See *Rubber tree, Sapodilla,* and *Sapote*.

SAPOTE, or marmalade plum, or mammee apple, a small West Indian tree with simple leaves and white flowers, producing large, sweet, edible berries containing a single, large seed.

The russet-brown fruit resembling a ripe pear in taste, is a local favorite, but does not ship well. A rich oil can be extracted from the seed to be used in confections. Family: Sapodilla (Sapotaceae); genus and species, *Calocarpum sapota*.

SARSAPARILLA. See *Smilax*.

SASSAFRAS, a shrub or tree native to eastern North America, growing 40 to 100 feet high in southern states, and 3 to 5 feet high in northern states. It has oval or lobed leaves, soft, yellow wood, corky roots, greenish-yellow flowers (the staminate and pistillate flowers on the same plant), and purplish-red berries with red bracts.

The wood is sometimes used for fence posts and small boats. An extract from the aromatic red bark of the roots is used in sassafras tea, and as the flavoring for root beer and other confections. The oil of sassafras, which is also obtained from the roots, is used in medicine and cosmetics. The leaves are sometimes used, along with okra, to flavor soups. Family: Laurel (Lauraceae); genus and species, *Sassafras albidum*.

SAXIFRAGE, any of about 300 different kinds of herbaceous plants native to lands from the highest Arctic to Tierra del Fuego. Many of the plants are alpine, low-growing annuals and perennials, usually with a basal whorl of leaves, and a short, upright stalk bearing a cluster of small flowers.

Some are among the first plants to bloom in the year; others are among those that grow highest on mountain slopes, where they bloom on rocks or in crevices between boulders. Family: Saxifrage (Saxifragaceae); genus *Saxifraga*.

SAXIFRAGE FAMILY (Saxifragaceae), a group of about 1200 species in 80 genera, widely distributed, growing as herbs, shrubs, or small trees with clustered, regular flowers. It includes grass-of-Parnassus (*Parnassia palustris*), a perennial herb of northern and alpine parts of the Northern Hemisphere that bears a single large, white flower from a basal whorl of leaves on each upright 12-inch stalk. See *Currant, Gooseberry, Hydrangea, Mock orange,* and *Saxifrage*.

SCHIZANTHUS. See *Butterfly flower*.

SCREWPINE, any of 180 different kinds of shrubs and small trees native to the Old World, from Africa, through Indonesia, to Australia, with stiff, shiny, sword-shaped leaves in a conspicuous spiral around the branching stems.

The trunk produces a good many stiltlike, prop-roots from above the ground, which sometimes remain after the lowest part of the trunk itself has died and decayed. Clusters of inconspicuous flowers, either staminate or pistillate, develop close to the branches; an aggregate fruit develops from them, on the outer surface of which the pattern of individual ovaries can be traced, much as on a pineapple. Family: Screwpine (Pandanaceae); genus *Pandanus*.

SEDGE, any of perhaps 1000 different kinds of grasslike herbs, chiefly of temperate regions and tropical mountains, with triangular, upright stems that are solid (never hollow like grass stems) and grow from a few inches to a few feet tall with narrow leaves that may be saw-edged and sharp enough to cut human skin.

Small green or brown flowers are borne in bristly spikes, the pistillate flowers in a saclike structure which persists and covers the hard nutlets that contain the seeds. Sedges are found mostly on marsh edges and in wet, poorly drained ground. Family: Sedge (Cyperaceae); genus *Carex*.

SEDGE FAMILY (Cyperaceae), a large group of more than 3000 species in about 85 genera, chiefly marsh plants of temperate and frigid regions, and widely distributed. Cotton grass (*Eriophorum species*), found in bogs and moorlands of the Northern Hemisphere, shows ball-like, white masses on tall, slender stalks, each ball composed of fine bristles that become hairs as they extend out in radial directions from each pistillate flower.

Saw grass (*Cladium Jamaicense*) is the most common plant in the Everglades of Florida, and with its sharp-edged leaves makes travel difficult through marshes and swamps in much of the southern United States and West Indies. See *Bulrush, Papyrus,* and *Sedge*.

SEDUM. See *Orpine*.

SELF-HEAL, or heal-all, a low-growing perennial herb native to the Northern Hemisphere, with a subterranean, creeping stem, many upright square stems, opposite leaves, and dense clusters of blue or purple, 2-lipped flowers. At one time it was believed to be useful as a salve for cuts and wounds. Family: Mint (Labiatae); genus and species, *Prunella vulgaris*.

SENECA SNAKEROOT, a perennial herb native to North America east of the Rockies but restricted to higher elevations in the Southeast. It grows to 18 inches, with smooth, pointed, alternate leaves clasping the erect stem at regular intervals, and a terminal cluster of greenish-white flowers; this green color appears in the petal-like sepals as well as the 3 petals. The medicine senegin was formerly extracted from the roots. Family: Milkwort (Polygalaceae); genus and species, *Polygala senega*.

SENSITIVE PLANT. See *Mimosa*.

SEQUOIA, a genus of mammoth, coniferous trees native to the western United States, with ridged, cinnamon-colored bark, short branches, sharp, scalelike needles barely longer than the diameter of the young stems in the big tree (*S. gigantea*) or flat, stiff needles growing to 1 inch in the coastal redwood (*S. sempervirens*).

It is thought that some sequoia trees may range in age from 3000 to 4000 years. The big trees grow at elevations of 5000 to 8500 feet on the west side of the Sierra Nevada in California. The trunks grow to 280 feet in height, 35 feet in diameter, and produce egg-shaped cones 2 to 3¾ inches long.

Coastal redwood trees often attain a height of 369 feet, a diameter of nearly 18 feet at chest height, and have cones ¾ to 1 inch in diameter; they grow in the fog belt of western California and Oregon in groves never more than 30 miles from the Pacific Ocean. Their lightweight, fungus-resistant wood is valuable for the construction of houses and furniture. Family: Bald cypress (Taxodiaceae).

SERVICEBERRY, or Juneberry, or shadbush, any of about 25 different kinds of shrubs or trees of the temperate Northern Hemisphere, growing to 30 feet, with simple leaves and white or pink flowers in loose clusters opening in early spring, followed by sweet, edible, purple fruits containing up to 10 seeds. Family: Rose (Rosaceae); genus *Amelanchier*.

SESAME, a woody herb native to India but now cultivated throughout the East, growing 2 to 4 feet tall, with lobed leaves and pink or yellow, trumpet-shaped flowers.

An oil is obtained from sesame leaves and seeds for use in cooking, confectionary, soap-making, lighting, medicine, and the manufacture of India ink. Sesame seeds themselves are flat, ivory-colored, and used to garnish baked goods or made into candy. Family: Pedalium (Pedaliaceae); genus and species, *Sesamum indicum*.

SHALLOT. See *Onion*.

SHAMROCK, the floral emblem of Ireland and the common name of several plants that bear 3-part, compound leaves with almost circular leaflets, including clovers (*Trifolium* species), the black medic (*Medicago* species of the pea family, Leguminosae), the wood sorrel (*Oxalis* species of the oxalis family, Oxalidaceae), and the European watercress (*Nasturtium officinale* of the mustard family, Cruciferae).

SHEEP LAUREL. See *Laurel*.

SHEEP SORREL, or field sorrel, or garden sorrel, a small annual or perennial herbaceous plant native to Europe but introduced into America and elsewhere, and widespread as a weed indicative of poor, acid soil. From a subterranean, branching, creeping, tough, horizontal stem, it sends up many erect, vertical stems growing to 1 foot, usually from the middle of a whorl of leaves shaped like arrowheads on long stalks.

The flowers, in a loose, branching cluster atop the stem, are either yellow and staminate or red and pistillate, on separate plants, flowering most of the summer and producing small seeds that drop to the ground and quickly germinate. The leaves have a pleasant, sour taste from the oxalic acid they contain but are poisonous if eaten in quantity. It is unrelated to wood sorrel (*Oxalis*). Family: Buckwheat (Polygonaceae); genus and species, *Rumex acetosella*.

SHEPHERD'S PURSE, a low-growing annual or perennial herb native to Eurasia but now cosmopolitan, with a basal rosette of notched leaves and a slender upright stem growing to 10 inches and bearing small, white flowers and, later, 3-cornered, pouchlike pods that open to release minute seeds. It is one of the most familiar of small weeds. Family: Mustard (Cruciferae); genus and species, *Capsella bursa-pastoris*.

SHOOTING STAR, any of about 30 different kinds of herbaceous perennials native to Eurasia and western North America, with basal, stemless leaves and pink or white flowers on tall stalks, suggesting those of cyclamens. Each blossom possesses stamens that protrude from the folded corolla. Family: Primrose (Primulaceae); genus *Dodocatheon*.

SISAL, a large perennial plant of arid and semiarid regions of tropical America, now cultivated in Florida, the West Indies, Africa, and the Far East, with a basal whorl of succulent, swordlike leaves about 5 feet long and 4 inches wide, containing sturdy fibers useful for making cord, twine, and rope.

At maturity sisal produces a tall, upright stem growing to 12 feet, with clustered, malodorous flowers. Family: Amaryllis (Amaryllidaceae); genus and species, *Agave sisalanx*.

SKUNK CABBAGE, a coarse herb, with broad leaves, growing in wet woodlands in eastern North America and eastern Asia. In very early spring before its leaves unfurl, it produces a number of greenish-yellow flowers on short stalks (spadixes), partly surrounded by purple-streaked, green hoods (spathes). The disagreeable odor of the flowers appears to attract flies, which act as pollen carriers. Family: Arum (Araceae); genus and species, *Symplocarpus foetidus*.

SMILAX, a genus containing about 300 different species of herbs, vines, and climbing shrubs, mostly of tropical and subtropical regions, with net-veined leaves and tendrils that are modified stipules. The prickly greenbrier (*S. rotundifolia*), native to dry woodlands in the eastern parts of North America, is regarded as an obnoxious pest.

Sarsaparilla is an oil extracted from the roots of several different kinds, particularly from *S. officinalis* of Honduras, *S. medica* of Mexico, and *S. ornata* of Jamaica. The "smilax" sold by florists is actually the mature, finely-divided foliage of either the prickly asparagus (*Asparagus asparagoides*) or of the asparagus-fern (*A. plumosus*); these are quite different plants of the same family. Family: Lily (Liliaceae).

SMOKE TREE, either of two shrubs or small trees, with leathery leaves and large clusters of minute flowers on fine stalks with multiple branches; these give the cluster the appearance of a cloud of brownish smoke. The cultivated European smoke-tree (*Cotinus coggygria*) is smaller than the American species (*C. americanus*), which is also known as chittamwood. In both the European and American species the staminate and pistillate flowers are on separate plants, and the few fruits consist of small, round berries. Family: Sumac (Anacardiaceae); genus *Cotinus*.

BURPEE SEEDS
SNAPDRAGON

SNAPDRAGON, an annual or perennial herb native to the Mediterranean region, cultivated as an ornament and horticulturally developed into many varieties popular in gardens of both hemispheres. The plants grow from 8 to 36 inches tall and are topped with handsome spikes of 2-lipped flowers with white, yellow, orange, rose, red, or purple corollas that open when squeezed at the sides and snap shut when released. Family: Figwort (Scrophulariaceae); genus and species, *Antirrhinum majus*.

SNOWDROP, an early-blooming, bulbous herb native to the Mediterranean region but widely cultivated for the small, bell-shaped, white flowers that often push through the late snows of winter, before the long, narrow, grasslike leaves appear. Family: Amaryllis (Amaryllidaceae); genus and species, *Galanthus nivalis*.

SNOW PLANT, a brilliant, red, saprophytic plant of California mountain country, often seen under big trees. It attains a height of 3 to 12 inches and opens waxy-red, bell-like flowers. The plant lacks chlorophyll and derives all of its nourishment from the decay of organic matter; it is a relative of the Indian pipe. Family: Pyrola (Pyrolaceae); genus and species, *Sarcodes sanguinea*.

SOAPBERRY, an evergreen shrub or small tree native to warm countries from Mexico to northern Argentina, with pinnately compound leaves, open clusters of small, white flowers, and globular, ivory-colored berries that blacken in autumn. The berries contain saponins that act like soap in water but may cause severe irritation of human skin.

A related deciduous tree (*Sapindus drummondi*) of the central and southwestern United States attains a height of 50 feet and yields wood used in making baskets and packsaddle frames. Family: Soapberry (Sapindaceae); genus and species, *Sapindus saponaria*.

SOAPBERRY FAMILY (Sapindaceae), a group of about 1100 species in some 130 genera, mostly tropical shrubs and trees with alternate leaves and clustered flowers. Many provide timber, edible fruits, or serve decorative purposes. See *Akee, Litchi* and *Soapberry*.

SOAPWORT. See *Bouncing bet*.

SOLOMON'S SEAL, any of about 30 different kinds of herbaceous perennials native to the North Temperate Zone, with large, fleshy, subterranean, horizontal stems marked with seal-like scars where the upright, vertical stems of previous years have separated at death. The vertical stems, growing to a height of 8 feet, arch over gracefully, bearing paired, oval leaves at the tip and paired, short stalks with pink or ivory, pendant, bell-like flowers and, later, purplish berries.

An allied genus (*Smilacina*), with about 20 different species native to America, is called false Solomon's seal or plumelily; the flowers and fruits are clustered in a terminal plumelike group. Family: Lily (Liliaceae); genus *Polygonatum*.

SORGHUM, a genus of coarse, tall grasses native to the Old World, found chiefly in tropical and subtropical regions, with 13 different species, of which several have been cultivated and developed horticulturally as important crops. Egyptian millet, or Johnson grass (*S. halepense*), is a valuable forage grass where it has been introduced in the southern United States, but it is a weed of cultivated fields farther north. The Eurasian broom corn or guinea corn (*S. vulgare*) is cultivated as a cereal in the Mediterranean countries.

Specialized varieties include kaoliang (var. *nervosum*, a cereal of China), durra (var. *durra*, a cereal of North Africa), kafir corn (var. *caffrorum*, a cereal of South Africa), shallu (var. *roxburghii*, a cereal of India), molasses sorghum (var. *saccharatum*, which yields a sweet juice similar to cane juice), and broomcorn (var. *technicus*, in which the stiff stalks that support the flowers and seeds are particularly long and useful in making brooms). Family: Grass (Gramineae).

SORREL. See *Sheep sorrel*.

SOURSOP. See *Custard apple*.

SPANISH MOSS, a feathery, silver-gray, epiphytic plant native to the southern United States, the West Indies, and Central America, with slender, threadlike stems several feet long, bearing short, pointed, scalelike leaves and small, yellow flowers, but no roots. It absorbs moisture and mineral nourishment from water vapor and dust in the air, and can grow equally well on a telephone wire or the outstretched limb of a live oak tree. It is often gathered for use as upholstery packing. Family: Pineapple (Bromeliaceae); genus and species, *Tillandsia usneoides.*

SPEEDWELL. See *Veronica.*

SPICEBUSH, a shrub native to eastern North America, growing to 15 feet, with flexible, aromatic, young branches, alternate leaves tapering at both ends, and small, yellow, fragrant flowers appearing in spring before the leaves. Some leaves are staminate and others are pistillate; they produce oval, red, fleshy, aromatic fruits.

The older wood will burn while still green. The bark and fruit can yield an astringent oil of supposed medical value; this oil is not related to the drug benzoin, which is extracted from Oriental trees of the genus *Styrax* (family Styracaceae). Family: Laurel (Lauraceae); genus and species, *Lindera benzoin.*

SPIKENARD, either of 2 unrelated herbaceous plants with enlarged, underground stems from which a fragrant, medicinal extract can be prepared.

The Old World spikenard (*Nardostachys jatamansi*) of the Far East is a member of the valerian family (Valerianaceae). The New World spikenard (*Aralia racemosa*) of eastern North America is a woodland plant with compound leaves and spherical clusters of minute, greenish flowers followed by purple-black berries; like its close relative, wild sarsaparilla (*A. nudicaulis*), it is a member of the ginseng family (Araliaceae).

SPINACH, a hardy, annual, herbaceous plant native to Asia, introduced into Europe in the 15th century and brought to America by early settlers. It has a thick cluster of oval or arrow-like, dark green leaves rich in iron, vitamins A, B complex, and C, and an upright branching stalk attaining a height of 2 to 3 feet in summer and bearing inconspicuous flowers in a cluster. It is regarded as a table vegetable and is prepared by boiling. Family: Goosefoot (Chenopodiaceae); genus and species, *Spinacia oleracea.*

SPINDLE TREE. See *Euonymus.*

SPIRAEA, a genus consisting of about 80 different species of shrubs native to the North Temperate Zone, found particularly in central and eastern Asia, many of them widely cultivated for their clustered flowers, each of which has 5 small petals of a red, pink, or white color.

Several of the wild species of spiraea found in North America are known as meadow sweet, while one, *S. tomentosa,* commonly found in pastures of eastern Canada and the northeastern states, is called steeplebush or hardhack. Bridal wreath (*S. prunifolia*), with delicate white flowers in clusters on a dense shrub about 10 feet tall, is an Oriental species raised in gardens of the temperate zones. Family: Rose (Rosaceae).

SPRUCE, any of about 45 different kinds of evergreen, coniferous trees native to cool and cold, temperate parts of the Northern Hemisphere, with needles borne on short, woody projections. These projections remain as roughness on the stem after the needles fall. The needles are angular in cross-section, but can be rolled between thumb and forefinger. The cones, which vary in size from 1 to 10 inches in length according to species, are always pendant.

Spruces yield valuable timber and are the world's most important source of pulp for paper. Norway spruce (*Picea abies*), a timber tree that is a handsome ornament, has been introduced to America from Europe. Sitka spruce (*P. sitchensis*), native to western America from California to Alaska, grows to 300 feet. The principal pulp spruces are eastern American red spruce (*P. rubra*) and black spruce (*P. nigra*). Family: Pine (Pinaceae); genus *Picea.*

SPURGE, any of several hundred different herbaceous and shrubby plants with milky juice, classified in genus *Euphorbia* and related genera, mostly native to warm, temperate, and subtropical regions, varying remarkably from one species to another in manner of growth, form of leaf, and details of flower. A spurge native to the north-central United States, but now widely cultivated as a decorative plant for gardens, is snow-on-the-mountain (*E. marginata*), an erect annual with broad, oval leaves; the uppermost leaves have broad, white edges.

Flowering spurge (*E. corollata*) of the eastern United States has conspicuous, white, round or oval appendages around its inconspicuous flower clusters; the flowers thus acquire a distinctive appearance without giving the impression that they have essentially the same form as the "flowers" of poinsettia (another spurge). Family: Spurge (Euphorbiaceae).

SPURGE FAMILY (Euphorbiaceae), a large group of about 7300 species in 283 genera, commonly cactus-like or heathlike, although many are herbs, shrubs, climbing vines, and trees. See *Cassava, Castor-oil plant, Croton, Euphorbia, Poinsettia, Rubber tree, Spurge, Tallow tree,* and *Tung tree.*

SQUASH, any of a number of closely related, coarse, prostrate, annual herbs or climbing vines native to tropical America, with large, rough leaves on thick, hollow stems and large, yellow flowers followed by edible fruits of many shapes. Fruits of winter squash (*Cucurbita maxima*) sometimes weigh more than 100 pounds.

Before Europeans arrived, the Indians were cultivating squashes in every section of the United States and depicting squash flowers in their cultural and religious rites. Family: Gourd (Cucurbitaceae); genus *Cucurbita.* See also *Pumpkin.*

SQUIRREL CORN. See *Dutchman's breeches.*

STAFF TREE, a low-growing evergreen tree native to the East Indies, bearing large clusters of small, regular flowers and, later, spherical, fleshy fruits with bright orange appendages attached to the seeds. From the seeds a medicinal oil called oleum nigrum is obtained. Family: Staff-tree (Celastraceae); genus and species, *Celastrus paniculatus.*

STAFF-TREE FAMILY (Celastraceae), a group of about 500 species in 45 genera, widely distributed, growing as shrubs, climbing vines, and trees, with simple leaves and clustered, small, greenish flowers. They usually have brightly-colored fleshy appendages (arils) attached to the seeds. See *Bittersweet, Euonymus,* and *Staff tree.*

STOCK, or gillyflower, a somewhat woody, erect biennial or perennial plant native to Mediterranean countries, growing 2 feet high, with narrow, blunt leaves. Both stem and leaves are coated with short hairs giving them a grayish, feltlike, or wooly appearance. The attractive flowers in terminal clusters are in pastel shades of yellow, orange, rose, blue or magenta, or white, and are usually fragrant. Many horticultural varieties have been developed for cultivation in gardens. Family: Mustard (Cruciferae); genus and species, *Mathiola incana.*

STONECROP. See *Orpine.*

STRAWBERRY, any of several related plants native to Europe and North America, with very short stems, 3-part, coarse, saw-edged leaves on long stalks, attractive white flowers, and bright red fruits. The fruits are composed of the fleshy, edible receptacle in the surface of which small, hard nutlets with seeds are embedded.

Cultivated berries are larger, softer, and often sweeter than the wild forms. American strawberries and some of the horticultural hybrids cultivated for this favorite fruit reproduce by runners (horizontal, naked stems above ground that produce new plants with roots at the tip). Family: Rose (Rosaceae); genus *Fragaria.*

SUDAN GRASS, a coarse cereal grass native to central Africa, introduced into the central United States as a drought-resistant hay and pasture plant, growing 5 to 9 feet tall with long clusters of tiny blossoms from which small, edible seeds develop. Family: Grass (Gramineae); genus and species, *Sorghum vulgare sudanensis.* See also *Sorghum.*

SUGARCANE, a tall grass, probably native to Southeast Asia, now cultivated throughout the tropics and subtropics for the sweet juice that can be obtained from its upright stems; it is the world's principal source of sugar. The plant grows to 6 to 16 feet, bearing coarse, narrow, grasslike leaves at intervals along its many-jointed stems, and a handsome plume of minute flowers at its summit.

The crop is prepared for harvesting when ripe by burning off the dry leaves and cutting the stems (canes) close to the ground. At the sugar mill the canes are crushed, their juice extracted, and the refuse (bagasse) used for fuel or processed into paper or wallboard. The juice is concentrated to produce molasses and purified to yield crystalline cane sugar.

Major producers of sugarcane are Cuba, India, Java, Hawaii, and countries of tropical America. Family: Grass (Gramineae); genus and species, *Saccharum officinarum*.

SUMAC, any of several shrubs and low trees native to North America and warm parts of Europe, with pinnately compound leaves, a milky juice, 4- or 6-lobed flowers, and clusters of bright red, hairy berries. The staghorn sumac (*Rhus typhina*) of eastern North America is often grown as a decorative plant. It grows to 30 feet, with angular branches; all of its young growth is covered with velvety hairs.

Some sumac plants produce clusters of greenish-yellow, fragrant, staminate flowers, and others, less conspicuous, pistillate flowers that mature into upturned, pyramidal clusters of crimson fruits. Aromatic sumac (*R. aromatica*), or polecat bush, of the central and eastern United States, which grows to 6 feet, is often planted along roadsides.

Related species include the poison sumac (*R. vernix*), which is also known as poison elder and poison dogwood and grows in swamps, and the poison oak (*R. toxicodendron*) of dry, sandy uplands in eastern North America. Like poison ivy (*R. radicans*), they cause a severe irritation of human skin. Family: Sumac (Anacardiaceae); genus *Rhus*. See also *Poison Ivy*.

SUMAC FAMILY (Anacardiaceae), a group of about 600 species in 73 genera, chiefly tropical, growing as shrubs or trees, with a milky sap and resin ducts, the leaves alternate and the flowers in clusters. Many cause inflammation of the skin. See *Cashew, Lacquer tree, Mango, Pepper tree, Pistachio, Poison Ivy, Smoke tree,* and *Sumac*.

SUNDEW, any of about 90 different low-growing, insectivorous plants native to all continents but most numerous and varied in Australia. They have basal rosettes of leaves bearing sticky, glandular hairs and slender, upright stems topped by clusters of small, white flowers. The glandular hairs produce shining droplets of secretion to which insects are attracted, and thus caught, enfolded by movements of the leaf, and digested.

The long-leaved sundew (*Drosera longifolia*) and the round-leaved sundew (*D. rotundifolia*), which has round leaves on narrow stalks, live on poorly drained hillsides and bog margins in cool, temperate, and arctic regions of Eurasia and North America. Family: Sundew (Droseraceae); genus *Drosera*.

SUNDEW FAMILY (Droseraceae), a small group of about 100 species in 5 genera, all insectivorous herbs with highly specialized leaves and small clusters of regular flowers supported by slender, upright stalks. *Aldrovanda vesiculosa*, a floating plant with no roots, native to the Old World from Central Europe to Australia, has whorls of leaves that close on and catch aquatic insects and worms. See *Sundew* and *Venus's-flytrap*.

BURPEE SEEDS
SUNFLOWER

SUNFLOWER, any of about 60 different kinds of herbaceous annuals and perennials native to North America, with large, daisy like flowers distinguished by a flat, central area of seed-producing disc florets surrounded by a handsome display of sterile ray florets, the strap-shaped petals of which are commonly bright yellow.

The common sunflower (*Helianthus annuus*) is native to Texas and Mexico, sacred to the Incas of Peru, and now the state flower of Kansas. It is widely cultivated as an ensilage crop and for its edible seeds, from which a valuable oil can be extracted. Its hairy stem grows 3 to 20 feet high, with coarse, saw-edged leaves and a flower head up to 18 inches in diameter. Sunflower stalks are used as fuel in many parts of eastern Europe and Asia.

The Jerusalem artichoke (*H. tuberosus*) is a sunflower native to central North America and cultivated by Indians for its edible, thick, underground stems, which grow to 4 inches long. It is an attractive garden plant and its roots are nourishing for livestock. Family: Daisy (Compositae); genus *Helianthus*.

SWEET BAY. See *Laurel*.

SWEET CLOVER, an erect tough annual or perennial herb, native to Eurasia but widespread in America. It has a deep, strong taproot, small, 3-part, compound leaves, and many slender spikes of small white or yellow flowers from which bees obtain a nectar that gives a distinctive flavor to honey.

It is grown extensively as hay, known as Bokhara clover, helps anchor the soil, and also enriches it with nitrogenous compounds produced by bacteria in the root nodules. Family: Pea (Leguminosae); genus and species, *Melilotus alba* (white-flowering) and *M. officinalis* (yellow-flowering).

SWEET GUM, a deciduous tree native to wet forests in North and Central America, growing to 150 feet in annually flooded areas of Mississippi, and often cultivated as an ornamental shade tree because of the strange, corky ridges that distinguish its younger stems and the gorgeous red or orange color that appears when its large, simple, star-shaped leaves take on their fall coloration. Its flowers lack a corolla and appear on the same plant in tight clusters that are either staminate or pistillate, the latter developing into spherical, burlike masses that drop ½-inch, winged seeds in autumn.

The reddish-brown wood of sweet gum is used instead of mahogany or walnut in furniture, flooring, and veneers. A related Asian species (*Liquidambar orientalis*) and an unrelated tree (*Styrax officinalis* of the storax family, Styracaceae) yield an aromatic resin called storax from their bark. Family: Witch-hazel (Hamamelidaceae); genus and species, *Liquidambar styraciflua*.

SWEET PEA, a herbaceous annual plant native to Sicily, introduced into northern Europe and then America in the 18th century for its handsome, fragrant butterfly-shaped flowers in white, lavender, blue, peach, pink, or red. The flowers grow in clusters of 3 or 4 on slender, climbing stems. The stems have pinnately compound leaves and twining tendrils, which are formed from modified, terminal leaflets. Family: Pea (Leguminosae); genus and species, *Lathyrus odoratus*.

SWEET POTATO, a perennial, trailing vine native to South America, introduced to Europe by Columbus, now widely cultivated in warm countries for its swollen, starchy, edible roots. It produces heart-shaped leaves and purple flowers. Although it is the original plant to be called a potato, and the "Irish" or white potato was named after it, the horticultural variety of sweet potato with the sweetest flavor is often incorrectly called a yam. Family: Morning-glory (Convolvulaceae); genus and species, *Ipomoea batatas*.

SWEETSOP, or Sugar Apple. See *Custard Apple*.

SWEET WILLIAM. See *Pink*.

SWISS CHARD. See *Beet*.

SYCAMORE. See *Plane-tree Family*.

SYRINGA. See *Lilac* and *Mock Orange*.

TALLOW TREE, a small tree native to China and Formosa, introduced to Europe and America as an ornament with glossy, oval leaves and long clusters of very small flowers, followed by seeds with a waxy covering. The wax has long been valued in China and India as a dressing for cloth, a material that could be made into soap, and a tallow for making candles that give a very clear light. The hardwood is sometimes used for engraving. Family: Spurge (Euphorbiaceae); genus and species, *Sapium sebiferum*.

TAMARACK. See *Larch*.

TAMARIND, an evergreen shade tree native to tropical Africa, but cultivated in India and other tropical countries. It grows to about 80 feet, with pinnately compound leaves bearing many leaflets, and clusters of white, yellow, or pink flowers followed by long, narrow, knotty, brown pods containing a juicy, brown pulp and small seeds. The pulp can be used to make a cooling drink, jellies, and preserves. The leaves yield a mordant used in dyeing cloth. The wood is hard and durable, suitable for cabinetmaking. Family: Pea (Leguminosae); genus and species, *Tamarindus indica*.

TAMARISK, any of about 80 different kinds of shrubs and small trees native to warm and tropical regions of the Old World, introduced also into semiarid parts of America, many of them tolerating extended drought and salty or alkaline soil. The densely branching stems bear smooth-edged, thick, or scalelike leaves, often suggesting those of heaths, and small, white flowers in slender spikes.

In desert areas, tamarisks provide shelter and break the wind. Along rivers and intermittent streams in arid lands, they absorb a great deal of water, which they lose in transpiration at the expense of other adjacent plants that are less well adapted to desert conditions. Family: Tamarisk (Tamaricaceae); genus *Tamarix*.

TANGERINE. See *Orange*.

TAPIOCA. See *Cassava*.

TARO, a horticultural variety of a perennial herb native to India and Malaysia, cultivated widely as the source of a staple food in much of the world's tropics, particularly in the Orient and the Pacific islands. The plant grows best in wet soil, producing long stalks, large, triangular leaves shaped like arrowheads, inconspicuous flowers resembling miniature calla lillies, and large, starchy, edible, underground stems (corms).

The wild ancestor of taro, dasheen (*Colocasia esculenta*), has sweeter but more slender corms containing less starch. Taro corms can be boiled or dried and ground into a meal; in the Hawaiian Islands the meal is fermented to a paste called poi that is often regarded as the native delicacy.

Florists sometimes offer dasheen or taro leaves, which they call elephant's ear, for decorative purposes. The term elephant's ear is also used to describe cultivated members of a related genus (*Caladium*) and certain unrelated begonias. Family: Arum (Araceae); genus, species, and horticultural variety, *Colocasia esculenta antiquorum*.

TARRAGON, a perennial herb native to Europe, with smooth branches, aromatic, simple leaves, and globular heads of tubular flowers. The foliage, which has a bitter taste, is used to flavor vinegar, pickles, and salads. The flavor is contained in an oil that can be extracted from the plant; the oil is known as tarragon oil or estragon oil. Family: Daisy (Compositae); genus and species, *Artemisia dracunculus*.

TEA, an evergreen shrub or small tree that grows to 30 feet, native to eastern Asia from India to Japan and cultivated extensively in Asia and equatorial Africa. The tree is pruned to 3 to 5 feet tall to facilitate the harvesting of its buds and young shoots. If these are allowed to mature, the shrub bears many leathery, oval, saw-edged leaves with thick veins and fine hairs below, as well as clusters of faintly fragrant, ivory-white or pink flowers, which produce woody fruits containing several seeds resembling hazelnuts.

The cultivated tea plants include many hybrid strains but the method of harvesting is much the same for all. Tea leaves are picked from the same bushes 20 to 30 times a year. The first picking (flush) yields buds and very young leaves, which contribute to the best grades of tea. New buds and leaf shoots induced to grow by the first plucking provide for the next pickings.

The final picking of the year includes the old leaves and completely strips the shrubs, providing the coarsest grade of tea. After the picked buds and leaves have wilted, they are rolled by hand. Those dried with a minimum of fermentation make green tea; those allowed to ferment more extensively before drying make black tea. Family: Tea (Theaceae); genus and species, *Camellia sinensis*.

TEA FAMILY (Theaceae), a group of about 500 species in 30 genera, chiefly of tropical and subtropical regions, growing as trees or shrubs with simple leaves and flowers bearing several whorls of stamens. The franklinia, or lost camellia tree (*Gordonia alatamaha*), is now extinct except in cultivation, although it was discovered in Georgia as recently as 1765; it has large, white flowers suggesting waxy poppies. See *Camellia* and *Tea*.

TEAK, a tall tree native to India and Malaysia, cultivated on huge plantations, with a straight trunk growing to 200 feet, a spreading crown, 4-sided branchlets with a central pith, and leaves attaining 24 inches in length and 12 in width, suggesting those of tobacco. The branches terminate in upturned clusters of small, white flowers.

The timber is fragrant, the heartwood a golden yellow that becomes darker and mottled with seasoning; it ranks with mahogany in value and is used for expensive furniture, homes, temples, and ships. Some teak carvings preserved in Indian temples are more than 2000 years old. In Burma an oil extracted from teak wood is used in medicine and commerce. Family: Vervain (Verbenaceae); genus and species, *Tectona grandis*.

TEASEL, any of 12 different kinds of prickly, stemmed, biennial plants native to Mediterranean countries, East Africa, and across the Caucasus to India. Wild teasel (*Dipsacus sylvestris*) is now a widespread weed, with long leaves that are toothed and prickly on the edges, the stem attaining a height of 5 or more feet and branching near the top to bear cone-shaped clusters of lavender, purple, or blue flowers among stiff bristles, each whole head guarded by about 6 narrow, modified leaves.

A cultivated variety of teasel, called fuller's teasel (*Dipsacus sylvestris fullorum*), has particularly stiff hooked bristles between the flowers in the head. When firm ripe heads are split lengthwise, they can be mounted on long wooden rollers under which new woolen cloth is shifted back and forth during the fulling process; the bristles raise the nap by picking gently at the cloth surface. Family: Teasel (Dipsacaceae); genus *Dipsacus*.

THISTLE, any of several different coarse, prickly, herbaceous plants, many widespread or cosmopolitan as weeds. Most are members of the daisy family (Compositae), with tubular flowers clustered in cylindrical heads, often surrounded by prickly, green bracts. The Scotch thistle (*Onopordum acanthium*), the national emblem of Scotland, falls into this category; it grows to 10 feet, bearing lobed, toothed, prickly, cotton-wooly leaves with a covering of gray hair. It is widespread as a weed.

Russian thistle (*Salsola kali tenuifolia*) is a very different plant. Native to Eurasia but now grown in America, it has short, stiff, prickly leaves on a repeatedly branched stem growing to 4 feet, which dries as a huge, loose, open globe and breaks loose from the root to become a tumbleweed, scattering its seeds as it rolls along in the wind; it is a member of the goosefoot family (Chenopodiaceae).

THORN APPLE. See *Jimsonweed*.

THYME, any of about 40 different kinds of low-growing, perennial shrubs native to Eurasia and Africa, most with a square, woody stem 1 to 2 feet high, narrow, aromatic, paired leaves, and clusters of lilac-colored, 2-lipped flowers. The garden thyme (*Thymus vulgaris*) of Mediterranean Europe and North Africa grows straighter than the wild, creeping thyme (*T. serpyllum*).

Thyme is more favored as a source of leaves, as a condiment, or as a source of the essential oil of thyme, which is used medicinally. Wild thyme has been introduced to America and has escaped from cultivation to become a weed. Family: Mint (Labiatae); genus *Thymus*.

TIMOTHY, a perennial grass native to Europe but widely introduced and cultivated as a leading hay crop. It is tolerant of cold weather and withstands drought well; some varieties have bulbous enlargements for food storage in the region where the stems arise from the roots. The minute, purple flowers are borne in an elongated, club-shaped head resembling a miniature cattail head; the purple color is that of the long stamens. Family: Grass (Gramineae); genus and species, *Phleum pratense*.

TOBACCO, a broad-leaved, annual herb native to Central and South America. Long before the coming of the Europeans to the New World, it was cultivated in the Caribbean islands and North America for the leaves, which were smoked in special pipes. The plant grows upright, bearing handsome leaves, a straight stem growing to 6 feet, and attractive white or pink tubular flowers. The leaves are stripped from the stems either before or after the stalks have been cut; they are dried and processed for manufacture into cigars, cigarettes, smoking tobacco, chewing tobacco, or snuff. Today the United States leads in all-purpose tobacco production.

Several related plants with larger flowers are favorites in gardens. They are known generally as nicotine and their flowers open mostly at night. Family: Potato (Solanaceae); genus and species, *Nicotiana tabacum*.

TOMATO, a herbaceous annual plant native to tropical South America, with a straggling, hairy stem, notched, pinnately compound leaves, small clusters of yellow flowers, and spherical, red or yellow berries. Introduced as a curiosity into Europe by Spanish explorers, tomatoes were known as "love apples" and thought to be poisonous.

Only within the last century has the tomato been widely recognized as harmless, edible, delicious, and rich in vitamins, whether eaten raw, cooked, pickled, canned, or crushed into juice. Family: Potato (Solanaceae); genus and species, *Lycopersicon esculentum*.

TONKA BEAN TREE, a tree of tropical South America, growing to 80 feet, with pinnately compound leaves and irregular flowers, producing fleshy pods containing black, fragrant seeds called tonka beans. The beans contain coumarin, a sweet-smelling carbohydrate. They are used in flavoring tobacco and in making artificial vanilla and perfumes. Family: Pea (Leguminosae); genus and species, *Dipteryx odorata*.

TREE OF HEAVEN, a deciduous tree native to China but commonly introduced into urban areas of Europe and North America, escaping from cultivation to become widespread. It grows to 90 feet in height and 40 inches in diameter at chest height, with large, pinnately compound leaves and either ill-smelling, small, greenish, staminate flowers or inconspicuous, pistillate flowers, which produce strange, 2-inch fruits with a seed at the center resembling twisted strips of brown paper.

The tree survives in cities despite polluted air and the paved soil that surrounds it. Family: Quassia (Simaroubaceae); genus and species, *Ailanthus altissima*.

TRILLIUM, a genus of delicate woodland wildflowers, native to North America and eastern Asia, with about 30 different species, all with short, thick, underground, horizontal stems from which they produce upright stems every spring. Each stem has a single whorl of 3 net-veined leaves and a terminal flower with 3 large petals.

In eastern North American woodlands, the most familiar are the large, white trillium (*T. grandiflorum*), the ill-smelling red trillium (*T. erectum*), and the attractive, painted trillium (*T. undulatum*), which has red stripes on its white petals. Family: Lily (Liliaceae).

TRUMPET CREEPER, or trumpet vine, either of two woody vines with bright-green, pinnately compound leaves and clusters of orange or scarlet, trumpet-shaped flowers. The stout stem clambers with the aid of tendrils over rocks, walls, trellises, trees, and sometimes roofs, occasionally reaching a height of 80 feet. Family: Bignonia (Bignoniaceae); genus and species, *Campsis radicans* (eastern North America) and *C. grandiflora* (native to China, but widely introduced as an ornament).

TUBEROSE, a herbaceous perennial plant native to Mexico, grown widely in gardens and greenhouses in temperate regions of both hemispheres for its long spikes of heavily perfumed, waxy, white, tubular flowers on stalks about 3 feet tall. The name tuberose has nothing to do with tubes or roses; instead, it refers to the tuberous, rather than bulbous, roots from which the narrow leaves and flower stalks grow. Family: Amaryllis (Amaryllidaceae); genus and species, *Polyanthes tuberosa*.

TULIP, any of about 50 different kinds of bulbous, perennial herbs native to north temperate parts of Eurasia, particularly to the steppes of Central Asia. Many kinds are now cultivated, especially in Holland, as the basis of an important horticultural industry. All tulips have sheathed bulbs, broad, tapering leaves, and large, showy, cup-like flowers. The original wild species (*Tulipa gesneriana*) is sometimes called the cottage tulip. The early-blooming, yellow-tipped, red, Van Thol tulips were derived from another wild tulip (*T. suaveolens*) from the vicinity of the Caspian Sea. Family: Lily (Liliaceae); genus *Tulipa*.

TULIP TREE, a handsome, tall, straight, deciduous tree native to the eastern United States, growing to 200 feet, with a cone-shaped top composed of branches bearing broad, simple, lobed leaves and strikingly tulip-like, greenish-yellow flowers. The soft wood, sometimes known as whitewood or canoewood, is still used for woodenware and interior finishes; for many years the Indians used the wood to make large canoes. The only close relative is a Chinese tree with similar blossoms. Unrelated tropical trees, such as the African tulipan (*Spathodea campanulata* of the bignonia family, Bignoniaceae), are sometimes called tuliptrees. Family: Magnolia (Magnoliaceae); genus and species, *Liriodendron tulipifera*.

TUMBLEWEED, any of a number of mostly unrelated plants of plains and prairies that break loose from their roots when mature and dry, curl into almost spherical masses, and tumble over and over, scattering their small seeds, as they are blown by the wind.

The native tumbleweed, covering much of North America, is usually *Amaranthus graecizans* of the amaranth family (Amaranthaceae). It might also be a winged pigweed (*Cycloloma*), a bugseed (*Corispermum*), a Russian thistle (*Salsola tragus* of the goosefoot family, Chenopodiaceae), or a member of the pea family (Leguminosae), such as the scurf pea (*Psoralea*) or wild indigo (*Baptisia*).

TUNG TREE, either of two kinds of small, deciduous trees native to China, now cultivated in vast orchards in the southeastern United States for the valuable oil that can be extracted from the seeds. The tree itself grows to 40 feet, flowering in early spring before leafing out. One to several pistillate flowers in the same cluster grow together with many staminate flowers; the apple-shaped fruit matures in early autumn.

Tung oil from the seeds is used in varnishes as a drying agent; it is also used in the manufacture of paints, oilcloth, linoleum, waterproof textiles, electrical insulation, and printing ink. Family: Spurge (Euphorbiaceae); genus and species, *Aleurites fordii* (semitropical) and *A. montana* (more cold-resistant).

TUPELO, or pepperidge, or sour gum, any of different kinds of small, water-loving trees native to India, eastern Asia, and North America, growing to 40 to 60 feet, with drooping lower branches, leathery simple leaves, and clusters of separate staminate and pistillate flowers on the same tree. The fruits are red, blue, or purple. Like the cherry, they have a central seed in a fleshy pulp. Both the cottongum or water tupelo (*Nyssa aquatica*), and the black gum (*N. sylvatica*) produce useful timber, and are often grown in parks for their brilliant red autumn foliage. Family: Dogwood (Cornaceae); genus *Nyssa*.

TURNIP. See *Mustard*.

UMBRELLA PLANT. See *Papyrus*.

VALERIAN, any of about 200 different sun-loving, hardy, perennial herbs of cool and alpine regions in the Northern Hemisphere, with thick, strong-scented roots and underground stems, simple or delicate pinnately compound leaves, and luxuriant clusters of tiny, sweet-smelling, pink, lavender, or white flowers. Common val-

BURPEE SEEDS
TOMATO

erian *(Valeriana officinalis)*, often called garden heliotrope, is frequently grown in the New World and the Old as a border plant. Its dried roots and underground stems yield a valuable drug used in nervous disorders. Unrelated plants with blue, cuplike flowers and showy foliage (genus *Polemonium* of the family Polemoniaceae) are often called Greek valerian or Jacob's ladder. Family: Valerian (Valerianaceae); genus *Valeriana*.

VALERIAN FAMILY (Valerianaceae), a group of about 370 species in 10 genera, chiefly of the North Temperate Zone and high elevations in the Andes. Most are herbs, usually with a 5-parted corolla, the calyx often developing later as a bristly appendage to the small dry seed. See *Spikenard* and *Valerian*.

VANILLA. See *Orchid Family*.

VEGETABLE SPONGE, or dishcloth gourd, or Loofah, a tropical vine with large, coarse leaves, yellow, bell-shaped flowers, and a slender fruit, 10 to 40 inches long, with a fibrous skeleton through the pulp. Although the fruit rind is edible, the fibrous portion is commonly saved, washed, and used as a sponge or in the preparation of cloth and hats. Family: Gourd (Cucurbitaceae); genus and species, *Luffa cylindrica*.

VENUS'S–FLYTRAP, a low-growing, insectivorous plant of North and South Carolina, displaying a rosette of shiny, green leaves with winged stalks and bilobed blades. The blades are edged with long, coarse projections and the upper surface of each lobe is armed with 3 sensitive bristles. If these are agitated, as by an insect crawling over them, the 2 lobes of the leaf fold abruptly and the long projections fit together, forming a cage.

Slowly the plant brings the leaf surfaces against the insect, secretes digestive juices, and absorbs the products of digestion. After closing without catching an insect, or after absorption is complete, the leaf blades spread apart, ready to act as a trap again. Mature plants send up a slender, vertical stalk to 7 inches high, with a cluster of white flowers at the top. Family: Sundew (Droseraceae); genus and species, *Dionaea muscipula*.

VERBENA, a genus of herbaceous plants native to temperate and tropical regions of both hemispheres, with about 230 species, bearing opposite leaves and spikes of flowers all through the summer. A few kinds, such as Eurasian vervain *(V. officinalis)*, have been introduced and grown in North America; it has branching, smooth stems and purple flower spikes.

Horticultural verbena hybrids include the sweet-scented verbena (referred to as *V. hybrida*). European moss verbena *(V. erinoides)* is often grown in hanging baskets. A related plant is the lemon verbena *(Lippia citriodora)* native to South America and cultivated in North America and Europe for the lemon fragrance of its leaves and its large pyramidal clusters

BURPEE SEEDS
WALLFLOWER

of flowers, which are smaller than those of true verbenas. Family: Vervain (Verbenaceae).

VERONICA, or speedwell, a genus of about 150 different species of small, herbaceous plants native to the North Temperate Zone, mostly with opposite, simple leaves on creeping or erect stems, and spikes of small, wheel-shaped, blue flowers. All contain large amounts of vitamin C, and some can be cooked as potherbs. One, called American brooklime *(V. americana)* because it grows along stream edges, has been recommended as a preventative for scurvy. Family: Figwort (Scrophulariaceae).

VETCH, any of about 150 different kinds of prostrate and climbing perennial herbs native to the Northern Hemisphere and temperate South America, with pinnately compound leaves often extended at the tip into tendrils, white or purple, pealike blossoms in short or solitary spikes, and a compressed pod from each flower.

The narrow-leaved, common vetch *(Vicia sativa)* of Europe and the British Isles, and the hairy or winter vetch *(V. villosa)* of eastern Europe are among those that have been widely introduced and become widespread in most temperate climates, sometimes planted and plowed under as a green manure, and often harvested as forage for livestock. Family: Pea (Leguminosae); genus *Vicia*.

VIBURNUM, a genus of shrubs and small trees native to temperate and subtropical regions, especially of Asia and North America, with simple leaves and clusters of white or pink flowers followed by fleshy fruits, usually red or black, for which the plants are sometimes called "wild raisins." The Eurasian guelderrose *(V. opulus)*, which has spherical flower clusters instead of flat-topped ones, has been developed into a widely cultivated ornamental shrub, the snowball bush

(V. o. roseum), which must be propagated by cuttings because its large flowers are sterile. Tree viburnums 15 to 30 feet tall include the nannyberry or sweet viburnum *(V. lentago)*, of eastern North America, and the twistwood or wayfaring tree *(V. lantana)*, native to Europe but introduced and widespread in the New World. Family: Honeysuckle (Caprifoliaceae).

VIOLET, any of about 400 small, herbaceous plants native to the North Temperate Zone, mountains in tropical Latin America, and tropical and southern Africa. They grow best in moist places, spreading oval or heart-shaped leaves on long stalks, and raising irregular, 5-petalled flowers on individual, long stalks; one long-spurred petal contains the nectar.

The widely cultivated perennial pansies, with flowers of many colors and patterns resembling human faces, have been developed by horticulturists from the wild European violet *(V. tricolor)* known as heart's-ease. Pansies escape from cultivation into lawns and wild areas, their flowers shrinking in size; the plant is then known as a Johnny-jump-up. A majority of violets have purple flowers; indeed, the flower gives its name to the color purple. Family: Violet (Violaceae); genus *Viola*.

VIRGINIA CREEPER. See *Boston Ivy*.

WAKE–ROBIN. See *Trillium*.

WALKING FERN, or walking leaf, a small fern native to eastern North America, with simple, lance-shaped, leathery, evergreen leaves tapering to slender, elongated tips, which droop down to the earth and take root, starting new plants. The base of each leaf is heart-shaped, and the spore cases are irregularly scattered on both sides of the midrib over the under surface of the blade. Family: Polypody (Polypodiaceae); genus and species, *Camptosorus rhizophyllus*.

WALLFLOWER, or gillyflower, a tall, herbaceous plant native to eastern Mediterranean countries, often cultivated in gardens as an ornament behind the flower bed or on the wall. The wild plant has yellow flowers with 4 petals, but horticultural varieties in many pastel shades have been developed. Family: Mustard (Cruciferae); genus and species, *Cheirinia cheiri*.

WALNUT, any of 15 different kinds of tall timber trees native to the Old World and the New, growing to 70 or 150 feet tall, with large, pinnately compound leaves; tiny, staminate and pistillate green flowers borne on the same tree; and usually, spherical, hard-shelled seeds enclosed in a leathery or fibrous husk. The commercial nuts, called walnuts, are from the Circassian or Persian walnut tree *(Juglans regia)*, native to western Asia from Iran to India, but much cultivated in England and known there as the English walnut; its seeds are particularly sweet and large, and its hard, gray-brown, mottled wood warps so rarely that it is prized for furniture-making.

The Black walnut (*J. nigra*) of the eastern United States is equally valuable for fine timber, but its seeds have a stronger flavor. Butternut (*J. cinerea*) of the eastern United States is less valuable, with smaller fruits that are oblong, pointed, and contain an oil from which a stain for dyeing homespun woolens was made in colonial days.

The California walnut (*J. californica*) is frequently used in walnut orchards of the western United States as the best root upon which to graft fruit-bearing branches of the Persian walnut; the trees are then called California budded walnuts. Family: Walnut (Juglandaceae); genus *Juglans*.

WALNUT FAMILY (Juglandaceae), a small group of about 60 species in 6 genera, all deciduous shrubs or trees with alternate, pinnately-compound leaves. The staminate flowers grow in catkins and the solitary, pistillate flowers mature into a hard shell around the seed that is enclosed by a leathery or fibrous husk. See *Hickory* and *Walnut*.

WATER CHESTNUT, or horn-nut, or water caltrop, an aquatic herb native to tropical Eurasia, with mottled, oval, floating, feathery, underwater leaves and spongy stalks. The small, white flowers are raised above the water surface, and produce large, horned, or spiny fruits with a thin shell that encloses a sweet, edible seed. In the Orient these seeds are roasted or eaten raw, whereas in Mediterranean countries they are ground into a flour. Family: Water chestnut (Hydrocaryaceae); genus and species, *Trapa natans*.

WATERCRESS. See *Cress*.

WATER LILY, any of several related kinds of aquatic plants native to ponds and shallow, slow-moving streams of many parts of the world. The fleshy stems grow in the bottom sediments of the marshes and produce flat, padlike leaves on long, slender stalks. The leaves float on the water's surface; the shiny green upper surface of the leaf is normally dry while the bottom is wet. Some leaves extend their flowers into the air, while others allow the flowers to float with them on the water's surface.

The yellow pond lily (*Nuphar advena*) of the eastern United States and Canada has almost spherical flowers. The yellow parts are sepals; the petals are tiny and usually overlooked. More fragrant is the white water lily (*Nymphaea odorata*) of the same region, with almost indistinguishable white sepals, and white petals that open widely, displaying the yellow stamens. The giant among water lilies is the *Victoria regia*, with leaves to 6 feet across that are turned up at the edges and prickly beneath; it is native to the Amazon valley and northeastern South America. Family: Waterlily (Nymphaeaceae).

WATER–LILY FAMILY (Nymphaeaceae), a small group of about 90 species in 8 genera, widely distributed in shallow, fresh waters. Aquarium fanciers often provide extra oxygen and food for their fish by cultivating fish grass (*Cabomba* species), native to tropical America, which has brushlike, green stems of finely divided leaves and grows completely submerged; or water shield (*Brasenia schreberi*), which has floating leaves on long stalks that come to the center of the under surface of the leaf. See *Lotus* and *Water lily*.

WATERMELON. See *Melon*.

WATER PLANTAIN, any of 6 different marsh plants of temperate regions, with fleshy stems growing in the bottom sediments of the marshes, and long-stalked leaves differing in shape according to the depth of the water in which they grow. Those that are submerged are generally grasslike; those that emerge from the water into the air are oval or lance-shaped and pointed at the tip; and those on the shore are more heart-shaped.

Submerged plants rarely open their flowers, which are self-pollinating; on the other hand those that grow in the air have small clusters of white or purple flowers that are visited by insects. Family: Water-plantain (Alismataceae); genus *Alisma*.

WATER–PLANTAIN FAMILY (Alismataceae), a small group of about 75 species in 14 genera, widely distributed, found mostly in wet ground or shallow, fresh water, and most common in the Northern Hemisphere. See *Arrowhead* and *Waterplantain*.

WATTLE TREE, any of several different kinds of low branching trees native to Australia, with pinnately compound leaves and clusters of bright yellow flowers. Young saplings are easily bent and are used for making fences and primitive dwellings. The common wattle (*Acacia longifolia*) is the national flower of Australia. Family: Pea (Leguminosae); genus *Acacia*.

WAXFLOWER, a climbing, evergreen, perennial plant native to southern China, with stiff, cylindrical stems, leathery, shiny, oval leaves, and clusters of pink, fragrant flowers, from which a copious and sweet nectar often drips. Cultivated indoors in temperate climates or outdoors where frost is rare, it is usually propagated by cuttings and requires much water. Family: Milkweed (Asclepiadaceae); genus and species, *Hoya carnosa*.

WAYFARING TREE. See *Viburnum*.

WHEAT, an annual grass native to central Asia and southern Europe, cultivated since prehistoric times for its cereal grains, and now one of the world's chief crops. It has tall, slender stems, ribbonlike leaves, and bearded, terminal clusters of flowers that mature into heads of grain. Wheat contains more gluten than many other cereal grains, and is especially suited for making into bread flour.

Spring wheat, planted in the spring and harvested in early summer, is grown in the northern United States, Canada, and other cold temperate regions. Winter wheat, planted in the fall and harvested late in the following spring, is preferred in warmer regions. Durum wheat has particularly hard, starchy grains, and yields semolina flour, which serves as the basis for most macaroni products. Family: Grass (Gramineae); genus *Triticum*, particularly the species *T. sativum*.

WILLOW, any of about 300 different kinds of fast-growing shrubs and trees with simple, narrow leaves and flowers in catkins; the pistillate flowers mature as loose capsules with numerous hairy seeds. Willows are found throughout the world—as creeping perennials between boulders in the Arctic and on high mountains, and as 100-foot trees along streams and in wet soil in warmer countries.

The young branches of many willows are used in making baskets and wicker furniture. These branches are called osiers. They take their name from a European basket willow (*Salix viminalis*).

One of the largest species is the black willow (*S. nigra*) of eastern North America. Weeping willow (*S. babylonica*), native to China, is popular as an ornamental tree because of its gracefully arching, drooping branches. Pussy willows (chiefly the eastern North American *S. discolor* and *S. humilis*) have gray, furry catkins that open in early spring before the leaves appear, generally after dropping their stiff, shiny brown bud scales on the snow. Family: Willow (Salicaceae); genus *Salix*.

WILLOW FAMILY (Salicaceae), a group of about 340 species in two genera, widely distributed, but most numerous in the North Temperate Zone and the Arctic. See *Poplar* and *Willow*.

WINTERGREEN, either of 2 unrelated types of evergreen plants with shiny, leathery leaves; one is native to heaths and northern woodlands in both the Old World and the New, and the other is characteristic of similar places in the eastern part of North America. The original wintergreens, members of genera *Chimaphila* and *Pyrola* of the pyrola family (Pyrolaceae), were so named before the discovery of America, and are known in the New World as "false wintergreens" to distinguish them from "true wintergreen" or checkerberry (*Gaultheria procumbens*) of the heath family, Ericaceae.

Wintergreen oil, used medicinally or as a flavoring, can be obtained from the leaves of *Gaultheria* or made synthetically. The leaves, the white, waxy flowers in small clusters, and the brilliant red berries all have the same pleasant flavor.

WISTERIA, or *wistaria*, a genus consisting of 6 species of climbing, woody vines native to eastern Asia and eastern North America, with pinnately compound leaves and handsome clusters of pea-shaped, white or lavender flowers. In horticultural varieties of the Chinese (*W. chinensis*) and

Japanese (*W. floribunda*) wistaria, the flower clusters range from 1 to 5 feet in length, and the pods that follow the flowers are hairy. In the shrubby species native to southeastern United States (*W. frutescens* and *W. macrostachya*), the clusters are smaller and more fragrant, the pods bare. Family: Pea (Leguminosae).

WITCH HAZEL, any of 6 different kinds of shrubs or trees native to eastern Asia and eastern North America, with alternate, simple leaves, and fragrant, yellow flowers with long, twisted, narrow petals that open in late autumn and sometimes again in early spring.

The fertilized ovules, enclosed by the hairy ovary wall, develop in the spring amid a mucilaginous material that becomes compressed as the fruit dries. Eventually the tip of the fruit opens and the brown seeds are shot out explosively for many feet. The astringent extract from the leaves and scaly bark is used in lotions and medicines. Family: Witch hazel (Hamamelidaceae); genus *Hamamelis*.

WITCH-HAZEL FAMILY (Hamamelidaceae), a group of about 100 species in 23 genera, all trees or shrubs with alternate simple leaves, chiefly Asiatic but found also in eastern North America, Africa, and Australia. See *Sweet gum* and *Witch hazel*.

WOLFSBANE. See *Aconite*.

WOODBINE, a common name given to several different, unrelated, climbing plants with tough stems that tend to tie together the bushes and trees upon which they grow.

They include the Virginia creeper (*Parthenocissus quinquefolia*) of the grape family, (Vitaceae); the common woodbine (*Lonicera periclymenum*) and Italian woodbine (*L. caprifolium*) of the honeysuckle family (Caprifoliaceae); and the virgin's-bower (*Clematis virginiana*), native to eastern North America and a member of the buttercup family (Ranunculaceae). See *Boston ivy* and *Clematis*.

WOOD SORREL. See *Oxalis*.

WORMWOOD, a coarse, perennial herb native to southern Europe and central Asia, with hairy, branching stems growing to 3 feet from a thick, subterranean branching stem. The twice or thrice pinnately compound leaves growing low on the stem have long stalks, whereas those higher up have short stalks. Several small heads of yellow flowers develop on each wormwood plant.

Once cultivated in Eurasia and introduced into North America, wormwood is generally regarded as a historically interesting weed, for a dark green, bitter oil extracted from it gave much of the flavor to absinthe and various tonics. Family: Daisy (Compositae); genus and species, *Artemisia absinthium*.

YAM FAMILY (Dioscoreaceae), a group of about 650 different species in 10 genera, mostly plants of warm, temperate, and tropical regions with herbaceous or woody climbing stems, large, net-veined leaves, and clusters of small, inconspicuous flowers followed by a fleshy berry or a dry capsule.

Most useful to man are members of the large genus *Dioscorea*, which have thick, starchy, underground stems or tubers worth cultivating for food. The edible parts of the common white yam (*D. alata*) grow to a length of 8 feet, weigh 30 to 100 pounds, and are made edible by roasting or boiling. In the United States the name yam is sometimes applied incorrectly to some varieties of the unrelated cultivated sweet potato.

YARROW, a milfoil, a herbaceous perennial, native to Europe but now widespread as a weed found on roadsides and in fields, bearing finely-divided leaves that have a pleasant aromatic fragrance and upright stems terminating in a flat-topped cluster of small, white or (rarely) pink flowers.

The name milfoil refers to the thousands of fine divisions on each soft leaf of the yarrow. Family: Daisy (Compositae); genus and species, *Achillea millefolium*.

YELLOWWOOD, a branching tree native to the central and southern United States, from 40 to 60 feet tall, with pinnately compound leaves that turn yellow in autumn. The tree has brittle, yellow wood from which a dye can be extracted, and long sprays of sweet-smelling, white flowers. It is sometimes known as gopherwood. Family: Pea (Leguminosae); genus and species, *Cladastris lutea*.

YEW, any of about 9 different kinds of shrubs and small trees native to the Northern Hemisphere, with evergreen needles more or less borne in 2 ranks along the outstretched branches. The seeds are dry or nutlike, surrounded except at their tips by a soft, fleshy, colorful enlargement of the tip of the flower stalk. English yew (*Taxus baccata*) has tough, flexible wood, and was formerly important in the construction of bows for archery. Western yew (*T. brevifolia*) of the Pacific coast of North America is a relatively scarce, medium-sized tree with fine-grained wood valuable in cabinet-making and for canoe paddles. Ground-hemlock (*T. canadensis*), a shrub of thickets in east-central North America, is often used decoratively around buildings and for making wreaths.

The foliage, bark, and seeds of all yews contan poisonous substances; English yew, in fact, is regarded as the most poisonous plant in Britain. Cattle will eat yew branches if given an opportunity, and children may be harmed if they swallow yew seeds while sampling the attractive, red, fruitlike covering. Family: Yew (Taxaceae); genus *Taxus*.

YUCA. See *Cassava*.

YUCCA, a genus of perennial plants native to southern North America and Central America, with a woody stem bearing a dense whorl of long, pointed, swordlike leaves, and majestic clusters of waxy, ivory-white flowers with a sticky pollen that is distributed only by certain small moths (*Pronuba yucca*).

A spirelike yucca (*Y. filamentosa*) of the eastern United States is called Adam's needle. A branching species (*Y. brevifolia*) of the southwestern states, which grows to 20 to 30 feet, is known as the Joshua tree. New Mexico has chosen the Spanish bayonet (*Y. gloriosa*) as its state flower. Other species of the genus are known as Spanish dagger, beargrass, and candle-of-God. Family: Lily (Liliaceae).

ZINNIA, a genus of 12 different species of herbaceous plants native to southern North America, with opposite leaves lacking stalks, and handsome, terminal heads of daisy-like flowers. The common cultivated zinnias of gardens are horticultural varieties of the species *Z. elegans*, introduced from Mexico. Family: Daisy (Compositae)—Lorus J. Milne, Margery Milne

BIBLIOGRAPHY

BOLD, HAROLD CHARLES. *Morphology of Plants*. Harper & Bros., 1957.
BOLD, HAROLD CHARLES. *The Plant Kingdom*. Prentice-Hall, Inc., 1960.
MULLER, WALTER HENRY. *Botany: A Functional Approach*. The Macmilan Co., 1963.
NORTHERN, H. T. *Introductory Plant Science*. The Ronald Press Co., 1958.
SCHERY, ROBERT W. *Plants for Man*. Prentice-Hall, Inc., 1952.
SELSAM, MILLICENT. *Plants That Move*. William Morrow, Inc., 1962.
SINNOTT, EDMOND WAPE. *Botany: Principles and Problems*. McGraw-Hill, Inc., 1963.
WILSON, CARL LEWIS and WALTER E. LOOMIS, *Botany*. Holt, Rinehart & Winston, Inc., 1962.

Biological Background

ORIGIN OF LIFE

Theories dealing with the origin of life attempt to account for the fact that there are living organisms on a planet that contained no life when it was formed. It is difficult to define what is meant by a "living organism" because there are many characteristics associated with living things. However, there are only two essential characteristics necessary for an organism to undergo evolution—the ability to *reproduce* and the ability to *mutate* (undergo change). Therefore, a *living organism* will be defined as an entity that is (a) capable of making a reasonably accurate copy of itself, and (b) subject to a low rate of mutation, with these mutations transmitted to its progeny.

Spontaneous Generation.—The problem of the origin of life in the modern sense was not considered by the ancient thinkers. They held that life could arise spontaneously from organic matter, as well as by sexual and asexual reproduction. The evidence for this belief was the common observation that insects and small animals arose from decaying meat and rotting grain. Thus life was considered to be originating at that time, the process was apparently a simple one, and there was no difficult problem to consider.

In 1668, Francesco Redi performed an experiment to disprove the theory of spontaneous generation. He placed some meat in a flask and covered the flask with muslin so that flies could not lay their eggs on the meat. No maggots, which are the larval form of flies, developed in the meat as long as the flask remained covered. This demonstration was sufficient to disprove the theory of spontaneous generation for higher organisms, but it did not apply to microorganisms. In 1765, Lazarro Spallanzani conducted similar experiments showing that microorganisms would not appear in various nutrient broths if the flasks were sealed and boiled. Objections were raised that the boiling had destroyed the "vital force" in both the nutrient broth and the air. This "vital force" was thought to be necessary for the spontaneous generation of life. Spallanzani could show that the broth was still suitable for the growth of organisms by readmitting air to the flasks, but he could not prove that the heating process had left the air in the flasks unchanged.

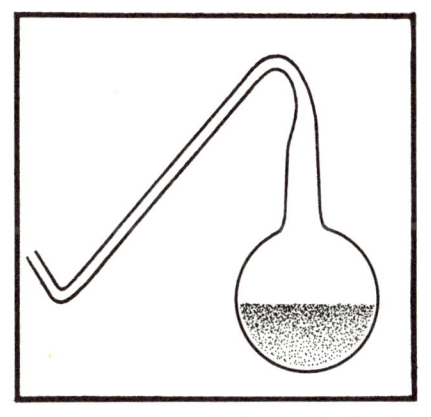

It was not until 1862 that the theory of spontaneous generation was conclusively disproved by Louis Pasteur. He placed a nutrient broth in a flask that had a long, S-shaped tube attached. This S-shaped tube allowed air to pass freely in and out of the flask. However, all dust, molds, and bacteria were caught on the sides of the curved tube. The broth was boiled to kill any microorganisms present, and the flask was then allowed to cool. No microorganisms formed in the cooled broth. Since the air could pass freely in and out of the flask, and the broth subsequently could be shown capable of growing microorganisms, this experiment showed that no "vital force" in the broth or the air had been destroyed. Pasteur and John Tyndall were able to extend these experiments to show that the "spontaneous generation" of organisms in nutrient broths is due to contamination by atmospheric microorganisms. These experiments were convincing, and no serious case has since been made in favor of the spontaneous generation of living organisms from nutrient broths.

Other Theories.—Charles Darwin's theory of evolution by natural selection simplified the problem of the origin of life. With this theory he could account for the evolution of the most complex plants and animals from the simplest single-celled organisms. Acceptance of his theory means the problem of origin of life is concerned with how this most primitive organism arose on earth.

It has been proposed that life was created by a supernatural event. This proposal, however, is not a scientific hypothesis since, by its very nature, it is not subject to experimental investigation.

In 1903, Svante Arrhenius offered a theory that life developed on earth as a result of a spore or other stable form of life coming to this planet in a meteorite from outer space or driven to the earth by the pressure of sunlight. One form of this theory assumes that life had no origin but, like matter, has always existed. Analysis of long-lived radioactive elements shows that the elements were formed about five billion years ago. If the elements have not always existed, it is difficult to understand how life could have always existed. Another form of this theory assumes that life was formed on another planet. However, most scientists doubt that any known form of life could survive for very long in outer space

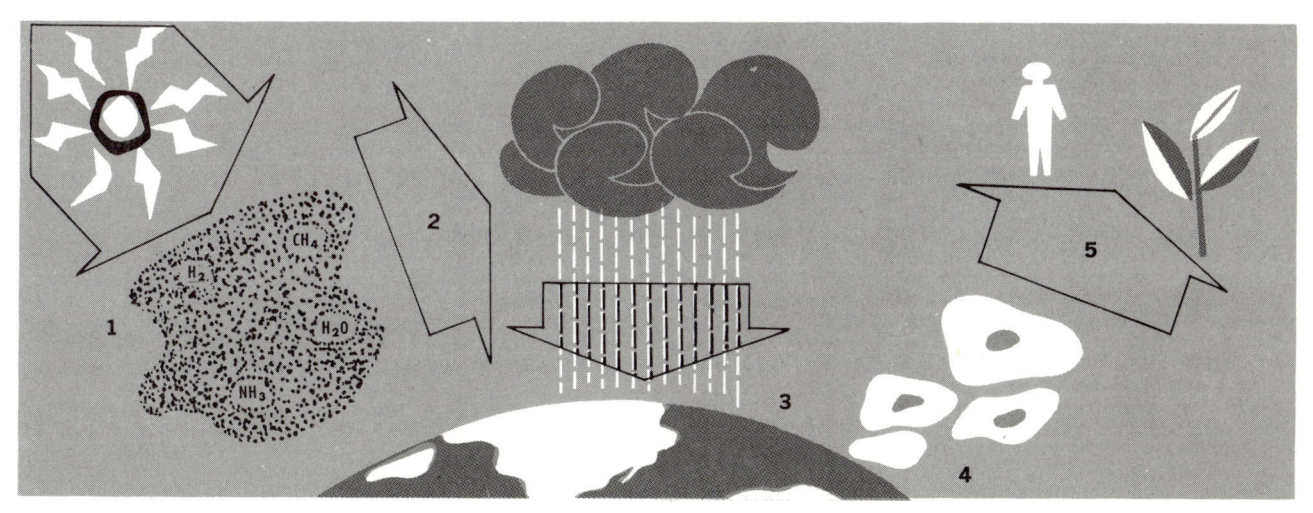

PASTEUR'S apparatus, by which he disproved spontaneous generation of life.

OPARIN'S THEORY maintained that sunlight caused a reaction of the materials in a reducing atmosphere (1), which contains hydrogen (H_2), ammonia (NH_3), methane (CH_4), and water (H_2O), to form simple organic compounds. These collected in clouds (2) and were carried to the earth (3) by precipitation. Continued reaction produced life forms (4) and, finally, more advanced life (5).

then fall through the earth's atmosphere without being destroyed. Therefore, although not disproved, this theory is held to be improbable.

It has been proposed that life developed from inorganic matter by a very improbable event—a spectacular accident. Such an organism would have had to live in an inorganic environment, and it would have had to synthesize all of its cellular components from carbon dioxide, water, and other inorganic materials. The chances for this improbable event are much too small for it to have occurred in the five billion years since the earth was formed.

■OPARIN'S THEORY.—The most plausible theory was proposed in 1938 by the Russian biologist, Alexander I. Oparin. He suggested that the first living organism arose spontaneously, not out of inorganic material, but out of the large quantities of organic material that he proposed were present in the oceans of the primitive earth. The simple organic compounds reacted to form structures of greater and greater complexity, until finally something was formed that could be called living. The formation of the first living organism was, then, the product of a series of simple reactions, none highly improbable.

Oparin's hypothesis is not in conflict with the demonstration by Pasteur that spontaneous generation does not take place. Pasteur only showed that spontaneous generation cannot take place at the present time and under present conditions. Such a demonstration does not say anything about spontaneous generation in the past and under different conditions. Two of the conditions necessary for spontaneous generation are that large quantities of organic compounds accumulate and that sufficient time is available for these compounds to organize into a living organism. This implies that spontaneous generation could occur on earth only when there was no life. Wherever there are living organisms, they will devour any organic compounds, thereby preventing their accumulation and reducing the time available for their organization into a living organism.

Oparin proposed that the organic compounds in the primitive oceans could have been formed if the atmosphere was not an *oxidizing atmosphere* as it presently is, but instead was a *reducing atmosphere* of methane, ammonia, water, and hydrogen. In 1952, Harold Urey showed that present theories on formation of the solar system require the earth to have had a reducing atmosphere in its early stages. He also showed that this reducing atmosphere would be present as long as there was molecular hydrogen in it, because methane and ammonia are the stable forms of carbon and nitrogen in the presence of hydrogen. The cosmic dust cloud, from which the solar system was formed, contained a large excess of hydrogen. The planets Jupiter, Saturn, Uranus, and Neptune still have reducing atmospheres. The planets Mercury, Venus, Earth, and Mars have developed oxidizing atmospheres since they were formed. This results from the fact that a water molecule, when exposed to the ultraviolet light from the sun, splits into oxygen and hydrogen; the hydrogen escapes into outer space. The free oxygen does not escape, thus helping to form an oxidizing atmosphere. The atmospheres of Jupiter, Saturn, Uranus, and Neptune have not become oxidizing because the escape of hydrogen is very slow on these planets due to their low temperatures and high gravitational attraction.

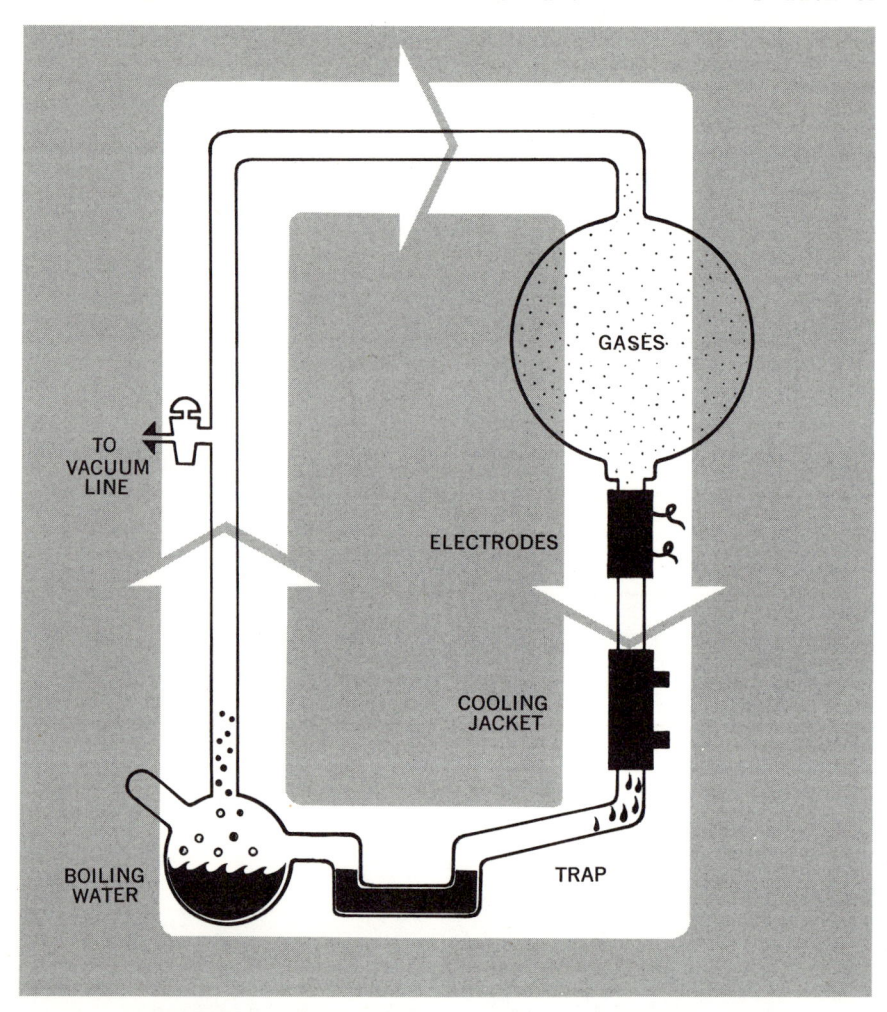

MILLER'S EXPERIMENT, in which the four gases found in an oxidizing atmosphere were passed through an electric discharge to produce amino acids, strengthened Oparin's theory.

Origin of Organic Compounds.—In 1953, Stanley Miller performed a series of experiments that strengthened the theories of Oparin and Urey. He circulated the gases that make up a reducing atmosphere (methane, ammonia, water, and hydrogen) past an electric discharge. Although ultraviolet light was the major source of energy on the primitive earth, electric discharges also were important. In addition, the products of ultraviolet light experiments would be similar to those of electric discharges. The result of Miller's experiments was the production of *amino acids,* the basic building blocks of proteins. In addition to the amino acids, the electric discharge experiments produced hydroxy acids, fatty acids, urea, and a number of other organic compounds.

The amino acids were not produced directly by the electric discharge, but rather by the reaction of smaller molecules produced by it. The smaller molecules included hydrogen cyanide and aldehydes.

In 1961, John Oro showed how hydrogen cyanide could be used to synthesize adenine, one of the purine bases in nucleic acids. He simply allowed a concentrated solution of ammonium cyanide to stand. A large amount of black *polymer* of unknown structure formed, as well as a number of smaller molecules, including adenine. A number of other bases that occur in nucleic acids can be synthesized by similar processes. Since hydrogen cyanide is synthesized by ultraviolet light and especially by electric discharges, such polymerizations were probably important on the primitive earth.

These experiments, as well as related ones, have shown how a number of simple organic compounds may have been synthesized on the primitive earth. This is a small part of the total problem. It is still necessary to understand in more detail how the amino acids, purines, pyrimidine, sugars, and fatty acids were synthesized. An important problem is to show how *peptides*, which are polymers of the amino acids, could have been synthesized under conditions that were present on the primitive earth. The same problem occurs for the synthesis of polymers containing purines, pyrimidines, sugars, and phosphate. These polymers are called *polynucleotides*. There are also the various difficulties of organizing these polymers into structures that are able to perform a primitive "biological" function.

These are difficult problems, but they are all subject to laboratory investigation. In this area of science, what had been thought to be extremely difficult has frequently turned out to be very simple. Therefore, although there are no explanations for these problems at the present time, it is reasonable to believe they eventually will be solved, and with relatively simple answers.

Nature of First Living Organisms.—In present living organisms, reproduction proceeds by duplicating the genes, followed by the synthesis of more enzymes and other cell constituents, and division of the cell into two fragments. The *genes*, which are located in the *chromosomes*, are composed of *deoxyribonucleic acid*, or DNA. Mutations occur when the base composition of the DNA is changed by an imperfect duplication, by ionizing radiation, or by other factors. Since the characteristics required in order to call an organism "living" are the ability to duplicate and the ability to mutate, it has been proposed that the first living organism was simply a strand of DNA, which, with the presence of necessary enzymes, could duplicate.

This organism would be similar to a virus except that it would have the enzymes necessary for its reproduction. A virus consists of DNA—in some viruses, the nucleic acid is *ribonucleic acid* (RNA) instead of DNA—surrounded by a coat of protein. A virus is capable of duplication, but only within another living cell, where the virus makes use of the cell's enzymes and metabolites.

Oparin proposed a different model for the first living organism, a *coacervate particle*. (A coacervate is a type of *colloid*—a substance that consists of very small particles suspended in solution.) These coacervates would accumulate organic material from their environment, grow in size, and then split into two or more fragments. In the course of time, the coacervate particles would develop the ability to form fragments more and more like each other. Later, these coacervate particles would incorporate a genetic apparatus to carry out very accurate duplication.

Our knowledge of present living organisms would speak in favor of the DNA model for the first living organism. DNA carries the biological information for the synthesis of the entire organism. The duplication of DNA appears to be a simpler process than the synthesis of protein and other cell constituents. DNA can be duplicated outside a living cell in a system containing the DNA to be duplicated, the *monomers* of the DNA, and a single enzyme. A system more complex than this would probably be needed to duplicate a strand of DNA on the primitive earth. A mechanism to accumulate the monomers and to hold the system together would probably be needed in addition to the single polymerizing enzyme. It might also be necessary for the first organism to synthesize this enzyme and perhaps several others. It is reasonable to think that such a system may have developed on the primitive earth.

Evolution of Early Organisms.—The first living organism must have obtained all of its small-molecule *metabolites* from the environment and then used these small molecules to build up polymers. There are many bacteria that obtain their metabolites from their environment. These are called *heterotrophic bacteria*. Many other bacteria and all plants synthesize their cell constituents from carbon dioxide, water, and other minerals; they are called *autotrophic organisms*. The first living organisms must have been heterotrophic organisms; it is necessary to explain how a heterotrophic organism could evolve into an autotrophic one, since the first organisms would have used up the available metabolites.

When the supply of a needed metabolite became exhausted, it must have been necessary for the organism to learn to synthesize this metabolite without which it would not have been able to live and to grow. A mechanism by which heterotrophic organisms could acquire various *biosynthetic pathways*, some of which are very long and complicated, was proposed in 1945 by Norman Horowitz. It has been found that the presence of an enzyme in an organism is often dependent on a single gene. This is known as the "one gene—one enzyme" hypothesis. Suppose that the synthesis of A involves the steps

$$D \xrightarrow{c} C \xrightarrow{b} B \xrightarrow{a} A$$

where *a*, *b*, and *c* are the enzymes, and A, B, and C are compounds that the organism cannot synthesize. If A becomes exhausted from the environment, then the organism must synthesize A in order to survive. It is extremely unlikely that there would be three simultaneous mutations to give the enzymes *a*, *b*, and *c*; but a single mutation to give enzyme *a* would not be unlikely. If compounds D, C, and B were in the environment when A was exhausted, an organism with enzyme *a* could survive while the others would die out. Similarly, when compound B was exhausted, enzyme *b* could arise by a single mutation, and organisms without this enzyme would die out. By continuing this process, the various steps of a biosynthetic process could be developed, with the last enzyme in the sequence being the first to develop, and the first enzyme developing last.

■**ENERGY SOURCES.**—Every organism must have a source of energy in order to carry out its metabolic functions. Animals obtain their energy from the oxidation of organic compounds. Plants obtain their energy from sunlight. There are many microorganisms that obtain their energy from simple fermentation reactions. For instance, the lactic acid bacteria obtain energy by fermenting glucose:

$$C_6H_{12}O_6 \rightarrow 2CH_3CH(OH)COOH + \text{energy}$$
glucose   lactic acid

The energy appears in the biologically useful form of adenosine triphosphate (ATP). Fermentation reactions do not require the use of molecular oxygen, which was absent from the primitive earth. The first organisms could have obtained their energy supply by fermentation until the supply of fermentable compounds in the environment was exhausted. Then it would have been necessary to develop the more complicated process of photosynthesis. *Photosynthesis* is the process whereby the energy in sunlight is used to make ATP and to reduce carbon dioxide to carbohydrate. With the development of photosynthesis and the pathways for the synthesis of necessary metabolites, organisms would become autotrophic.

The general picture of the origin of life and early evolution presented here is believed by many scientists to be basically correct. However, there is little detailed knowledge of any of the various steps in this process and no knowledge at all of some of the difficult steps.

Although this discussion is directed toward the events that have taken place on our planet, the same process could have taken place on other planets as well. Those planets with the proper temperature and atmosphere could undergo a similar process of chemical evolution. Mars is the nearest planet where life may be present, even though the temperature is barely high enough for life, as we know it, to persist. In a few years devices for the detection of life will be sent to Mars. The finding of life on Mars would confirm our ideas about the origin of life occurring under favorable conditions, and would be one of the greatest achievements of modern science.

It is likely that most stars have planetary systems. Life might also have arisen on many of these planets and may still be there. It follows that some of these planets may have very advanced civilizations that are attempting to communicate with other planets. Some attempts are being made to detect such signals. This is a very difficult technical problem, but the scientific results are of sufficient interest to warrant that some effort be made to detect these signals.

—Stanley Miller

BIBLIOGRAPHY

OPARIN, A. I. *The Origin of Life.* Dover Books, Inc., 1962.
SCHRODINGER, ERWIN. *What Is Life?* Cambridge University Press, 1963.

MICROBIOLOGY

Scope.—*Microbiology* is the study of microscopic living creatures. Generally, it is the study of viruses, *Rickettsiae*, bacteria, protozoa, yeasts, molds, and the small algae, thus including both plant and animal kingdoms. Some authorities do not use these kingdoms for the forms of life that show no tissue differentiation, but instead place them all in the kingdom *Protista*, a group established in 1866 by the German zoologist Ernst Heinrich Haeckel (1834–1919).

Cell Types.—Microorganisms, with the exception of viruses, are organized into two cell types, according to the structure of the nucleus. If there is a visible nucleus, the cell is *eucaryotic*. If the nucleus is not visible, the cell is *procaryotic*.

Eucaryotic cells have a definite outer cell membrane that varies from an unsupported, flexible membrane in animal-like cells to a fragile membrane inside a rigid cell wall in plant-like cells. The cell is filled with a more or less fluid material, *cytoplasm*, which contains a variety of granules (*plastids*) and membranes that function in the metabolism of the cell. The cytoplasm generally is in motion except during cell division.

■ **PLASTIDS.**—There are two kinds of plastids. One, the *protoplast*, is a colorless granule that contains many of the cell's respiratory and synthetic functions assembled in a highly organized state. All eucaryotic cells have at least one protoplast and cannot live without it.

The other plastid, the *chloroplast*, occurs in plant cells in addition to the protoplast. The chloroplast contains chlorophyll and all mechanisms for synthesizing chemical compounds through the process of *photosynthesis*. The simplest eucaryotic algae contain one protoplast and one chloroplast. Chloroplasts are not essential for life—since some single-celled plants may lose their chloroplast and still be able to live on dissolved food materials. Once a chloroplast has been lost, there is no evidence of its regeneration from the cytoplasm.

■ **NUCLEUS.**—The *nucleus* is suspended in the cytoplasm but is separated from it by a definite membrane. The nucleus contains the *chromosomes*, the hereditary material of the cell, which govern the structure and function of the rest of the cell. The cell usually multiplies by splitting in two. Prior to this, the chromosomes divide, half going into each new nucleus. Chromosomes are composed of *deoxyribonucleic acid* (*DNA*), which is not found in any other structure. Its sole function is to duplicate itself before cell division and to serve as a primary pattern or information center containing all the instructions that a cell or higher organism needs to grow and develop properly. If the DNA makes an error in duplicating itself, a mutation results. The mutant cell is either unable to function properly and therefore dies, or it lives on but is different from the parent cell; its *progeny*, or offspring, will continue to be different in the same way. Since a mutation is always inheritable, evolution is thought to have occurred through a series of mutations. Some mutations add characteristics to the cell or higher forms of life that make the organism better able to compete for food and the other necessities of life. Most mutations, however, cause the loss or damage of a characteristic; such mutations usually are harmful to the species and have no value in its evolution.

■ **EUCARYOTIC CELLS.**—Some eucaryotic cells either do not have a cell membrane, or have only an incomplete wall between nuclei. This is true of most of the molds. Such plants look and behave like a large cell with many nuclei. The eucaryotic microorganisms include most algae, protozoans, molds, and yeasts.

■ **PROCARYOTIC CELLS.**—Procaryotic cells differ from eucaryotic cells primarily in lacking a definite nucleus surrounded by its own membrane. They do, however, contain nuclear material in the form of many small strands of DNA that behave as a single chromosome. The internal organization of procaryotic cells, such as those of bacteria and blue-green algae, is not well understood. However, the cytoplasm is free of plastids and does not move. The chlorophyll of the blue-green algae and the photosynthetic bacteria is not in special organs, but is organized in some unrecognized fashion. Procaryotic microorganisms include the blue-green algae, bacteria, and *Rickettsiae*.

Viruses.—*Viruses* are the smallest of the microorganisms and lack the structural complexity of a cell. Their unit is a particle that is able to cause a host plant, animal, or bacterium to make more virus. This infective unit, called a *virion*, ranges in size from about 0.025 micron (poliomyelitis virus) up to about 0.3 micron (smallpox virus). A *micron*, μ, is $1/1{,}000$ of a millimeter, or about $1/25{,}000$ of an inch. Most viruses are too small to be seen with the light microscope, which has a maximum useful magnification of about 2,000 diameters. The electron microscope, which can produce magnifications of more than 100,000 diameters, can be used to photograph viruses. Some viruses are called *filterable viruses* because they can pass through a filter of unglazed porcelain that holds back bacteria.

A virus lacks usual cellular structure and instead consists of a nucleic acid associated with protein. The nucleic acid may be DNA, the material from which chromosomes are formed, or *ribonucleic acid* (*RNA*), which serves as a secondary pattern for synthesis of cellular components.

A virus is not capable of independent life and reproduction, and must multiply within the cells of a host. Hence, viruses are *obligately parasitic*. Apparently, viral nucleic acid intrudes into a cell in such a way that the host cell's nucleic acid loses control of the cell's function. The cell then makes more virus particles instead of its own nuclear and cytoplasmic materials. The presence of a virus in a host usually causes changes recognizable as a disease, although animal viruses have been found that cause no recognizable symptoms in the host. These are called *orphan viruses*.

■ **VIRAL PLANT DISEASES.**—Plant diseases of viral origin include the mosaics. The tobacco mosaic virus (TMV) was isolated by Wendell Stanley in a crystalline form and has remained infective after years of storage in a bottle. This virus has also been separated into its two components, protein and nucleic acid, and regenerated by their subsequent reunion. The protein, however, is not necessary for infection if it is possible for the nucleic acid to enter the cell without its aid. The protein may act as an enzyme, dissolving part of the cell wall to admit the nucleic acid fraction.

■ **VIRAL ANIMAL DISEASES.**—Animal and human diseases caused by viruses

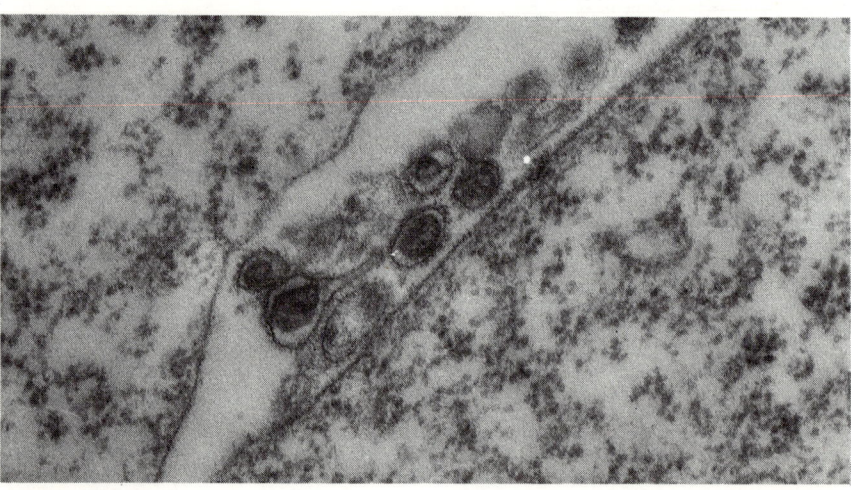

CHARLES PFIZER AND COMPANY

LEUKEMIA VIRUS in mouse tissue as seen through an electron microscope. Clearly visible are the outer shell of the virus, the dense nucleoid, and also the small, tail-like structure.

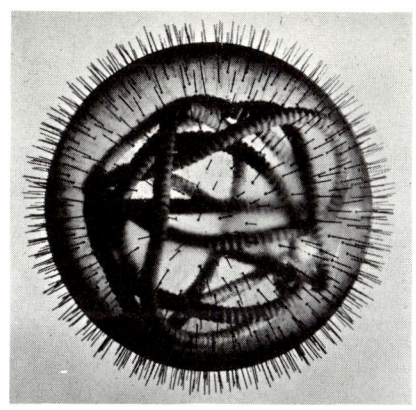

MEASLES VIRUS is classed as a cubic form. This model was designed from micrographs.

include yellow fever, distemper, hoof-and-mouth disease, influenza, psittacosis, measles, mumps, poliomyelitis, chickenpox, smallpox, and the common cold.

Viral diseases are transmitted to human beings and animals by various means. The virus that causes yellow fever is transmitted from person to person by the mosquito *Aedes aegypti*. The mosquito is infected when it bites a diseased person; if the mosquito later bites a healthy person, the virus may be transmitted. In the tropics, reservoirs of viral infection are maintained in monkeys, marmosets, and perhaps other species of animals. Psittacosis (parrot fever), primarily a disease of birds, is caused by a virus that infects parrots, parakeets, canaries, and other birds; human beings then contract it from infected birds. The disease, carried in bird droppings, is increasing in the United States as the sale of birds expands. The highly contagious hoof-and-mouth disease of livestock is of economic importance. The virus, transmitted by ingestion of contaminated particles, attacks the mouth and hoofs. Man may contract the disease in the same manner. Many viral diseases, such as measles, mumps, and influenza, are transmitted by simple contact with patients or by contact with infected materials. The virus of rabies is usually transmitted by the bite of an infected animal. Recently, an abundance of evidence has been found proving that some forms of animal cancers are caused by viruses. There is good reason to believe that some types of human cancer might also be caused by viruses.

Many human and animal viruses can be grown outside their normal hosts if they are inoculated into fertile chicken eggs before they hatch, or if they are inoculated into cultures of animal tissue cells maintained outside of the whole body. This use of chicken embryos and tissue cultures has made possible the laboratory cultivation of large quantities of viruses and has led to new methods of immunization against viral diseases.

A virus that appears to be of little if any importance to man, except as a tool, is the type that infects bacteria, a *bacteriophage*—literally, a "bacteria-eater." (The bacteriophages are treated more fully in the discussion of bacteria.)

Bacteria.—The *bacteria*, larger than viruses, are organized with a cellular structure contained within a rigid cell wall. They are usually divided into three large groups, depending on their shape. The spherical bacteria are *cocci* (singular, *coccus*), the cylindrical are *bacilli* (singular, *bacillus*), and the spiral ones are *spirilla* (singular, *spirillum*). Multiplication of bacterial cells occurs by simple splitting of the cell into two new cells, each of which can then grow and split again. Under ideal conditions this process can occur as often as every twenty minutes. Bacilli and spirilla usually split across the short diameter of the cell, and the newly formed cells seldom hang together for long. However, some species of bacilli form long chains of cells. The cocci have a more complicated system of multiplication that has led to their division into several groups. The *staphylococci* split in a random fashion, producing grapelike clusters. The *streptococci* always divide in the same plane and produce chains of cells. The *tetracocci*, or *gaffkya*, split alternately in two planes at right angles to each other, producing flat sheets of cells. The *sarcina* split successively in three planes at right angles to each other so that they tend to form cubical packets of eight cells.

The smallest bacteria are barely larger than some viruses, about 0.5 μ in diameter. Cocci are generally from 0.5 to 1.0 μ across. Bacilli vary in size, but most are from 0.5 to 1.0 μ across and 1 to 5 μ in length. Spirilla are about the size of bacilli or a little larger. A few giant bacteria will form cells over 50 μ long.

About 2,000 species of bacteria have been found. They are considered to be plantlike because of their rigid cell walls. Since there are so few basic shapes of bacteria, they are classified on the basis of size and shape, the materials they use as food, and the products formed from the food. The products are acids, alcohols, gases, pigments, and toxins. Oxygen relationship is also important. Those bacteria capable of growth only in the presence of air are called *aerobic*; those that cannot grow in the presence of air are called *anaerobic*. Bacteria able to grow in either situation are said to be *facultatively anaerobic*.

A few bacteria contain a special type of chlorophyll and hence are able to live photosynthetically in a manner similar to that of green plants. Bacterial photosynthesis differs from that of green plants mainly in that it is anaerobic and oxygen is not produced. Instead, oxidized organic compounds or sulfur compounds are the end products. Most photosynthetic bacteria contain a high concentration of *carotenoid pigments*; consequently, instead of appearing green, they are red or brown. There are a few green bacteria.

Most bacteria utilize nonliving organic materials for food and for growth, causing the materials' breakdown or decay. In fact, every naturally occurring organic material, including rubber, paraffin, and asphalt, can be used as a source of food by some microorganism. This breakdown is called *saprophytic action*. A few bacterial species are able to oxidize simple inorganic materials and secure their energy for growth from such processes. These processes include oxidations of ammonia, nitrites, sulfur, sulfides, hydrogen, carbon monoxide, iron, and manganese. Few, if any, bacteria are strictly parasitic. Many pathogenic (disease-causing) bacteria are unable to survive for long under natural conditions except in the host animal, but most of them have been cultivated in the laboratory on nonliving materials.

■**BACTERIAL MOVEMENT.**—Many bacteria cannot move by their own efforts. Some, however, have hairlike projections from the cell that enable them to swim rapidly in a liquid medium. These projections are called *flagella* (singular, *flagellum*). They may occur singly or in clusters at the ends of the cells, or may be scattered over the cell's surface. Bacterial species with a single terminal flagellum seem to swim as well as those having many flagella. How flagella are used to swim is not known. Most bacterial flagella are too small to be seen except when stained by a special method in which the stain accumulates around them so that they become visible under the microscope.

All bacteria have an outer slime layer that generally is thin and may be difficult to detect. Some bacteria, however, have a very thick gelatinous slime layer, a capsule, that can easily be seen. Some disease-causing bacteria, such as the *pneumococcus*, are able to resist defense mechanisms of the host because the latter react with the capsular material and do not

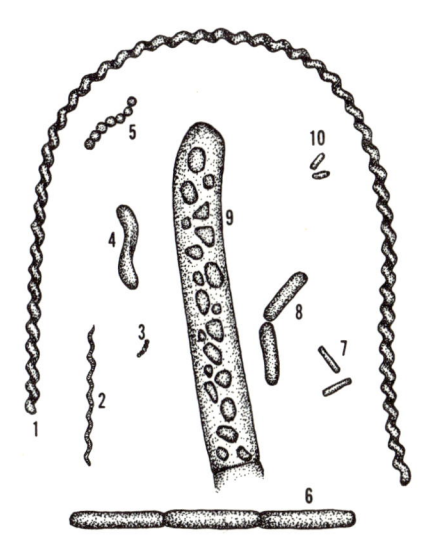

BACTERIA of various sizes and shapes: (1) *Spirochaeta plicatilis*; (2) *Treponema pallidum*; (3) *Peptostreptococcus parvulus*; (4) *Spirillum undula*; (5) *Streptococcus pyogenes*; (6) *Bacillus anthracis*; (7) *Mycobacterium tuberculosis*; (8) *Bacillus megatherium*; (9) *Beggiatoa alba*; and (10) *Bordetella pertussis*.

contact the bacterial cell itself.

A few species of the bacilli produce dormant forms that are more resistant to killing by heat, drying, and chemicals than are the original cells. These forms are called *spores* and are the most heat-tolerant form of life known. Spores of some species will survive boiling-water temperatures for several hours. The bacterial spore is thought to be a means of survival, not reproduction: a single cell usually forms but one spore, and when conditions are favorable for germination, that spore forms only one new growing cell.

The bacterial cell's nucleus is apparently not a clearly defined structure separated from the rest of the cell by its own membrane. The nucleus does, however, contain the cell's hereditary material (DNA), which controls the cell's processes in a manner that is probably similar to that in cells that have a well-defined nucleus. The bacteria that have been studied most completely appear to have only a single chromosome in the nuclear material. Since the chromosomes are not paired (*diploid*), the cell is *haploid*; and there are no dominant and recessive characteristics. Exchanges of nuclear material can occur in bacteria in at least three ways. These are recombination, transformation, and transduction. The latter two processes are apparently confined to bacteria.

■ **NUCLEAR MATERIAL EXCHANGE.** — *Recombination* occurs when two bacterial cells conjugate, or mate, and part of a chromosome is transferred from one to the other. Donor (F+) strains always transfer to recipient (F−) strains. Usually conjugation is a rare process, but a few F+ strains combine readily with F− strains and are therefore called *high-frequency recombinants* (HFR). After conjugation, the F− cell becomes F+ and gains the positive characteristics of the portion of the chromosome transferred. The F+ cell continues to grow because many such cells have more than one center of nuclear material and can use any center that has not been depleted by the conjugation.

Transformation is the incorporation into living bacterial cells of nuclear material (DNA) extracted from dead bacteria of the same species but of a strain having a few different characteristics. Some of the transformed cells will acquire some of the characteristics of the dead bacteria. The means of transfer of DNA into the cell is not known. Not all bacteria in a culture are competent to receive the DNA.

Transduction is the accidental transfer of bacterial DNA from a cell of one bacterial strain to a cell of another by a bacteriophage and the incorporation of this DNA into the chromosome of the recipient bacterium. The resulting cell has the positive characteristics of both cells for the portion of the chromosome transferred. This transfer requires that the bacteriophage be propagated on a bacterial strain that is destroyed by the virus, and that the recipient strain of bacteria be one that harbors the virus but is not ordinarily destroyed by it. Bacteria of the latter type are called *lysogenic* and may carry the virus with little or no evidence of infection.

Most of the work on transfer of nuclear material among bacteria has been done on the genera *Escherichia*, *Salmonella*, and *Shigella*. There is evidence that these three processes occur in most genera of bacteria.

■ **CLASSIFICATION.**—Bacteria have been classified in many ways. A completely *phylogenetic system*, one based upon obvious relationships and evolutionary patterns, is not possible with our present knowledge and perhaps may never be satisfactorily achieved. There are several large groups that have the status of orders and appear to be valid subdivisions of bacteria. The current system of classification, presented in the seventh edition of Bergey's *Manual of Determinative Bacteriology*, lists nine orders of bacteria. Four orders are listed below; the other five orders are of doubtful phylogenetic significance and may be listed as variations of true bacteria.

The *Eubacteriales* include the simple, or true, bacteria that have definite shapes and rigid cell walls. They multiply by transverse fission and do not show branching of cells. If they are motile, they move by means of flagella.

The *Myxobacteriales* are the slime bacteria that have no definite cell wall. They do not have flagella but are motile by a gliding motion, the explanation of which is unknown. The whole colony of cells may be motile and move across a surface in a small mound of secreted slime. The colony may organize into a complex fruiting body in which some cells form a base and others, a stalk. A few may become resting stages called *microcysts*. These dry and may be spread by the wind. New colonies of myxobacteria are started if they fall upon a suitable food source. Myxobacterial colonies are often found growing on animal dung deposits.

The *Actinomycetales* include the filamentous bacteria that often show true branching of the filaments. The intergradations between these and the eubacteria are so numerous that there is no clear line of demarcation.

The *Spirochaetales* form the order of the helical bacteria that are flexible, yet retain the coils of the helix. The spiral cell is wrapped around an axial filament that prevents the cell from straightening.

■ **CONTROL OF BACTERIA.**—Bacteria can be useful, harmful, or of no known importance to man. They are present in large numbers in most soils and waters and are carried in the air by dust particles. They are abundant on the skin, in the mouth, and in the digestive system of all animals. All ordinary objects have bacteria or microorganisms on their outer surfaces. Since some bacteria cause disease and many contribute to food spoilage, it is important to be able to control their activities. It is necessary to sterilize equipment to be used during surgical treatment of patients and to sterilize foods that are to be preserved for long periods. It is also necessary to sterilize containers for materials used in laboratory work when controlled changes are to be brought about by the use of a pure culture containing only one microbial species. The most common method of sterilization is use of steam under a pressure of about 15 pounds per square inch to give a temperature of 248° F. (121° C.) for 15 to 20 minutes. The apparatus used for this heat treatment is a large pressure cooker, an *autoclave*. Large containers of liquids or cans of dense, viscous material may have to be heated for an hour or more to ensure that all of the contents have been at 248° F. for the necessary length of time. Dry materials that should not be exposed to steam can generally be sterilized by heating them to 338° F. (170° C.) for two hours. If the material to be sterilized is severely altered by the heat treatment, chemical methods, although less convenient than heat, are available for sterilizing solid objects. Some liquids can be sterilized by passing them through a filter that holds back the bacteria. This will not, however, remove viruses; and if it is important that viruses be inactivated, this usually can be done by exposing thin layers of the liquid to high concentrations of ultraviolet light.

A reduction in the numbers of bacteria or complete sterility of water to be used for drinking, bottling, or industrial processes usually can be achieved by chemical treatment. Chlorine in a concentration of 0.1 to 1.0 parts per million bromine, or iodine is generally effective.

Where sterility is not as important as the destruction of disease-causing bacteria or the improvement of keeping quality by reducing the numbers of bacteria, pasteurization is the usual treatment. This relatively mild heat treatment was initiated by Louis Pasteur (1822–1895) to eliminate bacteria that spoil beer and wine. As it is commonly applied today to milk, pasteurization may use a temperature of 143° F. (61.3° C.) for 30 minutes or 161° F. (71.6° C.) for 15 to 20 seconds. Either process kills the bacteria that cause tuberculosis and brucellosis, as well as many of the common milk spoilage bacteria.

Early investigators did not understand that bacteria are everywhere and did not know that many of them can grow in the absence of air. Nor did they know that some species produce heat-resistant spores. Their crude methods of sterilization therefore generally failed, and subsequent growth of bacteria in the inadequately sterilized materials led them to believe that these living forms had originated spontaneously. The classical argument between J. T. Needham (1713–1781) and Lazzaro Spallanzani (1729–1799) in the eighteenth century pointed out the difficulties in establishing that spontaneous generation of life is not a common event under present conditions. The extensive experiments of Pasteur during the 1860's demonstrated that spontaneous generation of microorganisms does not occur—even bacteria must have ancestors.

■ **BACTERIAL DISEASES.**—The demonstration that bacteria can cause disease and that a particular bacterial species is always the cause of the same disease was made by the German physician Robert Koch (1843–1910) and his students during the period from 1870 to 1890. The rules for the establishment of this relationship are known as *Koch's postulates.* Four conditions must be achieved: (1) The suspected microorganism must be present in every case of the disease. (2) A pure culture of the microorganism must be obtained from a case of the disease. (3) The pure culture must cause the same disease when inoculated into a suitable experimental animal. (4) The original microorganism must be reisolated from the experimental case of the disease. These criteria often have been used to establish the cause-and-effect relationship between a particular bacterial species and a disease.

Some diseases in man caused by bacteria are scarlet fever, boils, diphtheria, bacillary dysentery, typhoid fever, whooping cough, pneumococcal pneumonia, asiatic cholera, tuberculosis, tetanus, gonorrhea, syphilis, and leprosy.

There are also many bacterial diseases of plants. Among these are fire blight of apple and pear trees, crown gall of trees and flowering plants, bean blight, tomato wilt, and soft rots of many vegetables.

Large quantities of foods are spoiled because of bacterial activities. Both stored fresh foods and canned foods that have been improperly sealed or processed are subject to spoilage. Several types of spoilage are of more than economic importance; poisonous toxins are sometimes produced and cause severe illness or death of persons who eat the affected food. *Staphylococci, streptococci, salmonellae,* and one of the anaerobic spore-forming bacilli, *Clostridium perfringens,* form toxins when they grow in food that has not been adequately refrigerated after preparation. These toxins may cause severe illness, but are seldom fatal. *Clostridium botulinum,* growing in canned or salted foods that have been inadequately processed, produces a toxin commonly fatal to man. Many cases of botulism have been caused by eating home-canned vegetables, but smoked fish have also been implicated. The toxin is destroyed by boiling food for ten minutes before it is eaten.

The manner in which a disease is transmitted depends in a measure on the living habits of the bacterium that causes it. Thus, the typhoid fever organism, *Salmonella typhosa,* which is carried in the feces, can contaminate meat, milk, shellfish, and water. It may infect subclinical carriers, who actually cause more outbreaks than persons with a full-blown case of typhoid. Infected food handlers are an important source of the disease. The gonococcus, *Neisseria gonorrhoeae,* attacks the mucous membranes of the genital tract and is usually transmitted during sexual intercourse. The whooping cough organism, *Bordetella pertussis,* is transmitted by inhalation of droplets from a coughing victim. Cholera is transmitted by contaminated water and food and by flies infected with the cholera organism, *Vibrio comma;* it may also be spread by person-to-person contact.

■ **INDUSTRIAL USES.**—Bacteria have important industrial uses. Indeed, many huge industries entirely depend upon bacterial action for their existence.

In the manufacture of cheese, cultures of bacteria are added to pasteurized milk. These bacteria slowly ferment the lactose to lactic acid and break down fats and proteins to produce substances that are responsible for the various flavors, textures, and aromas that characterize the different types of cheese. In fact, the "eyes" in Swiss cheese owe their existence to carbon dioxide made by bacteria.

To make commercial vinegar, the bacterium *Acetobacter* is used to oxidize alcohol to acetic acid, which in a concentration of about 4 per cent in water constitutes commercial vinegar. In the process, the alcohol trickles over a bed of shavings or other finely divided material that has been inoculated with the bacteria.

Bacterial fermentation is important in the manufacture of many other food products, such as sauerkraut, pickles, soy sauce, yogurt, and butter.

Bacteria are also used to make industrial chemicals. Species of the genus *Clostridium* ferment carbohydrates to produce butyl alcohol, isopropyl (rubbing) alcohol, acetone, and numerous other substances used in the manufacture of drugs, paints, synthetic rubber, explosives, and some plastics.

The brewing and related industries utilize bacteria. Species of the genus *Bacillus* produce enzymes from such organic wastes as soybean or peanut cake. These enzymes are used to convert raw starches into materials that can be fermented by yeasts. The textile and paper industries also make wide use of enzymes.

Mixtures of microorganisms are used in separating flax or hemp fiber from the woody plant tissue. Similarly, hides are subjected to bacterial action in leather-making. Bacteria are even used to remove sulfur compounds from petroleum.

Following Sir Alexander Fleming's (1881–1955) discovery in 1929 of the antibacterial action of penicillin (derived from the mold *Penicillium notatum*), Selman Waksman, René Dubos, and others sought other types of antibiotics among bacterial species. They found that the soil bacterium *Streptomyces* is especially antagonistic to pathogenic organisms, and species of this organism have yielded streptomycin, chloramphenicol, erythromycin, neomycin, and many other antibiotics useful in the treatment of a host of infectious diseases. Bacitracin and subtilin derive from species of *Bacillus.* Xerosin comes from *Achromabacter.* Millions of lives have been saved during the past 20 years because of the discovery of antibiotics. Today, drug manufacturers sell more than $75,000,000 worth of antibiotics annually; as a class of medicals their sales are rivaled only by the vitamins.

■ **BACTERIA AND WATER.**—Microorganisms are used in one of the methods for the purification of municipal water supplies and also in the purification of sewage in sewage disposal plants. In purifying water supplies by the slow sand filter, the raw water, perhaps from a river, is filtered through sand and gravel beds. As filtration proceeds, a slimy, jelly-like film accumulates around each sand grain, particularly in the upper few inches of sand. This film is composed of billions of bacteria and protozoa; and as it develops, it slows the flow of water through the sand. The water is purified by the action of enzymes, by biological oxidation and reduction processes, and by the ingestion of bacteria by the protozoa in the film. The filter removes about 99 per cent of the impurities from raw water.

The more recent and more commonly used rapid sand filter method of purifying water depends upon a thin layer of a chemical gel on the sand and upon other chemical treatments for removal of organic compounds and bacteria from the water. Both processes are generally followed by the addition of chlorine to com-

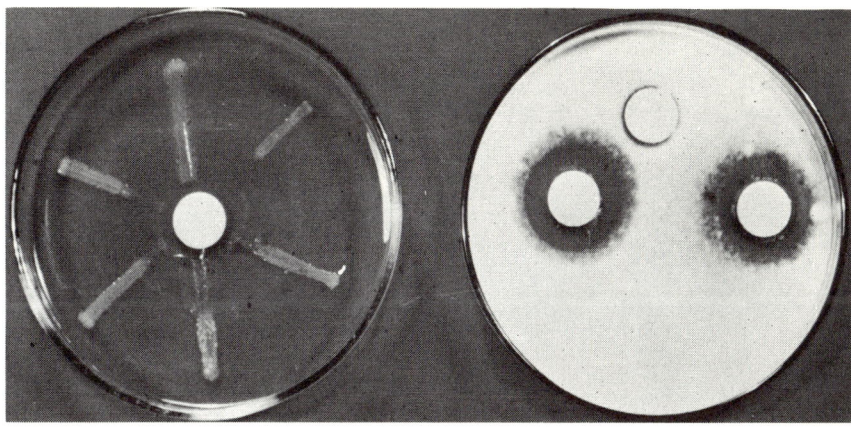

CHARLES PFIZER AND COMPANY

SCREENING PROCESS to test the antibiotic power of mold fluids. The dish on the left contains one mold fluid and six different germs; that on the right, four mold fluids and one germ organism. The dark rings signify fluids that are effective against the organisms.

plete the sterilization of the water.

BACTERIA AND SEWAGE.—Bacteria are vital to sewage disposal plants. Many different types of organisms abound in sewage; the abundance of any type changes as the sewage proceeds toward purification. One form of organism succeeds others as the environment changes.

Sewage disposal plants perform several functions. First, the sewage, which is about 95 per cent water, is screened to remove such large or inorganic matter as bottles and wooden boxes, and other large refuse. Then it is passed into separation tanks, where the heavier organic matter settles out. The supernatant liquid is then aerated by one of several processes to help the bacteria decompose the dissolved organic materials. This step is generally followed by another sedimentation, and the final water is chlorinated to remove harmful bacteria before it is discharged into a river, lake, or ocean.

The organic sediment from these treatments is pumped into closed tanks, or *sludge digesters,* and heated to about 100° F. Under these conditions the anaerobic bacteria produce a stable product that will not putrify later. The water from the sludge digesters is discharged with the other water; the sediment is dried and sold as fertilizer. The gases from the sludge digester are about 75 per cent methane, the same material as natural gas, which can be used to heat the digestion tanks and can be burned in gas engines to run the pumps in the sewage treatment plant.

Nearly all forms of organic materials are decomposed by bacteria during sewage treatment. Because of their slow rate of decomposition, however, greases and oils are usually skimmed off and burned.

BACTERIA IN AGRICULTURE.—Agriculture is largely dependent upon microorganisms for decomposition of plant roots and other items in the soil and for conversion of nitrogen-, phosphorus-, and sulfur-containing materials into forms useful to plants. Some soil bacteria can take nitrogen from the atmosphere and build it into their bodies, thus eventually contributing to the fertility of the soil. This process, called *nitrogen fixation,* also occurs in root nodules of many plants in situations where the plants and bacteria of various types grow together in an association beneficial to both. The best example of such a *symbiotic* (living together) association is that found between the bacteria of the genus *Rhizobium* and the legumes, plants such as peas, beans, clover, alfalfa, and locust trees. When the proper strain of *Rhizobium* invades the plant rootlet, a nodule containing the bacteria develops on the root. The nodule is the site of nitrogen fixation, which enables legumes to grow well in soils deficient in nitrogen and therefore unable to support other plants. There are various other symbiotic associations.

ANIMALS AND BACTERIA.— Although animals can live without bacteria in their environment, as has been shown by the raising of large colonies of "germ-free" animals, many animals benefit greatly from the presence of bacteria in their digestive systems. In the *rumen* (first stomach) of cattle, sheep, goats, deer, antelope, and other ruminant animals, bacteria and protozoa are responsible for the digestion of much of the food, especially the cellulose and other difficult-to-digest portions of the food. The microorganisms ferment these products and produce a number of acids from them. The acids, chiefly acetic, propionic, and butyric, are absorbed by the animal and metabolized as sources of energy. Microorganisms may help the animal by producing vitamins and proteins that can later be digested in the true stomach and utilized. A similar situation exists in the caeca of horses and some rodents.

Study of bacteria began as an applied science because of their relationship to disease, agriculture, and industrial processes. In recent years, investigators have attempted to study bacteria to learn more about the bacteria themselves. These studies have given much knowledge about the metabolism and genetics of higher plants and animals, because the basic chemical reactions of living creatures are all fundamentally similar. Because of rapid growth of bacteria, large crops of cells can be grown under carefully controlled conditions in a few hours. Similarly, genetic studies that need large populations or many generations have profited from observations of bacteria. The results of crossing various strains of bacteria can be observed in a few hours or days instead of the months or years that are required when higher plants or animals are used.

Rickettsiae.—*Rickettsiae* are intracellular parasites of the size and shape of small bacteria. They differ from bacteria in that they are dependent upon a host cell for part of their life processes. They have not been cultivated outside of a living host. Most *Rickettsiae* appear to be parasites of insects, ticks, or mites. They may or may not cause recognized illness in their normal host. Some, when transferred to other species, such as man, cause disease. Generally, rickettsial diseases are transmitted to man by the bite of their normal host—typhus fever by the body louse, tsutsugamushi fever by the mite, Rocky Mountain spotted fever by a tick. An exception to this is Q fever, caused by *Coxiella burnetii*. The fever is transmitted through milk from cattle to man, or by one's inhaling dust containing the dried manure of infected cattle. *Rickettsiae* usually can be cultivated in fertile chicken eggs; laboratory cultures are maintained in this manner.

Fungi.—The term *fungus* is poorly defined, but it includes those eucaryotic plantlike organisms that lack chlorophyll and the tissue differentiation of higher plants. Fungi vary in size from the single-celled yeasts, smaller than large bacteria, to mushrooms. Such related forms as puffballs may reach several feet in diameter.

The most commonly observed fungal growth is a cotton-like mass of filaments (*mycelium*) called *mold*. The individual filaments (*hyphae*) grow from the tip and may branch repeatedly. They have a chitin-like rigid wall and many nuclei. The nuclei may or may not be separated by cross walls (*septa*) in the hyphae; but even where septa are present, separation is generally incomplete, and the cytoplasm streams continuously through the mycelium.

Molds and other fungi with mycelia are abundant in the soil, where they are responsible for the decomposition of most dead plant material. Most of the mycelial structure is invisible to the naked eye. We become aware of it only when an unusually large amount of organic matter leads to the production of mycelia and mold fruiting bodies on its surface.

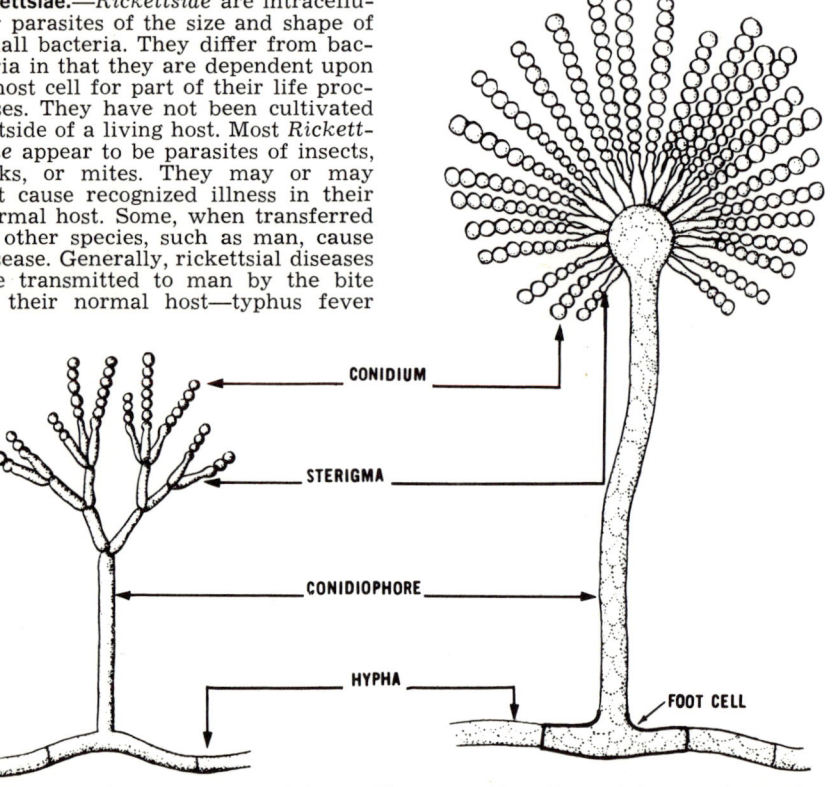

FUNGI occur in many types and forms. These two, *Penicillium* (*left*) and *Aspergillus* (*right*), are typical. Spores are produced at the tip of the branch called a *sterigma*.

REPRODUCTION OF FUNGI.—Fungi reproduce by forming a variety of small bodies called *spores*. Many of these, such as those most often formed by molds of the genus *Penicillium*, are small spheres exuded from the tips of special mycelial cells. They are called asexual spores because no nuclear fusion is required for their formation. Spores of this mold can often be seen on moldy oranges or cheese. They are green or blue-green and give it its characteristic color.

Most fungi have a sexual process for forming spores after the fusion of nuclei from two different mycelia or within multinucleated mycelia. Some of these processes are complex and lead to special spore-bearing organs such as the mushrooms.

FUNGAL DISEASES.—Many fungi cause diseases of plants; a few infect animals. Some fungi cause rust on grain and most other groups of plants. Many require different hosts for different stages of development. For example, black-stem wheat rust needs the common barberry for one phase of its sexual spore development. Another fungus, ergot, causes smuts of cereal crops and may cause death of animals and people who eat too much of the infected grain. However, ergot is also the source of a drug useful in controlling hemorrhage.

Human and animal diseases caused by fungi include athlete's foot, ringworm, and aspergillosis. Fungal diseases spread by contact with skin infected with the offending fungus. Athlete's foot is thought to be spread by the use of common showers and dressing rooms. In the course of this infection, the victim may become hypersensitive to the fungus or its products and develop allergic manifestations on parts of the body other than the feet, often the hands.

USES OF FUNGI.—Fungi are useful in the production of drugs and chemicals. The first of the antibiotics, penicillin, was discovered as a product of *Penicillium notatum*. *P. chysogenum* is now used for commercial preparation of penicillin. Fungi are also used to produce commercial quantities of citric and gluconic acids and such enzymes as amylase, cellulase, and glucose oxidase.

Yeasts.—A large miscellaneous group of fungi that seldom form mycelia but that generally grow as oval or round cells is known as yeasts. Many have a spore stage that follows fusion of nuclei from two cells. Others show only asexual reproduction, generally by *budding*. A small knob grows from the cell. As it increases in size, the cell nucleus divides and one of the new nuclei migrates into the protuberance. The bud is then walled off from the cell and is capable of forming its own buds. As seen in the figure, many buds may be formed by one cell. If a mass of cells stays attached, it may give the superficial appearance of a mycelium. A few yeasts multiply by fission in a manner similar to that of bacteria.

USES OF YEASTS.—Some of the yeasts, especially the species *Saccharomyces cerevisiae*, rapidly ferment sugars to carbon dioxide and alcohol. They have been used since antiquity to make beer and wine and to leaven bread. *S. cerevisiae*, variety *ellipsoideus*, is the yeast most often used in wine-making. Special distiller's yeast strains have been selected for making distilled alcoholic beverages and commercial ethyl alcohol. Yeasts also supplement human and animal diets because of their high content of B vitamins and protein. Food yeast may be recovered brewer's yeast, or it may be a special type, usually *Cryptococcus utilis*, grown on waste sugar solutions from a variety of industries.

YEAST INFECTIONS.—A few yeasts, such as *Candida albicans*, cause infections of human mucous membranes. *Candida* infection is not thought to be communicable; most persons unknowingly harbor the organism. Sometimes, when antibiotics are administered, the normal microbial flora of the body are disturbed and a *Candida* flare-up occurs. It is thought that administration of some antibiotics may stimulate its growth. *Cryptococcus neoformans*, a yeast found in the soil, may cause a fatal meningitis.

Algae.—Closely related to fungi and bacteria are the *algae*, which are mainly aquatic and marine plants. The algae vary greatly in size and characteristics; they include the large marine kelps and tiny single-celled plants. All, except for the blue-green algae, are eucaryotic. They all carry out the same photosynthetic reactions as the higher green plants do with the aid of chlorophyll.

The algae are among the most abundant of living things. The mass of microscopic algae in the oceans exceeds that of all green plants on land, making the oceans the principal sites of photosynthesis. Algae constitute a principal part of the diet of the largest whales.

The green algae are the most closely related to higher plants. They have cellulosic cell walls and store starch as a reserve food supply. Some of the unicellular green algae, such as *Chlorella*, are nonmotile while others, *Chlamydomonas*, for example, have flagella and are motile.

Euglena and related algae are quite similar to the green algae. However, they have no rigid cell wall, and hence resemble the protozoans more closely than other algae.

Other algae belong to the groups called *dinoflagellates, brown algae, red algae,* and *diatoms*. The diatoms are of interest because their walls are composed of overlapping halves, as shown in the figure, reinforced with silica. Diatoms are particularly abundant in the oceans and give the brown color to the foam seen on beaches. Their chlorophyll is obscured by carotinoid pigments. Large deposits of diatom shells have been found where prehistoric seas existed. They form a soft, white, powdery stone called *diatomaceous earth*, which is a common base for scouring powders.

Blue-green algae lack the organization of the other algae. They are procaryotic, and their chlorophyll is scattered throughout the cell instead of being separated from the rest of the cytoplasm in a chloroplast. Many blue-green algae can use gaseous nitrogen from the air and are therefore among the most self-sufficient microorganisms on Earth. They are the first plants to recolonize areas devastated by volcanic action or other catastrophes that kill all forms of life. They also can live in association with certain fungi, producing a complex plant structure called a *lichen*.

FLEISCHMANN LABORATORIES, STANDARD BRANDS, INC.

REPRODUCTION OF YEASTS by budding. These photomicrographs, taken over a four-hour period, show the firm cell wall. It appears to be formed of a material similar to that found in the cell walls of molds. The yeast cell, however, is usually ovoid or ellipsoidal and produces no flagella. Motility of yeasts has not been observed in any experiment.

Lichens grow in areas of extreme cold and dryness, such as the polar land masses and mountain heights.

Protozoa.—The *protozoa* are generally considered to be unicellular animals, but in some instances there is evidence that a protozoan has arisen from an alga that lost its ability to form chlorophyll. Most protozoans are sufficiently different from the algae so that no readily recognizable relationship can be established. Most protozoa lack a definite cell wall and vary greatly in size and shape. They are much larger than bacteria. *Paramecium*, a commonly studied form, is elliptical, with dimensions of 200 μ to 40 μ. Although they are regarded as the most primitive creatures in the animal kingdom, the protozoa are vastly more complex than the bacteria. The protozoa usually have well-defined portions that perform the functions of specialized organs in the more highly organized animals.

The four main groups of protozoa are *Sarcodina, Mastigophora, Sporozoa,* and *Ciliophora.* There are about 20,000 recognized species.

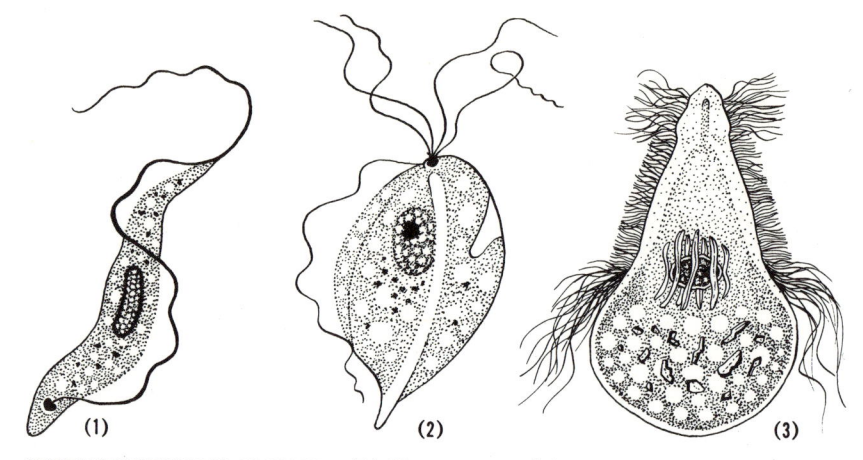

NONPHOTOSYNTHETIC PROTOZOA: (1) *Trypanosoma;* (2) *Trichomonas;* (3) *Trichonympha.*

■**SARCODINA.**—*Sarcodina* include the *amoebae,* the *foraminifera,* and the *radiolaria.* The adult amoebae lack definite shape or form and are bounded by a poorly defined cytoplasmic membrane. They move by extending arms of cytoplasm called *pseudopodia* ("false feet"), followed by movement of the rest of the cytoplasm into the pseudopod. Pseudopodia may completely surround food particles, thus bringing them into the cell. Multiplication is generally by fission of a single cell. This may, however, be preceded by conjugation of two cells. Many amoebae form resting stages, known as *cysts,* that are resistant to drying. When the environment is favorable, the cyst grows, producing an adult cell.

Most of the amoebae are free-living forms, but many are also parasitic on man and other animals. Only one of these, *Endamoeba histolytica,* causes human disease. This organism is carried in the feces and causes amoebic dysentery, a fairly common intestinal disease spread by contaminated water and food.

The foraminifera have a more or less complex outer shell structure, usually formed of calcium carbonate. Pseudopodia may extend through a mouth opening and also through holes in the shell to capture bacteria and other food materials. Geologists use the shells of foraminifera to determine geological age of rocks. Foraminifera occur only in salt water, and their skeletons make up a large part of the ooze of the ocean bottom. Throughout the world there are great chalk deposits, formed in the past geological ages, that consist largely of skeletons of foraminifera. The magnitude of these deposits is apparent when one considers that England alone produces over five million tons of chalk annually. The White Cliffs of Dover are shells of foraminifera.

The radiolaria have internal skeletons with radial spines that extend through and beyond the protoplasm. Their skeletons, which are siliceous, are almost indestructible. Their remains form the principal materials of millions of square miles of the bottoms of the Pacific and Indian oceans. They are thought to have been among the first animals on Earth; their skeletons form the oldest fossil-bearing rocks. Yet living forms closely resemble those of antiquity.

■**MASTIGOPHORA.**— The *Mastigophora* are protozoans that have from one to many long flagella in their principal phase. This group includes very simple organisms that appear to be flagellated amoebae and highly organized cells with definite shapes and internal structures; one finds protozoa that appear to be derived from algae. In fact, the protozoologist usually includes many species containing chlorophyll in the subclass *Phytomastigophora,* which contains the *Euglena* and related microorganisms. In this article all of the chlorophyll-containing protozoa have been classed as algae. Three important groups of flagellated protozoa are the trypanosomes, the trichomonads, and the trichonympha.

The *trypanosomes* and related protozoa have bladelike cells with a single terminal flagellum. An undulating membrane runs lengthwise along one side of the cell. Some of these protozoa cause diseases of insects and plants; others cause serious diseases in man and other animals. Among the latter are kala azar, caused by *Leishmania donovani* and thought to be transmitted by the bite of the sand flea. Another disease caused by a protozoan of this group is African sleeping sickness, caused by *Trypanosoma gambiense* and transmitted from man to man by an intermediate host, the tsetse fly. Most of the diseases of this group are spread by insects or other intermediate hosts.

Trichomonads are pear-shaped protozoans with four flagella at the smaller end. Many species of this group occur in animal intestines and can easily be observed in frogs and other amphibians. *Trichomonas vaginalis* causes an infection of the female genital tract; another form, *T. foetus,* causes abortion in cattle.

Trichonympha and related complex flagellates live in the digestive tracts of many insects, such as roaches and termites. In some instances they are beneficial to the insect, aiding in the digestion of such material as wood.

■**SPOROZA.**—All *sporozoa* are parasitic protozoans that at some stage of their life cycle form spores. Each species is usually restricted to one or two hosts in which different stages of its life cycle may occur. All groups of animals have sporozoan parasites. The most common sporozoan disease of man is malaria. Part of the sporozoan's life cycle occurs in the Anopheles mosquito, which may become infected from feeding on blood of persons suffering from malaria. After a developmental stage in the mos-

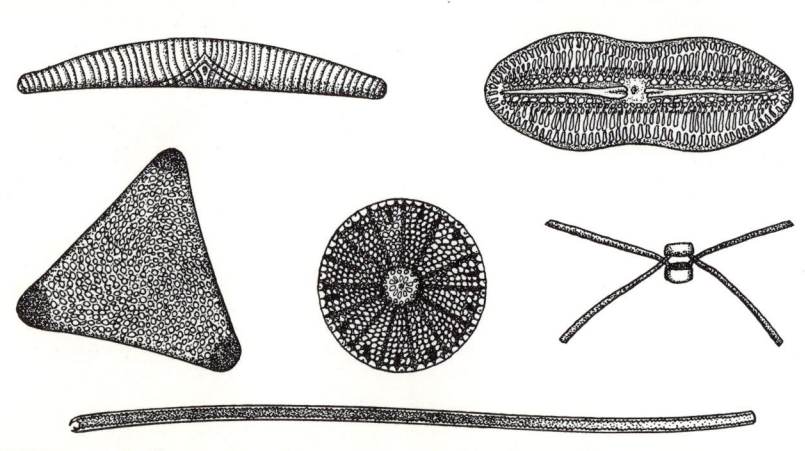

DIATOMS, a specific group of algae, occur in a wide variety of sizes, forms, and shapes.

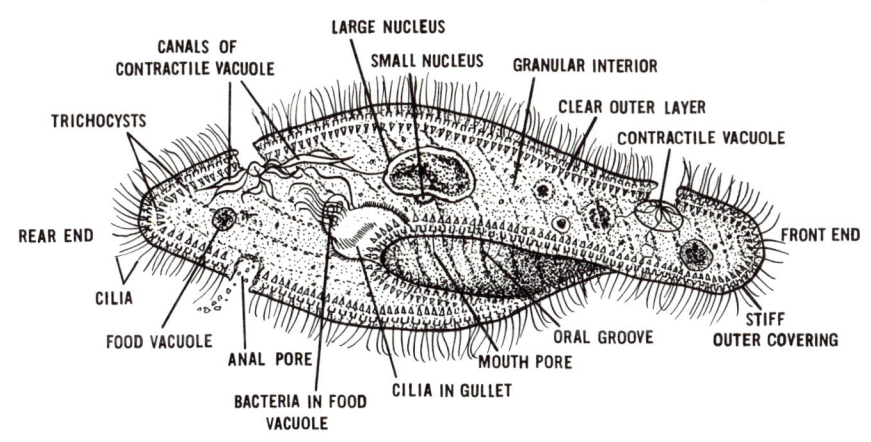

THE PARAMECIUM is one of the most highly developed of all of the unicellular animals.

quito, malaria can be transmitted to man again.

■CILIOPHORA.—The *Ciliophora* (*Infusaria*) are protozoa with *cilia,* short protoplasmic threads, on their surface. These cilia may cover nearly the whole surface, acting as organs of locomotion, as in paramecia, or they may be restricted to certain areas, such as around an oral opening where they help collect food. Most ciliates are free-living aquatic animals, but some inhabit the digestive tracts of animals. Many of them, such as the paramecia, readily develop in stagnant water containing dead plant materials. They live largely on other microorganisms, such as bacteria.

Some of the most complex ciliates, belonging to the genus *Diplodinium,* are found in the rumen of cattle and other ruminant animals. They appear to aid in the digestion of food particles and thus are beneficial, although not essential, to the well-being of the animal.

Immunity to Disease.—*Immunology* is the science that is concerned with the study of immunity to disease. The field developed in the course of study of viruses, bacteria, and *Rickettsiae*. Prior to the eighteenth century, people recognized that most persons and animals that recovered from some diseases did not get a second attack of the same disease. They had what we now call acquired immunity. Observation of this fact led to the intentional propagation of a mild form of smallpox, *variola minor,* that killed very few persons. This prevented a larger number of deaths than would otherwise have been the case during epidemics of a more severe form of smallpox, *variola major.* The severe form often killed 50 to 75 per cent of its victims. However, the practice was too risky for wide acceptance. The English physician Edward Jenner (1749-1823) observed that persons who had had a disease of cattle, cowpox, did not contract smallpox during epidemics. He dramatically demonstrated the value of this knowledge by artificially passing cowpox to a child and then later inoculating the child with material from a smallpox patient. The child did not contract smallpox. This discovery in 1796 was soon put to practical use to control smallpox, although the reasons for its effectiveness were not known for about another century.

Further studies during the period of 1879 to 1900 showed that immunity to several animal and human diseases could be induced by injections of bacteria or viruses treated to make them noninfective. Diseases in which poisonous bacterial products, *toxins,* are involved can be prevented by repeated small injections of toxin. Further, the toxin-neutralizing effect can be passed from an immunized person to a nonimmunized person by a transfer of blood serum. All of these immunities have been found to be specific—they protect the person only against the disease-causing agent used to develop the immunity. Acquired immunity is now known to be caused by the formation of substances called *antibodies,* which are altered blood-serum proteins. The substance inducing antibody formation is called an *antigen.*

The reaction of serum antibodies with the corresponding antigen can be demonstrated in a test tube by one of several means. If the antigen is particulate, such as dead bacterial cells, the antibody will cause it to *agglutinate,* or form clumps, and settle out. If the antigen is soluble, such as egg white or some other protein foreign to the host animal, the antibody will cause a visible precipitate to form. If the antigen is a suspension of living bacterial cells, the antibody will increase the rate at which they can be engulfed by living white blood cells. If the antigen is a toxin, the antibody (*antitoxin*) will neutralize it so that it may safely be injected into an experimental animal that it would otherwise kill. These reactions can be used to identify either the antigen or the antibody if the other half of the system is known.

The exact means whereby antibodies protect an animal from a disease caused by its corresponding pathogenic antigen are not known. They may, however, involve some of the same reactions that can be demonstrated outside the body.

■IMMUNIZATION.—Studies of antibody formation have led to many procedures that can be used successfully to protect man and domestic animals from disease. These include: (1) use of living but not virulent bacteria, such as the BCG (*bacille Calmette Guérin*) vaccine for tuberculosis; (2) use of dead bacteria to give immunity, as in vaccination against typhoid fever; (3) use of chemically modified extracts of bacteria, as in whooping cough vaccinations; (4) use of chemically modified toxins, *toxoids,* to form antitoxins against diphtheria and tetanus toxins; (5) use of dead *Rickettsiae,* as in vaccines for typhus fever and Rocky Mountain spotted fever; and (6) use of modified viruses to prevent such diseases as smallpox, measles, and poliomyelitis. Despite these many methods of immunization, present knowledge does not permit us to immunize against all diseases.

All of the above immunization procedures lead to what is called *active immunity;* the patient develops it himself. It is also possible to obtain *passive immunity* by transfer of antibodies, such as antitoxin, from one person to another or from an animal to a human being. Tetanus antitoxin is prepared by immunizing horses to tetanus toxin. The horse serum contains the antitoxin.

Active immunity is generally superior to passive immunity in preventing disease, since it lasts for a time from several months to the remainder of one's life; passive immunity disappears in a few weeks. Passive immunization is superior for treatment of a patient, since the maximum amount of antibody is present at the end of the injection. Active immunity generally requires several days or weeks to reach its maximum level.

The successful use of artificial immunity to prevent disease is dependent on an adequate vaccine, the length of immunity, the relative risk of immunization as compared with having the disease, and whether there are healthy carriers of the disease agent.

In addition to controlling disease, immunology includes studies of allergies and similar reactions and the response of a body to the transfer of material from a genetically different body of the same species.

—Richard H. McBee

BIBLIOGRAPHY

BROCK, THOMAS D. (ed.). *Milestones in Microbiology.* Prentice-Hall, Inc., 1961.

DUBOS, RENÉ JULES. *The Unseen World.* The Rockefeller Institute Press, 1962.

JACOBS, MORRIS B., and GERSTEIN, MAURICE J. *Handbook of Microbiology.* D. Van Nostrand, 1962.

STANIER, ROGER YATES, and others. *The Microbial World.* Prentice-Hall, Inc., 1963.

WALTER, WILLIAM G. *Dictionary of Microbiology.* D. Van Nostrand, 1962.

WALTER, WILLIAM G., and MCBEE, RICHARD H. *General Microbiology.* D. Van Nostrand, 1962.

GENETICS

Continuity of Life.—*Genetics* is the study of the inheritance of biological characteristics in living things—characteristics that are passed from one generation to the next. What is inherited is a code message in the genetic material (*genes*) of egg and sperm. The code directs embryonic development and organization of cells into tissues and organs, and the function of each tissue and organ. The development is also influenced by external and internal environment. Thus, the organism is the product of interaction between genetic material and environment.

What is the nature of genetic material? How is it reproduced? What is the material's mechanism of action in the cell's function and the individual's development? How is the material transmitted? What is its role in the process of organic evolution? Each of these questions is complex, but progress has been made in answering them.

Mendelian Genetics.—The first problem to be solved is related to the mechanism of transmission of genetic material. This was the basis of Mendelian, or classical, genetics. Even in the nineteenth century, biologists knew an embryo develops from fusion of egg and sperm. Hence, the new organism is the product of materials from each parent. However, biologists were under the false impression that hereditary traits were transmitted in a bloodlike fluid from each parent and were mixed in the offspring. Hence we have the terms "half-blooded" and "full-blooded."

Gregor Johann Mendel (1822–1884), an Austrian monk, analyzed the basic laws of inheritance in 1866. The results were lost until 1900, when investigators in Holland, Germany, and Austria each independently rediscovered the Mendelian concept.

■**MENDEL'S CONTRIBUTION.**—Mendel had proved hereditary traits are transmitted by pairs of distinct units, later called *genes*, which reshuffle, segregate, and redistribute, rather than blend, in the offspring.

Mendel used garden peas in his experiments because they hybridize easily. When a purebred tall plant was crossed with a purebred short plant, all hybrid offspring were tall, no matter which type was the mother and which the father. The hybrids self-fertilized. Mendel counted the offspring and found 787 tall and 277 short plants, a ratio of about 3 to 1. When the short plants self-fertilized, they produced only short offspring, but when the tall plants self-fertilized, there were two types of offspring: one-third had only tall offspring, and two-thirds produced both tall and short in a ratio of 3 to 1. Mendel crossed six other characters: round and wrinkled peas, colored and uncolored flowers, and yellow and green peas. He had approximately the same results.

Mendel then formulated the *law of segregation*. Today this principle states that hereditary traits (such as tallness or shortness of peas) are transmitted by *zygotes* (fertilized eggs). One member of the pair of traits comes from the male parent; the other, from the female. In the mature plant, these paired genes segregate during the formation of *gametes* (sperms and eggs) so that just one of the pair is transmitted by a particular gamete. The gamete has only one gene of each pair, and is called *haploid*. When the male and female gametes unite to form the zygote, it is called *double* or *diploid*.

Mendel's studies showed the *principle of dominance*. The trait of tallness is dominant over shortness. (When there is a gene for tallness and one for shortness, all peas are tall.) The opposite, unexpressed factor is *recessive*.

An individual with unlike paired genes can be represented as *Tt*. *T* represents the dominant gene for tallness, and *t* the recessive gene for shortness. Such an individual is called a *heterozygote*. If both genes are alike (*tt* or *TT*) the individual is a *homozygote*. The genetic makeup is called the *genotype*; the character determined by this genotype and expressed in the individual is the *phenotype*. If the genotype is *TT*, the phenotype is tallness. Another genotype that can give the phenotype tallness is *Tt*. The alternative forms of a gene are called *alleles*. This cross is illustrated in the diagram.

Mendel concluded that dominant and recessive genes do not affect each other; gametes are haploid and have only one of a pair of genes; each type of gamete is produced in equal numbers by a hybrid parent; and combination between gametes depends on chance—the frequency of each class of offspring depends on frequency of the gametes produced by each parent.

Mendel next determined how two or more pairs of genes would behave in crosses. He crossed plants with round, yellow seeds with those with wrinkled, green seeds. He knew a cross between round (*R*) and wrinkled (*r*) seeds produced round seeds in the F_1 generation and three round to one wrinkled seed in the F_2 plants; he knew crossing yellow (*Y*) with green (*y*) produced all yellow in the F_1 and three yellow to one green seed in the F_2 generation. This showed the dominance of roundness and yellowness over their respective contrasting alleles. When Mendel crossed round-yellow with

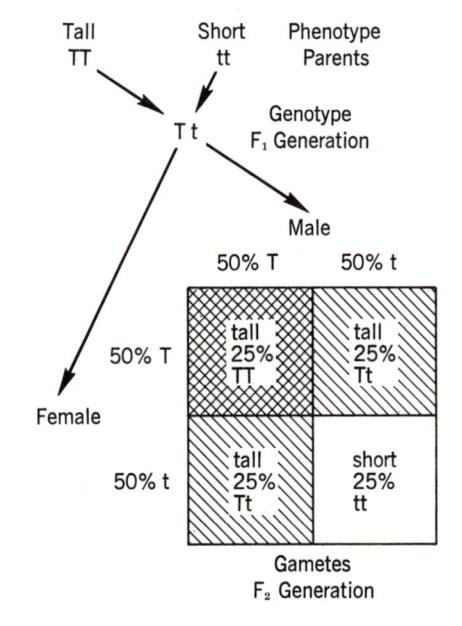

DROSOPHILA (FRUIT FLIES) aid geneticists in studying evolutionary characteristics. The Mendelian square (*right*) illustrates the principle of dominance. Since the trait of tallness is dominant, the combination *TT,tt* yields three tall individuals out of four offspring.

wrinkled-green, the F_1 produced all round-yellow seeds. In the F_2 generation, these seed types were obtained:

Two combinations, round-green and wrinkled-yellow, not present in either parental or the F_1 generation, have appeared. This result can be explained by Mendel's *law of independent assortment*, which states that members of one pair of genes segregate independently of other pairs. The various combinations are illustrated in the accompanying table.

Type	Proportion
Round-yellow	9/16
Round-green	3/16
Wrinkled-yellow	3/16
Wrinkled-green	1/16

Mendel also tested his F_2 plants to determine whether all of a single phenotype class, such as round-yellow, were alike in genotype. According to his hypothesis, there should be four different genotypes in this group: $RR, YY; RR, Yy; Rr, YY;$ and Rr, Yy. When F_2 plants self-fertilized, he found four classes of round-yellow seeded plants; the ratios fitted expectations. The breeding behavior of the F_2 round-green, wrinkled-yellow, and wrinkled-green were in accord with the hypothesis that each pair of genes segregates independently from other pairs of genes and is transmitted independently to the next generation.

Mendel's inheritance rules were later found to apply in other plants and in animals. More information explained the seeming exceptions.

In all characters studied by Mendel, the heterozygote was phenotypically identical with the homozygote dominant. In some cases, however, the heterozygote is intermediate. This is true in the color of the flower known as the "four o'clock." If a red parent is crossed with a white, all F_1 hybrids are intermediate in color, one-quarter of the F_2 offspring are red, one-quarter white, and one-half intermediate. In some cases, both alleles are equally "dominant," for example, those that determine the *MN* factors in blood. If one parent is *M* and the other *N*, all children will be *MN*. If both parents are *M*, or both *N*, all children will be *MM* or *NN*, respectively. If both parents are *MN*, one-quarter of the children are *M*, one-quarter *N*, and one-half *MN*. To understand other exceptions, where independent segregation does not seem to apply, one must consider the chromosomal basis of heredity.

Chromosomal Basis of Heredity.—All living things are composed of cells and begin life as a single cell. In organisms reproducing sexually, the cell is the fertilized zygote, which divides to form all the cells of the body of the organism (*somatic cells*).

Each cell has an inner body (*nucleus*) surrounded by a less dense semifluid material called *cytoplasm*, which is enclosed by a cell membrane. In the cytoplasm are various vital structures. In the nucleus, which is enclosed by its own membrane, are threadlike structures called *chromosomes*, and one or more bodies called *nucleoli*, which are dark when they are stained.

In 1902 a graduate student, W. S. Sutton, and a German cytologist, T. Boveri, decided independently that genes are in the chromosomes. Sutton's arguments were:

(1) Since sperm and egg give continuity from one generation to the next, the hereditary traits must be carried by the sperm and egg. (2) The sperm is almost all nucleus and yet contributes as much to heredity as does the egg, which has both cytoplasm and nucleus. Hence, the hereditary characters must be in the nucleus. (3) The visible nuclear parts that divide during cell division are chromosomes. The genes, then, must be on the chromosomes. (4) Chromosomes occur in pairs, as do genes. (5) Chromosomes segregate during maturation of egg and sperm. Genes segregate during formation of the gametes (law of segregation). (6) Members of one pair of chromosomes segregate independently of other chromosome pairs. (Mendel showed that one pair of genes also segregates independently of other pairs.)

This gives a logical basis for the hypothesis that genes must be on chromosomes. In sixty years, evidence has accumulated proving the truth of this hypothesis and identifying the chemical nature of the hereditary chromosomal material. Chromosomes are equally distributed during cell division (*mitosis*) and each member of the chromosome pair segregates during maturation of egg and sperm (*meiosis*).

■ MITOSIS.—Chromosomes are accurately reproduced and transmitted in a precise process that assures that each new cell formed receives one of each chromosome. The number of chromosomes characteristic of each species remains constant. Every somatic cell in the human being has 46 chromosomes; in the fruit fly, 8; in the garden pea, 14.

Although mitosis is a continuous process, it is described in terms of five phases:

Interphase. Chromosomes are usually not individually distinguishable; they are stretched out in long, diffuse threads. In this phase, each chromosome copies itself by a mechanism not yet understood.

Prophase. The chromosomes coil up and become short and thick. The nuclear membrane disappears and spindle fibers, denser than the cytoplasm, appear.

Metaphase. The chromosomes line up in a single plane across the center of the cell.

Anaphase. Each chromosome, at a fixed point on its body, has a minute structure called the *centromere*, attached to a spindle fiber. This fiber apparently contracts, and thereby guides each of the duplicated chromosomes away from the center of the cell in opposite directions.

Telophase. One complete set of chromosomes is in each half of the cell. The entire cell then divides between the two sets, and the chromosomes uncoil and lengthen. A new interphase is then begun in each daughter cell.

The number and make-up of chromosomes remain constant in each cell because successive chromosome duplication is followed by cell division.

■ MEIOSIS.—Each cell's chromosomes occur in pairs, one from the mother and one from the father. Each member of the chromosomal pair has similar genes; they are called *homologous chromosomes*, or *homologues*. Human somatic cells have 23 pairs of chromosomes each.

The egg and sperm must each have half the somatic number of chromosomes, or be haploid, so that when they unite, the fertilized zygote will be *diploid*, as will be all cells derived from it by mitosis. The chromosome number of somatic cells remains constant from generation to generation

THIS MENDELIAN SQUARE shows the many genetic combinations possible in hybrid peas.

Genetics

Interphase | Prophase | Metaphase

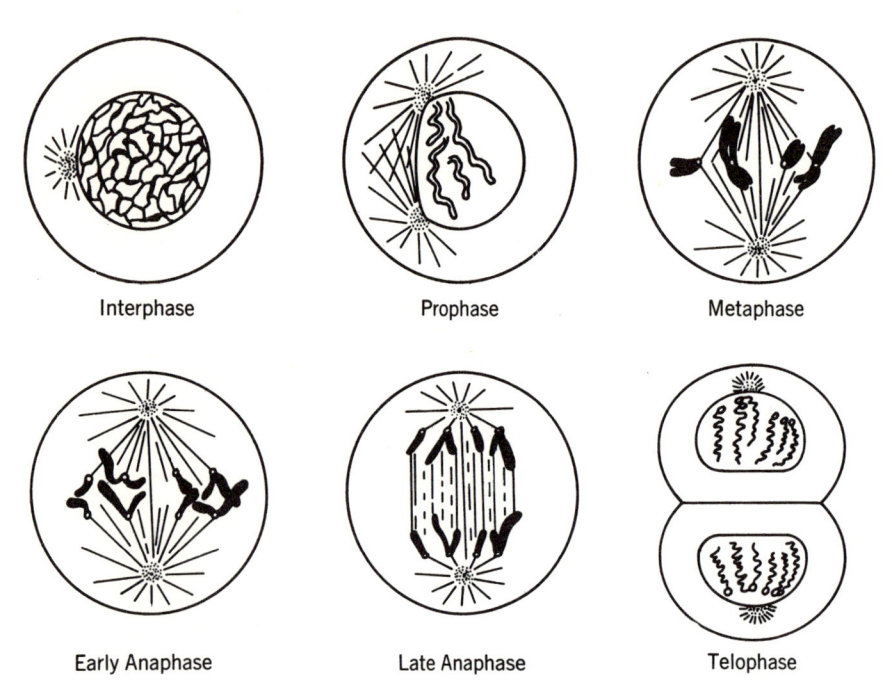

Early Anaphase | Late Anaphase | Telophase

MITOSIS, or cell division, is the process by which a cell splits into identical twins. The number and makeup of chromosomes remain constant in each cell during this process.

of the species and there is a mechanism to ensure that one member of each chromosome pair is in each gamete. The mechanism is known as *meiosis* and has two divisions:

First meiotic division. In this phase, each chromosome copies itself once, creating two *chromatids*; the chromatids are held together by the undivided centromere. The homologous chromosomes move toward each other and pair tightly, so that similar genes, or *alleles*, lie alongside each other. This makes a bundle of four chromatids and two centromeres. During this time the partner, or matching, strands twist around each other, break, and then reunite, thus exchanging homologous sections. As a result, chromosomes consist of parts from both paternal and maternal chromosomes. The centromere of each of the homologous chromosomes, attached to the spindle fiber and to the chromosome, is pulled to an opposite pole of the cell. The cell divides. Each new cell now has the haploid chromosome number, with either a maternally or paternally derived member of each chromosomal pair, depending on chance and on the random attachment of each centromere to the spindle fibers. This is the chromosomal basis for the independent assortment of each member of a pair of chromosomes with respect to the other.

Second meiotic division. In this phase, the centromeres divide so that each chromatid separates from its duplicate. Another division follows that is much like ordinary mitosis—two duplicate cells are formed.

Because of the two meiotic divisions, four cells are formed from the original cell; each has a haploid number of chromosomes, one of each homologous pair.

■**SEX-LINKAGE.**—Chromosomes occur in pairs, one maternal and one paternal. All but one pair are identical in both sexes. In one sex (usually the male) there is one pair of unidentical chromosomes—X and Y. In the human male, there are 22 pairs of identical (nonsex) chromosomes called *autosomes*, and one X and one Y chromosome. The female has 22 pairs of autosomes and a pair of X chromosomes. The X and Y chromosomes are called *sex chromosomes*. If an egg is fertilized by a sperm bearing an X chromosome, it becomes female (XX). If it is fertilized by a Y-chromosome-bearing sperm, it becomes male (XY). Thus, sex determination occurs at the moment of fertilization. Since segregation of the sex chromosomes takes place during meiosis exactly as does segregation of the other chromosomes, and is completely random, the chance is even that any sperm will contain a Y chromosome. Since all eggs contain one X chromosome, the probability of the offspring's being either a boy or girl is exactly equal.

The Y chromosomes of organisms contain few or no genes. (None are known to occur on the human Y chromosome.) The X contains many genes. Because of this, these genes are segregated differently in the two sexes, resulting in the phenomenon called *sex-linkage*.

Red-green color blindness is the most common sex-linked trait in human beings, occurring in about 8 per cent of men and in about .5 per cent of women. This is explained by the hypothesis that the recessive gene responsible is contained in the X chromosome and that there is no corresponding allele in the Y. A woman heterozygous for the trait married to a normal man would have daughters with normal vision, but probably half of her sons would be color-blind. The children of a homozygous (normal) woman married to a color-blind man would all be normal, but probably half the daughters would be heterozygous and would transmit the trait to half their sons.

■**X CHROMOSOME.**—It has long been a puzzle as to how males can function with only one X chromosome, and therefore only one set of sex-linked genes, whereas females have two X's and a double set of sex-linked genes.

Since 1949 geneticists have been able to distinguish between body cells from the male and female of many mammals, including human beings, by a simple staining technique. Cells from females contain a darkly staining body, the *Barr body* or *sex chromatin*, that is missing from male cells.

In 1961 the English geneticist, Mary Lyon, formulated a hypothesis based largely on experiments with mice, which resolved the riddle as to why a single X chromosome is enough for a male. She states that one X is also enough for a female, since only one of her two X's functions. The other is inactive and condensed, and so it stains deeply. This inactivation occurs early in the embryo's development. In some embryonic cells it may be the maternal X that is inactivated; in others, it may be the paternal X. All cells descended from the embryonic cells thus would only have the same single active X chromosome. The best evidence for this randomness of inactivation is the inheritance of certain sex-linked coat-color genes in mammals. Females heterozygous for any of these always show a mottled or dappled phenotype, with patches of normal and mutant color, as in a tortoise shell cat.

The Barr bodies in female cells fit the theory of the single active X. The theory is that all inactive X's show up as Barr bodies. Males (XY)

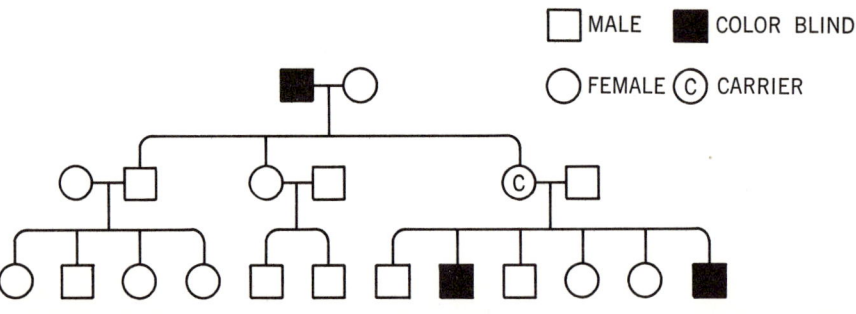

☐ MALE ■ COLOR BLIND
○ FEMALE Ⓒ CARRIER

COLOR BLINDNESS is a common sex-linked trait in human beings. A color-blind male passes his recessive trait to a male grandchild through his daughter, who serves as a carrier.

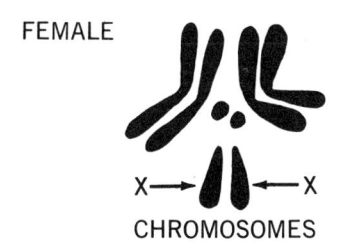

CHROMOSOMES in Drosophila. Two X's combine to make a female; X and Y, a male.

and females with an abnormal chromosome complement of one X and no Y (XO) have none; normal females (XX) and males with an abnormal chromosome complement (XXY) have one. Other abnormalities in sex chromosome number have been found. There are females with three X chromosomes and two Barr bodies. Females with four X's and three Barr bodies have also been reported.

The single active X chromosome hypothesis is not yet verified, but evidence indicates that it is true.

■**Y CHROMOSOME.**—Experiments with *Drosophila* (small two-winged flies) showed that two X chromosomes were necessary to produce a female, and one X to produce a male. The Y seemed to be neutral, as proved in certain flies with the XO chromosomal constitution (one X and no Y) that were sterile males. Female flies were found with two X chromosomes and a Y (XXY). Until recently, it was thought that sex was determined the same way in the human being. It is now known, however, that the Y chromosome is essential to determine maleness in human beings. Humans with rare chromosomal abnormalities have been studied, and those with the XO chromosome constitution (one X and no Y) are abnormal females. Some abnormal males have an XXY complement. Since the Y is essential in human beings for a male to develop, he will be abnormal if this is unbalanced by two X's. One X will produce a female, but two are necessary for normality.

■**CHROMOSOME MAPPING.**—The principle of independent assortment is explained in that the maternal and paternal members of each homologous pair of chromosomes are distributed independently to the gametes at meiosis. The seven factors Mendel studied were carried by different chromosomes and were independently inherited. Each chromosome has many genes; in *Drosophila* there are hundreds of genes known, but only four pairs of chromosomes. Genes located on the same chromosome tend to be inherited together and are said to be *linked*. During meiosis, when homologous chromosomes pair, they twist around each other with resultant breakage and reunion; hence, some parts of a chromosome segregated to the new cell can be either maternal or paternal. This process of chromosomal recombination is called crossover. There is indisputable evidence the crossover occurs at the stage of meiosis when there are four chromatids held together by the undivided centromeres.

Crossover occurs at random sites along the chromosome; the frequency is determined by the distance between the points—the closer the points, the less frequent the crossover; the farther apart, the more frequent.

This is the basis for mapping the locations (*loci*) of the genes; the crossover frequency is the unit of map distance between loci. To determine the order of the gene loci, crosses involving three different pairs of linked factors are used. Analysis of such crosses has proved that the genes within each chromosome are arranged linearly in a definite serial order at fixed loci.

Genetic maps of chromosomes are graphic representations of the relative distances of genes in each linkage group, as determined by the percentage of *recombination* (crossover) among the genes. The four pairs of chromosomes from *Drosophila melanogaster* have been extensively mapped. Corn has also been mapped; each of its ten linkage groups (corresponding to ten pairs of chromosomes) is represented by many genes. Other maps are available for pink bread mold (*Neurospora*), the colon bacillus (*Escherichia coli*), and the mouse. A few gene markers are mapped on the X chromosome of man, but the 22 autosomes (the non-sex chromosomes) are largely unmapped. New techniques in tissue culture may make possible mapping of all human chromosomes.

Correspondence between the genetic maps of chromosomes and morphologically detectable defects in the chromosomes has been good. The presence in the salivary glands of *Drosophila* of huge chromosomes has made possible detection of minor structural changes. Sometimes a portion of a chromosome is deleted; this defect is detected in salivary chromosomes. Flies missing a small region near one end of the X chromosome also lack the white eye gene; hence, the locus of the gene for white is in this region of the X chromosome. Likewise, the precise location of other genes has been ascertained; generally the relative distance as determined by linkage studies has been confirmed by cytological studies.

Nature of Genetic Material.—The chemical nature of genetic material and the chemical basis for its reproduction are important. Generally it is accepted that except for some viruses, genetic information is carried in *deoxyribonucleic acid* (DNA). Principally, the evidence is as follows: DNA is unique to the chromosomes. The amount of DNA is remarkably constant from cell to cell within any organism and within a single species. Only the egg and sperm cells have a different amount; they contain half the normal amount of DNA (and half the somatic chromosome number). *Proteins* and *ribonucleic acids* (RNA), other substances found in chromosomes, vary considerably in amount in different tissues within a species. Inheritable changes, *mutations*, are in the genetic material. These seldom occur spontaneously, but the frequency may be greatly increased by exposure to X rays, ultraviolet light, and certain chemicals. DNA and the genes are normally stable. A wavelength of 260 μ ultraviolet light is effective in producing mutations because it is most absorbed by nucleic acids.

The best direct evidence that DNA is the genetic material comes from experiments in transformation of certain bacteria; these show that the so-called transforming principle is pure DNA. Classic work by O. T. Avery, C. M. MacLeod, and M. McCarty in 1944 was based on earlier observations that when an extract from dead cells of one strain of *Pneumococcus* was added to living cells of another strain, it transformed some characters of the living cells so they were identical to the extract strain. The new characters were inherited by progeny of the transformed strain as if the latter had extract genes. Avery's group analyzed the extract and proved that the active part of the transforming extract was pure DNA, so the genetic material must be DNA.

Evidence that DNA transmits genetic information was obtained by the 1952 studies of Hershey and Chase on viral infection of colon bacilli. *Bacterial viruses*, or *bacteriophages*, consist of a protein coat and a DNA core. When viral protein is labeled with a radioactive isotope of

CROSSOVER brings about new combinations of genes in the offspring. This allows the offspring to have their own traits.

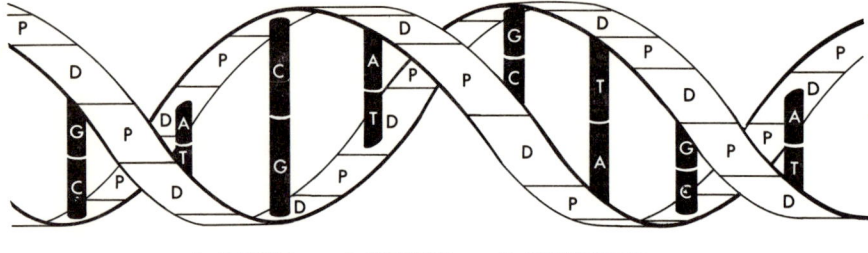

Genetics

A—ADENINE   **C**—CYTOSINE   **D**—DEOXYRIBOSE
T—THYMINE   **P**—PHOSPHATE   **G**—GUANINE

WATSON-CRICK MODEL of the DNA molecule is formed from a few simple molecules repeatedly linked. These various combinations represent a complex genetic code of life.

sulfur (S-35) and the DNA with radioactive phosphorus (P-32) and each is allowed to infect the bacterial host, S-35 remains outside and P-32 inside the host. The P-32 is found in the new viruses released when the bacteria open. Since the viral part (*phage*) within the bacterium contains genetic information that directs its host to make more phage (both DNA and protein), it must be DNA that is the genetic material.

N. Zinder and J. Lederberg discovered bacterial transduction, providing more proof that DNA transmits genetic information. In *bacterial transduction*, a hereditary trait can be transferred from one bacterial cell to another via a virus that infects first one cell and then the other. In transduction, the viral DNA picks up a tiny bit of its host's DNA. When the host cell ruptures and the virus infects a new host, the virus carries the genes of the first host with it. These genes are expressed in the new host and its offspring. A streptomycin-resistant bacterium may be infected with a viral strain of low virulence, a temperate bacteriophage. The virus may multiply within it, and some viral particles may pick up the streptomycin-resistant gene. If the virus is allowed to infect a streptomycin-sensitive bacterial strain, some of these bacteria and progeny are then found to be streptomycin-resistant. If two or more genes are transduced simultaneously, they are always closely linked. Transduction is indirect evidence that DNA is genetic material. Assuming that the part of the virus that enters the host is DNA and that the bacterial material carried by the virus is also DNA, then transduction is like transformation, except that instead of man transferring the DNA from donor to recipient, a temperate bacteriophage does so.

Some viruses, such as tobacco mosaic virus, consist of only RNA and protein. In 1957, Fraenkel-Conrat separated RNA and protein of related strains, recombining them so that strain *A*'s RNA was combined with protein of strain *B*, and vice versa. In each case, genetic properties of the hybrid virus particle, as determined by infection, were always of the strain from which the RNA came.

The Watson-Crick Model.—A high-molecular-weight polymer, DNA is a large molecule formed from a few simple molecules linked repeatedly by chemical bonds. Repeating units are *nucleotides*, each of which consists of a phosphate group; a five-carbon sugar, *deoxyribose;* and one of four different nitrogenous bases. The four bases are two *purines* called *adenine* (A) and *guanine* (G), and two *pyrimidines, cytosine* (C) and *thymine* (T). In polymerized form, as in nucleic acids, nucleotides are connected by a chemical bond between the phosphate group of one nucleotide and the 3-hydroxyl of an adjacent deoxyribose. The DNA has a deoxyribose-phosphate backbone with bases projecting inward and perpendicular to the axis.

Chargaff and co-workers showed that the ratio of adenine to thymine, and of guanine to cytosine, is about 1/1 in any DNA preparation. However, the ratio of adenine (or thymine) to guanine (or cytosine) varies. They thought that since A = T and G = C, each was associated with the other in DNA.

This ratio, together with X-ray diffraction studies of DNA by M. H. F. Wilkins, led James Watson and F. H. C. Crick, in 1953, to propose a DNA structure. Their structure is essentially a twisted ladder or *double helix;* the sides are made of the sugar-phosphate backbone and the rungs are the *bases*. The *base sequence* in one strand determines that in the complementary strand; an A must always be matched with a T, and a C with G. Weak hydrogen bonds hold A to T and G to C, giving the ladder firmness and ability to separate when replication takes place during mitosis.

The *Watson-Crick model* makes it possible to understand how genetic information is duplicated and transmitted. If double helix strands separate, each is a *template*, or mold that specifies the replication of its complementary copy. This would result in two identical DNA molecules, each with an original and a newly synthesized strand.

The model explains how DNA could carry genetic information, or *code*, translated into protein-producing instructions. The code depends on the sequence of the four bases in relation to each other; in effect, a four-letter alphabet. Many configurations are possible, since there are ten base pairs in each complete turn of the double helix; and this is a small portion of the entire molecule. For each turn, the number of configurations possible would be 4^{10}, or 1,048,576. Not all combinations of nucleotides are meaningful, but the storage potential of genetic information is vast.

The model gives a chemical basis for mutation. If DNA is genetic material, then a change in the DNA molecule should change the code and cause mutation. This could happen if an error is made during replication, or if A picks up C instead of T and the error is perpetuated. At one position, base pairs would be C-G instead of A-T, upsetting the code and preventing formation of a normal protein. If a compound similar to a normal base is introduced, a compound that differs so slightly that the replicating DNA could easily mistake it for the normal, mutations might occur. For example, 5-bromouracil can quantitatively replace thymine; in some cases this can produce mutation. Changing the code results in production of abnormal protein or of no protein.

The model fits requirements of linear arrangement of genes in linkage groups; the four bases are arranged linearly along the helix, forming a linear code.

The most direct work supporting the model is that done in 1958 by Meselson and Stahl. They grew many generations of bacteria in heavy nitrogen (N-15) and then transferred cells to ordinary N-14 medium for varying lengths of time. At specified times, they extracted the DNA from the cells and centrifuged it, using a technique that causes molecules to concentrate in bands at definite positions, depending on their density. DNA taken from bacteria grown for a long time in N-15 and allowed to divide once in N-14 formed a hybrid band halfway between that of DNA in bacteria grown in N-15 and in N-14. If the bacteria divided twice in N-14, two bands were visible, one a hybrid band and one the N-14 band. In succeeding divisions, the hybrid band became smaller and the N-14 band larger.

When the two strands of N-15 DNA separate, each is a template for information of a complementary N-14 strand. After one replication, two new DNA helices are formed—each a hybrid of N-14/N-15. At the next replication, each N-14 strand synthesizes another N-14 strand, forming a pure N-14/N-14 helix, and N-15 strands replicate, forming a hybrid N-14/N-15 helix. In succeeding generations, there is but one hybrid strand, but the number of pure N-14/N-14 molecules steadily increases. Facts and theory coincide, suggesting that the DNA helix unwinds into two single strands during replication.

Kornberg proved in a test tube the theoretical model of DNA synthesis. When he mixed a certain enzyme, triphosphates of each of the four nitrogen bases, and a primer, or starter, of a small amount of preformed DNA, more DNA would be synthesized. The DNA formed always had the same ratio of A, G, T, and C as the primer used had, showing that this had provided the template for new DNA.

Formation of Proteins.—DNA, now accepted as genetic material, is inactive in cellular metabolic processes, which are performed by proteins. Most proteins serve as enzymes and catalysts. To translate instructions carried within DNA into protein structure, DNA within the chromosomes gives its message to an RNA form present in the nucleus; RNA acts as messenger and transmits the message to the site of protein synthesis within the cytoplasm. This site is another form of RNA found in many particles (*ribosomes*) in the cytoplasm. On the ribosome, an RNA template is formed according to the messenger RNA's code. Proteins are long chains of amino acids hooked together linearly by *peptide bonds*. The chains are *polypeptides*. Twenty amino acids occur in proteins; the smallest protein (*ribonuclease*) has a molecular weight of 13,500 and is a single chain of 124 amino acids. Many amino acids are repeated several times; not all need be present in any individual protein. Proteins have a definite shape, on which their function depends. Polypeptide chains form a helix that folds into a characteristic shape. The amino acid sequence is believed to determine the nature of this folding.

To synthesize proteins on the RNA template on the ribosome, the amino acids must be brought to their proper positions. This is done by a soluble RNA (S-RNA or transfer-RNA), of which there is a specific one for each of the twenty-odd amino acids. S-RNA picks up its own amino acid, which has been activated by its specific enzyme, and brings it to a specific site on the template that it "recognizes," presumably by some kind of complementarity.

Once each amino acid fits into place on the template, sequence is established, peptide bonds are formed, RNA is sloughed off, and protein zips off the template and takes on the shape necessary to carry out its function in the cell.

Genetic Code.—DNA carries genetic information and gives its message to one form of RNA; this message is translated into protein structure, with the help of other forms of RNA. Although less is known about RNA structure than about either DNA or protein, it is known to be similar to DNA in that it is also a polymer containing four kinds of nucleotides. These nucleotides are similar to those of DNA except that *uracil* (U) replaces thymine as a pyrimidine base, and that the five-carbon sugar is ribose instead of a deoxyribose. The other components are the same as those in DNA. DNA may transmit its information to messenger RNA through complementarity between the bases, which by their alignment in both DNA and RNA contain the key to the code. The problem is how a four-letter code consisting of nucleotides can give a dictionary that is thought to contain the twenty amino acid "words."

Nirenberg and Matthaei, and Severo Ochoa's group, made an RNA, "poly-U" (polyuridylic acid), all of whose bases are uracil (UUUU...). When poly-U was put in a test tube with ingredients needed for protein synthesis, a long chain of repeating units of only one kind of amino acid, phenylalanine, was formed. The RNA code for phenylalanine is thus an unknown number of uracil bases. The favored number is three.

Since then, RNA's have been synthesized containing all possible combinations of A, G, C, and U. These experiments and others by Crick, Brenner, and others lead to the following conclusions: (1) The code message is read in groups of three bases (triplets), although multiples of three are not completely ruled out. (2) The message is read in nonoverlapping triplets, starting from a fixed point, probably one end. (3) Most triplets are meaningful. They allow the gene to function; each triplet probably represents an amino acid. (4) Since four bases combine into groups of three, there is the possibility of 4 × 4 × 4, or 64 triplets, more than enough to code the twenty amino acids found in protein.

In experiments with synthetic RNA, more than one triplet was found to code the same amino acid. A code such as the genetic code, in which more than one word can signify the same object, is called *degenerate*. This does not imply lack of specificity in protein structure; it simply means that more than one code word can direct the same amino acid to its specific site on the forming polypeptide chain. The accompanying table lists the RNA triplets that have been shown to code each of the twenty amino acids. This table must be viewed as tentative, since experiments to clarify it are in progress.

Present evidence suggests that the genetic code is universal—all species utilize approximately the same code.

Internal Structure of the Gene.—The gene, defined by classical genetics, is the unit of function, recombination, and mutation; the chromosome is pictured as a series of beads (genes) on a string. The genetic code resides in the nucleotide sequence of a long DNA molecule; mutation and recombination can be detected within the borders of the genes of rapidly reproducing organisms. This changes the classical concept of the gene.

In recombination of genetic material, sexual reproduction brings about a great variety in the number of possible genotypes. Crossover results in further recombination of parts of chromosomes. Many microorganisms have alternatives to sexual reproduction that produce new combinations of genes in their progeny. Some bacteria mate, and there even is a form of gene recombination in bacteriophagic viruses.

Because great numbers of progeny can be obtained in bacterial and viral "crosses," it is possible to "dissect" the gene. The following ideas have emerged: (1) The gene locus may have more than one function. The function unit is called a *cistron,* and is perhaps a coded sequence of nucleotide pairs in a DNA molecule. This sequence carries information needed to specify the order of amino acids in a large polypeptide chain. (2) Mutation can occur in a cistron. The mutation unit may be as small as a single nucleotide pair. (3) Recombination may occur almost anywhere along the DNA molecule. The recombination unit is called a *recon.*

■**GENES AND CHROMOSOMES.**—Knowledge obtained from chemical, X-ray, and electron microscope studies of chromosomes is summarized as follows: (1) Chromosomes consist of a complex of DNA and protein, with a variable amount of RNA. (2) The nucleoprotein complex forms individual fibrous particles with a molecular weight of about 18,000,000 each, of which 8,000,000 is attributable to a single DNA molecule. (3) The chromosomes may consist of a *fibril bundle;* each fibril may have either two or four DNA double helices with associated protein or a large strand made up of 1,000 to 100,000 DNA molecules combined with proteins.

Biochemical Genetics.—Genes may control metabolic activity. In 1902 A. E. Garrod studied a human metabolic

Summary of RNA Code Words

Amino Acid	RNA Code Words*			
Alanine	CCG	UCG†	ACG†	
Arginine	CGC	AGA	UGC†	CGA†
Asparagine	ACA	AUA	ACU†	
Aspartic acid	GUA	GCA†	GAA†	
Cysteine	UUG			
Glutamic acid	GAA	GAU†	GAC†	
Glutamine	AAC	AGA	AGU†	
Glycine	UGG	AGG	CGG	
Histidine	ACC	ACU†		
Isoleucine	UAU	UAA		
Leucine	UUG	UUC	UCC	UUA
Lysine	AAA	AAU		
Methionine	UGA			
Phenylalanine	UUU	CUU		
Proline	CCC	CCU	CCA	CCG†
Serine	UCU	UCC	UCG†	ACG
Threonine	CAC	CAA		
Tryptophan	GGU			
Tyrosine	AUU			
Valine	UGU	UGA†		

* Arbitrary nucleotide sequence.
† Probable.

disease, alcaptonuria, a hereditary defect caused by a block in the normal series of metabolic reactions of the amino acid tyrosine. He called alcaptonuria and similar conditions "inborn errors of metabolism." This was the first example of recessive inheritance recognized in man, and since then other inborn metabolic diseases have been found. Each is controlled by one mutant gene locus.

Human beings are not usually subject to experimental manipulation and breeding. However, George W. Beadle and Edward L. Tatum found that by studying biochemical mutants in a mold, they could determine how genes act in producing such diseases and in normal metabolism. They formulated a hypothesis called the "one gene–one enzyme hypothesis." To paraphrase in terms of DNA: The DNA of each gene carries the information to specify the formation of a single protein—in most cases an enzyme that controls a specific chemical reaction in the organism. Today, based on very recent work, the hypothesis is modified to state that one gene specifies one polypeptide.

Beadle and Tatum chose an organism in which it was possible to prove unequivocally that single genes affect single enzymes—which govern single biochemical reactions. They looked for and found an organism simple enough to show the direct relationship between a gene and its product. The organism was *Neurospora*.

Neurospora is a fungus that usually reproduces asexually by means of spores called *conidia*. All nuclei are haploid; hence, every gene is expressed: no allele interacts or proves dominant. *Neurospora* also undergoes sexual reproduction, which requires fusion of two haploid nuclei to produce a diploid zygote. This occurs only through the union of two strains of opposite mating types. These strains are indistinguishable morphologically, but can be shown to differ. If strains of opposite mating types are grown together, characteristic black sexual spores (*ascospores*) are formed; strains of the same mating type, if grown together, do not form such spores.

Fungi like *Neurospora* grow on a simple synthetic medium, called a *minimal medium*, containing inorganic salts, sugar, and the vitamin biotin. The ordinary wild type of *Neurospora* thrives on this, synthesizing all the organic compounds of which protoplasm is made: amino acids, nucleic acids, fats, vitamins, etc.

Beadle and Tatum irradiated conidia to produce mutations and crossed them with a strain of the opposite mating type. The sexual spores produced were then isolated and each spore grown separately on a medium supplemented with one class of ingredients, either amino acids or vitamins. The germinated spores were tested on minimal medium. If they grew, they were the wild type, still able to synthesize all necessary growth factors. If unable to grow on minimal medium, but able to grow on minimal medium supplemented with, say, amino acids, they were deficient in the ability to synthesize one or more of these acids. Conidia of the new mutant were tested separately on minimal medium supplemented with each amino acid until the one that permitted growth was found. To test that this was truly a genetic defect, each mutant strain was crossed with a wild type and the offspring were tested; a ratio of one mutant to one wild type was found. A large number of mutants were isolated. When a single supplementary compound produced normal growth, it meant that a single gene was affected by the mutagenic treatment. Thus, Beadle and Tatum demonstrated that genes have a single primary function in the process of metabolism. It is, of course, assumed that the normal, or wild type, gene performs the function that is deficient in the mutant.

Essential compounds, the amino acids and vitamins, are synthesized by each cell through a series of reactions. If by mutation each of several strains loses the ability to synthesize a particular amino acid, such as arginine, would all the strains be mutants for the same gene? Would they all be affected at the same step in the synthesis of the amino acid? Could one deduce the order of the processes from a study of mutants and their nutritional requirements?

In the case of arginine, three classes of mutants, designated as X, Y, and Z, were found to grow in media as indicated in the following table. This study suggests that a linear series of reactions results in arginine synthesis: Prior substance X → ornithine → Y → citrulline → Z → arginine. Strain Z grows only on arginine and is blocked at the step lettered Z, conversion of citrulline to arginine; thus Z is unable to grow on any of the earlier compounds in the series, but will grow if arginine, which comes after the block, is supplied.

Mutant Strain	X	Y	Z
Arginine	+	+	+
Citrulline	+	+	−
Ornithine	+	−	−
No supplement	−	−	−

+ indicates growth.
− indicates no growth.

Strain Y can grow on either citrulline or arginine, each of which comes after the block; but it will not grow on ornithine or minimal medium with no supplement. Strain X will grow on all three; it is blocked at a step preceding ornithine production, and because of this blocked step is unable to grow on unsupplemented minimal medium. Each step is blocked because an enzyme needed to catalyze that specific step is missing or defective.

Crosses involving mutants of each strain showed that each step involves mutation of one specific gene. Since there are three distinct enzymes, this is an example of the workability of the one gene–one enzyme hypothesis.

The same principle extends to all living organisms, including man. The hereditary disease *galactosemia* is caused by a single recessive gene that controls and prevents production of an enzyme essential for conversion of milk sugar, galactose, into glucose, the sugar that the body can use. A child homozygous for the galactosemia gene develops cataracts, mental retardation, and other defects because of abnormal accumulation of galactose in the body. By eliminating milk from the diet of children with galactosemia, the disease is controlled.

There is a test for the presence of the enzyme needed to convert galactose to glucose in red blood cells, and thus glactosemic infants can be identified before damage is extensive. A homozygote has virtually no enzyme, a normal person has a high level of enzyme, and a heterozygote usually has a level about halfway between. This intermediate level appears to be sufficient for normal function. If galactosemia runs in the family, parents and newborn infants can be tested.

There are many examples of inherited metabolic diseases that show that in man, as in microorganisms, genes control biochemical reactions.

■ GENES AND PROTEIN STRUCTURE.—The best evidence for the precise effect of mutation on protein structure comes from a study of the abnormal hemoglobins produced in certain inherited anemias of man, particularly of sickle cell anemia. In *sickle cell anemia*, the red blood cells form a sickle-shaped structure when oxygen concentration is low. The disease is serious, usually fatal in childhood. There is also a mild form of abnormality called *sickle cell trait*.

Both sickle cell trait and sickle cell anemia tend to occur in certain families originating in Central Africa, the central Mediterranean area, the Persian Gulf, and India. Since it is an inherited disease, those with sickle cell anemia are homozygous for a partially dominant gene, *S*. They are designated *SS*. People with sickle cell trait are heterozygotes, *AS*, with *A* the normal gene. Only if both parents are heterozygotes would a child have the disease. The cross would be as follows:

AS × AS

SS	AS	AA
anemia	trait	normal

Pauling and co-workers reported in 1949 that sickle cell anemia is a "molecular disease," since the large hemoglobin molecule of victims is different from that of normal people. More recent work by Ingram has defined the exact nature of the change. Hemoglobin, a globular protein with the molecular weight 66,200, consists of four polypeptide chains, two of one type (*alpha chains*) and two of another (*beta chains*). Each consists of about 140 amino acids.

Ingram broke the hemoglobin molecule into small fragments and analyzed each fragment for its amino acid sequence. The two alpha chains of normal hemoglobin A fragments were identical with those of hemoglobin S. One fragment from the beta chain showed a difference. This difference resided in only one amino acid in the fragment concerned.

Hemoglobin A	Hemoglobin S
Val	Val
His	His
Leu	Leu
Thr	Thr
Pro	Pro
GLU	VAL
Glu	Glu
Lys	Lys

The only difference is the substitution of valine for glutamic acid. This single amino acid substitution also changes other hemoglobin properties, making the red blood cells abnormal.

Mutation, then, can result in an altered protein, as in the hemoglobin, or in no recognizable product at all, as in galactosemia and other diseases caused by metabolic blocks. It is possible that in cases where no enzyme activity is found, an altered, nonfunctioning protein is produced that is undetectable by means available today.

Cytogenetics.—Information can be obtained about the hereditability of traits from the analysis of pedigrees.

Twin studies have been useful in determining the relationship between heredity and environment. There are fraternal twins and identical twins. Fraternal twins result from separate fertilization of two different eggs produced by the mother at the same time. Each zygote develops separately and is no more like the other than any two siblings (brothers and/or sisters). They can be of the same or opposite sex, depending on the sperm that fertilized each egg. Identical twins come from one fertilized egg that divides and separates into two parts at some stage in development. Since both children come from one egg, they have identical genes and must, of course, be of the same sex. Any difference between them is due to environmental influences. Studies of identical twins raised apart have been useful in assessing the relative roles of hereditary and environmental influences. Certain traits—blood groups, fingerprints, eye color—are inherited and not noticeably influenced by environment. Body build, height, weight, and I.Q. are examples of traits that have a very large hereditary component, but are also much influenced by environmental factors.

This fits with the concept of the norm, or range of reaction. Genotypes of living things react with the environment in which they develop. There is a range of potentiality as to what the final phenotypes might be, depending on the interactions. A child potentially tall because of his genotype might be stunted in growth by poor food, disease, etc. But a child whose genotype limits his height to 5½ feet could never be six feet tall, regardless of all the food, vitamins, and good health that might be provided for him.

Another aspect of human genetics has developed because of new cytological techniques for study of human chromosomes. *Cytogenetics* is the study of the role played by cell components, particularly chromosomes, in heredity. Certain congenital abnormalities are associated with abnormal numbers of chromosomes. The normal number of chromosomes is 46. Mongolism, an abnormality accompanied by mental retardation, is associated with 47 chromosomes, the extra chromosome being one of the smallest autosomes.

■**GENES AND DEVELOPMENT.**—A challenging genetic problem is the gene's role in the development of the embryo. Each cell in an embryo has the same chromosomal complement because it is derived from the original zygote by mitosis. Yet some cells become spindle-shaped muscle cells whose major protein is myosin; some, red blood cells whose major protein is hemoglobin; some, glandular cells that secrete digestive enzymes. Each cell type has the same genes, but is different from other cell types. Genes control formation of proteins found in each cell; but some genes are active in muscle cells and inactive in liver cells, and vice versa. Differentiation involves a continual interaction between the nucleus and the cytoplasm, with substances in the cytoplasm acting on the genes in the nucleus to repress or stimulate certain activities. The nature of this interaction is of interest.

There are two approaches to the study of how gene action is regulated. One may trace the development of an inherited defect back to the earliest stage of the embryo. There is a mutation in chickens known as the *creeper fowl*, which when homozygous (*CpCp*) usually kills the chick in the egg after three days of incubation. The mutant lags behind the normal in growth at as early as 1½ days, and the limb rudiments fail to grow, although in normal chicks they grow rapidly at this time.

Transplantation and tissue culture studies have revealed that most tissue taken from day-old embryos will grow normally for many days. Had they developed within a creeper embryo, they would have died with it. Mutant chick cells can also live normally if the environment supplies something that could be missing in their usual environment.

Heart tissue from early creeper chicks is an exception. It will not grow normally in tissue culture, regardless of what is supplied. Thus, the gene *Cp* in some way produces a substance that affects the development of one embryonic organ, the heart. This leads to a defective circulatory system that cannot distribute food and oxygen to normal cells of the developing chick. Limb buds, which normally grow rapidly at 1½ days, are most in need of food and oxygen and are affected. The defect spreads and the chick dies.

A partial verification of this hypothesis comes from the following experiments. Limb buds from normal embryos grown in tissue culture with too few nutrients show many characteristics of creeper limb rudiments. Also, if certain chemicals that suppress normal metabolism are added to nutritive tissue culture media in which early limb rudiments are growing, development is suppressed in a manner that mimics the creeper phenotype.

Another approach is to start with the genes themselves in a less complex system, usually a microorganism, to determine how gene action is regulated. The method of regulation discovered may provide a model for gene regulation in differentiation. Jacob and Monod in Paris studied the bacillus *Escherichia coli* and its ability to metabolize the sugar lactose. They found two kinds of genes: —those that specify, via messenger RNA, the protein's structure and those that regulate the time and rate of activity of the structural genes. A regulator gene produces a repressor which enters the cytoplasm and inhibits the structural gene. When there are specific molecules present in the cell that combine with the repressor and thus inactivates it, the enzyme may be made. One such specific molecule would be the material on which the enzyme acts, called its *substrate*. This control prevents the cell's energy and amino acids from being wasted by producing unnecessary protein, and thus would have a selective advantage.

The particular system the French scientists studied in *E. coli* consists of four genes, three of which are closely linked to form a so-called *operon*, while the fourth is an unlinked regulator gene. The operon has two structural genes, one which controls the synthesis of an enzyme, called a *permease*, which permits the sugar to enter the cell. The second gene controls the synthesis of another enzyme, *beta-galactosidase*, which changes the lactose to simpler sugars. The third, an operator gene, does not control the enzyme structure; it coordinates the activity of the structural genes as follows: The unlinked regulator gene constantly produces a repressor substance (possibly an RNA) that keeps the operator inert. As soon as lactose is present in the cellular environment, the repressor combines with some of it and is no longer able to inhibit the operator gene. This gene starts a chain reaction along the operon, diagramed below; and the two structural genes produce their enzymes, permitting more lactose to enter the cell and to be metabolized to simpler sugars.

operator gene	*beta-galactosidase gene*	*permease gene*
—o———	—o———	—o—

This is an example of coordination of gene action and interaction between genes and substances within the cytoplasm, as well as control of the movement of substances through the cell membrane from the extracellular environment, all influencing one another. Such actions and interactions must take place in a regular sequence of time and space to produce each stage of the embryo until the fully developed organism is formed.

■**CYTOPLASMIC INHERITANCE.**—The primary mechanism of heredity is the self-duplicating gene of the chromosome. There are also cases of hereditary factors carried within the cytoplasm. Self-duplicating cytoplasmic factors are detected by a test in sexually reproducing organisms. Both egg and sperm contribute equal amounts of nuclear material to the zygote. The egg contributes the cytoplasm as well as the other haploid nucleus. If chromosomal genes are involved, no difference will be observed in offspring from reciprocal crosses. However, if a cytoplasmic factor is involved, it will be inherited through the cytoplasmic donor, the egg. As a result, there will be a difference between offspring from reciprocal crosses. The clearest examples are in plants and involve *plastids*, the small self-reproducing bodies that carry chlorophyll. This type of inheritance accounts for many of the green-and-white spotted leaves on ornamental plants.

Other small bodies in the cytoplasm, including the *centrosomes*, *mitochondria*, viruses, and virus-like bodies, are thought to be self-duplicating. In addition to green plants, maternal inheritance has been found in mice, *Drosophila*, *Paramecium*, some other one-celled animals, and molds, like *Neurospora* and yeast.

Genes and Evolution.—The theory of natural selection (developed by Charles Darwin) as the mechanism of organic evolution has been the integrating force common to all biology. It is of interest to observe how the mechanism has been applied to large populations. Consider, for example, the blood groups. The most common in the American white population is group O at 45 per cent; next is group A at 38.5 per cent; group B is 13 per cent; and AB is 3.5 per cent. Blood groups are inherited in a Mendelian fashion. One might question how mutations caused by radiation or chemicals would affect the frequency of the blood group genes, or whether the same frequency occurs in different geographic locations, or whether the frequency is changing with time. These questions belong to the realm of population genetics. Since organic evolution involves the changes in gene frequencies in populations in time and place, this branch of genetics strives to explain the mechanism of evolution.

The principle of population genetics was developed independently in 1908 by the Englishman Hardy and the German Weinberg, and hence is known as the Hardy-Weinberg law. It states that relative gene frequencies remain constant from generation to generation in an infinitely large interbreeding population in which mating is at random, and in which there is no selection, migration, or mutation.

How, then, could evolution, which involves change in the genetic composition of populations take place? Obviously, both mutation and selection do occur, as well as some migration and isolation of small populations. These are the factors that influence evolution.

Let us consider mutation first. Mutations occur spontaneously, for unknown reasons, at predictable but

LEAFLIKE Kallima butterfly of India survives because of its natural camouflage.

low rates. Most mutations are harmful, because the genes already present in the populations have been the most successful survivors over millions of years that life has existed. Dominant lethal mutations are eliminated from the reservoir of genes in the population because the individuals in whom they occur die early in life. An occasional mutation is beneficial because it confers on the recipient a better chance to survive and pass the gene on to offspring. Such a gene is said to have a selective advantage.

Darwin observed that in most species of plants and animals the offspring produced are more numerous than their parents, yet most populations remain relatively stable in size. Also, many variations exist in nature, and most of these are inherited. As a result of the great numbers of offspring, competition exists; those best fitted by virtue of their variations will survive and pass on these variations to the next generation.

Beneficial genes remain in the gene pool, and dominant lethals are driven out. Unless they are disadvantageous to the heterozygote in the competition for food and mate, lethal recessive genes will be passed on, and not eliminated from the gene pool. If they are a disadvantage to the heterozygote, they will be eliminated very slowly over many generations. Many recessive harmful genes persist in populations because they are beneficial to the heterozygote. Sickle cell anemia is an example. The homozygote *SS* dies early, and the heterozygote *AS* has both normal and sickle cell hemoglobin. The trait is common in central Africa where a severe form of malaria exists. People with normal hemoglobin *AA* readily succumb to the disease, whereas heterozygotes *AS* are relatively resistant to this disease and have as much as a 25 per cent better chance of attaining adulthood than do the normal homozygotes.

Thus, a gene is maintained in the population even though individuals homozygous for it die before reaching productive age. This is a case of *balanced polymorphism*, which maintains alternative genotypes in a population by a balance between forces selecting for and against the gene. It is closely related to *heterosis*, or hybrid vigor, exemplified in hybrid corn in which a combination of genes makes it better than any homozygous line.

Although evolution is usually too slow a process for a person to observe in a lifetime, there are some examples of evolutionary change that have been observed recently. One is the development of DDT-resistant strains of insects. No doubt there were always some insects that could have survived DDT, but this was not a selective advantage in a DDT-free world. Once the chemical came into wide use, they were the ones who survived and reproduced, while the DDT-sensitive insects died. Thus, a change in environment (use of DDT) brought about a change in the characteristics of the insect world.

An important question to the population geneticist is: What is the genetic basis of the origin of species? He defines a single species as one in which members can crossbreed and produce fertile hybrids. New species arise through isolation of one group from another. Within each region of different environment, the population over many generations will become unique because of the selection of traits adaptively advantageous in that particular area. After a long time, the individual groups will have diverged to the extent that they no longer can interbreed. They are then separate species, and will remain separate even if they should occupy the same environment. This has happened many times in the course of evolution.

Progress in Genetics.—The significant advances made in the study of genetics are reflected by the number of Nobel Prize awards received by geneticists in recent years. Thomas Hunt Morgan received the award in 1934; Hermann Joseph Muller in 1946; George Wells Beadle, Edward Lawrie Tatum, and Joshua Lederberg in 1958; Arthur Kornberg and Severo Ochoa in 1959; Francis Harry Compton Crick, James Watson, and Maurice Hugh Frederick Wilkins in 1962; Francois Jacob, Andre Lwoff, and Jacques Monod in 1965.

—Selma Silagi

BIBLIOGRAPHY

CARSON, HAMPTON LAWRENCE. *Heredity and Human Life*. Columbia University Press, 1963.
DARWIN, CHARLES. *Evolution of Life*. The University of Chicago Press, 1960.
DOBZHANSKY, THEODOSIUS. *Genetics and the Origin of Species*. Columbia University Press, 1951.
ERLICH, PAUL R. *The Process of Evolution*. McGraw-Hill, Inc., 1963.
SAGER, RUTH and RYAN, FRANCIS JOSEPH. *Cell Heredity*. John Wiley & Sons, Inc., 1961.

BIOLOGICAL RELATIONSHIPS

Understanding Living Organisms.—In a world increasingly oriented toward technology it is sometimes difficult to remember our relationships to the earth and to other living things on it. Although it has become easy to make the false assumption that man is now independent of the old biological world, today we are almost as dependent upon our biological environment as our ancestors were thousands of years ago. We still require the same quantities of oxygen, water, and minerals from the soil that they did. We must still obtain the same quantity of energy from our food. The things that we eat must, as in the past, acquire this energy from sunlight and must still grow from the soil. We have not changed our tolerance to heat or cold, drought or humidity, radiation or pressure. Our advances have not come from any increased ability to adapt to a broader environment, but from learning how to maintain a suitable environment around us. Further technical advancement and survival in a world with an expanding population depend upon an understanding of ourselves as biological organisms and of our relationships with other organisms in the physical world.

In nature no living thing exists by itself. Each is part of an intricate structure composed of other living organisms and of the physical environment that encompasses them.

■ ECOLOGY.—The study of organisms in relation to each other and to their environment is known as *ecology*. One of the younger fields of biology, ecology has rapidly gained in importance; most of its developments have come since 1900 and more particularly since the 1940's. Ecology has been subdivided into two areas: *autecology*, concerned with the relation of the individual plant or animal to its environment; and *synecology*, concerned with the relation of populations of individuals to other groups and to their total environment.

Ecology has also been divided into the two fields of plant ecology and animal ecology, but one does not have to go very deeply into either field to realize that this separation is artificial. In studying the ecology of plants, an involvement with animals is inevitable. The study of animal ecology almost immediately entails the study of vegetation. There is fundamentally just one ecology, and it is concerned with the study of ecological systems, *ecosystems*, and the plants or animals of which these systems are composed.

Population, Community, Ecosystem.—Fundamental to the study of ecology are three different concepts: population, community, and ecosystem. A *population* is the total of all the individuals of a given species occupying a particular area. Each individual is necessarily part of a population; everything about it is affected by its place or status in the population; and even as an outcast it exists in relationship to the whole population.

But a population does not exist alone. Each occurs as part of a *biotic community*, a community of living creatures. Any species forms only a part of the community, for it is dependent upon other species for food or shelter, or in turn provides food or shelter for another species. Similarly, the biotic community is not an isolated entity, but bears relationships to other communities and to its physical environment. It cannot exist without the soil or rock, water, atmosphere, and sunlight. Thus each biotic community forms, in combination with its physical environment, an ecosystem.

■ POPULATION.—Although defined as the sum of individuals, a population is something more than the total of its parts and contains qualities not possessed by any individual member. Important properties of a population that are of interest to both ecologist and census-taker are the number of individuals and their relationship to the area occupied. Knowledge of these characteristics permits the calculation of *density*, which is the number of individuals per unit of area. Also important is the *structure* of the population. This refers to the sex and age composition of the whole: the number of males in relation to females and the age distribution of each sex. Finally, the student of population is interested in population *dynamics*, changes over a period of time and the forces that influence these changes. These are brought about by birth rates, or *natality;* death rates, or *mortality;* and *movements* of individuals into or out of the population.

In order to understand these movements, the factors influencing birth and death rates, and the determinants of population density, the student of animal population may investigate questions similar to those regarding the economic and social status of human populations. In a study of the Norway rat, investigators found that rat populations were essentially self-limiting. Even with abundant food and shelter their numbers were restricted by social factors, particularly an aversion to crowding. Other animals sometimes show no such aversion and, if their numbers are not checked by outside forces, eat themselves out of house and home.

Biotic Potential.—Populations that are not self-limiting are eventually checked in their growth by the pressures of environment. Each species is capable, if unchecked by mortality, of a high rate of increase, known as its *biotic potential*. Small animals with rapid breeding rates have a higher biotic potential than do large animals. But even the largest and slowest breeders could, if entirely unchecked, overrun the earth. Mankind, with a low biotic potential, currently shows signs of doing just that. But no population is long immune to mortality. Inevitably factors in the environment will cause losses or inhibit the birth rate. Predators kill other animals; diseases and parasites decimate species; weather causes loss or checks gains from natality. If all other factors fail, the lack of food, water, or some other essential will limit population growth. The total of all agents in an environment that cause loss or arrest population growth is known as the *environmental resistance*.

A *stable population* is one in which the biotic potential and the environmental resistance are in balance. Interference with such a population can affect this stability and cause severe fluctuations. Some populations normally fluctuate in a regular and predictable manner. These are known as *cyclic populations*. The snowshoe hare and Canada lynx, for example, regularly reach a population peak at nine- to ten-year intervals. This is followed by a marked decline. Other populations are normally stable, but occasionally show a striking increase to "plague" proportions, followed by a major decrease. Such population changes are called *irruptions*. However, most populations are relatively stable. This indicates the presence of constant environmental resistance.

■ COMMUNITY.—Studies of any population soon lead to questions about the total community of which the population is a part. The community of the ecologist differs from the community of the sociologist in that the biotic community is always composed of more than one species: for example, populations of plants and of the animals that feed upon those plants. Communities vary in complexity. A simple community would be that of hardy lichens growing on an exposed rock surface along with the few associated organisms, mostly small to microscopic, that can find food and shelter among the lichens. The lichen itself is an example of the close ecological relationship between species. It is not a simple plant, but consists of two different kinds of plants living in close association and depending upon one another: a green alga that manufactures food from sunlight, water, and atmospheric gases; and a colorless fungus that shelters and anchors the algae and in turn receives food from the algal cells. Such a close association and mutual dependence between species is an example of a relationship known as *symbiosis* or *mutualism*.

At the other extreme of complexity from the simple lichen community is the tropical rain forest. Here the growing conditions are so nearly ideal for plants that hundreds of different species of trees sometimes occur within a small area. Associated with the trees are an even greater variety of other plants, including *epiphytes* (plants such as the orchids that grow high on tree trunks) and giant vines, or *lianas,* that also depend upon the trees for their support. Finding food and shelter in this mass of vegetation are a greater variety of birds, insects,

152 Biological Relationships

SIMPLIFIED ECOSYSTEM with its five basic components: an energy source (the sun), consumer organisms (animals designated *A*, *B*, *C*, and *D*), producer organisms (plants *E*, *F*, and *G*), reducer organisms (remains *H* and *I*), and abiotic, or nonliving, chemicals (*J*, *K*, and *L*). Reducer organisms return these abiotic chemicals to the soil or the sea.

and other forms of animal life than one can find in any comparable area.

Biotic communities do not spring suddenly into existence, but instead develop through a long process known as *biotic succession*. Succession, in its primary form, occurs in areas that have not previously supported life: bare rocks or newly formed lakes or ponds. The first invaders of such areas are always the more hardy plants and animals. They change the environment so that it can be occupied in turn by more demanding species. A predictable series of changes which lead to greater complexity usually occurs. The soil is further developed and becomes able to support a greater variety of life. Eventually a relatively stable community, in balance with the prevailing climate and adjusted to a mature soil, occupies the area until some disturbance destroys it. When this occurs, the process of succession begins again. This secondary succession may have fewer stages than a primary succession and usually resembles a primary succession's later stages. The relatively stable community resulting from a succession is known as a *climax community*.

■ECOSYSTEM.—No biotic community exists apart from its physical environment. Each depends upon sunlight to provide energy, soil minerals, water, and atmospheric gases. Each is influenced by all the physical and chemical forces that characterize the area in which it is found. Since the interrelationship between the living portion of a community and the non-living (*abiotic*) environment is so intricate that the two are virtually inseparable, it is necessary to consider them together as an ecological system. The ecosystem therefore becomes the fundamental unit of study for the ecologist. Ecosystems, like the communities that comprise them, can be simple or complex. However, even the most simple artificial system, set up in a laboratory test tube, often reveals complexities that require detailed study. Natural ecosystems may seem to defy any complete analysis or understanding.

Any ecosystem has five basic components: (1) *Energy*, usually derived from sunlight, but rarely and in small quantities from other sources. This moves through the ecosystem along pathways known as food chains, which are described below. (2) *Abiotic chemicals,* including soil minerals, water, and atmospheric gases. (3) *Producer organisms,* usually green plants capable of capturing sunlight energy through the process of photosynthesis. They utilize the energy to construct the organic chemical compounds which form the plant body, or they store it in energy bonds and link the various atoms or molecules in these organic compounds. (4) *Consumer organisms,* such as some colorless, nongreen plants, and all animals in the community. Consumers do not obtain their energy directly, but acquire it secondhand from the sunlight energy originally stored in green plants. All animals are completely dependent upon the producers for energy and for the chemicals that they require for nutrition. Consumers are subdivided into two categories: *primary consumers,* or *herbivores,* that feed directly upon plants; and *secondary consumers,* or *carnivores,* that feed mainly on other animals and thus receive their energy or food chemicals after they have been processed through two other kinds of organisms. (5) *Reducer organisms,* mainly bacteria and fungi that decay and decompose the bodies of dead plants and animals. These organisms feed upon the plants' complex chemical compounds and in turn release simpler compounds. Through this process mineral materials that can be picked up and used once more by the roots of growing plants are eventually returned to the soil or water. Without such organisms an entire community would stagnate, choked by its own debris, and the fertility of the soil would be drained without being restored.

Concept of Niche.—Each of the many species within an ecosystem occupies a particular place in the environment. This place is known as the *ecologic niche* for the species and is not inhabited by any other group. In a broad sense the niche for a herbivore includes suitable green plants on which it can feed, and is influenced by the presence of secondary consumers that will in turn feed upon the herbivore. A herbivore such as the deer requires certain shrubs and herbs which are of a suitable height and contain essential nutritional elements in a palatable form. Drinking water should not be too far from the food supply, and both should be accessible. Shelter is also necessary so that the deer can escape from extreme heat or cold, avoid storms, and evade enemies. Salt licks to provide minerals lacking in food may also be essential. The presence and availability of these elements usually guarantee the deer's occupation of a place in the biotic community.

In turn, the deer's existence, along with other factors, will help create a niche for such other species as the mountain lion which feeds on the deer and the various parasites that depend upon the deer for food and shelter. Deer may also influence the vegetation and prevent the establishment of certain plants on which they feed too heavily, or alter the form or abundance of other plants.

Similar kinds of vegetation usually provide similar niches for animals. A tropical rain forest may harbor a leopard in Africa, a panther in Southeast Asia, and a jaguar in South America, each species occupying a similar niche. Grasslands everywhere provide niches for large, grazing herbivores. But the species of herbivore occupying the niche may vary from one continent to another.

Energy Flow.—The ancients worshipped the sun-god as the giver of life. Today's ecologists could have provided them with a much more complete justification for their religion than their high priest could have imagined. Until recently, all of the energy upon which life depended, and all of the power which made human civilization possible, came directly or indirectly from sunlight. With the discovery of atomic energy and the technology permitting its utilization, man has for the first time established a small degree of independence from solar energy. Complete independence, however, probably cannot be attained. The calories that sustain our work and maintain our bodies were originally sunlight calories. Heat given off by petroleum and coal runs our machinery. This heat was once trapped from solar energy by plants in the swamp forests and ocean waters. The water spinning the turbines in the hydroelectric dams was lifted from the oceans and transported to the streams by solar energy.

■ PHOTOSYNTHESIS.—In ecosystems the source of energy is sunlight, and only green plants are equipped to utilize it. A few kinds of plants, the iron and sulfur bacteria, can exist without sunlight because they use energy stored in iron or sulfur compounds. But they do not contribute significant amounts of energy or chemicals to the earth's ecosystems. The mechanisms by which green plants use solar energy, known as *photosynthesis,* are extremely complex, and plant physiologists and biochemists have been unable as yet to work out all of the details. Suffice to say that the presence of a complex green compound, *chlorophyll,* permits the capturing of particles of sunlight energy and their storage in chemical bonds in the various parts of the plant. The simple sugar *glucose* is one of the first of these storage compounds. Through further use of sunlight energy, molecules of glucose are broken down and linked with other chemicals. This results in the formation of the various carbohydrates, proteins, vitamins, and other substances that constitute the body of a plant.

During photosynthesis two chemical compounds, carbon dioxide from the air and water from the soil, are combined into simple sugars. In the process, oxygen is released back into the atmosphere. The presence of this gas in the earth's atmosphere is believed to be a contribution from the past generations of plants. Without green plants or some other means of restoring atmospheric oxygen, the continued respiration by animals would eventually exhaust the supply of oxygen on which we all depend.

■ LOSS OF ENERGY.—Green plants are the only organisms capable of storing large amounts of solar energy. Man has learned various ways of making direct use of this energy, but he has not yet devised effective ways of storing it in quantity. However, photosynthesis is not an efficient process. It has been calculated that only about 1 per cent of the total solar energy reaching the earth is actually fixed and stored by plants. The rest is lost, either because it is in wavelengths of light that plants cannot use; because it is reflected from the surface of plants or from bare soil, rock, or water; or because it is dissipated in the form of heat. Nevertheless, the total quantity of solar energy reaching the earth is so large that the 1 per cent remaining is more than adequate to maintain terrestrial life.

Inefficiency is also apparent in the step from plants to herbivorous animals. The energy stored within plant bodies cannot be transferred to animal tissues without loss. Some remains in the indigestible residue of plants; some is lost as heat generated in the process of digestion; and other fractions are lost during various metabolic processes in the animal's body. About 20 per cent of the energy is deposited in the body tissues of herbivores. A diminished amount of energy is thus available to the animals which feed on them. Further energy is lost in eating, digesting, and metabolizing the energy stored in a herbivore's body. Of the total herbivore supply of energy (which could be determined by burning tissues in a calorimeter), only a quarter or less will end up as energy stored in the body of a carnivore and available, therefore, to any creature that feeds upon carnivores.

It is obvious that this process cannot go on for long because one cannot have an unending chain of organisms feeding upon one another. Energy follows a one-way path through the ecosystem, with the initial supply rapidly dwindling as it passes from one organism to the next. In order for the system to function, energy must be supplied continually at the green end of the chain.

Energy relationships within an ecosystem illustrate the operation of the *second law of thermodynamics.* This law states that in any transfer of energy some energy is lost to the system and dispersed in a degraded form no longer capable of doing work. The various levels through which energy is transferred in a community are known as *trophic levels.* Producers, primary and secondary consumers, and reducers represent trophic levels. Food chains are the pathways over which energy is transferred from one organism to another.

Food Chains.—A simple predator food chain can be represented by the grass-steer-man linkage, where grass, steer, and man typify separate trophic levels and links. It is possible to have a longer food chain of this type. In a pond, for example, microscopic green algae are fed upon by small, floating animals (*zooplankton*). These in turn are fed upon by aquatic insects that provide food for small carnivorous fish. These small fish may in turn support a population of such large fish as bass or pike. Because of the energy relationships involved, it is rare to have more than five or six links in such a chain. In addition to predator food chains, other food chains go from large animals down through small. There are also food chains composed of reducer organisms which are involved in the breakdown of dead plant or animal tissues. Food chains are difficult to isolate in natural ecosystems because they are usually intertwined into complex

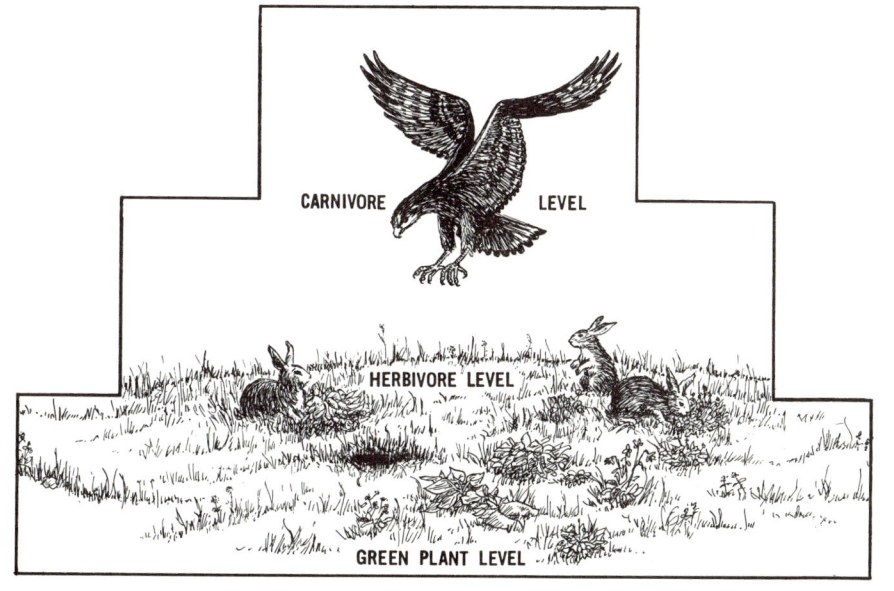

BIOTIC PYRAMID, which is based upon the diminishing quantities at each stage of the food chain, is illustrated by the large number of growths at the green-plant level, the three rabbits at the herbivore level, and the solitary eagle at the carnivore level.

food webs. Besides feeding a steer, a green plant furnishes food for a variety of small animals (including insects and microorganisms) which are then eaten by other species. Hence it is difficult to unravel the chains and webs in any complex community.

BIOTIC PYRAMIDS.—The necessary loss of energy between links in each food chain has a direct effect upon the number of organisms that can be supported at any trophic level. Thus the number of green plants upon which deer will feed is always greater than the number of deer that will be supported by them. The number of deer is in turn always greater than the number of mountain lions that feed upon them. These relationships can be diagramed in the form of *biotic pyramids*, which may illustrate either the number of organisms, the total weight of organisms, or the calories of energy stored in each layer of organisms. In a pyramid of numbers there will be more green plants than herbivores supported by them, and more herbivores than carnivores. Therefore the pyramid will show a broad base of plants and a narrow apex of carnivores. The picture would be similar if the relative weights were charted. It would take about 12,000 pounds of range forage to support a 1,000-pound steer for a year, and the steer could be converted into beef and support a 170-pound man.

Man, an omnivorous creature, can support himself largely upon a predominantly plant or animal diet. If he acts as a herbivore, or *vegetarian*, more food energy is available to him because energy is not lost in the transfer through another herbivore. Less food, but of higher nutritional quality, is available when man functions as a carnivore. This is not just a matter of theoretical interest. In order to feed the mass of people in an overpopulated country such as China, the waste of energy involved in feeding cereal grains to domestic animals must be eliminated. People must consume food plants directly, and dietary quality must be sacrificed to provide the calories needed to sustain life.

Chemical Cycles.—Besides aiding the flow of energy, food chains provide pathways for the chemical materials required by the body tissues of plants and animals. Some of these chemical materials enter the soil when the rocks in which they originate are decomposed. Others are washed away to ponds and eventually come to rest in the oceans. From any of these substrates—soil, fresh water, or the sea—these minerals can be taken up by green plants and introduced into food chains. Unlike energy flow, however, the flow of chemical materials is not one-way, but circular. The same atom or molecule is used again and again. Moving from plant to animal, it is returned to the soil only to be taken up once more by some other plant. It is likely that the calcium and phosphorus in the bones of a living man were once part of the bones of a now extinct animal. These same elements doubtlessly passed through countless generations of prairie plants, antelopes, buffaloes, and wolves before being taken up by a wheat plant and later ground into flour.

NITROGEN CYCLE.—One of the mineral pathways which have been thoroughly studied is the cycle through which nitrogen becomes available to living creatures. Nitrogen is essential for life because it forms an integral part of the proteins which must be present in each living cell. It is also one of the more common elements on earth and constitutes nearly 80 per cent of the atmosphere. Atmospheric nitrogen, however, is a relatively inert gas and does not combine readily with other elements. It cannot be used directly by most plants or animals, but must first be oxidized and converted to a nitrate. This conversion occurs when lightning ionizes atmospheric nitrogen and permits the gases to combine. The resultant nitrate dissolves and becomes dilute nitric acid, which enters the soil in rainwater.

Much of the soil nitrogen, however, is formed by the action of certain kinds of bacteria called *nitrogen fixers*. These live either free in the soil or in nodules found on the roots of legumes such as beans, peas, and alfalfa. Such bacteria can take nitrogen from the soil and convert it into nitrates. Plant roots then absorb these nitrates, and the plants combine them with other materials to form plant proteins. These in turn may be eaten by animals and reconverted into animal protein. From the animal they may pass back to the soil in the form of urea or other wastes. When the animal dies, its proteins are attacked by bacteria which break them down into simple nitrogen compounds such as ammonia or ammonium salts. These compounds are used by certain bacteria and oxidized once more into nitrates.

OTHER CYCLES.—Cycles similar to the nitrogen cycle have been traced for various other elements. Since the chemicals required for life are numerous, and the supply in the soil is not inexhaustible, there must be a continuous turnover of these materials if an area is to continue to grow living things and support living animals. In some complex biotic communities, such as dense, luxuriant forests, a high percentage of the chemicals derived from the soil may be within the bodies of the plants and animals. When soil nutrients are scarce, new growth depends upon the decay of dead plants and animals. Organisms such as earthworms process great amounts of plant litter through their bodies. Their actions accelerate decomposition and make available the materials necessary for new growth. Caterpillars that feed on leaves and add their excrement to the soil similarly hasten the rate of chemical turnover.

WATER CYCLE.—Water, which is essential to life, originates for the most part in the oceans. Transferred through the atmosphere, it reaches the vegetation and soil as rainwater. Not all of it becomes available to living things, however, for some accumulates on the surface of the ground and returns to the atmosphere through evaporation. Of the water which enters the earth, much moves through the soil and runs off through underground channels. In heavy downpours, or when the soil is soaked, much water may run off the surface and again be lost to the ecosystem. Some that enters the soil becomes closely bound to soil compounds and unavailable to plants. The rest is held as a soil solution which provides not only the water but also the dissolved chemicals necessary for plant life. The solution enters the plant roots and is drawn up by the leaves to be lost through their pores in the process known as *transpiration*. Therefore only some of it enters the plant cells and becomes part of their living protoplasm. From plants the water is transferred to animals, which may also obtain a supply directly from runoff held for a time in streams or pools or from underground sources

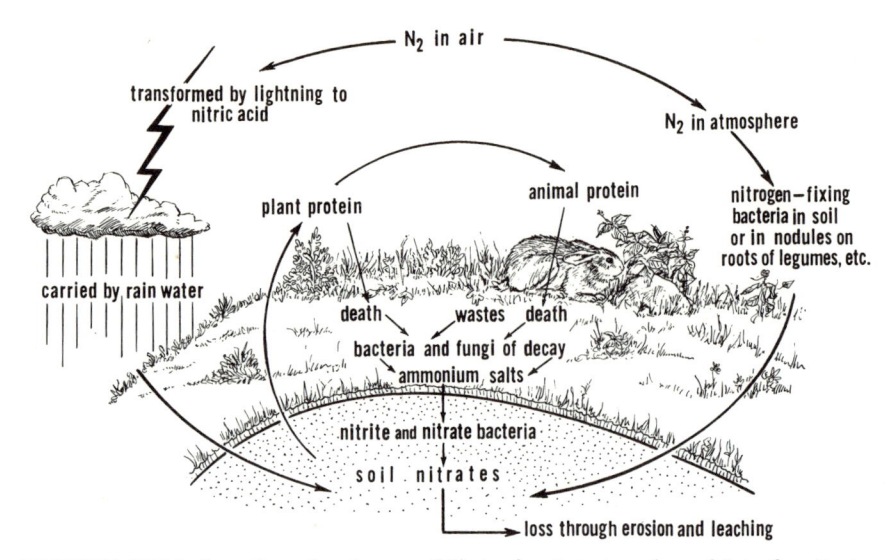

NITROGEN CYCLE shows how the nitrogen (N_2) in the air is transformed into the nitrates utilized by living organisms and then returned to the soil for further use. Nitrogen is essential to life because it is an integral part of the protein material present in living cells.

Biological Relationships

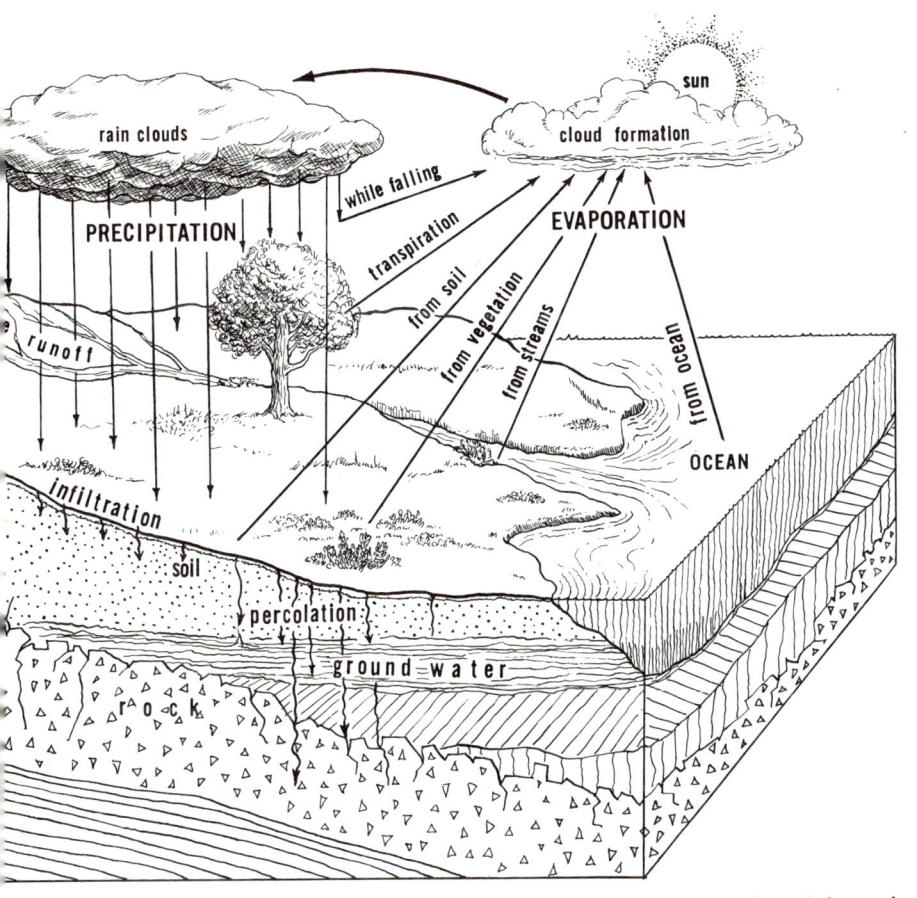

HYDROLOGIC CYCLE is composed of (1) evaporation of water from the surface of the earth to form water-vapor clouds, (2) precipitation of the water in the form of rain and snow back to the surface, and (3) infiltration and percolation of the water into the ground.

that reach the surface as springs. Eventually, however, all of the water used by plants and animals returns to the soil or is lost directly into the atmosphere. In either event it re-enters the complex cycle.

Varieties of Ecosystems.—Because their distribution is determined largely by climate and topography, the kinds of ecosystems vary greatly from one part of the world to another. Classifications of ecosystems vary according to the emphasis that ecologists place upon their distinguishing features. Perhaps the most useful broad classification of terrestrial ecosystems is the *biome* system, which recognizes certain major natural communities distributed over the world in accordance with the occurrence of the major types of climate. Climate, vegetation, and animal life are so closely related that in the past, when meteorological records were scarce, geographers mapped the boundaries of climatic regions according to the occurrence of major changes in the vegetation.

■ DISTRIBUTION OF BIOMES.—If you were to fly down the western coast of North America, starting at Point Barrow, Alaska, you would observe the sequence of biomes that extends between the Arctic and the tropics. First is an extensive region of treeless ground covered with low-growing vegetation. These arctic barren grounds are known as the *tundra*. In the vicinity of the Alaskan peninsula are the first fringes of dark spruce forest, the *taiga*. Next, across the peninsula, beyond the open spruce, are the northward reaches of the *temperate rain forest*. This is a tall, dense forest of Sitka spruce, cedar, and hemlock that continues, with some changes in species, all the way south along the coast to the San Francisco Bay region.

North of San Francisco the forest is broken; and to the south it is replaced by a lower-growing woodland of evergreen oaks or, more frequently, by the dense brush known as *chaparral*. Chaparral and woodland dominate as far south as Baja California, where they are replaced by open desert vegetation. Still farther south, on the mainland of Mexico, the desert vegetation is supplanted by dry tropical scrub and woodland. In Central America this gives way to the dense, luxuriant rain forests of the humid tropics. A continuation of the journey south along the western coast of South America would reveal a similar pattern of vegetation. However, the biomes would appear in a reverse order. Rain forest would give way to woodland and scrub, these regions to desert. In central Chile chaparral would replace the desert, and still farther south would be a dense temperate rain forest not unlike that of the Pacific Northwest. These changes in vegetation represent the major biomes of the continental west coasts of the world and the principal climatic regions of these coasts. Along the eastern coasts of continents some biomes will be different because of different climatic influences.

Ecologists classify the biomes of the regions of the world in a number of diverse ways. All of them, however, recognize the major divisions described below:

■ TUNDRA.—The tundra characterizes regions of arctic climate with long, cold winters when the sun hardly appears above the horizon, short summer growing seasons of perpetual daylight, and relatively little precipitation. The soil is underlain in most places by permanently frozen ground, the *permafrost,* because summer temperatures are too low to thaw more than the surface layers of ground. Poor drainage causes boggy ground at lower elevations. The vegetation consists of dwarf shrubs and trees, matlike, broad-leaved herbs, grasses, sedges, and, in places, extensive stands of reindeer moss or lichen. This is the home of the caribou, reindeer, and musk ox; of the ptarmigan, white fox, arctic hare, and lemming. North of it lies the barren icefield of the Arctic Ocean. Above it on the mountains are bare rock, snowfields, and glaciers. Composed of those hardy species of plant and animal that have adapted to the extremes of climate, the tundra is the farthest extension of life to the north. It covers the northern fringe of Canada and Alaska and then extends in a band across northern Europe and Asia. Tundra is found also in the higher mountains, above timberline, extending south along mountain ranges into the temperate zone.

■ BOREAL AND MONTANE FORESTS.—South of the tundra zone, or below it on the mountain ranges, is a forest dominated by needle-leaved evergreen conifers, mainly spruce and fir. This forest biome is the most extensive on the earth and covers much of Canada, Alaska, northern Europe, and Siberia. On its northern border the dark spruce trees are stunted and widely spaced where they merge with tundra. Farther south they grow in taller, denser stands and become mixed with fir, tamarack, or pine. In areas ravaged by fire the conifers are replaced by the broad-leaved birch and aspen. This biome occurs in regions of subarctic climate where winters are severe, but summer growing seasons are longer than in the tundra.

The summer heat is sufficient to prevent development of permafrost. Precipitation is higher than in the arctic region, averaging 15 to 30 inches a year. This biome is the home of the moose, snowshoe hare, northern grouse, goshawk, horned owl, red fox, and Canada lynx. Neither the tundra nor the boreal forest is found in the Southern Hemisphere, although some areas near the tip of South America are similar. This occurs because the southern continents do not have a large enough landmass close enough to the antarctic climatic regions to have the rigorous temperatures characteristic of the northern biomes. The climate of Antarctica is too extreme to support tundra.

156 Biological Relationships

■ TEMPERATE RAIN FOREST.—This forest is dominated in the Northern Hemisphere by a dense, luxuriant stand of tall conifers, usually spruce, cedar, hemlock, Douglas fir, and redwood. In the Southern Hemisphere a forest of similar appearance is dominated by the southern beech (*Nothofagus*) and such southern conifers as *Araucaria* and *Podocarpus*. For sheer volume of wood supported by each acre of land, the forests of coastal North America are unsurpassed. Some of the world's largest trees are found among the redwoods and Douglas firs of California and the Northwest. The reason for this vegetative abundance is the climate, which presents no extremes of cold or drought. Mild temperatures and high rainfall characterize the winters; the summers are cool and seldom without moisture. The growing conditions are thus second only to those of the humid tropical rain forest. The temperate rain forest supports no great mass of animal life, but provides a home for a great variety of smaller species. Characteristic of the North American region are the Roosevelt elk, mountain beaver, and black-tailed deer.

Because of the Gulf Stream influence, the climate necessary for a temperate rain forest does not occur in Europe. Neither Africa nor Australia reaches far enough south to have the necessary weather conditions. Similar climate and vegetation occur, however, on the western coast of New Zealand's South Island.

■ TEMPERATE DECIDUOUS FOREST.—In the eastern United States, western Europe, and northern China, the original vegetation was a forest of such broad-leaved trees as beech, maple, walnut, hickory, and oak. Man's influence has been felt more readily in these regions than in the others and has radically changed the environment. The climate of this biome is one of warm, wet summers and moderately cold, often snowy winters. A total rainfall of between 40 and 60 inches is adequate to support such a dense forest. Most of the trees adapt to the unfavorable winter growing conditions by shedding their leaves and becoming dormant. Unlike the conifers, which are mostly soft-wooded trees, the broad-leaved species are hardwoods and are considered among the most valued cabinet and furniture woods. In the United States this biome is the home of the white-tailed deer, wild turkey, gray squirrel, and cottontail rabbit.

■ MEDITERRANEAN FOREST AND SCRUB.—This biome exists in much of California, central Chile, the Cape of Good Hope region in South Africa, and southern Australia. It occurs most widely around the Mediterranean Sea in Europe, Asia, and Africa. The vegetation consists of broad-leaved evergreens and is called *sclerophyll* because the leaves are hard and waxy. Live oak, madroña, and laurel are most widespread in the California woodland, but over much of this biome brush (known as chaparral in California and maquis in Europe) has replaced the forest or woodland. The climate of this biome is one of warm, rainless summers and cool, moderately wet winters. Average rainfall is between 15 and 30 inches per year. In California the mule deer, gray fox, jackrabbit, and California quail are characteristic animals.

■ TROPICAL DECIDUOUS FOREST.—This is a grouping of similar biomes that includes the savanna forests, monsoon forests, thorn forests, and a variety of other tropical dry forest and scrub. They occur in tropical areas that are seasonally dry and stretch from the equatorial regions, where two wet and two dry seasons are normal, to the marginal tropics, where the summers are wet and the winters dry. Typically the trees and shrubs are leafless and the country barren during the dry season. In the wet season, however, the trees burst into bloom and leaf; and grasses and herbs cover the ground. In Africa these biomes form the big-game country and support great herds of antelope, zebra, buffalo, elephant, and other grazers and browsers, along with a variety of carnivores.

Because of fire, and to a lesser extent differences in soil, much of the area within these biomes is covered with *savanna*. This is an open interspersion of grassland with woody vegetation. Fires sweeping over these grassy regions kill the seedlings of invading shrubs or trees and keep the country open.

■ TROPICAL RAIN FOREST.—Several layers of trees of different heights characterize the luxuriant biome known

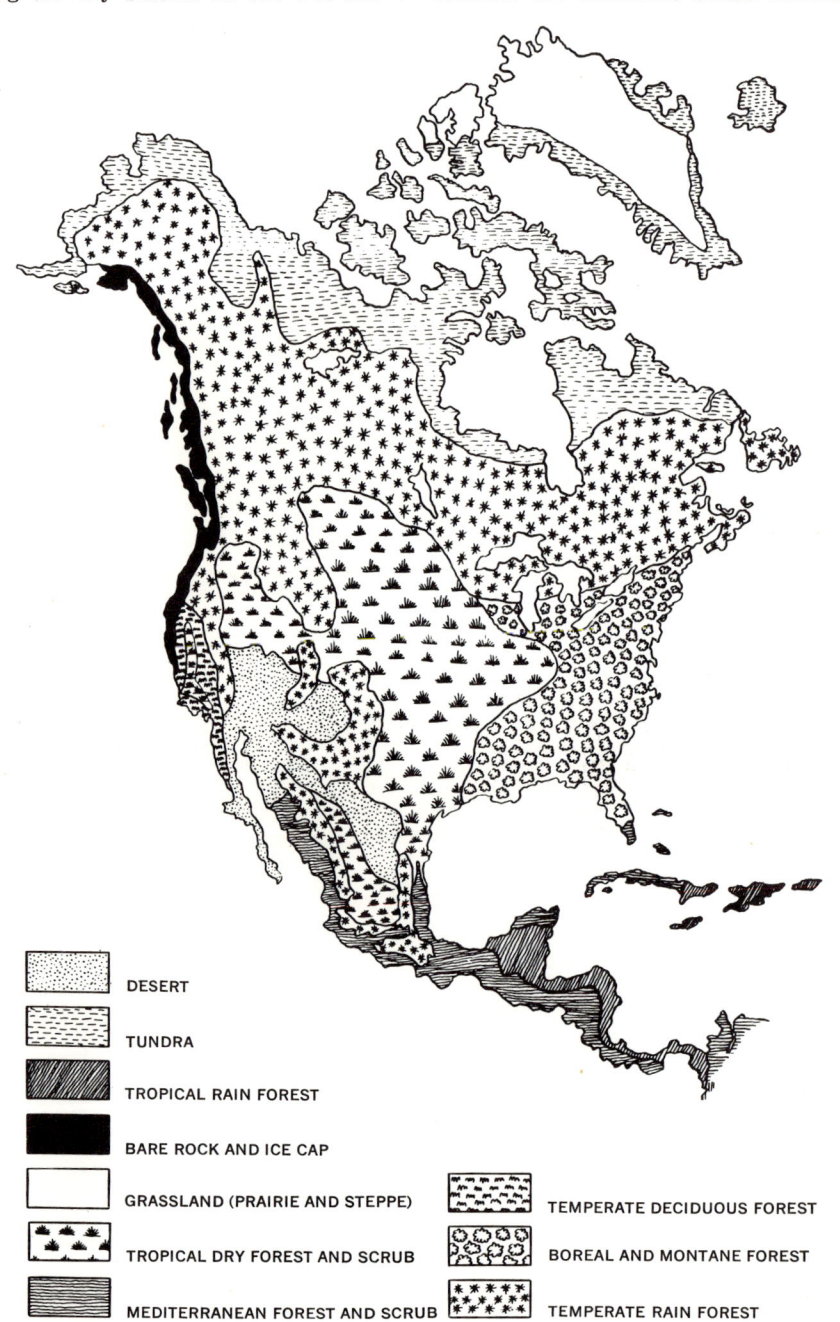

DESERT
TUNDRA
TROPICAL RAIN FOREST
BARE ROCK AND ICE CAP
GRASSLAND (PRAIRIE AND STEPPE)
TROPICAL DRY FOREST AND SCRUB
MEDITERRANEAN FOREST AND SCRUB
TEMPERATE DECIDUOUS FOREST
BOREAL AND MONTANE FOREST
TEMPERATE RAIN FOREST

BIOMES OF NORTH AMERICA

as the *tropical rain forest.* The trees are broad-leaved and evergreen, and in the mature forest the floor is relatively open. In some places one can walk on a dense mat of decomposing litter through aisles formed by the trunks of the rain forest trees. Where the mature forest has been cut or otherwise disturbed, however, a dense, almost impenetrable jungle springs up. This in turn is replaced, after many years, by another mature forest. Numerous species of trees occur within this region. However, it is unusual to find more than a few of each type in any one area. This has prevented the development of forest industries to any great extent, since the commercially valuable trees are widely scattered. Along with the great variety of plants, the rain forest supports more birds, insects, and small, tree-dwelling mammals than does any other biome.

This biome exists only in permanently warm and humid tropical areas. It is developed extensively in tropical areas with year-round rainfall; but in modified form, as gallery forest, it follows the banks of the larger permanent streams in the tropics. On tropical mountains, forests derived from the lowland rain forests occur, but these have fewer species and fewer layers of vegetation. The tropical rain forest is not as extensive as was once believed. It is found in the Amazon basin of South America and in other lowland areas of South and Central America. It occurs in the Congo basin and along the western coast of Africa, and is developed also in Southeast Asia.

■ GRASSLANDS.—*Grasslands* exist on all continents, either as extensive areas dominated exclusively by grasses and other herbaceous plants or as grassy areas interspersed among woodlands and scrub. North American grasslands once extended in an unbroken mass from Illinois to the Rocky Mountains and westward through the intermountain region to the Central Valley of California and the Palouse region of Washington. In Eurasia they stretched from Hungary to the Pacific. Formerly, huge herds of bison, antelope, and elk roamed the plains, and the North American grasslands supported the greatest mass of wild animal life on the continent.

Climatically, these areas are best developed in the zones between moist forests and arid deserts. Since this region is seasonally dry, it is subject to fires which suppress the invasion of woody vegetation. Grasslands can be divided into two general categories: the more humid prairies, dominated by tall grasses; and the dry steppes, where short grasses are the prevailing cover. Partly as a result of overgrazing, small shrubs such as the sagebrush (*Artemisia*) and saltbush (*Atriplex*) invaded widely and have changed the appearance of the dry steppes. Such areas of shrub invasion often look like deserts.

■ DESERTS.—The warm, dry areas of the earth can be considered together as the desert biome or group of biomes. In these areas rainfall is seldom in excess of 5 inches per year and is so erratic that some places often go without rain for a long time. The most barren deserts are lifeless, but when undisturbed by human influences the desert usually supports an open scrub vegetation. In the American deserts the creosote bush (*Larrea*) covers great areas in uniform, open stands. Elsewhere various cactuses or thorny leguminous shrubs are dominant. Deserts support an interesting and varied fauna including the desert fox, kangaroo rat, and desert jackrabbits in North America; and the oryx, gazelle, and jerboa in Asia and Africa. Many of these animals can live without drinking water and obtain all of their water from their food.

■ LIFE ZONES.—Biomes occupy broad continental areas corresponding to the major climatic regions. In the higher mountains, however, it is possible to find in one small area the same series of biomes that would ordinarily be

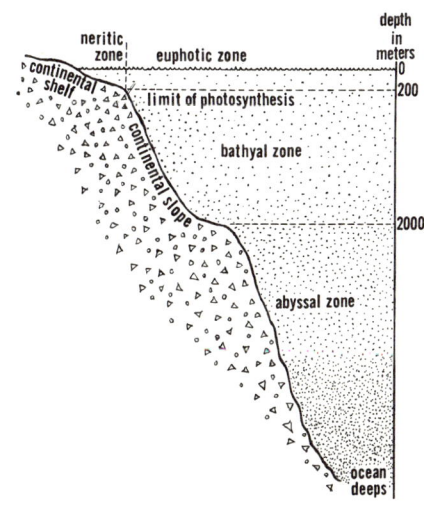

OCEAN is divided into the neritic zone, which lies above the continental shelf; the euphotic zone, in which all food is produced; and the bathyal and abyssal zones.

encountered in a journey over thousands of miles. The biomes in these mountain areas are distributed in altitudinally arranged belts known as *life zones.* In the western United States one can start at the base of a mountain range in the desert biome and pass successively through zones of grassland, Mediterranean scrub, and pine and fir forest until he finally reaches a tundralike zone above the timberline. Such life zone changes correspond to the decrease in temperature and increase in precipitation resulting from altitude changes.

Aquatic Ecosystems.—Most of the earth is covered with water, and most of the life on earth still finds its home in an aquatic environment. Life originated in the oceans and from them spread into fresh water, but relatively few of the many sea animals could adapt to the more rigorous conditions. Because the aquatic environment is much more uniform than that of dry land, it is difficult to divide it into separate biomes or easily recognizable ecosystems. Nevertheless, there are marked differences among the life of arctic, temperate, and tropical seas, and between various freshwater environments.

■ MARINE ENVIRONMENT.—Temperature and moisture are two major factors influencing the distribution of the major continental communities. In the oceans these are less important because of their tendency to be uniform and constant. On land, except beneath the canopies of dense forests, light is seldom a limiting factor. The distribution of life in the marine environment, however, is vitally determined by light. Much of the sunlight that strikes the face of the ocean is reflected back into the atmosphere. Only part of the total solar radiation penetrates the water; and of this, little reaches any great depth. To accomplish photosynthesis the green plants must live in the lighted surface layers of the water. Only here can they successfully produce the food and fix the energy that will support all other ocean life. Six hundred feet is the greatest depth at which this life-giving process can take place, and it usually occurs in more shallow water. Beyond that depth lie miles of water that are forever dark and unproductive. The lighted surface layer, termed the *euphotic zone,* produces all of the food and supports the greatest mass of marine life.

Since the organisms that live beneath the euphotic zone must depend for food upon materials that sink or are carried down from the surface, it was previously assumed that they were few in number. In recent decades, however, it has been found that this assumption is not necessarily true. Great layers of animal life have been located at depths well below the level of light penetration. Some of these layers consist of squid, which move to the surface to feed at night and submerge into the darkness during daylight. A great variety of other fish adjust to life in darkness in strange ways. In order to survive in their dark ocean homes they must feed either upon other organisms that move between the surface and the depths or upon materials that sink from above. Life can be found even in the great oceanic deeps, where animals must scavenge on the organic material that filters down through the upper layers of life. A diagram of life in the oceans, arranged according to mass, would be an inverted pyramid, with a broad base of living material near the surface and a narrow apex in the deeps.

The euphotic zone is not the only major life zone in the ocean. In the open ocean the zone below the euphotic, extending down to about 6,500 feet, is called the *bathyal region.* Still deeper lies the *abyssal region.* The principal way of life for plants and animals in the open ocean is termed *pelagic.* This is a free-swimming or free-floating existence, independent of contact with land. Of the pelagic types of life, those that have limited or no swimming ability are termed *plankton.* Their movements are dependent to a large degree upon the ocean currents, as opposed to those active swimmers that can move against or across currents.

Some animals in the open ocean region, however, live a *benthic* existence. This means that they are attached to, or moving over, the ocean floor. Around the edges of the main oceanic region is an extensive area called the *continental shelf*. This district represents the submerged portions of the continents. Life is usually more fruitful on a continental shelf than in the oceanic region beyond it. Here light can penetrate the water to support attached plants growing on the shelf's floor. These, in addition to the floating plants, constitute a great mass of productive plant material. Living a benthic existence on the continental shelf is also a much greater variety of attached or bottom-dwelling animal life than will be found on the main ocean floor. The water area on the continental shelf is classified as the *neritic zone*.

On its upper edge is the *intertidal zone*, that portion of the ocean with which most land dwellers are familiar. Here are found those plants and animals that can stand exposure to the air during periods of low tide. Although narrow by comparison with the great breadth of the oceans, the productive neritic zone occupies a considerable area. It follows the edges of all the continents, surrounds all of the islands, and occurs wherever there are submerged banks or reefs near the surface.

■ CHEMICAL NUTRIENTS.—Although light is the major factor limiting the distribution and amount of life in the ocean, chemical nutrients are also of great importance. Just as there are sterile soils on land that support little life, there are relatively sterile waters in the oceans. Those salts needed for plant nutrition are eroded from the land and carried in dissolved form down all of the streams and rivers to the oceans. Some come to rest in bays, in estuaries, or along the continental shelves. The salts that remain in the euphotic zone are available to green plants, but those that sink into the ocean depths are beyond the reach of food chains.

In a general sense there is no shortage of salt in the ocean. But not all of the salts necessary for nutrition are abundant. In particular, nitrates and phosphates are often in short supply. Those that are available are picked up by floating plants, *phytoplankton*, and pass from these to animals. When plants or animals die and their remains sink below the euphotic zone, the chemical nutrients in their bodies are removed from circulation. With a steady supply of nutrients flowing from the land and with an abundance of shallow, lighted water, it follows that the continental shelf areas are the most productive of life. Because mineral sources are unavailable, much of the oceanic euphotic zone is deficient in minerals and cannot support the mass of floating plankton on which larger marine organisms must feed.

The constant motion of the ocean waters encourages life in regions that would not ordinarily support it. Were it not for this motion, the required nutrients would have long ago sunk to the bottom and over the greater part of the seas the water would be lifeless. However, there are both deep and shallow currents in the ocean that keep the waters in constant movement and prevent stagnation. Deep currents can pick up those nutrients that have been lost to the surface waters. Where conditions are favorable, these deep currents can carry nutrient-rich water once more to the surface. Such favorable conditions exist along the western coasts of the major continents. Here the forces generated by the earth's rotation tend to push the warmer surface waters away from the land and to allow an *upwelling* of the cold waters from the depths. These fertile waters are then further distributed by surface currents. It is in these regions that some of the world's major fisheries are located.

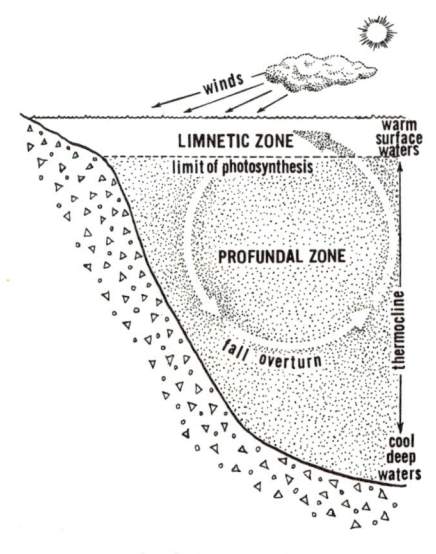

LAKES are divided into a limnetic and a profundal zone. The fall overturn replaces the nutrients that were depleted from the limnetic zone during photosynthesis.

■ FRESHWATER ENVIRONMENTS.—Since fresh water is less richly supplied with dissolved minerals than is the ocean, the availability of those minerals needed for plant and animal nutrition assumes a more controlling influence on the quantity and distribution of life. A common classification of freshwater environments separates the *oligotrophic* (low nutrient) waters from the *eutrophic* (high nutrient) waters. At one extreme is the glacial lake of the high mountains, fed by melting ice or snow, resting on a sterile substrate of granite; at the other, the farm pond in an area of rich soil, green with algae and teeming with animal life. Along with mineral content, the amount of dissolved oxygen in the water becomes limiting in fresh water more often than in the ocean. While photosynthesis occurs, shallow, eutrophic lakes are rich in oxygen; but in the winter light is screened out by a layer of ice and snow, and the abundant animal populations may exhaust the oxygen supply. Temperature also is much more variable in fresh water than in the ocean. The trout that can survive in a cold, oxygen-rich stream cannot live in the warm waters of sluggish streams or shallow lakes. Passing through several kinds of microorganisms and small invertebrates before ending in some large predatory fish, food chains in fresh water are also frequently complicated.

■ LAKES.—Deep lakes present many of the same problems for life that are encountered in the oceans. Below the limit of light penetration, called the *limnetic zone* in lakes, is a deeper layer in which no photosynthesis takes place. This is called the *profundal zone*. Fish dwelling in this deep zone depend upon the production of the limnetic zone for their food supply. Periodic mixing of the upper and lower layers of water is essential if their united capability for sustaining life is to be maintained. During the winter, for example, lake waters cool. Since water reaches its maximum density at 4° Centigrade, the water that cools to this temperature will sink to the bottom. As winter progresses, however, the surface layer of water cools below 4° C., expands, and at 0° C. becomes ice. At this stage the bottom waters are cut off from the surface layer; and a sharp temperature gradient, the *thermocline*, exists between the surface and the depths. Since no new oxygen can be added from the surface, animal life dwelling in the profundal zone can exhaust the oxygen supply during the winter.

In the spring, surface waters warm once more and soon reach the same temperature as the bottom waters. At this stage the thermocline disappears. Wind action induces mixing of the waters from the surface and the depths and thereby restores oxygen to the deeper waters. However, as summer approaches, the surface waters continue to warm and a new thermocline develops. A layer of light, warm water occupies the surface of the lake and may not mix with the deeper, cool waters. This condition can continue until declining autumn temperatures encourage another period of mixing. Following the period of mixing in the spring, the *spring overturn*, the surface waters usually experience a blooming of the algae and a consequent increase in animal life. This can exhaust the available nitrates, phosphates, and other essential materials in the surface layer. If this happens, the summer is a period of low productivity because the nutrients in the surface area cannot be replaced until the *fall overturn*.

Although the supply of nutrients controls the abundance of life in fresh water, there are some continental aquatic environments where an excess of salts presents a problem. Great Salt Lake, for example, is so much more saline than the oceans that a swimmer has difficulty in submerging. Mono Lake in California has such a high salt concentration that only two species of organisms, a salt-tolerant fly larva and a brine shrimp, can survive. Because drainage is interior rather than toward the oceans, high levels of salinity or alkalinity are usually found in most lakes in the intermountain region of the American West.

Biology and Conservation.—Since the early days of civilization, when man first domesticated plants and animals, human societies have exploited natural communities. Sometimes man has taken only the few products which he has needed and has left the community to restore itself through natural succession. Often, however, the wild community has been deformed and reshaped into a tamed community intended to serve the human welfare. At times, and in some places, people have managed to strike a balance with the forces of nature and have created stable ecosystems that include civilized man as a component. Too frequently, however, through failure to understand the biological forces involved, the deformation and change wrought in natural communities have initiated chains of consequences that in time have worked against human society. Many old civilizations are buried in jungle or have left their ruins standing windswept in what are now barren wastes. These ruins often reflect the failure to balance human demands against the biological necessities of ecosystems.

Today conservation movements attempt to counterbalance the destructive effects that formerly accompanied the exploitation of nature. *Conservation* is concerned primarily with maintaining a suitable world in which man can live. It is less involved with the quantity of production than with the quality of living. It seeks to preserve at least the remnants of unmodified natural communities and to balance man's demands upon the land and the capabilities of the land to produce; to substitute careful management of resources for unbridled, destructive use. Where it is involved with those resources that form a part of ecological systems, conservation depends upon a knowledge of biological relationships.

It is a recognized tenet of biological conservation that all living things grow, reproduce, and therefore show an annual growth. In a stable community this yearly increase represents a quantity of living material that can be safely harvested by man without destroying the basic resource. If it is not used by man, it will sooner or later die of natural causes, for no living thing can exist forever. Consequently, if the annual production of wood in a forest, brought about by tree growth, is balanced against the amount that is cut and converted into lumber, and if reasonable care is taken in removing this crop, the forest can remain permanently productive. Conversely, if too little is cut, old age, disease, insects, or other natural forces will eventually destroy the surplus. Balancing growth against harvest leads to a *sustained yield* of forest products. Sustained-yield management characterizes all modern systems of conservation-based forest management. The consequences of excessive harvesting and of careless handling of cut-over lands can be seen in the devastated hillsides of many parts of the world or in the scrubby growths of birch and aspen that have replaced the once magnificent pine forests of the Great Lakes states.

■**PRESERVATION OF WILD ANIMALS.**—A sustained-yield system of harvesting should characterize the commercial use of all living resources, including agricultural soils. Wild animal populations, for example, can be managed in this way. If the annual take by hunters is balanced against the annual replacement of adults by young, a game population can be permanently maintained. If an annual crop is not removed, the animals will die from natural causes; man's protection cannot make them eternal. In the United States game managers try to balance the annual increase of deer, quail, grouse, or rabbits against the annual demand from hunters. If game laws are tailored to allow a breeding stock to remain each year, the game populations will remain abundant. Game managers also attempt, through improving the vegetation or other aspects of the environment, to create a more suitable habitat for game and thus produce larger surpluses for the hunter.

In countries where hunting for sport is not extensive, as in Africa, it has been found that the annual crop of wild game can be taken for commercial purposes. The complex of wild grazers and browsers that forms a part of the biotic communities of Africa has been shown to produce more meat and other products of value, per acre, than can be produced when the same lands are used by domestic livestock. The Soviet Union has had similar experiences with some of its game animals. For example, the saiga antelope, an abundant game animal of the dry steppes and desert margins, is now managed for meat production. A harvest is taken each year by hunters; and the meat, hides, and other by-products enter the domestic economy.

It has become obvious with many kinds of wild animals that excessive protection can do as much harm as excessive hunting. A population of deer or elk, when completely protected, overbrowses and destroys the food plants on which it depends. Before man modified the natural scene, wild predators helped to remove the annual surplus and to keep populations in balance. But in order to protect his domestic animals, man has destroyed most of the wild predators, with the result that the wild herbivores are left without adequate checks on their biotic potential.

■**DOMESTIC ANIMALS.**—It is in the handling of domestic animals that man has done the most damage to his environment. A sparse human population maintaining great herds of cattle, sheep, or goats can destroy a vast region in a surprisingly short time. Failure to realize that range forage, like timber or wildlife, produces an annual surplus, and that only this annual surplus can safely be cropped, lies behind this devastation. The arid steppe and savanna regions are most susceptible to damage by domestic livestock. Here the plant production during a wet season or good rainfall year must hold the soil during the long, dry periods that follow. Because plant growth is usually slow, the annual surplus that can safely be cropped without injury to the grasses or shrubs is small. Such areas can sustain only light grazing.

If the land is overgrazed, the plants are destroyed; and the bare ground is subject to rapid erosion by wind or rain. When the layer of more fertile topsoil is lost, vegetation is slow to reoccupy the ground, and damage continues. Over wide areas of the globe the desert has expanded

U.S. DEPARTMENT OF AGRICULTURE

MAN'S ACTIVITIES tend to overbalance ecosystems, thus destroying their symbiotic existence. The dust bowl of the American Midwest was the end product of such an overbalancing.

into formerly productive lands following the impact of too many hoofs or grazing mouths of domestic livestock. The Sahara, the Arabian Desert, the deserts of Pakistan and of our American Southwest have all spread into lands that formerly were more productive. *Range management* is a relatively new field of conservation. It attempts to instill a knowledge of how best to harvest the annual forage crop from grasslands without damage to the growing stock of range plants.

Faulty management of farming lands has also resulted from a failure to understand biological necessities. Soils that developed as part of natural ecosystems cannot for long be separated from those forces that contributed to their development and guaranteed their stability. In the virgin prairie soil, structure was maintained by a dense network of plant roots. Erosion was checked by the perennial cover of growing plants. Fertility was held in balance by the annual return of dead plant and animal materials to the ground that had originally produced them.

When these prairie soils were first plowed, they were remarkable in both fertility and stability. With continued cultivation and annual planting of the same kind of crop, and with no effort to protect them from wind or rain, they began to deteriorate. Surface soil was lost to erosion. Structure was destroyed because the roots of wheat or corn failed to provide the mechanical or chemical action that was necessary to maintain it. Fertility was lost through the steady drain of nutrients into crops that were subsequently transported to distant markets.

Recent soil-conservation activities have attempted to repair this damage. The original soil-forming and soil-holding functions of natural vegetation have been replaced by techniques compatible with agricultural production. Crop rotation, cover-cropping, contour cultivation, mulching, and fertilizing all are part of sound, conservation-based agricultural practices today.

■ **FISHERIES.**—The early exploitation of the resources of fresh water and the oceans was based on a misunderstanding of the abundance of aquatic organisms. Too often fishermen have assumed that new sea fisheries can always be found to replace those that have been exhausted. In fact, commercially valuable fisheries are restricted to the few areas where nutrient supplies permit an abundant production of plants. Far from being inexhaustible, such localized fisheries can readily be overfished if sufficient pressure is placed upon them. Once it is reduced to a low population, a fishery may be a long time recovering, for the ocean environment cannot yet be controlled; and natural losses are high. Steady exploitation of depleted fish populations prevents any recovery. For the most part, excluding a few highly valued species of marine life, overfishing has been a localized problem. The ocean still has great resources of living materials suitable for human food. But with the increasing demands of growing human populations, biologically sound management of these marine resources is essential if they are to remain productive.

■ **PRESERVATION OF NATURAL AREAS.**—Since man is as dependent today upon the products of the lands and waters for his food as he was in ages past, it follows that much of the world must be used for the production of those things that people require. However, as more and more land comes into use, the value of the still wild, unmanaged parts of the world increases. Most nations have at least made gestures toward maintaining such natural areas in systems of national parks or wilderness reserves. However, no nation has gone far enough in this direction.

It is now clear that there is an acute need to preserve representative areas of all kinds of natural ecosystems, from humble tracts of bog or moor to vast areas of tropical rain forest. This is because it is important to have ecological check areas against which the progress or loss of the lands under management can be measured. In some parts of the world, devastation has been so complete that we do not know what the land could produce if it were left to recover. Some livestock owners have never seen an undamaged rangeland. They consistently settle for a lower productivity because they know no better. If natural grasslands of high productivity remained in each region, the range manager would better realize his goal.

Natural ecological systems contain the maximum variety and abundance of life that a climate and substrate will support. In development such ecosystems usually tend toward increased complexity. As each species moves in, it creates a niche for some new species that can feed or shelter upon it. Generally speaking, the more complex an ecosystem, the more stable it becomes and the less liable to extreme fluctuations in the abundance of any species. A herbivore that grows too numerous is fed upon by a variety of carnivores until its numbers are reduced. One that grows scarce is spared the pressure of predators that can turn to some other more abundant and readily available prey. Thus the entire system retains a natural balance.

Man, through his efforts at agriculture, pastoralism, logging, hunting, and fishing, tends to simplify complex ecosystems. The more they are simplified, the more likely they are to lose balance. A natural grassland is complex; a wheat field is simple. The wheat field provides an ideal environment for those things that prefer to live on, or feed upon, wheat—the wheat-destroying fungi and insect pests among them. Without natural enemies in this artificial system, these pests can increase to such proportions that they destroy the wheat crop. Similarly, an overgrazed range is simplified and supports fewer species of organisms than does a virgin rangeland. It is therefore out of balance. A species of rodent can increase to plague proportions and do serious damage, whereas such an increase would be prevented by natural checks in an undisturbed grassland community.

■ **CHEMICAL CONTROL OF INSECTS AND PESTS.**—Where agricultural or pastoral peoples have been, they have changed and simplified natural communities. Hence, they have often created an ideal environment for those pests, diseases, parasites, and predators that are the worst enemies of their crops and herds. In their efforts to control these pests that follow them, they have resorted to hunting, trapping, burning, and other techniques. Such attempts at regulation have usually been unsuccessful. With the development of the chemical industry, however, new weapons have been added to the battle against pests in the form of chemical insecticides, fungicides, and herbicides. For a while great progress was made by the use of these materials. Agricultural and pastoral losses were reduced, and production soared. Recently, however, it has become apparent that the use of poisonous chemicals on the land can, unless carefully controlled, wipe out the very species of plants and animals that man most wants to preserve. In the long run, the unrestrained and uninterrupted employment of some of these poisons could pollute the land and its waters to such an extent as to imperil man's very existence.

The pollution of the human environment, not just with pesticides but with all of the wastes and by-products of man's activities, creates the greatest problem for biological conservation today. As human populations increase, it will become even more severe. Perhaps it will finally force us to observe the biological rules of order that should govern our actions on this planet. It is the hope of the ecologist, who has an interest in natural things, that man will yet develop what Aldo Leopold has called an "ecological conscience." This involves a recognition that man is still a part of, not an enemy of, nature, and that other living things have as much right to a place on this earth in the future as they had in the past.

—Raymond F. Dasmann

BIBLIOGRAPHY

BATES, MARSTON. *Animal Worlds.* Random House, Inc., 1963.

BONNER, JOHN TYLER. *Cells and Societies.* Princeton University Press, 1955.

CARSON, RACHEL L. *Silent Spring.* Houghton Mifflin Co., 1962.

CLEMENTS, EDITH. *Adventures in Ecology: Half a Million Miles, from Mud to Macadam.* Pageant Press, 1960.

DASMANN, RAYMOND F. *Environmental Conservation.* John Wiley & Sons, Inc., 1959.

ODUM, EUGENE P. *Fundamentals of Ecology* (2nd ed.). W. B. Saunders Co., 1959.

WALLACE, BRUCE. *Ecology.* Prentice-Hall, Inc., 1961.

INDEX

A

Aardvark 9c, 11a
Abacá 78a
Abalone 11a
Abiotic chemicals 152c
Absorption (plants) 76a–76b
Abyssal zone 157c
Acacia 78a
Acanthaceae *see* Acanthus
Acanthus 78a
Aceraceae *see* Maple
Acetobacter 137b
Achene fruit 76a
Achromabacter 137c
Aconite 78a
Actinomycetales 136b
Active immunity 141c
Adam's needle *see* Yucca
Adder *see* Viper
Adenine 132c, 146b
Adenosine triphosphate (ATP) 133c
Adjutant bird *see* Stork
Adventitious roots 74b
Aedes aegypti 135a
Aerating roots 74b
Aerial roots 74b
Aerial stems 74b
Aerobic bacteria 135b
African sleeping sickness 140c
African violet *see* Gesneria family
Agave *see* Century plant
Ageratum 78a
Agouti 11a
Agrimony 78a–78b
Agronomy 68a
Airplant blossom *il* 95
Aizoaceae *see* Ice plant
Akee 78b
Alaskan brown bear 13c
Albacore *see* Tuna
Albatross 11a
Alcaptonuria 148a
Alder 78b
Alewife 11a–11b
Alfalfa 78b–78c
Algae 69c–70a, 139c–140a
  blue-green 69c–70a, 139c
  brown 70a, 139c
  diatoms 69a, 139c, *il* 140
  green 69c, 139c
  red 70a, 139c
Alganine *tab* 147
Algology 68a
Alleles 142c, 144a
Allergies 141c
Alligator *see* Crocodile
Alligator pear *see* Avocado
Allspice 78c
Almond 78c
Aloe 78c
Alpaca 11b
Alternation of generations (plants) 71c–72a
Altismataceae *see* Water-plantain family
Alyssum 78c
Amaranthaceae *see* Amaranth family

Amaranth family 78c
  see also Cockscomb; Pigweed; Tumbleweed
Amaryllidaceae *see* Amaryllis family
Amaryllis 78c–79a
Amaryllis family 79a
  see also Amaryllis; Century plant; Narcissus; Rose of Sharon; Sisal; Snowdrop; Tuberose
American brooklime *see* Bluebell
American elm *il* 98
American mandrake *see* Mayapple
Amino acids 132b, 147a
  genetics 147a
  RNA *tab* 147
Amoeba 11b, 140a
Amoebic dysentery 140a
Amphibia 8b
  Caudata *see* Newt; Salamander
  Salientia *see* Frog
Amphineura 4b
Amphioxus *see* Lancelet
Anacardiaceae *see* Sumac family
Anaconda *see* Boa
Anaerobic bacteria 135b
  sewage disposal 137c
Anatomy (plant) 67b–67c
Anchovy 11b
Anemia, sickle cell 148c
Anemone 79a
Angelfish 11b–11c
Angiosperms 72c–73b
Angleworm *see* Earthworm
Animal digestion
  bacteria 138b
Animal ecology *see* Ecology
Animals 1–66
  bibliography 66c
Anise 79a
Annelida 5a
  Hirudinea *see* Leech
  Oligochaeta *see* Earthworm
Annonaceae *see* Custard-apple family
Annual plants 74c
Annual rings 74c
Anopheles mosquito 140c
Anoplura 6b
  see also Louse
Ant 7a, 11c
Antarctic beech *see* Beech
Anteater 9a, 11c–12a, *il* 29
  scaly 9c
  spiny 8c
Antelope 9c, 12a
Anther (plant) 75c
Anthozoa 3c
  Actiniaria *see* Sea anemone
  Gorgonacea *see* Sea fan
Antibiotics 137c
Antibodies 141b
Antigens 141b
Antitoxin 141b
Ant lion 12a
Aoudad *see* Sheep
Ape 12a
Aphids 6c, 12a–12b
Apocynaceae *see* Dogbane family
Apple 79a
Apricot 79a
Aquatic ecosystems 157b–159a
  chemical nutrients 158a–158b

  freshwater environments 158b–158c
  lakes 158c–159a
  marine environments 157c–158a
Aquifoliaceae *see* Holly
Araceae *see* Arum family
Arachnida 7b–7c, 36b
  Acarina *see* Mite; Tick
  Araneae *see* Black widow; House spider; Tarantula; Trap-door spider
  Phalangida *see* Harvestman
  Scorpionida *see* Scorpion
Araliaceae *see* Ginseng family
Araucariaceae *see* Araucaria family
Araucaria family 79a–79b
  see also Norfolk Island pine
Arbor vitae 79b
Arbutus 79b
Argali *see* Sheep
Arginine *tab* 147
Aristolochiaceae *see* Birthwort family
Armadillo 9a, 12b
Arnica 79b
Arrhenius, Svante 131c
Arrowhead 79c
Arrowroot 79c
Arthropoda 5a
  Chilopoda 5c
  Diplopoda 5c
  Onychophora 5b
  Trilobita 5b
  see also Arachnida; Crustacea; Insecta; Merostomata
Artichoke 79c
Artiodactyla 9c
  see also Alpaca; Antelope; Bighorn; Bison; Buffalo; Camel; Cattle; Chamois; Deer; Gazelle; Giraffe; Gnu; Goat; Hippopotamus; Kudu; Llama; Musk ox; Okapi; Peccary; Pronghorn; Sheep; Swine; Yak
Arum family 79c
  see also Arrowroot; Calla lily; Jack-in-the-pulpit; Skunk cabbage; Taro
Ascidiacea *see* Tunicate
Asclepiadaceae *see* Milkweed family
Ascospores 148a
Ash 79c–80a
Asiatic cholera 137a
Asparagine *tab* 147
Asparagus 80a
Aspartic acid *tab* 147
Aspen *il* 98
  see also Poplar
Aspergillosis 139a
Aspergillus *il* 138
Asphodel 80a
Ass 12b
Assimilation (plant) 77a
Aster 80a
Athlete's foot 139a
Atmosphere
  origin of life 132a
  oxydizing 132a
  photosynthesis 132a
  planets 132a–132b
  reducing 132a
ATP *see* Adenosine triphosphate

Audubon, John James 49a
Auk 12c
Auklet *see* Auk
Autoclave 136c
Autoecology 151a
Autotrophic organisms 133b
Auxin 75a, 77c
Avery, O. T. 145c
Aves 8c
  Anseriformes *see* Black duck; Bufflehead; Duck; Eider; Fowl; Goldeneye; Goose; Mallard; Merganser; Pintail; Scaup; Swan; Teal
  Apodiformes *see* Hummingbird; Swift
  Apterygiformes *see* Kiwi
  Caprimulgiformes *see* Nighthawk; Whippoorwill
  Casuariiformes *see* Emu
  Charadriiformes *see* Avocet; Gull; Kittiwake; Phalarope; Plover; Puffin; Sanderling; Sandpiper; Skimmer; Snipe; Stilt; Tern; Woodcock; Yellowlegs
  Ciconiiformes *see* Flamingo; Heron; Ibis; Stork
  Columbiformes *see* Pigeon
  Coraciiformes *see* Kingfisher
  Cuculiformes *see* Cuckoo
  Falconiformes *see* Eagle; Falcon; Hawk; Kite; Osprey; Secretary bird; Vulture
  Galliformes *see* Bobwhite; Grouse; Guinea fowl; Partridge; Peafowl; Pheasant; Ptarmigan; Quail; Turkey
  Gaviiformes *see* Loon
  Gruiformes *see* Coot; Crane; Gallinule
  Micropodiformes *see* Chimney swift
  Passeriformes *see* Bird of Paradise; Blackbird; Bluebird; Bobolink; Brown thrasher; Bunting; Canary; Cardinal; Catbird; Chickadee; Cowbird; Crow; Finch; Flycatcher; Goldfinch; Grackle; Grosbeak; Jay; Junco; Kingbird; Kinglet; Lyrebird; Magpie; Mockingbird; Nightjar; Nuthatch; Oriole; Pewee; Phoebe; Redstart; Robin; Shrike; Sparrow; Starling; Swallow; Tanager; Thrush; Titmouse; Warbler; Water thrush; Waxwing; Wren; Yellowthroat
  Pelecaniformes *see* Cormorant; Frigate bird; Pelican
  Piciformes *see* Toucan; Woodpecker
  Podicepediformes *see* Grebe
  Procellariformes *see* Albatross; Petrel; Tube-nosed bird
  Psitaciformes *see* Lovebird; Parrot
  Sphenisciformes *see* Penguin
  Strigiformes *see* Owl
  Struthioniformes *see* Ostrich
  Trogoniformes *see* Trogon
Avocado 80a–80b
Avocet 12c
Axillary buds 74c
Axils (plant) 75b
Axolotl *see* Salamander
Azalea 80b
Aztecs
  sacred bird *see* Trogon

B

Baboon 12c–13a
Baby's breath 80b
Bachelor's button *see* Cornflower
Bacillary dysentery 137a
Bacille Calmette Guérin (BCG) 141c
Bacillus 135b, 137b
  anthracis *il* 135c

  megatherium *il* 135c
Bacitracin 137c
Bacteria 70c, 135b–138b, *il* 135c
  agriculture 138a
  animals and 138a–138b
  cheese making 137b
  classification 136b
  control 136b–136c
  food 135b–135c
  heterotrophic 133c
  industrial uses 137b
  lactic acid 133c
  movement 135c–136a
  nitrogen-fixing 76c

  nuclear material exchange 136a–136b
  nuclear structure 136a
  sewage disposal 138a
  species 135b
  transduction 146a
  water purification 137c–138a
Bacterial diseases 137a–137b
Bacterial fermentation 137b
Bacterial movement 135c–136a
Bacterial photosynthesis 135b
Bacterial transduction 146a
Bacterial viruses *see* Bacteriophages

Bacteriology 68a
Bacteriophages 135b, 145c
Badger 13a
Bagasse *see* Sugarcane
Balanced polymorphism 150c
Bald cypress 80b
Bald-cypress family 80b–80c
  see also Bald cypress; Cedar; Sequoia
Balm 80c
Balm-of-Gilead *see* Poplar

Balsa 80c
Balsam 80c
Balsam fir see Fir
Balsaminaceae see Jewelweed family
Balsier see Banana family
Bamboo 80c
Banana 80c–81a
Banana family 73a, 81a
  see also Abacá; Banana
Bandakai see Hibiscus
Baneberry 81a
Banyan tree see Fig
Baobab 81a
Barberry 81b
Barberry family 81b
  see also Barberry; Mayapple; Oregon grape
Barco il 95
Barley 81b, il 95
Barnacle 5b, 13a
Barr body 144c
Bass 13b
Basswood see Linden
Bat 9a, 13b–13c
Bathyal zone 157c
Bayberry 81b
Bayberry family 81b–81c
Bay-rum tree see Myrtle
BCG see Bacille Calmette Guérin
Beadle, George Wells 148a
  Nobel prize 150c
Bead tree see Chinaberry
Bean 81c
Bean blight 137a
Bean caper see Caltrop family
Bear 9b, 13c, il 28
Bear grass 81c, il 95
Beaver 9b, 13c–14a
Beche-de-mer see Sea cucumber
Bedbug 6c, 14a
Bedstraw 81c
Bee 7a, 14a–14c, il 27
Bee balm see Oswego tea
Beech il 74, 81c–82a
Beech family 82a
  see also Beech; Chestnut; Oak
Beet 82a
Beetle 7a, 14c
Beggiatoa alba il 135c
Begonia 82a
Belgian hare see Rabbit
Belladonna 82a–82b
Belladonna lily see Amaryllis
Beluga see Sturgeon
Benthic zone 158a
Berberidaceae see Barberry family
Bergamot 82b
Bergy, D. H.
  Manual of Determinative Bacteriology 136b

Berries 76a
Beta-galactosidase gene 149c
Betel pepper see Pepper
Betulaceae see Birch family
Bighorn 14c, il 29
Bignoniaceae see Bigonia family
Bigonia family 82b
  see also Calabash tree; Catalpa; Trumpet creeper
Bindweed 82b–82c
Binomial method 68b
Biochemical genetics 147c–149a
Biological conservation 159b–160c
  chemical control of insects and pests 160c
  domestic animals 159c–160a
  dust bowl il 159
  fish 160a–160b
  natural areas 160b–160c
  wild animals 159b–159c
Biological relationships 151–160
Biome
  life zones 157b
  North America il 156
Biome system 155a–155c
Biotic community 151b
Biotic potential 151b
Biotic pyramid il 153, 154a
Biotic succession 152a
Birch 82c
Birch family 82c
  see also Alder; Birch; Hazel; Hornbeam
Bird see Aves
  see also names of individual birds, such as Bluebird
Bird of paradise 15a
Bird-of-paradise (plant) see Banana family
Birthwort family 82c
  see also Dutchman's pipe
Bison 15a
Bittern see Heron
Bitterroot 82c–83c
Bittersweet 82c
Black alder see Holly
Black bear 13c
Blackberry 83c
Blackbird 15a
Black cherry see Cherry
Black duck 15a
Black-eyed pea see Cowpea
Black-eyed Susan 83a
Blackfish see Whale
Black gum see Tupelo
Black haw 83a
Black medic see Shamrock
Black widow 15a–15b
Bladderwort 83a
Bladderwort family 83a
  see also Bladderwort; Butterwort
Blanket flower see Gaillardia
Bleeding heart see Dutchman's breeches

Bligh, William 84b
Blood groups 150a
Bloodroot 83a–83b
Blowballs see Dandelion
Bluebell 83b
Blueberry 83b
Bluebird 15b
Bluebonnet see Lupine
Bluebottle see Cornflower
Blue crane see Heron
Bluefin tuna see Tuna
Bluefish 15b
Bluegill see Sunfish
Bluegrass 83c
Blue-green algae 69c–70a, 139c
Blue jay see Jay
Bluet see Madder family
Boa 15b–15c
Boat shell see Slipper shell
Bobolink 15c
Bobwhite 15c–16a
Bock, Hieronymous 68a
Boils 137a
Bokhara clover see Sweet clover
Boll weevil see Weevil
Bombacaceae see Bombax family
Bombax family 83c
  see also Balsa; Baobab; Kapok
Boneset 83c
Bony pike see Gar
Borage 83c
Borage family 83c
  see also Bluebell; Borage; Forget-me-not; Heliotrope
Boraginaceae see Borage family
Bordetella pertussis il 135c, 137a–137b
Boreal and montane forest zone 155c
Boston ivy 83c
Botany 67–69
  areas covered by 67a–68a
  classification of plants 68c–69b
  history 68a–68c
Botfly 16a
Botree see Fig
Botulism 137a
Bougainvillea 83c
Bouncing bet 84a
Boveri, T. 143b
Bowwood see Osage orange
Box 84a
Box elder see Maple
Brachiopoda 7c
Bracken 84a
Brake see Bracken
Brazil nut 84a
Brazil-nut family 84a
Breadfruit 84a–84b, 110c
Brenner, Sydney 147b

Bridal wreath see Spiraea
Bristletail 6a, 16a
Broccoli see Mustard
Bromeliaceae see Pineapple family
Broom 84b
Broomcorn 84b–84c
Brown algae 70a, 139c
Brown bear 13c
Brown thrasher 16a
Brunfels, Otto 68a
Brussels sprouts see Mustard
Buckeye see Horse chestnut
Buckhorn see Plantain family
Buckthorn 84c
Buckthorn family 84c
  see also Buckthorn; Jujube
Buckwheat 84c
Buckwheat family 84c
  see also Buckwheat; Dock; Rhubarb; Sheep sorrel
Buddhism
  sacred tree 93a
Buddleia see Butterfly bush
Budgerigar see Parrot
Buds (plant) 74c
Buffalo il 15, 16a–16b
Bufflehead 16b
Bugseed see Tumbleweed
Bulbs (plant) 74c
Bullbat see Nighthawk
Bullhead see Catfish
Bulrush 84c–85a
Bunchberry 85a
Bunting 16b
Burdock 85a
Burning bush see Euonymus
Burro see Ass
Bushmaster see Pit viper
Butcherbird see Shrike
Butterball 16b
Buttercup 85a
Buttercup family 73b, 85a
  see also Aconite; Anemone; Baneberry; Bluebell; Buttercup; Clematis; Columbine; Hellebore; Hepatica; Larkspur; Marsh marigold; Peony; Woodbine
Butterfly 6c, il 6–7, 16b–16c
Butterfly bush 85a
Butterfly flower 85a–85b
Butterfly weed see Milkweed
Butternut see Walnut
Butterwort 85b
Buttonbush see Madder family
Buttonwood see Plane-tree family
Buxaceae see Box
Buzzard see Vulture
By-the-wind sailor 3c, 16c–17a

C

Cabbage see Mustard
Cabuya see Century plant
Cacao 85b
Cachalot see Whale
Cactaceae see Cactus family
Cactus family 85b, il 95
  see also Night-blooming cereus; Saguaro
Caddis fly 17a, il 73
Calabash tree 85b–85c
Calcarea 3b
Calceolaria 85c
Calcium
  in plants 76b
Calendula see Pot marigold
California sea bass see Squeteague
Calla lily 85c
Caltrop 85c–86a
Caltrop family 86a
  see also Caltrop; Creosote bush; Lignum vitae
Calyx (plant) 75c
Camass see Bear grass

Cambium 73c, 74c
Camel 9c, 17a
  South American see Alpaca
Camellia 86a
Camomile 86a
Campanulaceae
  see Bluebell
Camphor see Cinnamon
Canada lynx 151c
Canary 17a
Canarybird flower see Nasturtium
Cancer 135a
Candida albicans 139c
Candleberry see Bayberry
Candolle, Augustin de 68c
Candytuft 86a
Canker worm 17a–17b
Canna 86a
Cannabinaceae see Hemp family
Cannaceae
  see Arrowroot; Canna
Cannonball tree see Brazil-nut family
Cantaloupe see Melon
Canterbury Bell see Bellflower
Canvasback see Duck
Cape jasmine see Gardenia
Cape primrose see Gesneria

family
Caper 86b
Caper family 86b
  see also Caper; Cleome
Capparidaceae see Caper family
Caprifoliaceae see Honeysuckle family
Caraway 86b
Carbon
  in plants 76b
Cardamom 86b
Cardinal 17b, 35a
Cardinal flower see Lobelia
Caribou see Reindeer
Caricaceae see Papaya
Carnation see Pink
Carnivora 9b
  see also Badger; Bear; Cat; Cheetah; Civet cat; Coyote; Dog; Fox; Hyena; Kinkajou; Lynx; Marten; Mongoose; Otter; Polecat; Raccoon; Skunk; Weasel; Wolf; Wolverine
Carob see Locust
Carotenoid pigments 135b
Carp 17b
  see also Minnow
Carpels 75c

Carrageen see Irish moss
Carrion crow see Vulture
Carrot 86b, il 87
Carrot family 86c
  see also Anise; Caraway; Carrot; Celery; Dill; Fennel; Parsley; Parsnip; Poison hemlock
Caryophyllaceae see Pink family
Caryopsis (fruit) 76a
Cascara sagrada see Buckthorn
Cashew 86c
Cassaba melon see Melon
Cassava 86c
Castor-oil plant 86c–87a
Cat 9b, 17b–18a
Catalpa 87a
Catbird 18a–18b
Caterpillar 6c, 18b
Catfish 18b
Catkins 73a
Catnip 87a
Cattail 87a–87b
Cattle 18b–18c
Cauliflower see Mustard
Cavy see Guinea pig
Cayman see Crocodile
Cedar 87b

INDEX

Celandine 87b
Celastraceae *see* Staff-tree family
Celery 87b
Cells 134a–134b
 plant 73b–73c
Centipede 18c
Centromere 143c
Centrosomes 149a
Century plant 87b–87c
Cephalochordata *see* Chordata
Cephalopoda 4c
 Branchiostoma *see* Lancelet
 Dibranchia *see* Cuttlefish; Octopus; Squid
 Tetrabranchiata *see* Nautilus
Cephalotaceae *see* Pitcher plant
Cesalpino, Andrea 68a
Cestoda 4a
Cetacea 10a
 see also Dolphin; Porpoise; Whale
Chacma *see* Baboon
Chaetognatha 8a
Chaffinch *see* Sparrow
Chameleon 18c–19a
Chamois 19a
Chamomile *see* Camomile
Chard *see* Beet
Chargaff, Erwin 146b
Chase, H. B. 145c
Checkerberry *see* Wintergreen
Checkered lily *see* Fritillary
Cheetah 19a
Chemical cycles 154a–154b
 nitrogen cycle 154b
Chemical elements (plants) 76b
Chenopodiaceae *see* Goosefoot family
Cherimoya *see* Custard apple
Cherry 87c
Cherry pie *see* Heliotrope
Chestnut 87c
Chian turpentine *see* Pistachio
Chickadee 19a
Chicken *see* Fowl
Chickenpox 135a
Chickweed 87c
Chicory 87c–88a
Chiffchaff *see* Warbler
Chilopoda 5c
Chimney swift 19b
Chimpanzee 9a, 19b
Chinaberry 88a
Chinagrass *see* Nettle
Chinch bug 19b
Chinchilla 19b
Chinese cabbage *see* Mustard
Chinese lantern *see* Potato family
Chinese liver fluke *see* Fluke
Chinese sacred lily *see* Narcissus
Chinook salmon *see* Salmon
Chipmunk 19c
Chiroptera 9a
 see also Bat; Vampire
Chive *see* Onion
Chittamwood *see* Smoke tree
Chlamydomonas 139c
Chloramphenicol 137c
Chlorella 139c
Chlorophyll 153b
Chloroplasts 73c, 134a

Chocolate *see* Cacao
Cholera (Asiatic) 137a
Chondrichthyes 8b
 Batoidea *see* Ray
 Selachii *see* Dogfish; Shark
Chordata 8a, 40b
 Cephalochordata 8a
 Leptocardii *see* Lancelet
 Tunicata 8a
 Vertebrata *see* Amphibia; Aves; Chondrichthyes; Cyclostomata; Mammalia; Osteichthyes; Placodermi; Reptilia
Christmas berry 88a
Christmas cactus *see* Cactus
Christmas fern *see* Polypody family
Christmas rose *see* Hellebore
Chromatids 144a
Chromoplasts (plant) 73c
Chromosomal basis of heredity 143b–145b
Chromosomes 133a, 134a, 143b–145b, *il* 145, 147c
 deoxyribonucleic acid (DNA) 145c–146a
 mapping 145a–145b
 meiosis 143c–144a
 mitosis 143c
 in plants 73b
 sex-linkage 144a–144c
 X chromosome 144c–145a
 Y chromosome 145a
Chrysanthemum 88a, *il* 96, *il* 97
Cicada 6c, 19c–20a, *il* 27
Cigarette plant *see* Orpine family
Cilia 141a
Ciliata 3b
Ciliophora 141a
Cinchona 88a–88b
Cineraria 88b
Cinnamon 88b
Cistron 147c
Citron 88b
 see also Melon
Citrulline 148b
Civet cat 20a
Clam 4c, 20a
Clamworm *il* 6
Classes (plant) 69a
Classification of plants *see* Taxonomic system
Clematis 88b
Cleome *il* 96
Climax community 152b
Clostridium 137b
 botulinum 137a
 perfringens 137a
Clover 88b–88c
Clove tree 88c
Club moss 72a, 88c
Coacervates 133a
Cobra 20a–20b
Coca 88c–89a
Cocci (spherical bacteria) 135b
Cochineal insect *see* Scale insect
Cockatoo *see* Parrot
Cockle *see* Clam
Cockroach 20b
Cockscomb 89a
Cocoa *see* Cacao
Cod 8b, 20b–20c
Coelenterata 3c

 see also Anthozoa; Hydrozoa; Scyphozoa
Coffee 89a
Coffee tree *see* Kentucky coffee tree
Cold (viral disease) 135a
Coleoptera 7a
 see also Beetle; Firefly; June bug; Ladybeetle; Weevil
Collembola 5c
 see also Springtail
Collenchyma tissue 73c
Colloid 133a
Color blindness *il* 144, 144a
Colugo *see* Flying lemur
Columbine 89a–89b
Columbus, Christopher 125c
Combretaceae *see* Mangrove
Combretum family *see* Mangrove
Community (ecology) 151a–152b
Compositae *see* Daisy family
Conch 20c
Condor *see* Vulture
Cone shell 20c–21a
Conger eel *see* Eel
Conidia 148a
Conifers 72c
Conservation, biological *see* Biological conservation
Consumer organisms 152c
Continental shelf *il* 157, 158a
Continental slope *il* 157
Conure *see* Parrot
Convolvulaceae *see* Morning-glory family
Cony 9b, 21a
Cook, James 84b
Coon *see* Raccoon
Coontie *see* Arrowroot
Coot 21a
Copperhead *see* Pit viper
Coquina 21a
Coral 21b
Coral snake *il* 30
Coral vine *see* Buckwheat family
Coreopsis 89b
Corkwood *see* Balsa
Cormorant 21b
Cornaceae *see* Dogwood family
Corms (plant) 74c
Corn 89b
Cornborer 21b
Cornel *see* Dogwood
Cornflower 89b
Corolla (plant) 75c
Cosmos *il* 96
Cotton 89b
Cotton grass *see* Sedge family
Cottonmouth *see* Pit viper
Cottonwood *see* Poplar
Cotyledon 72c
Cougar *see* Cat
Cow 9b
 see also Cattle
Cowbird 21b
Cowpea 89c
Cowpox 141a
Cowrie 21b–21c
Cowslip
 see Marsh marigold; Primrose
Coxiella burnetii 138c
Coyote 9b, 21c, *il* 20

Coypu *see* Nutria
Crab 5b, 21c
Crabgrass 89c
Cranberry 89c
Crane 21c–22a
Cranesbills *see* Geranium
Crape myrtle 89c
Crappie *see* Sunfish
Crassulaceae *see* Orpine family
Crayfish 22a
Cream-of-tartar tree *see* Baobab
Creeper fowl 149b
Creosote bush 89c
Cress 90a
Crick, Francis Harry Compton 146b
 Nobel prize 150c
Cricket 22a–22b
Crocodile 22b
Crocus 90a
Cross pollination 75c
Croton 90a
Crow 8c, 22c
Crowfoot *see* Buttercup
Crown gall 137a
Crown-of-thorns *see* Euphorbia
Cruciferae *see* Mustard family
Crusades 52b, 102a
Crustacea 5b
 Amphipoda *see* Shrimp
 Cirripedia *see* Barnacle
 Cladocera *see* Water flea
 Decapoda *see* Crab; Crayfish; Lobster; Shrimp
 Isopoda *see* Sowbug
 Mysidacea *see* Shrimp
Cryptococcus neoformans 139c
Cryptococcus utilis 139c
Ctenophora 3c
Cubeb *see* Pepper
Cuckoo 23a
Cucumber 90a
Cucurbitaceae *see* Gourd family
Cupressaceae *see* Cypress family
Currant 90a–90b
Custard apple 90b
Custard-apple family 90b
 see also Custard apple; Papaw
Cutch *see* Acacia
Cuttlefish 4c, 23a
Cycad 72b, 90b
Cycad family
 see Arrowroot; Cycad; Sago palm
Cyclamen 90b–90c
Cyclic population (ecology) 151c
Cyclostomata 8a, 40a
 Hyperoartia *see* Lamprey
Cylindrical bacteria 135b
Cyperaceae *see* Sedge family
Cypress 90c
Cypress family 90c
 see also Arbor vitae; Cedar; Cypress; Juniper
Cysteine *tab* 147
Cytogenetics 149a–150a
Cytology 67c–68a, 73b
 see also Cells
Cytoplasm 134a
 heredity 148a, 149c–150a
 plant 73b
Cytosine 146b

D

Daddy longlegs *see* Harvestman
Daffodil *see* Narcissus
Dahlia 90c, *il* 97
Daisy 90c
Daisy family 73b, 90c–91a
 see also Ageratum; Arnica; Artichoke; Aster; Black-eyed Susan; Boneset; Burdock; Camomile; Chickory; Chrysanthemum; Cineraria; Coreopsis; Cornflower; Dahlia; Daisy; Dandelion; Edelweiss; Elecampane; Everlasting; Gaillardia; Golden glow;

Goldenrod; Guayule; Hawkweed; Ironweed; Joe-Pye weed; Lettuce; Marigold; Mayweed; Pot marigold; Ragweed; Rubber tree; Safflower; Sagebrush; Salsify; Sunflower; Tarragon; Thistle; Wormwood; Yarrow; Zinnia
Damselfly 6b, 23a–23b
Dandelion 91a
 seed *il* 75
Daphnia *see* Water flea
Darwin, Charles 68c
 evolution 131c
Dasheen *see* Taro
Deadly nightshade *see* Belladonna
Deciduous plants 75a
Deer 9c, *il* 22, 23b
Demospongiae 3c

Density (population) 151b
Deoxyribonucleic acid (DNA) 133a–133b, 134a, 145b–147c
Deoxyribose 146b
De Plantis (Cesalpino) 68a
Dermaptera 6a
 see also Earwig
Dermoptera *see* Flying lemur
Deserts 157a–157b
Devil's-paintbrush *see* Hawkweed
Dewberry *see* Blackberry
Diatomaceous earth 139c
Diatoms 69a, 139c, *il* 140
Dibatag *see* Gazelle
Dicotyledons 68a, 72c, 73a–73b
Digestion (plants) 76c
Dill 91a
Dingo *see* Dog

Dinoflagellates 139c
Dioscoreaceae *see* Yam family
Dioscorides 68a
Diplodinium 141a
Diploid gamete 142b
Diplopoda 5c
Dipsacaceae *see* Teasel
Diptera 6c
 see also Botfly; Fly; Fruit fly; Midge; Mosquito; Tick
Diptheria 137a
 antitoxin 141c
Disease
 amoebic 140a
 bacterial 137a
 fungal 139a–139b
 immunity 141a–141c
 metabolic 148a
 molecular 148c

164 Dishcloth gourd

protozoan 140c, 141a
rickettsial 138b-138c
viral 134c-135b
Dishcloth gourd see **Vegetable sponge**
Distemper 135a
Diver see **Loon**
DNA see **Deoxyribonucleic acid**
Dobsonfly 23b
Dock 91a
Dodder 91a-91b
Dog 9b, 23c
Dogbane 91b
Dogbane 91b
   see also Dogbane; Indian hemp; Oleander; Periwinkle; Rubber tree
Dog fennel see **Mayweed**
Dogfish 23c
Dogtooth violet 91b
Dogwood 91b
Dogwood family 91b
   see also Bunchberry; Dogwood; Tupelo
Dolphin 10a, 23c-24a
Dominance, principle of (genetics) 142b-142c
Donkey see **Ass**
Doodle bug see **Ant lion**
Douglas fir 91c
Dove see **Pigeon**
Dragonfly 6b, 24a
Drill see **Baboon**
Dromedary see **Camel**
Droseraceae see **Sundew family**
Drosophila il 142
   chromosomes il 145
   maternal inheritance 150a
   see also Fruit fly
Drupes 76a
Dubos, René 137c
Duck 8c, 24a-24b
Duckbill 8c, 24b
Duck hawk see **Falcon**
Dugong see **Sea cow**
Durra see **Sorghum**
Durum wheat see **Wheat**
Dust bowl il 159
Dutch elm disease 92a
Dutchman's-breeches 91c
Dutchman's-pipe 91c
Dwarf banana il 95
Dynamics (population) 151b
Dysentery
   amoebic 140a
   bacillary 137a

E

Eagle 24b
Earth
   atmosphere 132a-132b
Earthworm 5a, 24c
Earwig 6a, 24c
Ebenaceae see **Ebony family**
Ebony 91c
Ebony family 91c
   see also Ebony; Persimmon
Echinodermata 7c
   Asteroidea 7c
     see also Sea star
   Crinoidea 7c
   Echinoidea 7c
     see also Sea urchin
   Holothuroidea 7c
     see also Sea cucumber
   Ophiuroidea 7c
Ecological conscience 160c
Ecologic niche 152c-153a
Ecology 68a, 151-160
   aquatic ecosystems 157b-159a
   autoecology 151a
   bibliography 160c
   biological conservation 159a-160c
   chemical cycles 154a-154b
   community 151c-152b
   definition 68a, 151a
   ecosystem 152b-152c
   energy flow 153a
   food chains 153c-154a
   niche 152c-153a
   population 151a-151b
   synecology 151a
   water cycle 154c-155a
Ecosystem 151a, 152a-152b
   aquatic 157b-159a
   classification 155a
Edaphosaurus il 25
Edelweiss 91c-92a
Edentata 9a
   see also Anteater; Armadillo; Sloth
Eel 8b, 24c-31a
Eft see **Newt**
Eggplant 92a
Egret see **Heron**
Egyptian millet see **Sorghum**
Eider 31a
Elder 92a
Elecampane 92a
Elephant 9c, 31a-31b
Elephant's ear see **Begonia; Taro**
Elk see **Deer**
Elm 92a
Elm family 73a, 92a
   American elm il 98
   see also Elm; Hackberry
Embryo (plant) 76a
Emu 31b
Endamoeba histolytica 140a
Endive see **Chicory**
Endosperm (seed) 72c, 76a
Energy
   flow 153a
   loss 153b
   sources 133c
Environmental resistance 151c
Ephemeroptera 6b
   see also Mayfly
Epiphytes 113a, 151c
Equisetaceae see **Horsetail**
Ergot 139a
Ericaceae see **Heath family**
Ermine see **Weasel**
Erosion 160a
Erythromycin 137c
Erythroxylaceae see **Coca**
Escherichia 136b
Escherichia coli 149c
Eubacteriales 136b
Eucalyptus 92b
Eucaryotic cells 134a, 134b
Eucaryotic microorganisms 134b
Euglena 139c
Euonymus 92b
Euphorbia 92c
Euphorbiaceae see **Spurge family**
Euphotic zone 157c
Eutrophic waters 158b
Evening primrose 92c
Evening-primrose family 92c
   see also Evening primrose; Fireweed; Fuchsia; Godetia
Evergreens 72c
Everlasting 92c
Evolution 133b
   Darwin, Charles 150a
   genes 148a
   natural selection 150a
   organic 150a
   requirements for 131a

F

Facultatively anaerobic bacteria 135b
Fagaceae see **Beech family**
Falcon 31b
Fall overturn 158c
Family (plant) 69a
Farewell-to-spring see **Godetia**
Fennel 92c
Fer-de-lance see **Pit viper**
Fermentation 137c
   yeasts 139b-139c
Ferns 7lc-72b
   tree 71c
   see also Polypody family
Fibril bundle 147c
Field sorrel see **Sheep sorrel**
Fig 93a
Figwort 93a
Figwort family 93a
   see also Bluebell; Calceolaria; Figwort; Foxglove; Mullein; Snapdragon; Veronica
Filamentous bacteria 136b
Filbert see **Hazel**
Filterable virus 134c
Finch 31b
Fique see **Century plant**
Fir 93a-93b
Fire blight 137a
Firefly 31b
Fireweed 93b
Fisher see **Marten**
Fisheries 160a-160b
Flagella 135c
Flame tree see **Bigonia family**
Flamingo 31c
Flatfish 31c
Flatworm 4a
Flax 93b
Flea 31c-32a
Fleming, Alexander 137c
Flicker see **Woodpecker**
Flossflower see **Ageratum**
Flounder see **Flatfish**
Flowering cherry see **Cherry**
Flowering plants 72c-73b
Flowering quince see **Japonica**
Flowers 75c-76a, il 96-97
   parts of 75c
   pollination 75c-76a
Fluke 4a, 32a
Fly 32a
Flycatcher 32b
Flying fish 32b
Flying fox see **Bat**
Flying lemur 32b
Food chains 153c
Food spoilage 137a
Food storage and digestion (plant) 76c
Food webs 154a
Foraminifera 140a-140b
   geologic dating 140b
Forestry 68a
Forget-me-not 93b-93c
Formation of proteins 147a
Forsythia 93c
Four o'clock 93c
Four-o'clock family 93c
   see also Bougainvillea; Four o'clock
Fowl 8c, 32b-32c
Fox 32c
Foxglove 93c
Fraenkel-Conrat, Heinz 146a
Frangipani see **Dogbane family**
Franklinia see **Tea family**
Fraternal twins 149a
Freesia 93c
Freshwater environments 158b-158c
Frigate bird il 26, 32c
Fritillary 93c-94a
Frog 8b, 32c-33a
Fronds 71c
Fruit fly 33a
   see also Drosophila
Fruits 76a
   aggregate 76a
   dry 76a
   fleshy 76a
   multiple 76a
   simple 76a
   structural differences 76a
Fuchs, Leonhard 68a
Fuchsia 94a
Fumariaceae see **Fumitory family**
Fumitory 94a
Fumitory family 94a
   see also Dutchman's-breeches; Fumitory
Fungal diseases 139a-139b
Fungi 70a-71a, 138c-139c
   bacteria 70c
   diseases 139a-139b
   lichens 70c-71a
   reproduction 139a
   slime molds 70c
   uses 139b
   yeasts 139b-139c
Fur seal see **Sea lion**
Furze see **Gorse**

INDEX

G

Gaffkya 135b
Gaillardia 94b
Galactosemia 148b–148c
Gallinule 33a
Gametes 142b
Gar 33b
Gardenia 94b
Garden sorrel see Sheep sorrel
Garlic 94b
Garrod, A. E. 147c
Gastropoda 4b
   Aspidobranchia see Limpet; Periwinkle (animal)
   Opisthobranchiata see Slug
   Pectinibranchia see Cowrie
   Prosobranchiata see Abalone; Conch; Cone shell; Slipper shell
   Pulmonata see Slug
Gazelle 33b
Gecko 33b
Genera Plantarum (Jussieu) 68c
Generations, alternation of 71c–72a
Genes 133a, 147b
   beneficial 150a
   crossover il 145
   development role 149b–149c
   evolution 150a–150c
   genetic code 146b, 147a–147b
   internal structure 147b–147c
   lethal 150b
   material of 145b–146a
   metabolic function 148b
   mutations 145c
   protein structure 148c
Genetic code 146b, 147a–147b
Genetics 68a, 142–150
   balanced polymorphism 150c
   bibliography 150c
   biochemical genetics 147a–149a
   cytogenetics 149a–150a
   evolution 150a–150c
   genetic code 147a–147b
   heterosis 150c
   internal structure of genes 147b–147c
   population genetics 150a
   protein formation 147a
   Watson-Crick model il 146, 146a–146c
Genotype 142c, 149a
Gentian 94b–94c
Gentianaceae see Gentian family
Gentian family 94c
   see also Gentian
Genus 68b, 69a
Geotropism (plant) 77b
Geraniaceae see Geranium
Geranium 94c
Germination 77b–77c
Gesneriaceae see Gesneria family
Gesneria family 94c–99a
   see also Gloxinia
Gibbon 33b–33c
Gigartinaceae see Irish moss
Gigartina family see Irish moss
Gila monster il 30
   see also Lizard
Gill-over-the-ground see Ground ivy
Gillyflower see Stock; Wallflower
Ginger 99a
Ginger family 99a
   see also Arrowroot; Cardamom; Ginger
Ginkgo 72b, 99a
Ginkgoaceae see Ginkgo
Ginseng 99a–99b
Ginseng family 99b
   see also Ginseng; Ivy; Spikenard
Giraffe 9c, il 29, 33c
Gladiolus il 97, 99b
Glasswort see Goosefoot family
Gloxinia 99b
Glucose
   photosynthesis 153b
Glutamic acid tab 147
Glutamine tab 147
Glutton see Wolverine
Glycine tab 147
Gnu 33c
Goat 9c, 34a
Godetia 99c
Golden bell see Forsythia
Golden chain see Laburnum
Goldeneye (duck) 34a
Goldeneye (insect) see Lacewing
Goldfinch 34a–34b
Golden glow 99c
Goldenrod 99c
Goldfish see Minnow
Gonorrhea 137a
Goose 34b–34c
Gooseberry 99c
Goosefoot family 99c
   see also Beet; Lamb's-quarter; Pigweed; Saltbush; Spinach; Thistle; Tumbleweed
Gopher 34c
Gorilla 9a, 34c
Gorse 99c–100a
Gourd 100a
Gourd family 73b, 100a
   see also Cucumber; Gourd; Melon; Pumpkin; Squash; Vegetable sponge
Grackle 34c
Gramineae see Grass family
Grape 100a
Grape family 100a
   see also Boston ivy; Grape; Woodbine
Grapefruit 100a–100b
Grape hyacinth 100b
Grass family 72c, 100b
   see also Bamboo; Barley; Bluegrass; Broomcorn; Corn; Crabgrass; Millet; Oat; Pampas grass; Reed; Rice; Rye; Sorghum; Sudan grass; Sugarcane; Timothy; Wheat
Grasshopper il 27
Grasslands 157a
Grebe 35a
Green algae 69c, 139c
Greenbrier see Smilax
Green fly see Lacewing
Grenadine see Pomegranate
Grizzly bear see Bear
Grosbeak 35a
Ground cedar see Club moss
Ground fir see Club moss
Groundhog see Marmot
Ground ivy 100b–100c
Ground laurel see Arbutus
Groundnut see Peanut
Ground pine see Club moss
Ground pink see Phlox
Grouse 35a–35b
Grunting ox see Yak
Guaiacum see Lignum vitae
Guanine 146b
Guard cells (plant) 75b
Guava 100c
Guayule 100c
Guelderrose see Viburnum
Guillemot see Auk
Guinea fowl 35b
Guinea pig 35b
Gull 35b
Gumbo see Hibiscus
Gum tree see Eucalyptus
Gunny see Jute
Guppy 35b–35c
Gutta-percha see Rubber tree
Guttiferae see Rose of Sharon
Gymnosperms 72c
Gypsophila see Baby's-Breath
Gyrfalcon see Falcon

H

Hackberry 100c
Haddock 35c
Haeckel, Ernst Heinrich 134a
Hake 35c–36a
Halibut see Flatfish
Hamamelidaceae see Witch-hazel family
Hamster 36a
Haploid gamete 142b
Hardhack see Spiraea
Hardy, Godfrey Harold 150a
Hardy-Weinberg law 150a
Hare 36a
Harebell see Bluebell
Harpy eagle il 26
Harvestman 7b, 36a–36b
Haustoria see Mistletoe
Hawaiian Islands Bird Reservation 11a
Hawk 36b
Hawkweed 100c
Hawthorn 101a
Hazel 101a
Heal-all see Self-heal
Heartsease see Violet
Heath 101a
Heather 101a
Heath family 101a
   see also Arbutus; Azalea; Blueberry; Cranberry; Heath; Heather; Huckleberry; Madroña; Manzanita; Mountain laurel; Pipsissewa; Rhododendron; Wintergreen
Heath hen see Grouse
Hedgehog 9a, 36b
Hedgehog cactus il 95
Helical bacteria 136b
Heliotrope il 97, 101a–101b
Hellbender see Salamander
Hellebore 101b
Hemlock 101b
Hemoglobin 148c–149a
Hemp 101b–101c
Hemp family 101c
   see also Hemp; Hop
Henequen see Century plant
Henna plant see Loosestrife family
Hepatica 101c
Herbaceous stems 74b, 74c
Herb Christopher see Baneberry
Heredity
   blood groups 150a
   chromosomal basis 143b
   cytogenetics 149a–150a
   cytoplasmic inheritance 149c–150a
   twin studies 149a
Heron 36c
Herring 8b, 36c–37a
Hershey, Alfred D. 145c
Heteroptera 6b
   see also Bedbug; Chinch bug; Water boatman; Water strider
Heterosis 150c
Heterotrophic organisims 133b
Heterozygote 142c
HFR see High-frequency recombinants
Hibiscus 101c
Hickory 101c–102a
High-frequency recombinants (HFR) 136a
High nutrient waters see Eutrophic waters
Hinny (hinnies) see Mule
Hippocastanaceae see Horse chestnut
Hippopotamus 9c, il 36, 37a
Hirudinea 5a
   see also Leech
Histidine tab 147
Histology 67c, 73c
Hog see Swine
Holly 102a
Hollyhock 102a
Homologous chromosomes 143c
Homologues see homologous chromosomes
Homoptera 6c
   see also Aphids; Cicada; Leafhopper; Louse; Scale insect
Honeybee see Bee
Honeydew melon see Melon
Honey locust see Locust
Honeysuckle 102a
Honeysuckle family 102b
   see also Black haw; Elder; Honeysuckle; Viburnum; Woodbine
Hoof-and-mouth disease 135a
Hookworm 37a
Hop 102b
Horehound 102b
Hormone (plant) 77c
Hornbeam 102b
Horned beetle il 27
Horned toad see Toad
Hornet 37a–37b
Horn-nut see Water chestnut
Horowitz, Norman 133b
Horse 10a, 37b
Horse chestnut 102b–102c
Horseradish 102c
Horseshoe crab 7b, 37b–37c
Horsetail 72a–72b, 102c
Horticulture 68a
Hourglass spider 15a
House spider 7b, 37c
Huckleberry 102c
Hummingbird 37c
Hyacinth 102c
Hyalospongiae 3b
Hydra 37c–38a
Hydrangea 103a
Hydrocaryaceae see Water chestnut
Hydrogen
   in plants 76b
Hydrotropism (plant) 77b
Hydrozoa 3c, 38a
   Hydroidea see Hydra
   Siphonophora see By-the-wind sailor; Portuguese man-of-war
Hyena 38a
Hymenoptera 7a
   see also Ant; Bee; Hornet; Sawfly; Wasp
Hyracoidea 9c
   see also Cony

I-J-K

Ibis 38a
Ice plant 103a
Ichneumon *see* Mongoose
Ichneumon fly 7b
Identical twins 149a
Iguana *il* 30, 38a–38b
Immortelle *see* Everlasting
Immunity to disease 141a–141c
  active 141c
  passive 141c
Immunization 141b–141c
Immunology 141a
Incas
  sacred flower *see* Sunflower
Indehiscent fruit 76a
Indian corn *see* Corn
Indian hemp 103a
Indian pipe 103a
Indians, American
  corn 89b
  pumpkin 119a
Indian tobacco *see* Lobelia
Indian turnip *see* Jack-in-the-pulpit
Indigo 103a
Influenza 135a
Ingram, Vernon 148c
Inheritance
  cytoplasmic 149c–150a
  see also Genetics; Heredity
Insecta 5c–7b
  Amphipoda *see* Louse
  Anoplura 5c
    see also Louse
  Coleoptera 7a
    see also Beetle; Firefly; June bug; Ladybeetle; Weevil
  Collembola 5a
    see also Springtail
  Dermaptera 6a
    see also Earwig
  Diptera 6c
    see also Botfly; Fly; Fruit fly; Midge; Mosquito; Tick
  Ephemeroptera 6b
    see also Mayfly
  Heteroptera 6b
    see also Bedbug; Chinch bug; Water boatman; Water strider
  Homoptera 6c
    see also Aphids; Cicada; Leafhopper; Louse; Scale insect
  Hymenoptera 7a
    see also Ant; Bee; Hornet; Sawfly; Wasp
  Isoptera 6a
    see also Termite
  Lepidoptera 6c
    see also Butterfly; Cankerworm; Caterpillar; Cornborer; Moth; Silkworm; Swallowtail; Tent caterpillar
  Mallophaga 6b
    see also Louse
  Neuroptera *see* Ant lion; Dobsonfly; Lacewing
  Odonata 6b
    see also Damselfly; Dragonfly
  Orthoptera 6a
    see also Cockroach; Cricket; Katydid; Locust; Praying mantis; Stick insect
  Plecoptera *see* Stone fly
  Siphonaptera 7a
    see also Flea
  Thysanura 6a
    see also Bristletail
  Trichoptera *see* Caddis fly
Insect control 160c
Insectivora 9a
  see also Hedgehog; Mole; Shrew
Integument 72c
Intertidal zone 158a
Iridaceae *see* Iris family
Iris 103a–103b
Iris family 103b
  see also Crocus; Freesia; Gladiolus; Iris

Irish moss 103b
Iron
  in plants 76b
Ironweed 103c
Irritability (plant) 77a
Irruptions (population) 151c
Isoleucine *tab* 147
Isoptera 6a
  see also Termite
Istle *see* Century plant
Ivy 103c
Jacaranda *see* Bigonia family
Jackal *see* Dog
Jackfruit *see* Mulberry family
Jack-in-the-pulpit 103c
Jack rabbit *see* Hare
Jacob, François 149c
Jacob's ladder *see* Bluebell
Jade plant *see* Orpine family
Jaguar 17c–18a, *il* 28
Jamaica pepper *see* Allspice
Jandaia *il* 26
Japonica 103c
Jasmine 103c–104a
Jay 38b
Jellyfish *see* Medusa
Jenner, Edward 141a
Jerusalem artichoke *see* Artichoke; Sunflower
Jessamine *see* Jasmine
Jewelweed 104a
Jewelweed family
  see Balsam; Jewelweed
Jimsonweed 104a
Joe-Pye weed 104a
Johnny-jump-up *see* Violet
Johnson grass *see* Sorghum
Johnston, Sir Harry 46b
Jonquil *see* Narcissus
Joshua tree *see* Yucca
Judas tree *see* Redbud
Juglandaceae *see* Walnut family
Jujube 104a
Juncaceae *see* Rush
Junco 38b–38c

Juneberry *see* Serviceberry
June bug 38c
Junegrass *see* Bluegrass
Juniper 104a–104b
Jupiter (planet)
  atmosphere 132a–132b
Jussieu, Antoine de 68c
Jute 104b
Kaffir thorn *see* Potato family
Kafir corn *see* Sorghum
Kaka *see* Parrot
Kakapo *see* Parrot
Kala azar 140c
Kale *see* Mustard
Kalong *see* Bat
Kangaroo 38c
Kaoliang *see* Sorghum
Kapok 104b
Katydid 38c–39a
Kauri pine *see* Araucaria family
Kentucky coffee tree 104b
Kiang *see* Ass
Killdeer *see* Plover
Kingbird 39a
King crab *see* Horseshoe crab
Kingfisher 39a
Kinglet 39a–39b
Kinkajou 39b
Kiskadee *see* Flycatcher
Kite 39b
Kittiwake 39b
Kiwi 8c, 39b
Knot *see* Sandpiper
Koala *il* 28, 39b–39c
Koch, Robert 137a
Koch's postulates 137a
Kodiak bear 13c
Kohlrabi *see* Mustard
Kornberg, Arthur 146c
  Nobel prize 150c
Kudu 39c
Kudzu 104b
Kulan *see* Ass
Kumquat 104b

L

Labiatae *see* Mint family
Laburnum 104c
Lac bug *see* Scale insect
Lacewing 39c
Lacquer tree 104c
Lactic acid bacteria 133c
Ladybeetle 7a, 39c–40a
Lady's slipper 104c
Lagomorpha 9b
  see also Cony; Hare; Rabbit
Lakes
  ecosystem 158c–159a
Lamb's-quarters 104c
Lamina (plant) 75a
Lammergeier *see* Vulture
Lamprey 8b, 40a
  see also Eel
Lancelet 8a, 40a–40b
  see also Chordata
Land iguana *il* 30
Larch 104c–105a
Largemouth bass *see* Sunfish
Lark 40b
Larkspur 105a
Lateral buds 74c
Laughing jackass *see* Kingfisher
Lauraceae *see* Laurel family
Laurel 105a
Laurel family 105a
  see also Avocado; Cinnamon; Laurel; Sassafras; Spicebush
Lavender 105a
Law of independent assortment (Mendel) 143a
Law of segregation (Mendel) 142b
Leaf *see* Leaves
Leafhopper 6c, 40b–40c
Leaflets 75a
Leaf scar 75b

Leatherflower *see* Bluebell
Leaves 74c–75c, *il* 76
  arrangement 75b
  bud scales 75a
  form 75a
  internal structure 75b–75c
  lamina 75a
  longevity 75a–75b
  petiole 75a
  spines 75a
  veins 75a
  venation 75a
Lecythidaceae *see* Brazil-nut family
Lederberg, Joshua 146a
  Nobel prize 150c
Leech 5a, 40c
Leek 105b
Legume 76a
Leguminosae *see* Pea family
Leishmania donovani 140c
Lemming 40c
Lemon 105b
Lemur 9a, 40c
Lentibulariaceae *see* Bladderwort family
Lentil 105b
Leopard *see* Cat
Leopold, Aldo 160c
Lepidoptera 6c
  see also Butterfly; Cankerworm; Caterpillar; Cornborer; Moth; Silkworm; Swallowtail; Tent caterpillar
Leprosy 137a
Leucine *tab* 147
Leucoplasts (plant) 73c
Leukemia virus *il* 134
Lettuce 105b–105c
Lianas 151c
Lichen 70c–71a, 139c–140a, 151c
Lichenology 68a
Licorice 105c

Life origins 131–133
  bibliography 133c
  evolution 131c–132a
  Miller experiment *il* 131, 131b–131c
  Oparin theory *il* 131, 131a–131b
  spontaneous generation 131a–131c
Life plants *see* Orpine family
Life zones 157b
Lignum vitae 105c
Lilac 105c
Lilac butterfly *see* Swallowtail
Liliaceae *see* Lily family
Lily 105c–106a
Lily family 73a, 106a
  see also Aloe; Asparagus; Asphodel; Bear grass; Bluebell; Dogtooth violet; Fritillary; Garlic; Grape hyacinth; Hyacinth; Leek; Lily; Lily of the valley; Mariposa lily; Onion; Rose of Sharon; Smilax; Solomon's seal; Trillium; Tulip; Yucca
Lily of the valley 106a
Lime 106a
Limnetic zone 158c
Limpet 40c–41a
Linaceae *see* Flax
Linden 106a
Linden family 106a
  see also Jute; Linden
Ling (animal) 41a
Ling (plant) *see* Heather
Lingcod *see* Ling (animal)
Linnaeus, Carolus 68b
Linné, Karl von *see* Linnaeus, Carolus
Lion *see* Cat
Litchi 106a–106b
Live-forever *see* Orpine
Live oak *see* Oak
Liverleaf *see* Hepatica
Liverworts 71c

Living fossils *see* Merostomata; Monoplacophora; Onychophora
Lizard *il* 30, 41a–41b
Llama 41b
Lobelia 106b
Lobeliaceae *see* Lobelia
Lobster 5b, 41b
Locoweed 106c
Locust (animal) 6a, 41b
Locust (plant) 106c
Logan, J. H. 106c
Loganberry 106c
Loganiaceae *see* Logania family
Logania family 106c
  see also Butterfly bush; Jasmine; Nux vomica
Logwood 106c
Loofah *see* Vegetable sponge
Loon 41c
Loosestrife family 107a
  see also Crape myrtle
Loquat 107a
Loranthaceae *see* Mistletoe
Lorikeet *see* Parrot
Lost camellia tree *see* Tea family
Lotus *il* 96, 107a
Louse 41c–42a
Lovebird 42a
Low nutrient waters *see* Oligotrophic waters
Lucerne *see* Alfalfa
Luffa *see* Vegetable sponge
Lungfish 8b, 42a
Lupine 107a
Lycopodiaceae *see* Club moss
Lynx 42a–42b
  see also Canada lynx
Lyon, Mary 144c
Lyrebird 42b
Lysine *tab* 147
Lysogenic bacteria 136b
Lythraceae *see* Loosestrife family

M

Macaw see Parrot
Mackeral 42b
MacLeod, C. M. 145c
Madder 107b
Madder family 107b
  see also Bedstraw; Chinchona; Coffee; Gardenia; Madder
Madroña 107b
Madroño see Madroña
Magnesium
  in plants 76b
Magnolia 107b–107c
Magnoliaceae see Magnolia family
Magnolia family 107c
  see also Magnolia; Tulip tree
Magpie 42b–42c
Mahogany 107c
Mahogany family 107c
  see also Chinaberry; Mahogany
Maidenhair fern see Polypody family
Maidenhair tree see Ginko
Maize see Corn
Malaria 140c
Malayan sun bear 13c
Mallard 42c
Mallophaga 6b
  see also Louse
Mallow family 107c
Mallow family 107c
  see also Cotton; Hibiscus; Hollyhock; Mallow; Marshmallow; Rose of Sharon
Malvaceae see Mallow family
Mammalia 8c–10a
  Artiodactyla 9c
    see also Alpaca; Antelope; Bighorn; Bison; Buffalo; Camel; Cattle; Chamois; Deer; Gazelle; Giraffe; Gnu; Goat; Hippopotamus; Kudu; Llama; Musk ox; Okapi; Peccary; Pronghorn; Sheep; Swine; Yak
  Carnivora 9b
    see also Badger; Bear; Cat; Cheetah; Civet cat; Coyote; Dog; Fox; Hyena; Kinkajou; Lynx; Marten; Mongoose; Otter; Polecat; Raccoon; Skunk; Weasel; Wolf; Wolverine
  Cetacea 10a
    see also Dolphin; Porpoise; Whale
  Chiroptera 9a
    see also Bat; Vampire
  Dermoptera see Flying lemur
  Edentata 9a
    see also Anteater; Armadillo; Sloth
  Hyracoidea 9c
    see also Cony
  Insectivora 9a
    see also Hedgehog; Mole; Shrew
  Lagomorpha 9b
    see also Cony; Hare; Rabbit
  Marsupialia 8c
    see also Kangaroo; Koala; Opossum; Wallaby; Wombat
  Monotremata 8c
    see also Duckbill
  Perissodactyla 10a
    see also Ass; Horse; Mule; Rhinoceros; Tapir
  Pinnipedia 9c
    see also Seal; Sea lion; Walrus
  Primates 9a
    see also Ape; Baboon; Chimpanzee; Gibbon; Gorilla; Lemur; Marmoset; Monkey; Orangutan
  Proboscidea 9c
    see also Elephant
  Rodentia 9b
    see also Agouti; Beaver; Chinchilla; Chipmunk; Gopher; Guinea pig; Hamster; Lemming; Marmot; Mouse; Muskrat; Nutria; Porcupine; Prairie dog; Rat; Squirrel; Vole
  Sirenia 10a
    see also Sea cow
  Tubulidentata 9c
    see also Aardvark
Mammee apple see Sapote
Mammoth see Elephant
Manatee see Sea cow
Mandrake il 69, 107c–108a
Mandrill see Baboon
Mangel-wurzel see Beet
Mango 108a
Mangosteen family see Rose of Sharon
Mangrove 108a
Manila hemp see Abacá
Manioc see Cassava
Man-of-war see Portuguese man-of-war
Man-of-war bird see Frigate bird
Manta see Ray
Manual of Determinative Bacteriology (Bergey) 136b
Manx cat see Cat
Manzanita 108a
Maple il 98, 108a–108b
Marabou see Stork
Marantaceae see Arrowroot
Marguerite see Daisy
Marigold 108b–108c
Marine environment 157c–158a
Mariposa lily 108c
Marjoram 108c
Marlin 42c
Marmalade plum see Sapote
Marmoset 42c–43a
Marmot 43a
Mars (planet)
  atmosphere 132a–132b
  life on 133c
Marshmallow 108c
Marsh marigold 108c
Marsupialia 8c
  see also Kangaroo; Koala; Opossum; Wallaby; Wombat
Marten 43a
Martin see Swallow
Marvel of Peru see Four o'clock
Mastigophora 3a, 140b–140c
Mastodon see Elephant
Maté see Holly
Materia Medica (Bock) 68a
Matrimony vine see Potato family
Matthaei 147a
Mauritius hemp see Century plant
Mayapple il 77, 108c
Mayas
  sacred bird see Trogon
May beetle see June bug
Mayflower see Arbutus
Mayfly 43a–43b
Mayweed 108c–109a
McCarty, M. 145c
Meadowlark see Lark
Meadow mouse see Vole
Meadow sweet see Spiraea

Measles 135a
  vaccine 141c
  virus il 135
Mediterranean forest and scrub zone 156a–156b
Medlar 109a
Medusa (animal) 3c, 43b
Meiosis 143c–144a
Meliaceae see Mahogany family
Melon 109a
Melville, Herman 65a
Membrane (plant) 76b
Mendel, Gregor Johann 142a
  Law of independent assortment 143a
  Law of segregation 142b
Mendelian genetics 142a–143b
Mendelian square il 142c, il 143
Menhaden 43b
Meningitis 139c
Merganser 43b–43c
Mercury (planet)
  atmosphere 132a–132b
Meristem 73c
Meristematic zone 77c
Merostomata 7b
  Xiphosura see Horseshoe crab
Meselson, Matthew Stanley 146c
Mesophyll 75b
Mesquite 109a–109b
Metabolic diseases 148a
Methionine tab 147
Mice
  maternal inheritance 150a
  see also Mouse
Michaelmas daisy see Aster
Microbiology 68a, 134–141
  bibliography 141c
Microcysts 136b
Midge 43c
Mignonette 109b
Milkweed 109b–109c
Milkweed family 109c
  see also Milkweed; Waxflower
Milkwort 109c
Milkwort family see Milkwort; Seneca Snakeroot
Miller, Stanley L. 132b
Miller experiment il 132, 132b–132c
Millet 109c
Mimosa 109c–110a
Minimal medium 148a
Mink see Weasel
Minnow 43c
Mint 110a
Mint family 73b, 110a
  see also Balm; Bergamot (wild); Catnip; Ground ivy; Horehound; Lavender; Marjoram; Mint; Oswego tea; Rosemary; Sage; Self-heal; Thyme
Mistletoe 110a
Mite 43c–44a
Mitochondria 73c, 150a
Mitosis 143c, il 144
Moby Dick (Melville) 65a
Moccasin see Pit viper
Mockingbird 44a
Mock orange 110a–110b
Molds 70c
  see also fungi
Mole 9a, 44a
Mollusca 4b
  see also Cephalopoda; Gastropoda; Pelecypoda
Monarch butterfly il 6
Mongoose 44a–44b
Monkey 9a, 44b
Monkeycup family see Pitcher plant

Monkey puzzle tree see Araucaria family
Monkshood see Aconite
Monocotyledons 68a–68b, 72c–73a
Monod, Jacques 149c
Monoplacophora 4c
Monotremata 8c
  see also Duckbill
Moose see Deer
Moraceae see Mulberry family
Morel mushroom il 95
Morgan, Thomas Hunt
  Nobel prize 150c
Morning glory il 110
  see also Bindweed
Morning-glory family 110b
  see also Bindweed; Dodder; Sweet potato
Morphology 67b
Mortality 151b
Mosquito 44b–44c
  aedes aegypti 135a
  anopheles 140c
Mosses 71a–71c
  club 72a, 88c
Mosslike plants 71a–71c
Moss pink see Phlox
Moth 6c, 44c
Mouflon see Sheep
Moundbuilder see Fowl
Mountain ash 110b
Mountain laurel 110b
Mountain sheep see Bighorn
Mountain tobacco see Arnica
Mouse 9b, 44c
Movement (plant) 77b
Movement (population) 151b
Mud dauber see Wasp
Mud puppy see Salamander
Mulberry 110b–110c
Mulberry family 110c
  see also Breadfruit; Fig; Mulberry; Osage orange; Paper mulberry; Rubber tree
Mule 44c–45a
Mullein 110c
Muller, Hermann Joseph
  Nobel prize 150c
Mullet 45a
Mumps 135a
Musaceae see Banana family
Mushroom il 70, il 95
Muskmelon see Melon
Musk ox 9c, 45a–45b
Muskrat 45b
Musquash see Muskrat
Mussel 4c, 45b
Musserana il 30
Mustard 110c–111a
Mustard family 111a
  see also Alyssum; Candytuft; Cress; Horseradish; Mustard; Peppergrass; Radish; Shamrock; Shepherd's purse; Stock; Wallflower
Mutation 134b, 145c
  chemical basis 146c
  cistron 147c
  creeper fowl 149b
  metabolic diseases 148a
  population genetics 150a–150b
  protein structure 148b
Mycobacterium tuberculosis il 135c
Mycology 68a
Myricaceae see Bayberry family
Myristicaceae see Nutmeg
Myrtaceae see Myrtle family
Myrtle 111a
Myrtle family 111a–111b
  see also Allspice; Clove tree; Eucalyptus; Guava; Myrtle; Pomegranate
Myxobacteriales 136b

N

Narcissus (plant) 111b
Narwhal see Whale
Naseberry see Sapodilla
Nasturtium 111b–111c

Natality 151b
Natural selection (Darwin) 150a
Nautilus 4c, 45b–45c
Nectar 75c
Nectarine see Peach
Needham, J. T. (1713–1781) 136c
Needles (pine) 72c
Neisseria gonorrhoeae 137a
Nematoda 4a

Rhabditida see Hookworm
Neomycin 137c
Nepenthaceae see Pitcher plant
Neptune (planet)
  atmosphere 132a–132b
Neries virens see Clamworm
Neritic zone il 157, 158a
Nettle 111c
Neurospora 148a

maternal inheritance 150a
Newt 45c
Niche, ecologic see Ecologic niche
Night-blooming cereus 111c
Nighthawk 45c
Nightingale 45c–46a
Nightjar 46a
Nightshade 111c–112a

Nirenberg, Marshall Warren 147a
Nitrogen
  cycle 154b
  fixation 138a, 154b
  in plants 76b
Nitrogen-fixing bacteria 76c
Norfolk island pine 112a

North America
  biomes *il* 156
Norway maple *il* 98
Norway rat 151b
Nucleic acids 132c
Nucleoli 143b
Nucleotides 146b

Nucleus 134a
  genetics 143b
  plant cell 73b
Nuthatch 46a
Nutmeg 112a
Nutria 46a–46b

Nutrients
  plant absorption 76a–76b
Nux vomica 112a
Nyctaginaceae *see* Four-o'clock family
Nymphaeaceae *see* Water-lily family

O

Oak 69a, 112a–112b
Oat 112b
Ocean zones *il* 157
Ocelot *see* Cat
Ochoa, Severo 147a
  Nobel prize 150c
Octopus 46b
Odonata 6b
  see also Damselfly; Dragonfly
Okapi 46b
Okra *see* Hibiscus
Old-man's-beard *see* Clematis
Oleaceae *see* Olive family
Oleander 112b
Oligochaeta 5a
  Megadrili *see* Earthworm
Oligotrophic waters 158b
Olive 112c
Olive family 112c
  see also Ash; Forsythia; Jasmine; Lilac; Olive; Privet
Olm *see* Salamander
Onager *see* Ass

Onagraceae *see* Evening-primrose family
Onion 112c
Onychophora 5b
Oparin, Alexander I. 132a
Operator gene 149c
Operon 149c
Opossum 8c, 46b–46c
Orange 112c–113a
Orangutan 9a, 46c
Orchidaceae *see* Orchid family
Orchid family 73a, 113a
  see also Lady's slipper
Orchis *see* Orchid family
Orders (plant) 69a
Oregon grape 113a
Organic compounds 132b–133a
Origin of life
  see Life origins
Oriole 66c
Ornithine 148b
Ornithomimus *il* 25
Oro, John 132b
Orphan virus 134c
Orpine 113a–113b
Orpine family 113b
  see also Orpine

Orris root *see* Ivy
Orthoptera 6a
  see also Cockroach; Cricket; Katydid; Locust; Praying mantis; Stick insect
Osage Indians 113b
Osage orange 113b
Osier *see* Willow
Osmosis (plant) 76b
Osprey 46c–47a
Osteichthyes 8b
  Acanthopteri *see* Angelfish; Bluefish; Mackerel; Tuna
  Acanthopterygii *see* Acanthopteri
  Anacanthini *see* Cod; Haddock; Hake; Ling (animal)
  Apodes *see* Eel
  Chondrostei *see* Sturgeon
  Cyprinodontes *see* Guppy; Swordtail
  Dipnoi *see* Lungfish
  Eventognathi *see* Carp; Sucker
  Ginglimodi *see* Gar
  Haplomi *see* Pike
  Heterosomata *see* Flatfish
  Isospondyli *see* Alewife; Anchovy; Herring; Menhaden; Salmon; Shad; Smelt; Tarpon; Trout; Whitefish
  Ostariophysi *see* Catfish; Minnow; Piranha
  Percomorphi *see* Bass; Marlin; Mullet; Perch; Squeteague; Swordfish
  Plectognathi *see* Sunfish
  Solenichthyes *see* Sea horse
  Synentognathi *see* Flying fish
  Thoracostei *see* Stickleback
Ostrich 8c, *il* 9, 47a
Oswego tea 113c
Otter 47a
Ovule sac (plant) 75c
Owl 47a–47b
Ox *see* Cattle
Oxalidaceae *see* Oxalis family
Oxalis *il* 112, 113b–113c
Oxalis family *see* Oxalis; Shamrock
Oxidizing atmosphere 132a
Oxygen
  bacteria 135b
  freshwater 158c
  photosynthesis 153b
  in plants 76b
Oyster 4c, 47b–47c
Oyster plant *see* Salsify

P

Painted leaf *see* Poinsettia
Painted tongue *see* Salpiglossis
Paleobotany 68a
Palmaceae *see* Palm family
Palma Christi *see* Castor-oil plant
Palmetto *see* Palm family
Palm family 73a, 113c–114a
  see also Sago palm
Paloverde 114a
Pampas grass 114a
Pandanaceae *see* Screwpine
Pangolin 9b
Pansy *see* Violet
Panther *see* Cat
Papaveraceae *see* Poppy family
Papaw 114a
Papaya *il* 95, 114a–114b
Paper mulberry 114b
Paprika *see* Pepper, red
Papyrus 114b
Parakeet *see* Parrot
Paramecium 140a, *il* 141
  maternal inheritance 150a
Parenchyma tissue (plant) 73a
Parrot 47c
Parrot fever *see* Psittacosis
Parrotlet *see* Parrot
Parsley 114c
Parsnip 114c
Partridge 47c
Pasqueflower *see* Anemone
Passifloraceae *see* Passionflower
Passionflower 114c
Passive immunity 141c
Pasteur, Louis
  bacteria control 136c
  spontaneous generation 131b
Pasteurization 136c
Pathology 68a
Pauling, Linus 148c
Pawpaw *see* Papaw

Pea 114c–115a
Peach 115a
Pea family 115a
  see also Acacia; Alfalfa; Bean; Broom; Clover; Cowpea; Gorse; Indigo; Kentucky coffee tree; Kudzu; Laburnum; Lentil; Licorice; Locoweed; Locust; Logwood; Lupine; Mesquite; Mimosa; Paloverde; Pea; Peanut; Redbud; Sandalwood (red); Shamrock; Sweet clover; Sweet pea; Tamarind; Tonka bean tree; Tumbleweed; Vetch; Wattle tree; Wisteria; Yellowwood
Peafowl 48a
Peanut 115a
Pear 115a
Pecan *see* Hickory
Peccary 48a
Pedaliaceae *see* Sesame
Pedalium family *see* Sesame
Peepul tree *see* Fig
Pekan *see* Marten
Pelagic life 157c
Pelargonium *see* Geranium
Pelecypoda 4b
  Eulamellibranchia *see* Shipworm
  Filobranchia *see* Mussel; Scallop
  Prionodesmacea *see* Oyster
  Teleodesmacea *see* Coquina
Pelican 48a–48b
Penguin 8c, *il* 26, 48b
Penicillin 137c
Penicillium *il* 138
Penicillium notatum 137c
Pennyroyal *see* Mint
Peony 115b
Pepper 115b–115c
Pepper family 115c
  see also Pepper
Peppergrass 115c
Pepperidge *see* Tupelo
Peppermint *see* Mint
Pepper, red 115c–116a

Peppertree 116a
Pepperwort *see* Peppergrass
Peptides 133a
  bonds 147a
Peptostreptococcus parvulus *il* 135c
Perch 8b, 48b
Percheron *see* Horse
Perching plants *see* Epiphytes
Perissodactyla 10a
  see also Ass; Horse; Mule; Rhinoceros; Tapir
Periwinkle (animal) 48b
Periwinkle (plant) 116a
Perennial plants 74c
Permease gene 149c
Persian melon *see* Melon
Persimmon 116a
Pest control 160c
Petals 75c
Petiole (plant) 75c
Petrel 48c
Pe-tsai *see* Mustard
Petunia *il* 96, 116a
Pewee 48c
Phalarope 48c–49a
Pheasant 49a
Phenotype 142c, 149a
Phenylalanine *tab* 147
Phloem (plant) 73c
Phlox *il* 97, 116a–116b
Phlox family *see* Bluebell; Phlox
Phoebe 49a
Pholidota 9b
Phosphorus
  in plants 76b
Photoperiodism (plant) 77b
Photosynthesis 76b–76c, 133c, 134a, 153b–153c
  bacteria 135b
  marine environment 157c
Phototropism (plant) 77a
Phylogenetic system
  bacteria 136b
Physiology (plant) 67c
Phytolaccaceae *see* Pokeweed family

Phytomastigophora 140c
Phytoplankton 77a
Pia *see* Arrowroot
Pickerel *see* Pike
Pie *see* Magpie
Pie plant *see* Rhubarb
Pig *see* Swine
Pigeon 8c, 49b
Pigeonberry *see* Pokeweed family
Pignut *see* Hickory
Pigweed 116b
Pika *see* Cony
Pike 49b
Pimento *see* Allspice
Pimiento *see* Pepper, red
Pimpernel 116b–116c
Pinaceae *see* Pine family
Pine 116c
  seed *il* 75
Pineapple 116c–117a
Pineapple family 117a
  see also Pineapple; Spanish moss
Pine family 116c
  see also Cedar; Douglas fir; Fir; Hemlock; Larch; Pine; Spruce
Piñon nuts *see* Pine
Pink 117a
Pink family 73a–73b, 117a
  see also Baby's breath; Bouncing Bet; Chickweed; Pink
Pink, ground *see* Phlox
Pinnipedia 9c
  see also Seal; Sea lion; Walrus
Pintail 49c
Pinworm 4b
Pipal *see* Fig
Piperaceae *see* Pepper family
Pipsissewa 117a
Piranha 49c
Pistachio 117a
Pistil 75c
Pitcher plant 117b
Pit viper 49c–50a
Placodermi 8b

INDEX

Plane-tree family 117b
Planets
  atmosphere 132a–132b
Plankton 157c
Plantaginaceae see Plantain family
Plantain family 117c
Plant ecology see Ecology
Plant lice see Aphids
Plant rust 139a
Plants 67–130
  alternation of generations 71c–72b
  annual 74c
  assimilation 77a
  bacteria 70c
  bibliography 130c
  botany 67–69
  cells 73b–73c
  classification 68c–69b
  deciduous 75a
  digestion 76c
  embryonic tissue 73c
  flowers 75c–76a
  food storage 76c
  fruits 76a
  germination 77b–77c
  growth 77b–77c
  guard cells 75b
  herbaceous stems 74c
  leaves 74c–75c
  long-day 77b
  main characteristics 67a
  nutrient absorption 76a–76b
  number of known forms 68c
  perennial 74c
  permanent tissue 73c–74a
  photoperiodism 77b
  photosynthesis 76b–76c
  physiology 76a–77c
  pollination 75c–76a
  respiration 76c–77a
  roots 74a–74b
  seed 72b–73b, 74a–76a
  short-day 77b
  stems 74b–74c
  stimulus and response 77a–77b
  structure 73b–74a
  study of 68a–68c
  subterranean stems 74c
  taxonomy 68a–68c
  tissues 73c–74a
  transpiration 76b
  tropisms 77a–77b
  water absorption 76a–76b
  woody stems 74c
Plastids 73c, 134a, 150a
Platanaceae see Plane-tree family
Platyhelminthes 4a
Platypus see Duckbill
Pliny the Elder 68a
Plover 50a–50b
Plum 117c
Plumelily see Solomon's seal
Pneumonia (pneumococcal) 137a
Poinsettia 117c
Poison dogwood see Sumac
Poison elder see Sumac
Poison hemlock 117c–118a
Poison ivy 118a
Poison oak see Sumac
Pokeweed family 118a
Polar bear 13c
Polecat 50b
Polemoniaceae see Bluebell; Phlox
Polio see Poliomyelitis
Poliomyelitis 135a
  vaccine 141c
Pollination 75c–76a
  cross 75c
  self 75c
Pollock see Cod
Polychaeta 5a
Polygalaceae see Milkwort; Seneca Snakeroot
Polygonaceae see Buckwheat family
Polymers 132c–133a
Polymorphism, balanced see Balanced polymorphism
Polynucleotides 133a
Polypeptides 147a
Polypodiaceae see Polypody family
Polypody family 118a
  see also Bracken; Ferns; Walking fern
Pomegranate 118b
Pomelo see Grapefruit
Pomes 76a
Pond lily see Waterlily
Pond skater see Water strider
Poplar 73a, 118b
Poppy 118b–118c
Poppy anemone see Anemone
Poppy family 118c
  see also Bloodroot; Celandine; Poppy
Population (ecology) 151a–151c
Population genetics 150a
  balanced polymorphism 150c
Porbeagle see Shark
Porcupine 9b, 50b–50c
Porifera 3b
Porpoise 50c
Portuguese man-of-war 3c, 50c–51a
Portulaca see Purslane
Portulacaceae see Bitterroot; Purslane
Potassium
  in plants 76b
Potato 118c
Potato family 118c
  see also Belladonna; Bittersweet; Butterfly flower; Eggplant; Jimsonweed; Mandrake; Nightshade; Pepper (red); Petunia; Potato; Salpiglossis; Tobacco; Tomato
Pot marigold 118c–119a
Prairie chicken see Grouse
Prairie dog 51a
Prawn see Shrimp
Praying mantis il 27, 51a
Pressure
  root (plant) 76b
Pride of India see Chinaberry
Primates 9a
  see also Ape; Baboon; Chimpanzee; Gibbon; Gorilla; Lemur; Marmoset; Monkey; Orangutan
Primrose 119a
Primrose family 119a
  see also Cyclamen; Pimpernel; Primrose; Shooting star
Primulaceae see Primrose family
Prince's pine see Pipsissewa
Principle of dominance 142b–142c
Privet 119a
Proboscidea 9c
  see also Elephant
Procaryotic cells 134a, 134b
Producer organisms 152c
Profundal zone 158c
Proline tab 147
Pronghorn 51a–51b
Prop roots 74b
Protein
  formation 147a
  structure 148c
Protoplasm 73b
Protoplasts 134a
Protozoa 3a, 140a–141a
  Ciliata 3b
  Ciliophora 141a
  diseases 140c, 141a
  Mastigophora 3a, 140b–140c
  nonphotosynthetic protozoa il 140
  Sarcodina 3a, 140a–140b
  Sporozoa 3a–3b, 140c–141a
Prune see Plum
Pseudopodia 140a
Psittacosis 135a
Ptarmigan 51b
Pteranodon il 23
Puffin 51b
  see also Auk
Pukeko see Gallinule
Puma see Cat
Pumpkin 119a
Pumpkinseed see Sunfish
Purine 146b
Purple martin see Swallow
Purslane 119b
Purslane family see Bitterroot; Purslane
Pussley see Purslane
Pussy willow see Willow
Pyrimidines 146b
Pyrolaceae see Pyrola family
Pyrola family 119b
  see also Indian pipe; Snow plant; Wintergreen

Q-R

Q fever 138c
Quagga see Ass
Quail 51c
Quassia family see Tree of heaven
Queen Anne's lace see Carrot
Queensland arrowroot see Canna
Quercus see Oak
Quetzal see Trogon
Quince 119b–119c
Rabbit 9b, 51c
Rabies 135a
Raccoon il 29, 51c–52a
Radiolaria 3a, 140b
Radish 119c
Raffia see Palm
Ragweed 119c
Rail 52a
Ramie see Nettle
Range management 160a
Ranunculaceae see Buttercup family
Rape see Mustard
Raspberry 119c
Rat 9b, 52a–52b
  see also Norway rat
Ratel see Badger
Rattlesnake il 30
  see also Pit viper
Raven see Crow
Ray 52b
Ray, John 68a, 68c
Recessive traits 142c
Recombination (bacterial) 136a
Recon 147c
Red algae 70a, 139c
Red-banded leafhopper il 27
Redbird see Cardinal
Redbug 119c
Red-footed booby chick il 26
Redi, Francesco 131a
Redstart 52b–52c
Redwood il 98
  see also Sequoia
Reed 120a
Reedbird see Bobolink
Reindeer see Deer
Reptilia 8b
  Crocodilia see Crocodile
  Squamata
    Sauria see Chameleon; Gecko; Iguana; Lizard
    Serpentes see Boa; Cobra; Pit viper; Viper
  Testudinata see Tortoise
Resedaceae see Mignonette
Respiration (plant) 76c–77a
Response (plant) 77a–77b
Reticulate 72c
Rhabditida see Hookworm
Rhamnaceae see Buckthorn family
Rhinoceros 12a, il 28, 52c
Rhizobium 138a
Rhizomes (plant) 74c
Rhizophoraceae see Mangrove
Rhododendron 120a
Rhodora see Azalea
Rhubarb 120a
Ribonuclease 147a
Ribonucleic acid (RNA) 133a, 134c, 145c
  ribosomes 147a
  RNA code words tab 147
Ribosome 147a
Rice 120a–120b
Ricebird see Bobolink
Rickettsiae 138b–138c
Rickettsial diseases 138b–138c
Ringworm 139a
RNA see Ribonucleic acid
Robin 52c
Rock melon see Melon
Rocky Mountain spotted fever 138c
  antitoxin 141c
Rodentia 9b
  see also Agouti; Beaver; Chinchilla; Chipmunk; Gopher; Guinea pig; Hamster; Lemming; Marmot; Mouse; Muskrat; Nutria; Porcupine; Prairie dog; Rat; Squirrel; Vole
Root cap (plant) 74a–74b
Root hairs 74b
Roots (plant) 74a–74b
  adventitious 74b
  aerating 74b
  aerial 74b
  pressure 76b
  prop 74b
  specialized 74b
  structure 74a–74b
  systems 74b
Rosaceae see Rose family
Rose il 97, 120b
Rosebay see Rhododendron
Rose family 73b, 120b–120c
  see also Agrimony; Almond; Apple; Apricot; Blackberry; Cherry; Christmas berry; Hawthorn; Japonica; Loganberry; Loquat; Medlar; Mountain ash; Peach; Pear; Plum; Quince; Raspberry; Rose; Serviceberry; Spiraea; Strawberry
Rose mallow see Hibiscus
Rosemary 120c
Rose moss see Purslane
Rose of China see Hibiscus
Rose of Sharon 120c
Rotifera 4b
Roundworm 4a
Rowan see Mountain ash
Rubber plant see Fig
Rubber tree 120c
Rubiaceae see Madder family
Rue 120c–121a
Rue family 121a
  see also Bergamot; Citron; Grapefruit; Kumquat; Lemon; Lime; Orange; Rue
Running myrtle see Periwinkle (plant)
Rush 121a
Russian thistle see Tumbleweed
Rutabaga see Mustard
Rutaceae see Rue family
Rye 121a

S

Sable *see* Marten
Saccharomyces cerevisiae 139b
Safflower 121a–121b
Saffron *see* Crocus
Sage 121b
Sagebrush 121b
Sago Palm 121b
Saguaro 121b
Saiga *see* Antelope
Saintpaulia *see* Gesneria family
Salamander 8b, 52c–53a
Salicaceae *see* Willow family
Salmon 53a–53b
Salmonella 136b, 137a
Salmonella typhosa 137a
Salpiglossis 121b–121c
Salsify 121c
Saltbush 121c
Salvia *see* Sage
Samara fruit 76a
Samphire *see* Goosefoot family
Sandalwood 121c
Sand dollar *see* Sea urchin
Sanderling 53b
Sandpiper 55b
Sangue-de-bois *il* 26
San Juan Capistrano Mission 59a
Santalaceae *see* Sandalwood
Sapindaceae *see* Soapberry family
Sapodilla 121c
Sapodilla family 121c
 see also Rubber tree; Sapodilla; Sapote
Sapotaceae *see* Sapodilla family
Sapote 121c–122a
Saprophytic action 135c
Sapsucker *see* Woodpecker
Sarcina 135b
Sarcodina 3a, 140a–140b
Sardine *see* Herring
Sargasso Sea 70a
Sarraceniaceae *see* Pitcher plant
Sarsaparilla *see* Smilax
Sassafras 122a
Saturn (planet)
 atmosphere 132a–132b
Sausage family *see* Bignonia family
Sawfish *see* Ray
Sawfly 7b, 53c
Saw grass *see* Sedge family
Saxifragaceae *see* Saxifrage family
Saxifrage 122a
Saxifrage family 122a
 see also Currant; Gooseberry; Hydrangea; Mock orange; Saxifrage
Scale insect 6c, 53c
Scallop 4c, 53c–54a
Scaphopoda 4b
Scarab *see* June bug
Scarlet fever 137a
Scaup 54a
Schizanthus *see* Butterfly flower
Sclerenchyma tissue 73c
Scorpion 7b, *il* 27, 54a
Scorpion grass *see* Forget-me-not
Scouring rush *see* Horsetail
Screwpine 122a
Scrimshaw *see* Whale
Scrophulariaceae *see* Figwort family
Scud *see* Shrimp
Scurf pea *see* Tumbleweed
Scyphozoa 3c
Sea anemone 54a
Sea cow 10a, 54b
Sea cucumber 7c, 54b
Sea fan 54b–54c
Sea grape *see* Buckwheat family
Sea horse 8b, 54c

Seal 9c, 54c
Sea lily 7c, 54c
Sea lion 9c, 54c–55a
Sea parrot *see* Puffin
Sea squirt *see* Tunicate
Sea star 7c, 55a
Sea swallow *see* Tern
Sea trout *see* Squeteague
Sea urchin 7c, 55a
Secretary bird 55a
Sedge 122b
Sedge family 122b
 see also Bulrush; Papyrus; Sedge
Sedum *see* Orpine
Seed coat 76a
Seed plants 72b–73b, 74a–76a
 anatomy 74a–76a
 buds 74c
 flowers 75c–76a
 leaves 74c–75a
 pollination 75c–76a
 roots 74a–74b
 stems 74b–74c
Seeds 76a
 germination 77b–77c
Self-heal 122b
Self-pollination 75c
Seminole bread *see* Arrowroot
Seminole Indians 90b
Semipermeable membranes (plant) 76b
Seneca snakeroot 122b
Sensitive plant *see* Mimosa
Sepals (flower) 75c
Sequoia 122b–122c
Serine *tab* 147
Serviceberry 122c
Sesame 122c
Sewage disposal 138a
Sex chromatin (Barr body) 144c
Sex chromosomes 144b
Sexual system (plant) 68b
Shad 55a–55b
Shadbush *see* Serviceberry
Shadfly *see* Mayfly
Shallot *see* Onion
Shallu *see* Sorghum
Shamrock 122c
Shark 55b
Shasta daisy *see* Daisy
Sheep 9c, 55b–55c
Sheep laurel *see* Laurel
Sheep sorrel 122c
Shepard's purse 123a
Shigella 136b
Shiner *see* Minnow
Shipworm 55c
Shoeblack plant *see* Hibiscus
Shoeflower *see* Hibiscus
Shooting star 123a
Shrew 9a, 55–56a
Shrike 56a
Shrimp 5b, 56a
Sickle cell anemia 148c, 150b
Sickle cell trait 148c
Silk-cotton tree *see* Kapok
Silkworm 56a–56b
Silverfish *see* Bristletail
Simaroubaceae *see* Tree of heaven
Siphonaptera 7a
 see also Flea
Sirenia 10a
 see also Sea cow
Sisal 87c, 123a
Skate *see* Ray
Skimmer 56b
Skunk 56b
Skunk cabbage 123a
Slater *see* Sowbug
Slime bacteria 136b
Slime molds 70c
Slipper shell 56b–56c
Slipperwort *see* Calceolaria
Sloth 9a, 56c
Sloth bear 13c
Sludge digesters 138a
Slug 4b, 56c–57a
Smallpox 135a, 141a–141b
 cowpox 141a
 vaccine 141c
 variola major 141a
 variola minor 141a

Smelt 57a
Smilax 123a
Smoke tree 123a–123b
Snapdragon 123b
Snappers *see* Bluefish
Snapweed *see* Jewelweed
Snipe 57a
Snout beetle *see* Weevil
Snowdrop 123b
Snow-on-the-mountain *see* Spurge
Snow plant 123b
Snowshoe hare 151c
Soapberry 123b–123c
Soapberry family 123c
 see also Akee; Litchi; Soapberry
Soapwort *see* Bouncing Bet
Soft rot 137a
Soil conservation 160a
Solanaceae *see* Potato family
Sole *see* Flatfish
Solomon's seal 123c
Sorghum 123c
Sorrel *see* Sheep sorrel
Sotol *see* Bear grass
Sour cherry *see* Cherry
Sour gum *see* Tupelo
Soursop *see* Custard apple
Sowbug 57a
Spallanzani, Lazzaro 131a–131b, 136c
Spanish bayonet *see* Yucca
Spanish moss 123c–124a
Sparrow 8c, 57a–57b
Speargrass *see* Bluegrass
Spearmint *see* Mint
Species 68b, 69a
Spectacled bear 13c
Speedwell *see* Veronica
Spermatophyta 72b–73b
 angiosperms 72c–73b
 gymnosperms 72c
Spherical bacteria (cocci) 135b
Spicebush 124a
Spider *see* Arachnida
Spiderflower *see* Caper family
Spider mite *see* Mite
Spikenard 124c
Spinach 124a
Spindle tree *see* Euonymus
Spines (plant) 75a
Spiraea 124a
Spiral bacteria *see* Spirilla
Spirilla 135b
Spirillum undula *il* 135c
Spirochaetales 136b
Spirochaeta plicatilis *il* 135c
Spleenwort *see* Polypody family
Sponges 3c
Spontaneous generation 131a–131c
Spores (bacterial) 136a
Spores (fungal) 139a
Sporozoa 3a, 140c–141a
Springbok *see* Gazelle
Spring overturn 158c
Springtail 5c, 57b–57c
Spruce 124a–124b
Spurge 124b
Spurge family 124b
 see also Cassava; Castor-oil plant; Croton; Euphorbia; Poinsettia; Rubber tree; Spurge; Tallow tree; Tung tree
Squash 124b
Squeteague 57c
Squid 57c
Squirrel 9b, 57b–58a
Squirrel corn *see* Dutchman's breeches
Stable population (ecology) 151c
Staff tree 124b–124c
Staff-tree family 124c
 see also Bittersweet; Euonymus; Staff tree
Stag beetle *see* June bug
Stagbush *see* Black haw
Staghorn *see* Polypody family
Staghorn evergreen *see* Club moss
Stahl, Franklin W. 146c
Stamens (flower) 75c
Stanley, Wendell 134c

Staphylococci 135b, 137a
Starfish *see* Sea star
Starling 58a
Star of Bethlehem *il* 72
Steeplebush *see* Spiraea
Stems (plant) 74b–74c
 aerial 74b
 bulbs 74c
 corms 74c
 herbaceous 74b, 74c
 rhizomes 74c
 subterranean 74b, 74c
 tubers 74c
 woody 74b, 74c
Sterculiaceae *see* Cacao
Sterilization
 bacteria control 136b–136c
Sterlat *see* Sturgeon
Stick insect 58a
Stickleback 58b
Stigma (flower) 75c
Stilt 58c
Stimulus (plant) 77a–77b
Sting ray *see* Ray
Stint *see* Sandpiper
Stoat *see* Weasel
Stock 124c
Stockfish *see* Hake
Stomata (plant) 75b
Stonecrop *see* Orpine
Stone fly 58b
Stork 58b–58c
Storksbills *see* Geranium
Strawberry 124c
Streptococci 135b, 137a
Streptococcus pyogenes *il* 135c
Streptomyces 137c
Streptomycin 137c
Structure (population) 151b
Sturgeon 8b, 58c
Style (flower) 75c
Substrate 149c
Subterranean stems 74b, 74c
Subtilin 137c
Succory *see* Chicory
Sucker 58c–59a
Sudan grass 124c
Sugar apple *see* Custard apple
Sugarcane 124c–125a
Sulfur
 in plants 76b
Sumac 125a
Sumac family 125a
 see also Cashew; Lacquer tree; Mango; Pepper tree; Pistachio; Poison ivy; Smoke tree; Sumac
Summer's darling *see* Godetia
Summer squash *see* Pumpkin
Sundew 125a
Sundew family 125a
 see also Sundew; Venus's-fly-trap
Sunfish 59a
Sunflower 125b
Sustained yield management 159a–159b
Sutton, W. S. 143b–143c
Swallow 59a
Swallowtail 59b
Swan 59b–59c
Sweet bay *see* Laurel; Magnolia
Sweet cherry *see* Cherry
Sweet clover 125b
Sweet fern *see* Bayberry family
Sweet gale *see* Bayberry family
Sweet gum 125b–125c
Sweethaw *see* Black haw
Sweet pea 125c
Sweet potato 125c
Sweetsop *see* Custard apple
Sweet William *see* Pink
Swift 59c
Swine 59c
Swiss chard *see* Beet
Swordfish 59c–60a
Swordtail 60a
Sycamore *see* Plane-tree family
Symbiosis 138a, 151c
Synecology 151a
Syphilis 137a
Syringa *see* Lilac; Mock orange

INDEX

T

Taccaceae *see* Arrowroot
Tadpole *see* Frog
Taiga 155b
Takahe *see* Gallinule
Tallow tree 125c
Tamarack *see* Larch
Tamaricaceae *see* Tamarisk
Tamarind 125c–126a
Tamarisk 126a
Tanager 60a
Tangerine *see* Orange
Tannin *see* Mangrove
Tapeworm 4a, 60a–60b
Tapioca *see* Cassava
Tapir 10a, 60b
Tap-root systems 74b
Tarantula *il* 27, 60b
Taro 126a
Tarpan *see* Ass; Horse
Tarpon 60b–60c
Tarragon 126a
Tatum, Edward Lawrie 148a
  Nobel prize 150c
Taxaceae *see* Yew
Taxodiaceae *see* Bald-cypress family
Taxonomy 67b, 68a–69b
Taxus *see* Yew
Tea 126a–126b
Tea family 126b
  see also Camellia; Tea
Teak 126b
Teal 60c
Teasel 126b–126c
Teju lizard *il* 30
Temperate deciduous forest zone 156a
Temperate rain forest zone 156a

Template 146b
Temple tree *see* Dogbane family
Tent caterpillar 60c–61a
Tercel *see* Falcon
Terebinth tree *see* Pistachio
Terminal buds 74c
Termite 6a, 61a
Tern 61a
Terrapin *see* Tortoise
Tetanus 137a
  antitoxin 141c
Tetracocci 135b
Thallophytes 69b–70a
  algae 69c–70a
  fungi 70a–71a
Theaceae *see* Tea family
Theophrastus 68a
Thermocline 158c
Thistle 126c
Thorn apple *see* Jimsonweed
Threonine *tab* 147
Thrush 61a
Thyme 126c
Thymine 146b
Thysanura 6a
  see also Bristletail
Tick 7b, 61b
Tickseed *see* Coreopsis
Tiger *see* Cat
Tiliaceae *see* Linden family
Timothy (plant) 126c
Tissue (plant) 73c–74a
  bast 73c
  collenchyma 73c
  complex 73c
  embryonic 73c
  epidermal 74a
  fibrous 73c
  permanent 73c–74a
  sclerenchyma 73c
  sieve 73c
  simple 73c
  soft 73c
  stone 73c
  vascular 74a

Titmouse 61b
Toad 8b, 61b
  Brazilian Horned Toad *il* 30
Tobacco 126c–127a
Tobacco mosaic virus (TMV) 134c
Tomato 127a
Tomato wilt 137a
Tonka bean tree 127a
Tooth shell 61b
Tortoise 61b–62a
Totuava *see* Squeteague
Toucan *il* 26, 62a
Touch-me-not *see* Jewelweed
Toxins 141b
Transduction (bacterial) 136a
Transformation (bacterial) 136a
Transpiration 76b, 154c
Trap-door spider 62a
Traveler's-tree *see* Banana family
Tree of heaven 127a
Trematoda 4a
Trepang *see* Sea cucumber
Treponema pallidum *il* 135c
Trichomonads 140c
Trichomonas *il* 140
  foetus 140c
  vaginalis 140c
Trichonympha 140c
Trillium 127a
Trilobita 5b
Trogon 62a–62b
Tropaeolaceae *see* Nasturtium
Trophic levels 153c
Tropical deciduous forest zone 156b–156c
Tropical rain forest zone 156c–157a
Tropisms (plant) 77a–77b
Trout 62b
Trumpet creeper 127a–127b
Trumpet tree *see* Mulberry family
Trumpet vine *see* Trumpet creeper

Trypanosoma *il* 140
  gambiense 140c
Trypanosomes 140c
Tryptophan *tab* 147
Tsetse fly *see* Fly
Tsutsugamushi fever 138c
Tube-nosed bird 62b
Tuberculosis 137a
  vaccine 141c
Tuberose 127b
Tubers (plant) 74c
Tubulidentata 9c
  see also Aardvark
Tuftybell *see* Bluebell
Tulip 127b
Tulipan *see* Bigonia family
Tulip tree 127b–127c
Tumbleweed 127c
Tuna 62b
Tundra 155a, 155c
Tung tree 127c
Tunicata *see* Chordata
Tunicate 62b–62c
  see also Chordata
Tupelo 127c
Tupi Indians 60a
Turbellaria 4a
Turkey 62c
Turnip *see* Mustard
Turtle *il* 61
  see also Tortoise
Tusk shell *see* Tooth shell
Twins 149a
  studies of 149a
Tyndall, John 131c
Typhaceae *see* Cattail
Typhoid fever 137a
  vaccine 141c
Typhus fever 138b
  vaccine 141c
Tyrosine *tab* 147

U–V

U *see* Uracil
Ulmaceae *see* Elm family
Umbelliferae *see* Carrot family
Umbrella plant *see* Papyrus
Unicorn (tapestry) *il* 67
Uracil (U) 147a
Uranus (planet)
  atmosphere 132a–132b
Urey, Harold 132a
Urticaceae *see* Nettle
Urubu *see* Vulture
Urushiol *see* Poison ivy

Vacuoles 73c
Valerian 127c–128a
Valerianaceae *see* Valerian family
Valerian family 128a
  see also Spikenard; Valerian
Valine *tab* 147
Vampire 62c
Vanilla *see* Orchid family
Variola major 141a
Variola minor 141a
Varnish tree *see* Lacquer tree
Vascular bundles (plant) 74c, 75c
Vegetable bran *see* Akee
Vegetable sponge 128a
Veins (plant) 75a
Venation 72c, *il* 73, 75a

Venus (planet)
  atmosphere 132a–132b
Venus's-flytrap 128a
Verbena 128a–128b
Verbenaceae *see* Teak; Verbena
Veronica 128b
Vertebrata *see* Chordata
Vetch 128b
Vibrio comma 137b
Viburnum 128b–128c
Violaceae *see* Violet
Violet 128c
Viper 62c–63a
Viral diseases 134c–135b
  animal 134c
  plant 134c
Virginia creeper *see* Boston ivy

Virginian cowslip *see* Bluebell
Virgin's bower *see* Clematis
Virion 134b
Viruses 134b–135b
  animal diseases 134c–135b
  bacterial 145c
  cultivation 135a
  filterable 134c
  genetics 146a
  leukemia *il* 134
  measles *il* 135
  plant diseases 134c
  reproduction 134c
Vitaceae *see* Grape family
Vole 44c, 63a
Vulture 63a–63b

W

Wahoo *see* Euonymus
Wake-robin *see* Trillium
Waksman, Selman 137c
Walking fern 128c
Walking leaf *see* Walking fern
Wallaby 63b–63c
Wallflower 128c
Walnut 128c–129a
Walnut family 73a, 129a
  see also Hickory; Walnut
Walrus 9b, 63c
Warbler 63c
Wasp 7a, 64a
Water
  plant absorption of 76a–76b
Water boatman 64a

Water caltrop *see* Water chestnut
Water chestnut 129a
Watercress *see* Cress
Water cycle 154c–155a
Water dog *see* Salamander
Water ecosystems *see* Aquatic ecosystems
Water flea 64a–64b
Water lily *il* 96, 129a
Water-lily family 73b, 129a–129b
  see also Lotus; Water lily
Watermelon *see* Melon
Water plantain 129b
Water-plantain family 129b
  see also Arrowhead; Water plantain
Water purification 138a
Water strider 6c, 64b
Water thrush 64b
Watson, James 146b
  Nobel prize 150c

Watson-Crick model 146a–146c
Wattle tree 129b
Waxflower 129b
Wax myrtle *see* Bayberry
Waxwing 64b–64c
Waxwork *see* Bittersweet
Wayfaring tree *see* Viburnum
Weasel 9b, 64c
Weevil 7a, 64c
Weinberg, Wilhelm 150a
West Indian cedar *see* Mahogany family
Whale 10a, 64c–65a
Whippoorwill 65a–65b
Wheat 129b–129c
Whin *see* Gorse
Whistler *see* Goldeneye (duck)
White ant *see* Termite
White Cliffs of Dover 140b
Whitefish 65b
White grub *see* June bug
Whiting *see* Cod

Whooping cough 137a
  vaccine 141c
Widgeon *see* Duck
Wild canary *see* Goldfinch
Wildcat *see* Cat
Wildebeest *see* Gnu
Wild indigo *see* Tumbleweed
Wild jalap *see* Mayapple
Wild sweet william *see* Phlox
Wilkins, Maurice Hugh Frederick 146b
  Nobel prize 150c
Willow 129c
Willow family 73a, 129c
  see also Poplar; Willow
Windflower *see* Anemone
Winged pigweed *see* Tumbleweed
Winkle *see* Periwinkle (animal)
Wintergreen 129c
Wiregrass *see* Bluegrass
Wisent *see* Bison
Wistaria *see* Wisteria

Wisteria 129c–130a
Witch hazel 130a
Witch-hazel family 130a
  see also Sweet gum; Witch hazel

Wolf 9b, 65b
Wolfsbane *see* Aconite
Wolf spider *il* 27
  see also Tarantula
Wolverine 65b–65c

Wombat 65c
Wood anemone *see* Anemone
Woodbine 130a
Woodchuck *see* Marmot
Woodcock 65c–66a

Woodpecker 66a–66b
Wood sorrel *see* Oxalis
Woody stems 74b, 74c
Wormwood 130a
Wren 66b

X-Y-Z

X chromosome 144c–145a
Xerosin 137c
Xylem 73c
Yak 66b
Yam family 130a–130b

Yarrow 130b
Y chromosome 145a
Yeasts 139b–139c
  infections 139c
  maternal inheritance 150a
  reproduction 139b
  uses 139b
Yellow-bellied sapsucker *see* Woodpecker
Yellowbird *see* Warbler

Yellow fever 135a
Yellowfin tuna *see* Tuna
Yellow jacket *see* Hornet
Yellowlegs 66b–66c
Yellowthroat 66c
Yellowwood 130b
Yerba maté *see* Holly
Yew 130b–130c
Yuca *see* Cassava

Yucca 130c
Zebra 10a
  see also Ass
Zinder, N. 146a
Zingiberaceae *see* Ginger family
Zinnia *il* 96, 130c
Zygophyllaceae *see* Caltrop family
Zygote 76a, 142b